HB
139
.F69
1968

D1287138

JACKSON LIBRARY
LANDER UNIVERSITY
GREENWOOD, SC 29649

Intermediate Economic Statistics

Intermediate
Economic Statistics

KARL A. FOX

Professor of Economics and Head of Department
Iowa State University

JOHN WILEY & SONS, INC.,
NEW YORK · LONDON · SYDNEY

JACKSON LIBRARY
LANDER UNIVERSITY
GREENWOOD, SC 29649

COPYRIGHT © 1968 BY JOHN WILEY & SONS, INC.

All Rights Reserved
This book or any part thereof must not
be reproduced in any form without the
written permission of the publisher.

LIBRARY OF CONGRESS CATALOG CARD NUMBER: 67-27273
PRINTED IN THE UNITED STATES OF AMERICA

Preface

This is a challenging time to write an intermediate text on economic statistics. At the research frontier of economics, dramatic changes have been accumulating since the mid-1930s. So far, I believe, these newer developments have not been satisfactorily integrated into undergraduate instruction in economic statistics.

I believe this book will also fill a major gap at the graduate level. Much graduate instruction in econometrics has emphasized the theory of statistical estimation more or less in isolation from actual problems of economic research. I am very much in favor of advanced training for economists in statistical theory, economic theory, and the relevant fields of mathematics. However, I believe an additional course focused squarely on problems of quantitative economic research will help to consolidate the gains accruing from the theoretical instruction. I see no dichotomy between theory and application but rather an opportunity to encourage their more effective integration.

The object of the book is suggested by the titles of its first three chapters: Economics and Statistics, A Review of Economic Concepts, and A Review of Statistical Concepts. The review chapters help to make the book self-contained for the purposes of a one-semester course. They also assume that the student has had an adequate course in economic principles and an introductory course in statistics covering frequency distributions, measures of central tendency and dispersion, relations between populations and samples, and the interpretation of measures such as the standard error of the mean. Students who have had more advanced training in economics and statistics will be able to progress very rapidly through the first four chapters and to concentrate on the later ones.

Thus some teachers of undergraduates may choose to cover only Chapters 1 through 9 during the semester. A graduate-level course might include Chapters 5 through 14, with particular emphasis on Chapters 10, 11, 12, 13, and 14. These later chapters deal with the construction of large-scale economic models; identification, causal ordering, and estimation in economic models; a survey of estimation techniques; multicollinearity and the use of *a priori* information; and the measurement of economic aggregates. Some graduate students will, I believe, find the chapter on aggregation both demanding and enlightening. The weakest elements in our models of national, regional, and urban economies are the links between properties of individual decision-making units and the properties of aggregates. Chapter 12 by Drs. J. K. Sengupta and B. C. Sanyal provides an introduction to more advanced topics in estimation such as two-stage and three-stage least squares, maximum likelihood methods, and the Bayesian approach.

A number of colleagues at Iowa State University have given me advice and assistance. Drs. J. K. Sengupta and B. C. Sanyal contributed the special chapter on estimation mentioned. Dr. James A. Stephenson supplied most of the chapter questions. Dr. B. C. Sanyal prepared the glossary and list of equations, supplied many of the chapter references, and rendered invaluable assistance in seeing the final manuscript through production. Drs. William C. Merrill and Hylke Van de Wetering read an intermediate version of the manuscript and made helpful comments. Drs. T. Krishna Kumar and M. V. R. Sastry monitored some of the calculations and commented on a still earlier version of the material.

Helen M. Brown and Rita Bauman typed successive drafts of the manuscript with dispatch and with careful attention to the mathematical and technical sections. Karen Fox prepared drafts of many of the diagrams appearing in the earlier chapters and handled some of the calculations.

The emphasis of the book reflects my experience in adapting statistical techniques to the analysis of substantive economic problems. Many of these problems grew out of the needs of policymakers in federal agencies. I cannot recall a single instance in which their needs would have been met by a purely *statistical* analysis. In essence, they needed quantitative estimates of structural relationships among economic variables; reassurance or caution as to the stability of these relationships over time; and judgments concerning the accuracy with which the outcomes of proposed policy actions could be predicted. The choice of statistical techniques grew out of the prior (and more demanding) tasks of specifying the economic relationships connecting the variables of interest and investigating problems of measurement error, aggregation, and bias in the series available for representing these variables.

I believe this conception of the relationship between statistics and economics is the dominant one among economists doing quantitative research in the 1960s. Seriously intended models of national economies, such as the Brookings quarterly econometric model of the United States, are cases in point. Operations research involves a similar integration of statistical techniques with the properties of economic (and other) structural systems.

Karl A. Fox

July 14, 1967

Contents

Intermediate Economic Statistics

CHAPTER 1

Economics and Statistics

This book is intended for students of economics. It is concerned primarily with the estimation or measurement of relationships among economic variables.

The central concepts of economic theory can be stated as functional relationships among variables, using the symbols of algebra, calculus, and/or set theory. If we wish to apply economic theory to concrete situations, we must replace these symbols with the appropriate numbers.

However, the appropriate numbers are not easy to come by. First, they require the individual variables of concern to be defined and measured. These measurements may be derived by means of sampling procedures or they may be built up from incomplete reports. Some variables are expressed as index numbers, and different choices of base periods and weights result in different numerical values for what is, in concept, a single variable.

Hence the variables of quantitative economic research are subject to error. The real relationship between any two such variables may be obscured or disturbed by fluctuations in other variables. The attempt to ascertain the slope of a demand curve involves us in a combination of economic and statistical problems.

Statistics is a discipline in its own right. Its principles are of wide applicability in many sciences. In this book we do not attempt a balanced coverage of statistics. We confine ourselves to those particular aspects of statistics that are relevant to the estimation of economic relationships.

1.1 ECONOMICS AND OTHER SCIENCES

Economics is concerned with the use of scarce resources to produce commodities and distribute them among the members of society. This central

1

theme ramifies in many directions, including the allocation of resources and commodities over time, over space, among individuals, and among nations.

Economics is one of a number of sciences which deal with man and society. The boundaries between these sciences are somewhat arbitrary and change over time.

As a biological organism, man is a part of nature. His needs for food nutrients and for the insulating properties of clothing and shelter are jointly related to his biological makeup. In advanced contemporary economies the desire to reduce environmental stress expresses itself as an effective demand for central heating and air conditioning. Medical research and public health measures to control certain aspects of man's microbiological environment are having profound effects on the world economy, including the population explosion in less developed economies and increasing proportions of elderly persons in the more advanced ones.

Psychology has been described as a two-way funnel, into which the biological sciences converge and from which the social sciences diverge.[1] As a social science, psychology deals in part with the formation of human personality. Personality expresses itself largely in terms of attitudes toward and expectations of other people and expectations of oneself in relation to other people. The goals and personality traits described by psychologists and the terminology used by them appear to be several steps removed from the economist's area of concern. But the two disciplines are both talking about the same human beings and they are both relatively successful in predicting behavior in certain interpersonal and interfirm situations.

Cultural anthropology tries to encompass all social aspects of human life. It has been most successful and illuminating in the study of small, relatively isolated and self-contained groups of primitive people. In hunting and food-gathering societies, man's impact upon his environment was not greatly different from that of other species. Man had little storable wealth. Most of the foods captured or collected were perishable and were quickly consumed. A good deal of art and ritual was directed toward economic ends (successful hunting, bumper crops of acorns, etc.) through "sympathetic magic." Boys quickly learned the economic roles of their fathers and girls those of their mothers. Within a group consisting of at most a few hundred individuals we could find an integrated complex of phenomena which, in advanced societies, would have been separated into small clusters for study under the specialized headings of economics, political science, psychology, and sociology.

Complex modern societies provide the rationale for specialization within the social sciences. Economics gives much attention to the "rational" pursuit

[1] Henry W. Nissen, "Axes of Behavioral Comparison," in Anne Roe and George Gaylord Simpson (eds.), *Behavior and Evolution* (New Haven: Yale University Press), p. 187, 1958.

of stipulated objectives—for example, the pursuit of maximum utility or maximum real income by a consumer or the pursuit of maximum profit by a business firm. Political science deals mainly with topics such as the distribution and use of political power within a society. An economist has put forward a normative or optimizing model for political parties in a democracy— the party in power is conceived as trying to maximize its anticipated number of votes in the next election.[2] If so, the party should adopt a policy if it appears likely to gain more votes from citizens benefiting or approving than it will lose from citizens who will be adversely affected or who disapprove on other grounds.

Sociology is concerned with human beings as participants in and products of groups, organizations, and institutions. Many of the human wants which economists take as given are culturally determined. Sociologists may interpret the expenditures of a given household as an effort to emulate the expenditure patterns of some "reference group." Economists explain the same expenditures in terms of the more or less rational allocation of a given income among competing wants.

Economics also interacts with technology and with the physical and natural sciences. For example, materials and principles first developed for military purposes may displace other materials and technologies in production for civilian use. The depletion of a natural resource accompanied by a sustained increase in its relative price will direct the attention of private and public research and development organizations toward the development of substitute materials.

Thus economics deals only with certain facets of human activity. Economic statistics deals with those aspects of economics which require quantitative measurement or estimation in the presence of errors and disturbances, some of which are of a random or probabilistic character.

1.2 SUBDIVISIONS WITHIN ECONOMICS

Economic theory has selected its major problems from observations of real economic activities. Proprietors and other self-employed persons in a great many different industries and occupations are all guided in part by the desire to realize larger net incomes out of their existing limited resources. Economic theory expresses the essential features of all these situations in a compact body of rules and principles.

Although most elements of economic theory can be stated verbally, their validity and internal consistency can be subjected to more rigorous tests if the theories are expressed in mathematical form. *Mathematical economics* may

[2] Anthony Downs, *An Economic Theory of Democracy* (New York: Harper), 310 pp., 1957.

best be regarded as an extension of, or adjunct to, economic theory. New theoretical insights—or insights concerning kinds of economic phenomena that had previously escaped careful study—may occur to economists in a form that is not consciously mathematical. But mathematics is required to demonstrate the validity of the intuitive formulation and to define clearly the conditions under which the theory will hold.

During the past century, the principal contributors to economic theory have also been capable, and sometimes highly gifted, mathematicians. The further development of economic theory appears to require an even higher level of mathematical power and sophistication than it has in the past.

For economists economic theory is clearly antecedent to and takes precedence over economic statistics. Once it has been rather fully developed, economic theory is our primary guide in deciding what economic magnitudes are worth measuring and how they should be measured. Economic statistics then enters the picture as a guide to measuring individual variables and estimating relationships between variables.

Economic policy involves the exercise of governmental powers to influence the course of economic development and current economic activity.

Governments at various levels find themselves concerned with human values, some of which are not included in the conventional realm of economics. Intervention by governments to conserve or enhance essentially noneconomic values nevertheless changes the economic situations and opportunities of some people. A local zoning ordinance prevents an industrialist from building a factory on an otherwise desirable piece of property. Pure food and drug laws limit the economic opportunities of potential manufacturers and vendors while protecting potential consumers against probable ill effects.

Public regulatory activities often involve implicit comparisons between economic values and values which are generally regarded as noneconomic. As economists develop more elaborate and complete models for comparing economic benefits and economic costs, some of these "noneconomic" effects may be assigned price tags. For example, the effects of a smoky factory chimney upon the cleaning and painting bills and housekeeping energies of families living nearby could be estimated. Many such detailed effects could be lumped together with esthetic considerations by estimating the decline in the market values of neighboring residential properties resulting from the smoky chimney. Federal projects for irrigation, hydroelectric power production, flood control, and navigation on major river basins involve exceedingly complex calculations of economic costs and economic benefits to many groups of interested parties in many states.

Some economic policies are designed to impede the growth of extremely large business firms and to preserve the competitive structures of various industries. Some states have laws which prohibit the development of branch banking. Some states seek to maintain the gross margins of retailers through retail price maintenance laws. Taxes on cigarettes and alcoholic beverages may be imposed partly to produce revenue and partly to inhibit consumption. Labor legislation is adjusted from time to time in response to changing technology and economic conditions in addition to changing concepts of public welfare and governmental responsibility for it.

A great deal of economic policy takes the form of restrictions upon the activities of particular categories of economic agents. However, a very important branch of economic policy deals with the role of government, particularly national government, in promoting economic stability and growth.

For economists, economic policy, like economic theory, precedes and takes precedence over economic statistics. However, the need for quantifying the favorable and unfavorable effects of alternative economic policies upon various groups presents a tremendous challenge to economic statistics. If the economic statistician can demonstrate, within a moderate range of error, that a proposed policy will transfer about 100 million dollars of annual income from Group A to Group B, legislators are at least placed under pressure to decide consciously whether they wish to impose a penalty of this magnitude upon Group A in order to achieve a similar increase in income for Group B. The chains of causation and interaction which determine the ultimate effects of national economic policies are extremely complex and require a highly sophisticated combination of economic theory and statistical technique for their analysis.

The scope of applied economics may be illustrated further by enumerating some of the standard topics or specialties within economics as they appear in college and graduate school curricula. Agricultural economics, labor or manpower economics, urban or regional economics, economics of education, money and banking, public finance, national income analysis, monetary policy, fiscal policy, business cycle analysis, consumption economics, marketing, industrial organization, international trade, and economic development suggest the many institutional contexts in which economic principles may be applied. A great many of these applications in almost all fields of economics involve statistical problems of measurement and estimation.

Many topics in economic theory involve the mathematical principles of maximization and minimization. Problems involving maxima and minima are extremely widespread in other sciences as well as in economics. There are so many formal analogies between economic activities directed toward maximizing net income or profit, political activities directed toward maximizing the probability of election, and other human activities involving ends-means systems that many of the principles and techniques of economic theory find applications in other fields. Conversely, mathematical and statistical techniques initially developed while designing guidance systems for space vehicles may prove highly adaptable to the analysis of complex subsystems in an economy or the stability properties of the economy as a whole.

The fruitfulness of such analogies has led to the development of fields such as "operations research," "systems analysis," "control systems engineering," and "general systems analysis." These fields are essentially and consciously multidisciplinary in nature, although advanced training in mathematics, probability theory, and statistics appear to be prerequisite for creative work in them. The same disciplines, plus economic theory, also appear necessary for highly creative work in economic statistics. Economic statisticians are rapidly adapting themselves to the availability of large-scale electronic computers, and their interests, along with those of other scientists, are stimulating the development of faster computers with the capacity to handle larger and more complex problems.

The main points in the preceding discussion can be summarized as follows.

1. Economics deals with only a portion of human activity.

2. Economic and noneconomic goals and values jointly influence the economic behavior of households and business firms and the nature of public economic policy.

3. The scope of economic statistics is broad enough to include problems of measurement and estimation of relationships in all fields of applied economics.

4. "Applied economics" is essentially the application of economic theory to clusters of problems arising in particular economic sectors or in particular kinds of economic activity.

5. As economic theory is essentially mathematical in nature, new ideas, concepts, and techniques developed in other disciplines may be transmitted into economic theory and analysis through the common medium of mathematics.

6. Probability theory and statistics are of almost universal applicability (although of varying degrees of importance) throughout the sciences. Hence new concepts and analytical techniques can be expected to enter economic statistics from other disciplines via the common media of probability theory and mathematical statistics.

7. Formal analogies between problems of optimal decision-making in many fields of applied science have encouraged the development of consciously multidisciplinary fields such as management science and operations research. The self-conscious development of these fields as professional specialties can be expected to increase the rate of importation of new methods into economic statistics from other disciplines.

8. The rapidly expanding use of electronic computers in many disciplines,

including economics, further encourages the recognition of formal similarities between some problems in economics and some problems in other sciences.

9. On the negative side, these recent developments threaten to devalue the professional capital of economists who do not learn the new skills or ally themselves in constructive interactions with those who do. A "cook book" knowledge of descriptive statistics, meaning thereby the mere compilation of raw data into frequency distributions, the routine processing of time series, and the construction of index numbers, no longer suffices for professional economists.

10. On the positive side, an economist who learns those parts of mathematics, probability theory, and statistics which are most relevant to applied economics will at the same time acquire a key to the understanding of important segments of several other disciplines, and his work in economics will be broadened by his ability to recognize the relevance for economics of new techniques developed in other disciplines.

1.3   MEASUREMENT IN ECONOMICS

Much of economic theory is concerned with the principles of optimizing behavior for individual consumers or business firms.[3] The study of the behavior of individual units is sometimes called *microeconomics*. In contrast, the study of economic relationships and interactions in terms of large aggregates, often national totals, is sometimes called *macroeconomics*. Consistent with these categories, variables reflecting the behavior of an individual economic unit may be called *microvariables* and magnitudes reflecting the summation of all similar economic units in a region, a nation, or a sector of the economy are called *macrovariables*.

1.3.1   *The Measurement of Microvariables*

In concept, it would be quite possible to record every economic transaction made by the members of *a particular household*. The household members could, of course, keep such a record for themselves. Each item purchased could be precisely identified (with brand names, sizes, quality designations, and the like); the number of units of the commodity purchased at a given store on a given day could be noted, along with the price paid for it by the particular household member.

---

[3] "Optimizing" means maximizing when the best value is a maximum (for example, profit for a business firm) and minimizing when the best value is a minimum (for example, the total variable cost of producing a stipulated amount of output).

At this level of detail, members of each household would be involved in many thousands of economic transactions in the course of a year. Some of these transactions are conveniently lumped or aggregated. For example, a salaried worker's only money income may come in the form of a monthly paycheck. The household's use of electricity for many kinds of uses (lighting, washing clothes, cooking meals) may similarly be summarized in a single monthly bill from the power company.

Without belaboring these points further, we may simply note that most of the economic activities of a household can be measured in the forms of prices, quantities, amounts of money paid out, amounts of money received, and assets owned.

Most *businesses* of any size keep rather detailed sets of accounts. Every economic transaction reflected in the family income and expenditures of a household will be reflected in the receipts of the firm that sold the commodity or the disbursements of the firm that paid the salary or wages to the household member.

As a rule firms purchase inputs (raw materials and factors of production) and sell outputs (goods or services). Thus the economic activities of a firm can be expressed for the most part in terms of prices, quantities, expenditures, and receipts, just as can the activities of a household.

Government enterprises, such as municipal water or electrical utilities, keep books much like those of business firms. The receipts and expenditures of other public agencies are also entered in their accounts.[4]

Finally, the receipts and expenditures of private nonprofit institutions and organizations, religious, educational, and social, also give rise to microvariables such as numbers of employees, wage and salary disbursements, and purchases of goods and services.

1.3.2 *The Measurement of Macrovariables*

A set of accounts for a household should enable us to calculate its real level of consumption and the net change in the value of its assets—both measures of the household's economic welfare. Similarly, a set of accounts for a business firm should enable us to calculate its current earnings and the net change in the value of its assets, which are appropriate measures for appraising the economic success of the firm.

---

[4] There is some ambiguity in deciding how large a government enterprise must be before the records of its receipts and expenditures are regarded as *macro-* rather than *microvariables*. But similar ambiguity might logically be attached to variables describing the economic behavior of General Motors or the American Telephone and Telegraph Corporation. Certainly, most enterprises and agencies of state and local governments would be subjects for microanalysis.

"Social accounts," or national income and product accounts, are in concept simple summations of the accounts of individual households, business firms, nonprofit institutions, and governmental units. If every microeconomic unit kept accurate and detailed accounts according to some uniform format, we could simply process them all through a computer, arriving at the corresponding set of macrovariables by direct addition.

In practice, of course, we do not have such detailed and uniform records covering all the economic transactions of all microunits. Hence the construction of national income and product accounts for (say) the United States requires the matching, splicing, and reconciliation of economic records and estimates from many sources.

Macrovariables also differ from microvariables in one very important respect. Microvariables reflect the decision-making activities of an identifiable household or an identifiable business firm. Members of the individual household actually observe the prices that we describe as microvariables and, in the light of these prices and of the household's income and assets, select the quantities of each good and service purchased. The particular set of quantities that the household selects influences the level of satisfaction attained by members of the household. As a rule its purchases are made without consultation with other households and its purchases have only a diffuse effect, if any, on the sense of well-being of other households.

The corresponding macrovariables on average prices paid and total quantities purchased by millions of households cannot be related directly to the economic welfare of a corresponding "macrohousehold." None of the individual households are trying to optimize the economic position of such a mystical macrohousehold. Hence we must use considerable care in attaching welfare connotations to changes in macrovariables or in assuming that relationships between macrovariables will have the same interpretation as those between microvariables for a particular household. The same cautions apply to macrovariables that reflect the total outputs, inputs, receipts, and expenditures of a great many business firms.

Nevertheless, comprehensive sets of macrovariables such as national income and product accounts can tell us a great deal about the over-all performance of a national economy. Additional light can be provided by more elaborate macroeconomic frameworks, such as input-output tables and econometric models.

An interesting and potentially fruitful approach to problems of economic decision-making by national governments is the concept of a preference function which is ascribed to "the policymaker" who makes the final decision on government actions. The policymaker is assumed to appraise the performance of the economy in terms of macrovariables. He is regarded as capable of defining alternative positions of the national economy in terms of sets of values of macrovariables such as employment, real consumer expenditures, and the balance of international payments, and stating that he prefers some positions of the national economy to others. In a democracy, "the policymaker" arrives at his decisions after listening to the advice of many people and within limits set by law or convention. He may be the spokesman of a political party or the announcer of what appears to him to be the most desirable compromise between divergent interests. But the idea of a preference function held by a policymaker does provide a starting point for discussing economic policy in a quantitative, optimizing framework.

1.3.3 *Problems of Aggregation in Economics*

The human mind cannot encompass and interpret the totality of economic activity as reflected in every transaction of every microeconomic unit. If we had a running record of every economic transaction made by the members of a household hour by hour through a calendar year, we would be obliged to classify and summarize or aggregate the basic transactions before we could begin to make sense of them or use them in some way to evaluate the purchasing behavior of the household.

For example, even if we preserved full commodity detail, we might choose to aggregate the purchases over time into weekly, monthly, or quarterly units or even into annual totals. Already we do some violence to the real economic behavior of the household. The price of a commodity may have differed from day to day within any of these time units, so that "the average price" during a given month or year is itself an abstraction which was never directly observed or experienced by members of the household.

To summarize the accounts of an individual household, we would also find ourselves aggregating over commodities. First, we might lump together the different brands of a commodity such as (say) canned tomatoes purchased during the year. Next, we might proceed to higher levels of commodity aggregation such as *all canned vegetables, all vegetables, all fruits and vegetables,* and *all foods.* We might go on to even more comprehensive classifications, such as those of *consumer durable goods, consumer nondurable goods,* and *services* which figure in the national income and product accounts of the United States. At each successive level of aggregation the concept of an average price and a total quantity purchased becomes increasingly abstract.

Some aspects of aggregation and classification will be discussed in Chapters 5 and 14. But it is important to recognize that problems of aggregation are omnipresent in constructing, estimating, and interpreting economic macrovariables of all sorts. They are not essentially statistical in the sense of "probabilistic," but they must be faced by the economic statistician as he applies his techniques to the estimation of relationships among such variables.

1.4   THE PLAN OF THE BOOK

The object of this book is to integrate a knowledge of relevant statistical techniques with the central problems and concepts of modern economics. All chapters except Chapter 3 are concerned with the estimation or measurement of relationships between two or more variables.

As we have noted, the scope of economic statistics is broad enough to include all problems of estimation and measurement in economics that involve statistical or probabilistic elements. The chapters also include one or two topics, such as aggregation, which are presented initially in terms of exact functions rather than statistical relationships.

Chapter 2 includes a brief review of economic concepts (indifference curves, production functions, market demand, and supply curves, etc.) which are mentioned in introductory economics courses and are drawn upon in the subsequent statistical chapters.

Chapter 3 presents a similarly brief review of statistical concepts relating to a single random variable, including frequency distributions, relations between populations and samples, the rudiments of statistical inference, and the use of tables based on the normal, t and F distributions. We assume that the student has had an introductory course in statistics covering most of these topics.

Chapter 4 introduces simple regression analysis in terms of relationships between two frequency distributions. It presents the logic and the arithmetic of simple regression calculations but does not make use of sampling concepts.

Chapter 5 deals with index numbers and time series from the traditional point of view. Because of the limitation of space, these topics are not discussed in detail. The student who is interested in descriptions of particular index numbers can refer to the annotated references at the end of the chapter. The traditional approach to analysis of economic time series has been somewhat modified to show its relationship to regression analysis. Also, the partitioning of the variation of the original observations into seasonal, trend, cyclical, and random or erratic components is related to frequency distributions and variance analysis.

Chapters 6 and 7 deal with simple and multiple regression analysis. The interpretation of regression results differs considerably between two basic types of situations. Interpretation is clearest for experimental observations— namely, observations in which values of the independent or explanatory variables have been deliberately preassigned by an experimenter. The *regression model*, as this situation may be called, has been very highly developed in the biological sciences and in other fields in which experimentation is easily possible.

During the 1920s and 1930s many economists absorbed uncritically the terminology and emphasis on *correlation* that was appropriate to the kinds of data with which some of the pioneer biometricians were concerned. The meaning of correlation coefficients is unequivocal only when the observations that are being correlated have been randomly drawn from a normal bivariate or multivariate population. A clear recognition of the difference between the *correlation model* and the *regression model* should enable the next generation of economists to avoid many of the mistakes of its predecessors.

Chapter 8 treats a few aspects of the analysis of variance that are particularly germane to regression analysis.

Chapter 9 emphasizes what may be called the multivariate approach to economic time series, in that the movements of a particular variable are explained primarily in terms of its relationship to other measurable variables which are themselves changing over time.

Chapters 10, 11, and 13 relate economic statistics to the revolution in macroeconomic theory which has occurred since the middle 1930s. Chapter 10 discusses some recent attempts to construct large-scale models of the economy of the United States. Each equation of a well-known model of the United States economy is approximated by means of an ordinary least-squares regression equation, using techniques thoroughly explained in Chapters 6 and 7. Discussion of this model and of the new (1965) Brookings Institution-Social Science Research Council model of the United States discloses several clusters of statistical problems, which are enumerated in Chapter 10. Then, each major cluster of problems is treated in detail in Chapters 11 and 13.

Chapter 11 gives a clear discussion of the identification problem; a clear statement of the circumstances under which ordinary least-squares regression methods are not only adequate but preferable to alternative estimation methods; a discussion of causal ordering and its usefulness in deciding what techniques of statistical estimation are most appropriate for various equations and subsystems in a multiple-equation model; and an exposition of the method of two-stage least squares.

Chapter 12 includes a brief survey of the maximum likelihood method and other methods of estimation.

Chapter 13 extends the treatment of multicollinearity or high intercorrelation among independent variables into the setting of multiple-equation models. Considerable attention is given to the meaning of *a priori* or extraneous information, that is, information from other economic or statistical analyses used to supplement the information contained in a given sample of (usually time series) observations. For practical purposes high intercorrelations among economic time series often force us to use other information to arrive at regression coefficients and equations that warrant structural interpretations. The use of *a priori* or extraneous information and conditional regression analysis has a fairly long history (several decades) in disciplines other than economics. At its best, the use of *a priori* information is an appeal to good economics to save an analysis from ambiguous statistics.

Chapter 14 discusses the measurement of economic aggregates. Most of the pure theory of economics deals with individual decision-making units, particularly consumers and business firms. All too often economists engaged in the analysis of market data or in the construction of macroeconomic models make little attempt to identify the coefficients of their aggregative relationships with those of the basic decision-making units. Chapter 14 includes a simple exposition of the concept of "perfect aggregation" which shows, under certain assumptions, the exact connection between the coefficients of demand curves and other microrelations of individual households and firms and the corresponding coefficients of relationships (*macrorelations*) among aggregates of many households or firms.

The traditional subject of index numbers is treated here as one aspect of the broader problem of measuring economic aggregates. The use of implicit price deflators in connection with the national income and product accounts of the United States is shown to have an affinity both with Theil's concept of perfect aggregation and with Irving Fisher's "Ideal Index Number" which figured so prominently in discussions of economic measurement during the 1920s and 1930s.

In general, we have selected examples either for their expository value or because they involve sets of data and sectors of the economy with which we are familiar as a result of our own research.

Real competence in the use of economic statistics tends to develop in close association with a sophisticated understanding of economic theory, institutions, and sources of data in the area or areas of economics with which one is concerned. An appropriate integration of the relevant economic theory and statistical techniques should become second nature to a practicing economist, although never too deeply engrained for scrutiny and reevaluation.

CHAPTER 2

A Review of Economic Concepts

Economic theory is almost exclusively concerned with relationships between two or more variables. Chapter 4 and other chapters will deal with the estimation of relationships between variables. This chapter therefore provides a brief review of economic concepts, most of which are used later.

Most of the economic concepts referred to can be found in textbooks on economic principles. They will also be found in more rigorous form in textbooks on economic analysis or prices and resource allocation written for undergraduate majors in economics.

2.1 THEORY OF THE CONSUMER

Figures 2.1 through 2.4 present some basic concepts of "rational" consumer behavior.

The curved solid line in Figure 2.1 represents an indifference curve. Let us assume we have defined two composite commodities that we will call *food* and *clothing*. We assume further that the consumer can respond to the following kind of experiment: If an experimenter places before him two alternative combinations of quantities of food and quantities of clothing, he is able to tell the experimenter that he prefers one to the other or that he is *indifferent* between the two.

The consumer will always prefer larger quantities to smaller quantities. Hence he will prefer the combination represented at point A (five units of food and five of clothing) to the combination represented at A_1 (three units of food and three of clothing). Similarly, he will prefer the combination represented by A_2 (eight units of food and eight of clothing) to the combina-

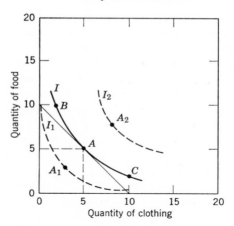

Figure 2.1 Indifference curves.

tion represented by point A. Since at these three points food and clothing are
combined in fixed proportions, we are offering the consumer three different
quantities of the single composite commodity "one unit of food plus one unit
of clothing"; we would expect him to prefer more units to fewer units of such
a commodity.

At points B, A, and C food and clothing are combined in different proportions. We assume the consumer has told the experimenter that the three
combinations (ten units of food and two of clothing; five units of food and
five of clothing; or two units of food and ten of clothing) are equally acceptable to him. He feels no better off with one combination than with another.

In deciding that combinations B, A, and C are equally desirable to him and
therefore lie on the same indifference curve, the consumer has considered only
quantities of the two commodities; the experimenter has not raised the
question of price at all. Now suppose our consumer sallies forth into the real
world. He visits a food store and he visits a clothing store and determines
how many dollars (1) a unit of food and (2) a unit of clothing will cost. We
further assume that the total amount of income the consumer is able to spend
on food and clothing combined is fixed at (say) $100 a month. If a unit of
food and a unit of clothing are each priced at $10, his income is sufficient to
buy ten units of food or ten units of clothing. It is not sufficient to buy ten
units of food plus two units of clothing; therefore his income does not permit
him to attain point B. Similarly, his income is not sufficient to purchase two
units of food plus ten units of clothing, so he cannot attain point C. He *can*
afford five units of food and five units of clothing, so the best allocation of
his income between food and clothing is that which brings him to point A.

The diagonal line in Figure 2.1 is sometimes referred to as a *budget line* or income constraint. The slope of the budget line is equal to the ratio of the price per unit of clothing to the price per unit of food. In this particular instance, we have assumed that the two prices are the same.

The budget line is the locus of all possible combinations of food and clothing which can be bought for precisely $100 at the stipulated prices. However, the only allocation of his $100 that will make him feel as well off as combinations *B* and *C* (either of which would cost $120) is combination *A*.

Indifference curve *I*, which includes points *A*, *B*, and *C*, is only one of a family of indifference curves which collectively constitute an *indifference map*. The indifference map may be thought of as a topographic map—the projection onto a plane of contour lines of an indifference *surface* in three dimensions. The two dimensions of the plane are quantity of food and quantity of clothing; the height of the surface, measured perpendicular to the plane, is utility or consumer satisfaction. Any other allocation of his income than that represented by point *A* would place the consumer on a lower indifference curve or utility level than *I*.

The slope of the indifference curve at any point given is the *marginal rate of substitution* of food for clothing, $-(\Delta Q_f / \Delta Q_c)$. It is the number of units of food which can be sacrificed for an additional unit of clothing if the consumer is to remain on the same indifference curve.

The slope of the budget line represents the number of units of food which must be forgone in order to purchase an additional unit of clothing. At the point of tangency of the budget line and the indifference curve, namely point *A*, the slopes of the line and of the curve are equal. Hence if the slope of the indifference curve is written as $-(\Delta Q_f / \Delta Q_c)$ and the slope of the budget line as P_c / P_f, at the point of tangency we have $-(\Delta Q_f / \Delta Q_c) = P_c / P_f$, and $-\Delta Q_f P_f = \Delta Q_c P_c$. At this point the allocation of one more dollar to clothing just compensates for the loss of satisfaction associated with a reduction of one dollar in outlays for food.

The indifference curves in Figure 2.1 are convex toward the origin of the quantity axes. This reflects a presumption of competitive or substitution relationships between the two commodities. This slope also implies a *diminishing marginal rate of substitution*: As the amount of clothing is increased, the consumer is willing to sacrifice smaller and smaller quantities of food for an additional unit of clothing. One economist has stated this succinctly as "the more you have of a thing, the less you want more of it."

A diminishing marginal rate of substitution gives rise to a downward sloping demand curve for a commodity by an individual consumer. For example, we might think of the horizontal axis in Figure 2.1 as representing a commodity for which the consumer spends only a small fraction of his income; the vertical axis could be regarded as measuring the quantity of all other commodities purchased by the consumer. If the prices of all other commodities remain constant, the shape of the indifference curve I implies that the consumer will sacrifice successively smaller quantities of "all other commodities" (or generalized purchasing power) to acquire successive additional units of the specific commodity represented on the horizontal axis. This means that the consumer will purchase larger quantities of the commodity only at lower prices. As we shall note later, this inverse relationship between price and consumption is also characteristic of market demand curves.

Figure 2.2 demonstrates the effects upon consumer purchases and welfare of a reduction in the price of one commodity, in this case, food. We assume our consumer to have an income of $100 a month, as in Figure 2.1, and that the price of clothing continues at $10 per unit. However, the price of food is reduced to $5 per unit, so that the consumer's income would now be sufficient to buy 20 units of food.

The price reduction obviously makes the consumer better off, for he could now acquire his original combination of five units of food and five units of clothing for only $75, leaving $25 to spend on additional quantities of food and/or clothing. If he continued to buy food and clothing in equal proportions, his $100 would now suffice to buy $6\frac{2}{3}$ units of each rather than five units of each as before.

However, the slope of the budget line is twice as steep as before. The best allocation of his income between the two commodities will occur at the point of tangency of the new budget line with a higher indifference curve I_1.

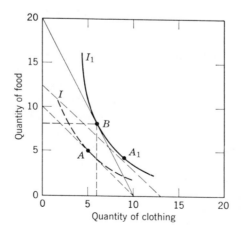

Figure 2.2   Effect of a price reduction.

The movement of the consumer's point of optimal allocation from A to B may be broken down into a *substitution effect* (a movement along a given indifference curve) and an *income effect* (a movement from a lower to a higher indifference curve). For example, if the price of food had remained at $10 a unit, and if the consumer had been given sufficient additional income to reach the indifference represented by I_1, he would have chosen A_1 involving an outlay of approximately $130 for nine units of clothing and four units of food. However, given the sharp reduction in the price of food *relative to* the price of clothing, the consumer achieves the same level of welfare at point B by purchasing six units of clothing and eight units of food.

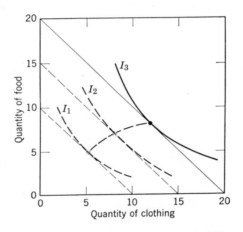

Figure 2.3   Effects of an increase in household income.

Figure 2.3 illustrates the effects of increasing consumer income upon consumer purchases if the prices of the two commodities remain constant. The three straight lines in Figure 2.3 are budget lines reflecting successively incomes of $100, $150, and $200 a month. Successively higher incomes enable the consumer to attain successively higher indifference curves. However, he may change the proportions of his income allocated to commodities even though their actual and relative prices remain constant. In this instance, the consumer is willing to allocate $50 of a $100 income to food, but only $80 of a $200 income. Thus a 100% increase in his income is associated with a 60% increase in his expenditures for food and a 140% increase in his expenditures for clothing. Roughly speaking, we may say that the income elasticity of his demand for food is 0.6 and the income elasticity of his demand for clothing is about 1.4.

Figure 2.4 shows five indifference curves that form a portion of the assumed indifference map of a consumer. The shape of the indifference curve I_5 implies that additional quantities of food beyond about 13 units will not increase the consumer's utility level or sense of well-being. His desire for food is completely satiated at this point.

The principles embodied in Figures 2.1 to 2.4 can, of course, be generalized to any number of commodities. If a "rational" consumer experienced changes in his income and changes in the prices of various commodities over a period of time, the quantities which he purchased of the various commodities could be explained in terms of movements along indifference curves in response to

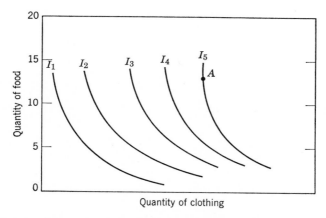

Figure 2.4 Indifference curves showing point of satiation for one commodity.

changes in relative prices and movements from one indifference curve to another in response to changes in real income. If the consumer's indifference map (his set of tastes, preferences, and attitudes) remained fixed, the changes in his purchases could be explained in terms of changes in the levels and slopes of the budget lines in successive time periods. (If we deal with three or more commodities, our budget lines become planes or hyperplanes and our indifference curves become surfaces in three or more dimensions. Fortunately, mathematical analysis can cope with any number of dimensions and hence any number of commodities.)

2.2 RESOURCE ALLOCATION AND THEORY OF THE FIRM

Figures 2.5 to 2.9 illustrate various aspects of the theory of production and resource allocation, which is usually treated as part of the theory of the firm.

Figure 2.5 shows a simple production function relating outputs (per unit of a fixed factor of production) to inputs of a variable factor of production (per unit of a fixed factor). For concreteness we might conceive of the fixed factor in each case as an acre of land, the variable factor as fertilizer, and the output as yield per acre (for example, bushels of corn).

The slope of the production function at Y_1 indicates the number of units increase in yield that will result from an additional input of one unit of the variable factor. The increment in Y in response to this last unit of A may be called the *marginal physical product* of A. The marginal physical product

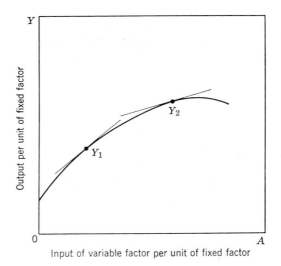

Figure 2.5 Diminishing returns.

ΔY multiplied (under perfect competition) by its price P_y is called the *marginal value product* of A.

But a unit of A has a cost which we will call P_a. If $\Delta YP_y > P_a$ at the point Y_1, the producer can increase his net income by applying additional units of A to each acre of land.[1] The shape of the production function in Figure 2.5 reflects *diminishing returns* or *diminishing marginal productivity*. The slope of the production function at Y_2 is considerably less than its slope at Y_1. For any given pair of prices of Y and A, namely P_y and P_a, the most profitable

[1] We assume that the demand curve facing the producer is horizontal, so that the increase in his own production, ΔY, does not appreciably affect the market price, P_y. The more general rule, which also covers the case in which the demand curve facing the producer is downward sloping, is that the marginal value product $\Delta YMR_y \geq \Delta AMFC_a$, where MR stands for marginal revenue and MFC for marginal factor cost.

level of application of A occurs at the point where $\Delta Y/\Delta A = P_a/P_y$. This also implies that $\Delta YP_y = \Delta AP_a$, or that the marginal value product equals the marginal cost of producing it.

Suppose the point of maximum profit in a given year occurs at Y_1. If the price of the output rises while P_a remains constant, a unit of Y will buy more units of A than before; hence it is profitable to increase the amount of A applied so that the marginal value product is again equated to the marginal cost.

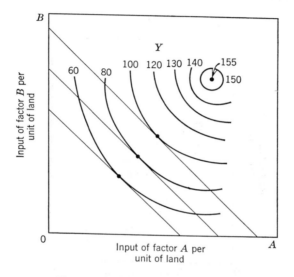

Figure 2.6 Isoquants and isocost lines.

A reduction in P_a would have the same effect as an increase in P_y. It is the *ratio* of P_a to P_y that determines the point of maximum profit on the production function and not the absolute levels of the prices.[2]

Figure 2.6 depicts a *production surface* in which the level of output Y depends jointly on two variable inputs. The shape of the production surface reflects the fact that the variable inputs are used in conjunction with a fixed factor and the output is also limited by a fixed factor. We might visualize the factors A and B as two kinds of fertilizer, nitrogen and phosphate, applied to an acre of land and Y as measuring the yield of corn per acre.

[2] We leave out of this presentation the many qualifications concerning attitudes toward uncertainty, price expectations, capital rationing, and imperfect knowledge which influence the behavior of producers under various circumstances. Similar abstractions were made in presenting the theory of consumer demand.

The successive curves in Figure 2.6 are successively higher *isoquants* or "equal output" contours on a three-dimensional production surface which is convex from above, implying diminishing marginal physical returns to both of the variable inputs A and B. The isoquant nearest the origin includes all combinations of B and A that are capable of producing 60 bushels of corn per acre.

If B and A are used to denote the quantities of the two factors, the slope of the isoquant at any given point may be written as $-(\Delta B/\Delta A)$. The slope of the lines drawn tangent to the isoquants is equal to the ratio of the prices of the

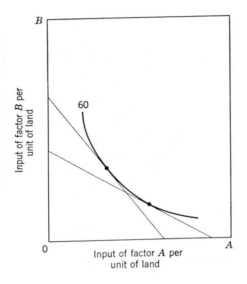

Figure 2.7 Effect of a change in relative prices of two inputs.

two inputs P_a/P_b. The shape of the isoquants implies a *diminishing marginal rate of substitution* of B for A in production. As more and more units of A are applied, the number of units of B which can be sacrificed for an additional unit of A *while maintaining Y at a specified level* (for example, on a given isoquant) rapidly decreases.

At a point of tangency the slopes of the isoquant and of the relative price line (sometimes called the *isocost* or *iso-outlay line*) are equal. The equality may be written as $-(\Delta B/\Delta A) = P_a/P_b$, which in turn implies that $-\Delta B P_b = \Delta A P_a$. This means that a dollar's worth of B can be withdrawn in exchange for an additional dollar's worth of A, leaving production unchanged. At the given price ratio P_a/P_b any other combination of B and A necessary to achieve a given isoquant would be more expensive than the combination needed to reach this isoquant at the point of tangency.

If we assume a situation of capital rationing, so that the producer has only (say) \$100 to allocate between the two factors, he should try to attain the highest isoquant or yield level possible under this budget restriction. A reduction in the price of B will increase the total amounts of one or both inputs which he can afford and will enable him to reach a higher isoquant. At the same time, the lower price of B will induce him to use more of B and less of A in achieving any given yield level.

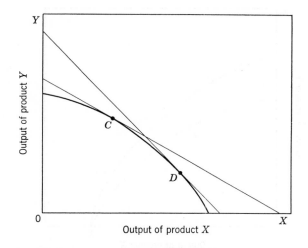

Figure 2.8 Production possibilities curve and isoincome lines.

Thus there is a close formal analogy between movements along an isoquant (a substitution effect) and a movement from one isoquant to another which, under capital rationing, might be called a purchasing power effect of the reduction in P_b. The movement along an isoquant in response to a change in the relative prices of B and A is illustrated in Figure 2.7. (We assume, of course, that marginal revenue exceeds marginal cost; otherwise it would be better not to produce at all.)

Figure 2.8 illustrates the allocation of a fixed bundle of resources between the production of alternative outputs or products, Y and X. The curved line CD is sometimes called a *production possibilities curve*. With respect to a particular firm, the curve includes all feasible combinations of outputs of Y and X which could be produced with the resources available to the firm.

The slope of the production possibilities curve at any point may be written as $-(\Delta Y/\Delta X)$. To increase the production of X by one unit, we must reduce or sacrifice the production of Y in the ratio of $\Delta Y/\Delta X$ units. This ratio (with a negative sign) is sometimes called the *marginal rate of transformation* of Y into X. As the output of X is increased, larger and larger amounts of Y must be sacrificed to achieve an additional unit of output of X.

The production possibilities curve implies a fixed bundle of resources or inputs available for use in production. In effect, the level of production expenditures is assumed constant. The producer is then visualized as allocating these fixed expenditures among Y and X in such a way as to maximize

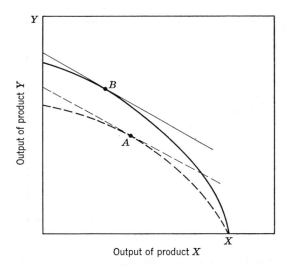

Figure 2.9   Effect of a reduction in cost of producing an output.

his gross income, $YP_y + XP_x$. (As production expenditures are assumed constant, maximizing gross income would also maximize net income.)

The straight line tangent to the production possibilities curve at C has a slope equal to P_x/P_y. The straight line itself (sometimes called an *isoincome line*) includes all combinations of Y and X which, at the given prices, would bring a given gross income. Given the shape of the production possibilities curve, under the specified price conditions any other point on the production possibilities curve would yield a smaller gross income than the combination represented by point C. At point C we have the relationship $-(\Delta Y/\Delta X) = P_x/P_y$, or $-\Delta YP_y = \Delta XP_x$. Thus in order to increase the output of X by one dollar's worth we must reduce the value of output of Y by an equal amount.

If P_y falls or if P_x rises, the relevant point of tangency is found at D. Under the new price relationships, maximum gross and net incomes are achieved by producing considerably more of X and considerably less of Y.

Finally, Figure 2.9 illustrates the effects of an improvement in technology which reduces the cost of Y or, what is the same thing, which increases the quantity of Y that can be produced with the given bundle of resources.

The production possibilities curve moves outward away from the origin, although the maximum amount of X which can be produced remains unchanged. If the prices of Y and X remain as before, gross income is increased. At the same time, production of Y is increased both absolutely and relative

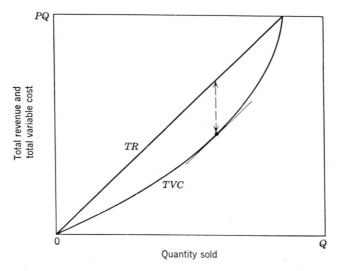

Figure 2.10   Constant average revenue and increasing marginal cost.

to production of X. We may note that an even more drastic reduction in the unit cost of producing Y *could* result in an absolute increase in the amount of X produced, although the output of Y would be increased still further relative to that of X.

Figures 2.5 to 2.9, then, summarize the "rational" responses of producers to changes (1) in the relative prices of outputs and inputs, (2) in the relative prices of alternative inputs, and (3) in the relative prices of alternative outputs. In each figure, we assume that the producer must take the prices of outputs and inputs as given and that he adjusts the quantities of his inputs and outputs in such a way as to maximize net income under these price conditions.

Revenue and Cost Curves. Figures 2.10 to 2.13 express other aspects of the theory of the firm. Figure 2.10 characterizes a firm operating in a purely competitive market such that the firm's own output does not affect the price it receives for its products. In such a case, average revenue and marginal revenue for the firm are equal (see Figure 2.12). Thus the total revenue curve *TR* is a straight line; its slope is equal to the price of the product. We assume total variable costs *TVC* to rise at an increasing rate; this implies a rising marginal cost curve for the firm (note that marginal costs are always variable costs). The most profitable level of output for the firm is that at which marginal revenue is equal to marginal cost. If the cost of producing an additional unit is less than the increased revenue which could be obtained from the sale of an additional unit, it obviously pays to increase production.

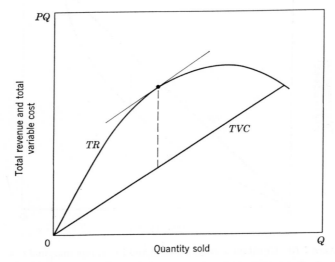

Figure 2.11   Decreasing average revenue and constant marginal cost.

In Figure 2.10, the *slope* of the total variable cost curve is equal to the marginal cost *MC*. Hence a tangent to the total variable cost curve parallel to *TR* identifies the production level at which marginal cost and marginal revenue are equal and net income is a maximum. In Figure 2.10 the difference between total revenue and total variable cost is available to cover fixed costs. Under perfect competition, the minimum average total cost per unit of each firm would be equal to the market price. The marginal cost curve would also intersect the average cost curve at its minimum point, which would be its point of tangency to the horizontal line *AR* = *MR*, or price = average revenue = marginal revenue, in Figure 2.12.

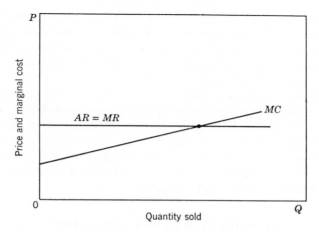

Figure 2.12   Constant average revenue and increasing marginal cost.

Figures 2.11 and 2.13 illustrate the situation of a firm which produces a highly differentiated commodity or which produces such a large proportion of total output that an increase in the volume of its own output decreases the price it receives for its product. In this case, the average revenue curve is shown as a downward sloping straight line. The corresponding total revenue curve is a second-degree parabola, convex from above. In Figure 2.13, we have also assumed a constant marginal cost curve. The corresponding total variable cost curve is a straight line, as shown in Figure 2.11.

The most profitable output for the firm is again achieved at the point where marginal revenue is equal to marginal cost, as indicated in Figure 2.13. In

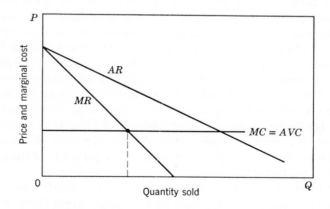

Figure 2.13   Decreasing average revenue and constant marginal cost.

Figure 2.11, the slope of the total variable cost curve is equal to marginal cost and the slope of the total revenue curve is equal to the marginal revenue. Hence if we draw a tangent to TR parallel to TVC we identify the level of output at which marginal revenue and marginal cost are equal (as in Figure 2.13) and at which net income is a maximum.

Clearly, average revenue is the price of an output or collection of outputs and marginal cost is a function of the prices of one or more inputs. Hence the implications of Figures 2.10 to 2.13 are consistent with those of Figures 2.5 to 2.9—an increase in the prices of outputs or a decrease in the prices of inputs will tend to expand the profit-maximizing output of the firm. Conversely, an increase in prices of inputs or a decrease in prices of outputs will tend to reduce the most profitable output of the firm.

2.3 MARKET DEMAND AND SUPPLY

In discussing the concept of diminishing marginal rate of substitution in consumption, we presented a basis for the downward slope of the consumer demand curve. The demand curve for a particular commodity by a given consumer would indicate that, in general, the consumer would buy larger quantities of the commodity if its price were reduced (other prices and the consumer's money income remaining constant). It is a simple matter conceptually and graphically to add up the demand curves of two or more consumers to obtain a relationship between the price charged for the commodity to all consumers and the total quantity purchased by all consumers included in the aggregate.

Similarly, we could aggregate the supply curves of two or more firms to give an aggregate or market supply curve for the group of firms as a whole. This process is illustrated in Figure 2.15 for firms operating under conditions of pure competition. As in Figure 2.12, the horizontal lines imply that marginal revenue and average revenue for each firm are equal and are, in fact, the same for both firms. At successively higher market prices, each firm will find it profitable to expand its output to the point at which its marginal cost is equal to the market price (and which is also the marginal revenue under pure competition). Unless the market price equals or exceeds the minimum level of the average variable cost curve for a given firm, no production will take place; for higher prices, the supply curve of the firm is its marginal cost curve. Hence the market supply curve for an aggregate of many firms operating under pure competition is in concept an aggregate of the marginal cost curves of the individual firms.

Figure 2.14 simply illustrates the determination of market price by the intersection of a market demand curve and a market supply curve. If market demand, as represented by D, remains constant, whereas costs of production

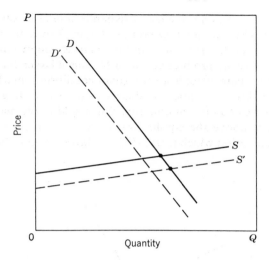

Figure 2.14   Market demand and supply curves.

are reduced, prices in a competitive market will fall. Output will increase less than if price had remained at its previous level, and the quantity demanded or purchased will increase somewhat above its previous level. Shifts in the market demand curve arising from changes in consumer income and in prices of competing commodities will also influence market prices and hence the quantities produced by suppliers.

Figures 2.1 to 2.15 are all essentially static and represent situations at a particular moment in time. Figures 2.16 and 2.17 depict the simplest form of

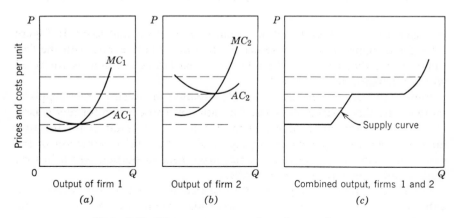

Figure 2.15   Firm cost curves and market supply curve.

dynamic model in economic theory (a dynamic model involves time lags). The equilibrium price and quantity point in Figure 2.16 is given by the intersection of the market demand curve and the market supply curve. If for any reason suppliers actually produce and offer for sale a larger-than-equilibrium quantity, the immediate effect is a lower-than-equilibrium market price.

In reacting to this lower price producers in the succeeding time interval supply *less* than the equilibrium quantity. When sold in the market, it brings a price somewhat above the equilibrium price. This in turn encourages a supply in the next period which is still slightly above the equilibrium amount;

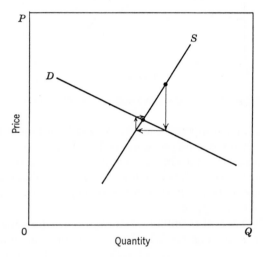

Figure 2.16 Cobweb model, convergent case: demand more elastic than supply.

this leads to a price slightly below the equilibrium price, and so on. In Figure 2.16, the demand curve is more elastic than the supply curve, with the fortunate result that an initial disturbance of market equilibrium is corrected within a few production periods.

Figure 2.17 depicts the less fortunate situation in which market supply is more elastic than market demand. An initial overproduction for any reason leads to a substantial reduction in market price as a result of the inelastic demand. Because suppliers are highly sensitive to a price reduction in the situation illustrated, there is a drastic curtailment of output, which in turn leads to an extremely large rise in price.

Figures 2.16 and 2.17 represent two particular aspects of the well-known cobweb model, which can be generalized and extended to many economic situations involving sequential impacts and reactions over time.

Derived Demand. Consumption is the object of a large proportion of economic activity, and consumer demand is often referred to as a *final demand*. This means that the great majority of goods and services purchased by consumers do not reappear in the economy as objects of purchase by others.

The retailer confronts the final demand curve of consumers, and the prices he charges consumers will (other things equal) determine the quantities he is able to sell to them.

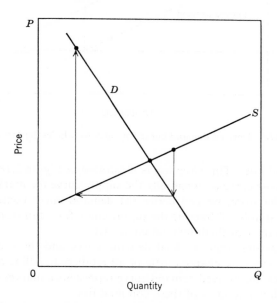

Figure 2.17   Cobweb model, explosive case: supply more elastic than demand.

However, the retailer buys the products he sells from wholesalers (including manufacturers' sales branches). His interest in buying is derived from his interest in selling. In terms of Figures 2.12 and 2.13, he is motivated to buy only as much as he can sell at that point at which the increase in his total revenue obtained by selling one additional unit to consumers is just equal to the invoice cost of the last unit bought from wholesalers *plus* the labor and other variable costs associated with handling the additional unit in the store.

Roughly speaking, if the marginal variable cost of labor and other inputs used in the retailer's store is about ten cents a unit over a considerable range of sales volumes, the price he can afford to pay to wholesalers is about ten cents a unit lower than the price he can charge to consumers for any given

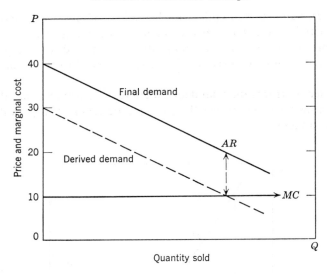

Figure 2.18 Derived demand curve for sales by wholesalers to retailers.

volume of final sales. This situation is illustrated in Figure 2.18. If we regard the marginal cost curve as essentially the supply curve for marketing services provided in the store, we can *derive* the demand curve confronted by the wholesaler by simply subtracting the supply curve for retail store services *MC* from the consumer or final demand curve *AR*.

If we now assume that the final demand curve and the supply curve for retail store services are characteristic of all retailers handling a given cluster of commodities, the derived demand curve represents a market demand curve confronting all wholesalers of these commodities.

Figure 2.19 compares the consumer demand curve for food with the derived demand curve confronting farmers on the assumption that the supply curve for all food marketing and processing services is horizontal over the relevant range of experience. In the early 1960s, a representative wage earner's household of three persons was spending about $1000 a year for a composite food unit known as "the Food Market Basket." Food processors and distributors received about $600 for their services in handling a Food Market Basket unit and farmers received about $400 for the raw products from which a Food Market Basket unit was assembled.

Since the consumer demand curve for food is quite steep (in the United States) and the supply curve for food marketing services appears to be nearly horizontal for a significant distance above and below the current volume of sales, the derived demand curve confronting farmers is less elastic than the consumer demand curve. As the figure is drawn, an increase of 1% in the

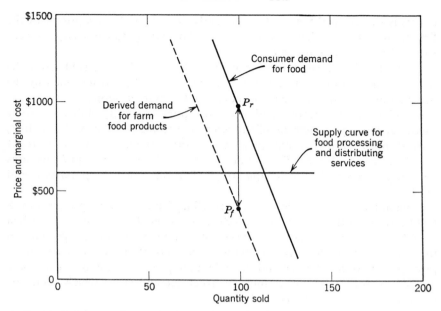

Figure 2.19 Consumer demand for food and derived demand for farm products.

volume of food sold to consumers would reduce the retail price of the Food Market Basket about $33 or 3.3%. The price received by farmers for the raw materials entering into the Food Market Basket would also decline about $33, but on a base of only $400. Hence the *percentage* decline at the farm level would be 8.25, compared with a percentage decline at retail of only 3.3.

A similar situation confronts producers of raw agricultural and mineral products in some countries for export to others. Processing, distribution, and transportation charges, and tariffs and excise taxes, if any, cause the demand curve confronting primary producers to be much less elastic than the demand curve of the final consumers themselves. This situation lends itself to large percentage fluctuations in prices of primary products.

The demand for factors of production may also be viewed as a derived demand. The rising marginal cost curve in Figure 2.12 might result from the fact that increased inputs of a variable factor (for example, labor) combined with fixed factors such as the existing floor area and layout of a store will after a point increase total cost more than it will increase total revenue from sales.

If the final or consumer demand curve shifts to the right, the retail price that can be charged for any given volume of sales is increased; for any given firm the point of intersection of the marginal cost and marginal revenue curves is shifted to the right. Consequently, it will pay the proprietor of the firm to hire more workers and increase his borrowings to carry larger inventories of goods ready for sale.

Similarly, the demand for factor A in Figure 2.5 is derived from the demand for the output Y. The price of the output, P_y, is determined by the intersection of a market demand curve and a market supply curve for Y. The optimal level of output (and hence the optimal quantity of factor A to be used) depends upon the *ratio* of the price of A to the price of Y, P_a/P_y. If P_y falls, P_a must fall by the same percentage if the initial level of use of factor A is to be justified. Hence if P_y is set at successively lower levels and P_a remains constant, successively smaller quantities of factor A will be purchased and used.

A manufacturer or wholesaler who is selling factor A to the producer of Y will be aware of the fact that this producer buys smaller quantities of A when P_y falls. If there are many producers of Y and we know the production functions of each (the "transformation functions of A into Y") we can in principle determine the demand for A by each producer and aggregate these derived microdemand curves into a market demand curve which confronts the sellers or manufacturers of A.

Some economic models or frameworks assume a special form of the production function and at the same time assume away the existence of substitution of one factor for another in response to changes in their relative prices. For example, suppose that the production function in Figure 2.5 is simply a straight line passing through the origin of the Y and A axis. If this is the production function, Y and A will always change in precisely the same proportion. The number of units of A required to produce a unit of Y is a constant regardless of the level of output. The ratio of units of input to units of output is called a *technical coefficient* in the terminology of input-output analysis.

Because there is no such thing as a tangent to a straight line, there is no room for relative prices to influence the technical coefficient if the production function is indeed a straight line.

2.4 SOME CONCEPTS OF MACROECONOMICS

We will make brief mention here of two of the most important frameworks used in macroeconomic analysis, the national product and income accounts (or "social accounts") and input-output analysis.

2.4.1 *National Product and Income Accounts*

The *gross national product* of an economy may be classified into major types of final sales or deliveries to final demand. Deliveries to final demand include personal consumption expenditures, gross private domestic fixed investment (construction of new buildings and purchases of new durable equipment), government purchases of goods and services, the net change in inventories of goods in the economy, and net exports of goods and services. In the United States in 1966 the gross national product and its major components were as follows:

	Deliveries to Final Demand, 1966 (billions of dollars)
Gross national product	739.5
Personal consumption expenditures	465.0
Gross private domestic investment	116.5
Net exports of goods and services	4.9
Exports	42.9
Imports	(−) 38.0
Government purchases of goods and services	153.1
Federal	77.0
State and local	76.2

The *gross national income* is equal to the gross national product. The reasons for this equality require some elucidation.

Personal consumption expenditures are a component of gross national product. Money paid by consumers to business firms is distributed by firms as payments for the factors of production which they use. Thus business firms disburse wages and salaries to their employees; they pay interest to lending agencies for borrowed capital; they pay rent on the buildings they occupy if these are owned by others; and most firms also realize a proprietary net income or profit.

In addition to these disbursements to the owners of factors of production (including human skills "owned" by wage and salaried workers), business firms must use part of their gross receipts to cover depreciation—the physical deterioration of buildings and machinery and/or the shrinkage in their economic value as a result of obsolescence (essentially economic displacement by newer and more efficient types of structures and models of machinery). Sooner or later, this deterioration and obsolescence of fixed capital must be made good if the productive capacity of the economy is to be maintained at a constant level. If the construction of new plants and purchases of new equipment are barely sufficient to maintain the value of fixed capital, gross investment is just equal to depreciation and net investment is zero.

In short run, depreciation charges may simply appear as an entry in the books of a business firm; in the longer run, these depreciation allowances must be offset or more than offset by gross investment, which involves tangible economic activities.

Indirect business taxes, such as sales and excise taxes, appear implicitly in the gross national product so they must also appear in the gross national income. In this particular case, the disbursements are made by business firms to local, state, and federal governments.

For the United States in 1966 the gross national income and its major components were as follows:

	Outlays for Factors of Production, 1966 (billions of dollars)
Gross national income	739.5
Capital consumption allowances (depreciation)	63.1
Indirect business taxes (and minor items)	65.5
Compensation of employees	433.3
Proprietors' income	57.8
Business and professional income	41.8
Net income of farm operators	16.0
Rental income of persons	18.9
Corporate profits and inventory valuation adjustment	79.8
Net interest	20.0

Intermediate sales from one business firm to another do not enter into the gross national product. If we added to the price paid for a new automobile by a consumer the price paid for that same automobile by the dealer to the manufacturer, we would clearly be counting the same thing twice.

The amount paid by the consumer for the automobile is included in personal consumption expenditures and hence in the gross national product or deliveries to final demand. If we subtract from the price of the automobile paid by the consumer the price paid for the automobile by the dealer, we have a measure of the "value added" by the dealer. The dealer may, of course, buy other goods and services, such as natural gas to heat his building and electricity to light his garage and display rooms. But the "value added" by the dealer is the amount available to him over and above these purchases from other firms, and this "value added" is the amount which he distributes to the owners of factors of production used directly in his own firm.

The automobile manufacturer in turn may buy steel, tires, and various parts and accessories from other firms. Here too only the "value added by manufacture" enters into the gross national product and is available for distribution to the owners of factors of production.

Thus the gross national product may be regarded as the sum of *values added* by the use of factors of production. The entire economic system may be viewed as a machine for transforming factors of production (land, labor, capital, and management) into goods and services delivered to final demand (personal consumption expenditures, gross private domestic investment, government purchases of goods and services, and net exports). The efficiency of the economic system may be measured by the volume of goods and services it delivers to final demand through the utilization of given quantities of the basic factors of production.

From this Olympian point of view, all intermediate sales are merely incidental to the basic function of the economic system in transforming factors of production into goods delivered to final demand. The only derived demands of consequence would then be the demands for basic factors of production as derived from the final demands of consumers, businesses, government, and foreign buyers (less quantities imported from other countries for use in the nation with which we are concerned).

If we personified "*the* final demander" (an intellectually dangerous thing to do) and endowed him with an indifference map of which the curve I in Figure 2.20 is one contour, the optimal production program for the economy as a whole would be identified by the point of tangency between the production possibilities curve RS and the indifference curve I. At this point A the marginal rate of transformation of Y into X in production is equal to the marginal rate of substitution of Y for X in satisfying final demand. Technological improvements in the production of either Y or X or both would

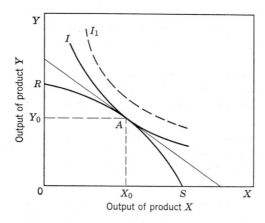

Figure 2.20   Final demand and total output equilibrium for a national economy.

shift the production possibilities curve upward and to the right, so that the new optimal production program for the economy would be found at the point of tangency of the new production possibilities curve with a higher contour of the final demander's indifference map. The real income and the sense of well-being of the final demander would be increased.

The straight line tangent to both RS and I at A has a very interesting interpretation. On the one hand, it serves as the budget line or income constraint of the final demander—the total amount available with which to pay for *deliveries to final demand*. From this viewpoint ($Y_0P_y + X_0P_x$) is the *gross national product*. On the other hand, the straight line serves as an isorevenue line for the producer. Since we have cancelled out all intermediate sales, the resources underlying the production possibilities curve consist exclusively of the ultimate factors of production. Hence from this viewpoint ($Y_0P_y + X_0P_x$) is the *gross national income*—the gross amount available for compensating owners of the basic factors of production.[3]

2.4.2 *Input-Output Analysis*

Input-output analysis can be regarded as an extension of national product and income accounts to depict the flow of intermediate sales between groups of similar firms (industries). On certain assumptions concerning the shape of production functions, an input-output table or *transactions matrix* enables us to estimate the effect of one industry's increasing its deliveries to final demand upon the required output levels of all other industries in the economy.

The special form of the production function assumed in input-output analysis is illustrated in Figure 2.21. If the output of industry j, X_j, is increased by one unit, its purchases of inputs from industry 1 are increased by a_{1j} units, where $a_{1j} = X_{1j}/X_j$. Because of aggregation problems previously mentioned, X_j and X_{1j} are usually measured in terms of dollar values at specified fixed prices—usually, average prices in a particular year. Similarly, purchases of inputs by industry j from industry 2 would change in proportion to $a_{2j} = X_{2j}/X_j$.

Our X_j is a measure of the total gross output or gross sales of industry j. Total gross output is equal to total gross outlay or purchases, including purchases of intermediate goods as well as payments to the basic factors of production.

Suppose that an economy is subdivided into 20 industries or sectors. Then the total gross output of industry j is distributed among intermediate sales to some or all the other 19 industries and deliveries to various categories of final demand.

---

[3] Gross national income also includes indirect business taxes, as we have seen. Technically it is as if governments had an equity in business firms—or in the rights of business firms to try to pass on excise and sales taxes to consumers.

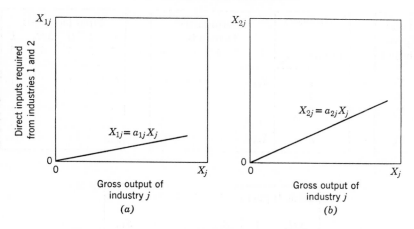

Figure 2.21 Basic relationships in input-output analysis.

Figure 2.22 outlines the structure of an economy in the input-output format. Total economic activity is divided into n categories. Deliveries to final demand are divided into five broad categories, personal consumption expenditures (C), gross private domestic fixed investment (I), government purchases of goods and services (G), the increase in inventories in each industry where an increase occurs (ΔH_a), and gross exports (E). The basic inputs are divided into eight categories: inventory depletions for those industries showing depletions ($-\Delta H_d$), gross imports (M), depreciation (D), indirect business taxes (T_b), wage and salary payments (W), interest (i), net rent (R), and before-tax profits (π).

The national product and income accounts incorporate the following identities:

$$(2.1) \qquad \text{GNP} = C + I + G + (\Delta H_a - \Delta H_d) + (E - M)$$

$$= \text{TG output} - \Delta H_d - M - \sum_{i=1}^{n} \sum_{j=1}^{n} X_{ij}$$

$$(2.2) \qquad \text{GNI} = D + T_b + W + i + R + \pi$$

$$= \text{TG outlay} - \Delta H_d - M - \sum_{i=1}^{n} \sum_{j=1}^{n} X_{ij}$$

and

$$(2.3) \qquad \text{GNI} = \text{GNP}$$

In these equations, GNP stands for gross national product and GNI for gross national income.

Total Gross Output	=	Industry \ Industry	Interindustry Demands					+	Final Demands				
			1	2	3	$\cdots$	n		C 1	G 2	ΔH_a 3	E 4	5
X_1		1	X_{11}	$\cdot$	$\cdot$	$\cdots$	X_{1n}	+	f_{11}	$\cdot$	$\cdot$	$\cdot$	f_{15}
X_2		2	$\cdot$				$\cdot$		$\cdot$				$\cdot$
X_3		3	$\cdot$				$\cdot$		$\cdot$				$\cdot$
$\vdots$		$\vdots$	$\vdots$				$\vdots$		$\vdots$				$\vdots$
X_n		n	X_{n1}	$\cdot$	$\cdot$	$\cdots$	X_{nn}		f_{n1}	$\cdot$	$\cdot$	$\cdot$	f_{n5}

+

Basic Inputs		1	2	3	$\cdots$	n
ΔH_d	1	S_{11}	$\cdot$	$\cdot$	$\cdots$	S_{1n}
M	2	$\cdot$				$\cdot$
D	3	$\cdot$				$\cdot$
T_b	4	$\cdot$				$\cdot$
W	5	$\cdot$				$\cdot$
i	6	$\cdot$				$\cdot$
R	7	$\cdot$				$\cdot$
π	8	S_{81}	$\cdot$	$\cdot$	$\cdots$	S_{8n}

=

Total Gross Outlay or Income	X_1	X_2	X_3	$\cdots$	X_n

Figure 2.22 Input-output structure of an economy.

The double summation term in (2.1) and (2.2) represents the interindustry demands—flows of raw materials, semimanufactures, components, and services—which are pronounced and relatively stable features of a mature economy. These intermediate flows are "netted out" in calculating GNP and GNI, but they constitute an extremely important mechanism for transmitting changes in activity in a given industry into changes in output and employment in other industries. Whenever economic measures are adopted which stimulate consumption, investment, or exports, or which increase government purchases of goods and services, this interindustry purchase and sales mechanism is called into play. It also operates when measures are taken to reduce final demand.

The input-output nexus between final demand and total gross output may be stated as follows:

Let

$$(2.4) \qquad a_{ij} = \frac{X_{ij}}{X_j} \qquad i, j = 1, 2, \ldots, n$$

so that $X_{ij} = a_{ij}X_j$. An increase of one million dollars in X_j (the gross output of industry j) will require *directly* an increase of a_{ij} million dollars of inputs from industry i. But the increase in output of industry i will in turn call for an increase in inputs from industry k, which might call for additional inputs from industry j.

It is possible to convert the set of technical coefficients a_{ij} into another set of coefficients α_{ij} which enable us at once to calculate *both the direct and indirect effects* of an increase in X_j upon the output levels required of each of the other $n - 1$ industries. Thus, if ΔF_j denotes an increase in deliveries to final demand from industry j, the required increase in output from any industry i is

$$(2.5) \qquad \Delta X_i = \alpha_{ij}(\Delta F_j)$$

An increase in the output of industry j requires increased employment in industry j. The input-output mechanism reflected in (2.5) indicates that an initial increase in X_j will also lead to some increases in employment in the other $n - 1$ industries, with some, of course, more than others. Hence, if government policy makers can find and use means for increasing deliveries to final demand, they also have a means for increasing employment. If policy makers are in a position to increase deliveries to final demand from a single industry (for example, by simply stockpiling its products for some future contingency), they can also focus the bulk of the employment effect upon workers associated with that industry.

Other means available to policy makers might be more general and diffuse in their impacts. For example, a reduction in personal income tax rates will increase the disposable personal incomes of nearly all households, and personal consumption expenditures will be increased for virtually all categories of consumer goods and services. Although employment increases may be more concentrated in some industries than in others, employment will rise in activities as remote from the consumer as steel production and the mining of iron ore as well as in automobile factories and clothing stores.

We will not go into the subtleties of multiplier theory and Keynesian economics here. However, the nature of multiplier processes can be illustrated with the aid of Figure 2.22 and, in fact, the coefficients α_{ij} as a group may be regarded as a generalization of the simple Keynesian multiplier.

An increase in the rate of business investment in plant and equipment increases the levels of sales and of factor payments on the part of several industries. Persons receiving these factor payments will pay additional income taxes and lay aside additional personal savings. Their personal consumption expenditures will increase by a smaller amount than the increase in their before-tax incomes.

The increased consumer expenditures, if prices remain stable, represent increased deliveries to final demand. These require increases in outputs and hence in factor payments in many or all industries. (Some of the increased expenditures go ultimately to pay for increased imports from other countries.) The "second round" increase in factor payments leads to an additional, but smaller, increase in consumer expenditures, so the first cycle is repeated. This is the basic process involved in the Keynesian multiplier. In a more general and complex form, it enters into most uses of input-output analysis and of macroeconomic models.

We will not introduce at this point a discussion of more complex models of national economies. The study and execution of economic policy at the national level more and more involve sophisticated analysis and the use of macroeconomic models. The national income and product accounts are an integral part of virtually all such models. The more sophisticated models by the middle of the 1960s were incorporating input-output transaction tables or coefficient matrices.

It is quite possible to conceive of the factors of production used in an industry as being related to one another and to the industry's output by means of a production function. Similarly, we could regard the retail prices of consumer goods and services and the quantities of them delivered to final demand as being related to one another through aggregative consumption functions.

Our verbal description of the transmission of successive rounds of effects through an input-output model suggests (although it does not necessarily require) a succession of time periods. Some economic policies achieve their effects with a time lag. The cobweb models of Figures 2.16 and 2.17 embody a simple one-period time lag structure, but they illustrate the nature of possible dynamic processes in more complex macroeconomic models.

EXERCISES

1. Show carefully why the slope of the budget line for two goods is the ratio of the prices of these two goods. Is it always a straight line?

2. Why are indifference curves convex to the origin? What effect does this convexity have on the slope of the demand curve for a commodity?

3. Using indifference curve analysis, where A and B are two commodities which are substitutes for each other, what is the effect on the quantity demanded of commodity A of

(a) an increase in the consumer's income.

(b) a decrease in the price of commodity *A*.

(c) a decrease in the price of commodity *B*.

4. Explain carefully the *income* and *substitution effects* in demand analysis.

5. Define carefully the concept of productivity in the theory of the firm. Distinguish between marginal productivity and returns to scale.

6. In terms of revenue and cost curves, explain carefully the relationships among total, average, and marginal curves. Why are economists so interested in marginal curves rather than total or average?

7. What is the economic meaning of the statement that a perfectly competitive firm faces a horizontal demand curve?

8. Explain carefully the distinction between "final demand" and "derived demand." Why is it necessary to draw this distinction between them in economics?

9. If we have a production function which exhibits diminishing marginal productivity, show that the demand curve for a factor of production which is in the production function is downward-sloping in perfect competition.

10. Illustrate the theoretical relationship between the Keynesian "multiplier theory" and the input-output analysis described in this chapter.

REFERENCES

1. Ferguson, C. E., *Microeconomic Theory*, Homewood, Illinois: Richard D. Irwin, 1966.
2. Henderson, J. M. and R. E. Quandt, *Microeconomic Theory: A Mathematical Approach*, New York: McGraw-Hill Book Co., 1958.
3. Leftwitch, R. H., *The Price System and Resource Allocation*, Revised edition, New York: Holt, Rinehart and Winston, 1964.
4. Liebhafsky, H. H., *The Nature of Price Theory*, Homewood, Illinois: The Dorsey Press, 1963.
5. Scitovsky, Tibor, *Welfare and Competition*, Chicago, Illinois: Richard D. Irwin, 1951.
6. Watson, D. S., *Price Theory and Its Uses*, Boston: Houghton Mifflin Co., 1963.

CHAPTER 3

A Review of Statistical Concepts

We have noted in Chapter 2 that economic theory is mainly concerned with functional relationships among variables. These relationships are certainly systematic and we usually assume them to be exact and continuous.

Probability theory is largely concerned with the properties of random variables. The notion of "randomness" has often been illustrated in terms of tossing coins, rolling dice, or drawing cards. The foundations of probability theory were laid by mathematicians who were fascinated by games of chance, but not particularly interested in natural science.

Later, astronomers and physicists faced the problem of dealing with errors of measurement. Annoying variations were encountered in repeated measurements of the same thing—the weight of a small object, the length of a metal bar, or the speed of sound.

Similarly, observations of the positions of a planet at successive points in time did not occur precisely on the smooth path called for by theory. Mathematically, an ellipse could be made to pass through three previously specified points, but through no more than three. If we had a hundred observations, we could select three points in

$$C_3^{100} = \frac{100!}{97!\,3!} = \frac{100 \cdot 99 \cdot 98}{1 \cdot 2 \cdot 3} = 161{,}700 \text{ ways}$$

and obtain 161,700 different ellipses. Yet our theory would specify that in fact there was only one "true" ellipse.

Astronomers were anxious to get rid of all but one of these ellipses, but felt obliged to do so in a dignified and reproducible way. Reasonable assumptions led the mathematician Gauss to the method of least squares for arriving at a unique curve (or a unique point estimate) from the complete set of

44

observations. These assumptions imply that the errors of measurement are essentially random drawings from a normal distribution. Probability theorists had arrived at this same distribution two or three generations earlier but with different purposes in mind.

Our interest in statistics in this book is that of the applied scientist. Typically, we seek to estimate systematic relationships among economic variables on the basis of empirical data. To arrive at a unique estimate of the systematic relationships, we must make assumptions about the nature of the deviations of actual observations from these relationships. The usual assumption is that the "deviation component" in each observation can be regarded as a random drawing from a normal distribution.

In the following discussion we shall highlight a few points that may be useful preliminaries to the real substance of the book which begins in Chapter 4. It is assumed that the reader has had an introductory course in "statistics for economists" or its equivalent. We will present some ideas on an intuitive basis and state a number of results and formulas without proof. They will cover a narrow range of topics and involve somewhat special assumptions.

The probability distributions used implicitly or explicitly in the remaining chapters include the normal distribution, the t-distribution, and the F-distribution. They all have a strong family resemblance. The simplest way into them lies through coin-tossing experiments and the binomial distribution.

3.1 THE BINOMIAL DISTRIBUTION

If we toss a single coin the possible outcomes are two, a head (H_1) or a tail (T_1). If we toss two coins in succession, the four possible sequences are

$$H_1H_2 \qquad H_1T_2$$
$$T_1H_2 \qquad T_1T_2$$

If we toss three coins in succession, the eight possible sequences are

$$H_1H_2H_3 \qquad H_1H_2T_3 \qquad H_1T_2H_3 \qquad H_1T_2T_3$$
$$T_1H_2H_3 \qquad T_1H_2T_3 \qquad T_1T_2H_3 \qquad T_1T_2T_3$$

For each toss of a single coin, let us call the probability of a head p and that of a tail q. The probability of getting either a head or a tail is $(p + q)/(p + q) = 1$. We define "probability" in such a way that $p + q = 1$. Then $p/(p + q) = p$, and $q/(p + q) = q = 1 - p$. If p is constant for all possible tosses of the coin, we can generate a binomial distribution for sequences of n tosses, where n is any number from one to infinity:

n	$(p + q)^n = 1$
1	$p + q = 1$
2	$p^2 + 2pq + q^2 = 1$
3	$p^3 + 3p^2q + 3pq^2 + q^3 = 1$
4	$p^4 + 4p^3q + 6p^2q^2 + 4pq^3 + q^4 = 1$
5	$p^5 + 5p^4q + 10p^3q^2 + 10p^2q^3 + 5pq^4 + q^5 = 1$
$\vdots$	
n	$p^n + np^{n-1}q + \dfrac{n!}{(n-2)!\,2!}p^{n-2}q^2 + \dfrac{n!}{(n-3)!\,3!}p^{n-3}q^3 \cdots = 1$

In the distribution for $n = 5$, p^5 is the probability of a sequence of five heads, p^4q is the probability of a sequence of five tosses resulting in four heads and a tail, pq^4 is the probability of a sequence of five tosses resulting in one head and four tails, and so on. The numerical coefficient of each term (1, 5, 10, 10, 5, 1) is the number of different sequences in which the specified numbers of heads and tails could appear. These coefficients can be calculated from the basic formula for the number of combinations of n things taken x at a time ($x \le n$):

$$C_5^5 = \frac{5!}{5!} = \frac{5 \cdot 4 \cdot 3 \cdot 2 \cdot 1}{5 \cdot 4 \cdot 3 \cdot 2 \cdot 1} = 1$$

$$C_4^5 = \frac{5!}{4!\,1!} = \frac{5 \cdot 4 \cdot 3 \cdot 2 \cdot 1}{4 \cdot 3 \cdot 2 \cdot 1(1)} = 5$$

$$C_3^5 = \frac{5!}{3!\,2!} = \frac{5 \cdot 4 \cdot 3 \cdot 2 \cdot 1}{3 \cdot 2 \cdot 1(2 \cdot 1)} = 10$$

$$C_2^5 = \frac{5!}{2!\,3!} = \frac{5 \cdot 4 \cdot 3 \cdot 2 \cdot 1}{2 \cdot 1(3 \cdot 2 \cdot 1)} = 10$$

$$C_1^5 = \frac{5!}{1!\,4!} = \frac{5 \cdot 4 \cdot 3 \cdot 2 \cdot 1}{(1)4 \cdot 3 \cdot 2 \cdot 1} = 5$$

$$C_0^5 = \frac{5!}{5!} = \frac{5 \cdot 4 \cdot 3 \cdot 2 \cdot 1}{5 \cdot 4 \cdot 3 \cdot 2 \cdot 1} = 1$$

The number of different possible sequences of heads and tails is 32 ($= 2^5$). If $p = \frac{1}{2}$ and $q = \frac{1}{2}$, each of these sequences is equally likely, and the probability distribution is as given in Column (3) of Table 3.1.

The mathematical expectation of the number of heads in a sequence of five tosses is $5(\frac{1}{2}) = 2.50$, and the variance is $5(\frac{1}{2})(\frac{1}{2}) = 5(\frac{1}{4}) = 1.25$.

We can calculate these two parameters of the probability distribution by treating it as though it were an ordinary frequency distribution. Thus to get Column (4) we multiply the numbers of heads in Column (1) by the numbers of sequences (frequencies) in Column (2). The total number of heads appearing in the 32 sequences is 80. Hence the *arithmetic mean* number of heads per sequence is $\sum X/N = 80/32 = 2.50$.

Table 3.1

(1)	(2)	(3)	(4)	(5)	(6)
Number of Heads in a Sequence of Five Tosses X	Number of Possible Sequences Containing Specified Number of Heads	Probability of Obtaining Specified Number of Heads If All 32 Sequences Are Equally Likely	Col. (1) Times Col. (2), Total No. of Heads	$[\text{Col. (1)}]^2$ X^2	Col. (5) Times Col. (2)
5	1	0.03	5	25	25
4	5	0.16	20	16	80
3	10	0.31	30	9	90
2	10	0.31	20	4	40
1	5	0.16	5	1	5
0	1	0.03	0	0	0
Totals	32	1.00	80		240

The *variance* of the frequency distribution of numbers of heads per sequence can be calculated from the following formula:

$$\sigma^2 = \frac{\sum x^2}{N} = \frac{1}{N} [\sum X^2 - N\bar{X}^2]$$

In this case $N = 32$ and the arithmetic mean $\bar{X} = 2.50$. We calculate $\sum X^2$ in Column (6) by squaring the numbers of heads, X, in Column (1) and multiplying them by the frequencies in Column (2). Thus,

$$\sigma^2 = \frac{\sum x^2}{32} = \frac{1}{32} [240 - 32(2.50)^2] = 7.50 - 6.25 = 1.25$$

The square root of the variance is $\sigma = 1.118$.

The binomial distribution is discrete or discontinuous in that the number of heads (or "successes") in sequences of n tosses (or "trials") can take on only the $n + 1$ discrete values 0, 1, 2, 3, 4, . . ., n. The mean or *expected value* is equal to np and the variance to npq. On the special assumption that $p = q = \frac{1}{2}$, we have $\mu = \frac{1}{2}n$ and $\sigma^2 = \frac{1}{4}n$, where μ is the expected value and σ^2 is the variance.

The expected value or mean is a measure of the *central tendency* of the distribution. The square root of the variance, called the standard deviation, is a measure of the *dispersion* of the distribution. If two distributions had approximately the same shape, it appears intuitively that we could compare them in terms of these two summary measures, their means and their standard deviations.

In the distribution for $n = 5$ and $p = q = \frac{1}{2}$, 62% of the equally probable sequences lie in the range $\mu - \sigma$ to $\mu + \sigma$, or 1.382 to 3.618; 94% of the equally probable sequences lie within $\mu - 2\sigma$ to $\mu + 2\sigma$, or 0.264 to 4.736. But with all the occurrences massed at a few data points, these percentages might change substantially depending on whether some data point were just inside or just outside the $\mu \pm \sigma$ or $\mu \pm 2\sigma$ range.

These hazards would presumably be reduced if the total probability, $P = 1$, were distributed over a very large number of data points. But consider the distribution of $p(X)$ for the binomial distribution $(p + q)^n$ when $n = 100$ and $p = q = \frac{1}{2}$; $\mu = np = 50$, $\sigma^2 = npq = 25$, and $\sigma = 5$. The problem of discontinuity is still present, for $p(50) = 0.080$, $p(55) = 0.048$, and $p(60) = 0.010$ and these are precisely the end points of the intervals $\mu + \sigma$ and $\mu + 2\sigma$. The distribution is symmetrical about $\mu = 50$, so the same applies at the points $X = 45$ and $X = 40$. The distribution of $p(X)$ over the range $34 \leq X \leq 66$ follows.

Table 3.2

X	$p(X)$	X	$p(X)$
34	0.001	50	0.080
35	0.001	51	0.078
36	0.002	52	0.073
37	0.003	53	0.067
38	0.004	54	0.058
39	0.007	55	0.048
40	0.010	56	0.039
41	0.016	57	0.030
42	0.023	58	0.023
43	0.030	59	0.016
44	0.039	60	0.010
45	0.048	61	0.007
46	0.058	62	0.004
47	0.067	63	0.003
48	0.073	64	0.002
49	0.078	65	0.001
50	0.080	66	0.001

If we assume arbitrarily that the basic distribution is continuous and that the point $X = 50$ really stands for the class interval $49.50 < X < 50.50$, we can allocate half of $p(50) = 0.080$ to the interval $\mu + \sigma$ and half to the interval $\mu - \sigma$. We can make similar allocations of $p(45)$, $p(55)$, $p(40)$, $p(60)$, $p(35)$, and $p(65)$, arriving at the following tabulation:

Table 3.3

Class Interval	Probability
$X < \mu - 3\sigma$	0.0025
$\mu - 3\sigma < X < \mu - 2\sigma$	0.0205
$\mu - 2\sigma < X < \mu - \sigma$	0.1370
$\mu - \sigma < X < \mu$	0.3400
$\mu < X < \mu + \sigma$	0.3400
$\mu + \sigma < X < \mu + 2\sigma$	0.1370
$\mu + 2\sigma < X < \mu + 3\sigma$	0.0205
$X > \mu + 3\sigma$	0.0025
	1.0000

The foregoing distribution is almost identical with the well-known normal distribution. We might translate the binomial distribution for $p = q = \frac{1}{2}$ into a nearly continuous distribution by letting n become very large. For example, if $n = 1,000,000$, $\mu = np = 500,000$; $\sigma^2 = npq = 250,000$ and $\sigma = 500$. Within the class interval $\mu + \sigma$ there would be 501 data points instead of the six data points which exist when $n = 100$ (counting both end points of the $\mu + \sigma$ intervals). The probability of obtaining (say) precisely 500,001 heads in 1,000,000 tosses of a coin is less than 0.001.

3.2   THE NORMAL DISTRIBUTION

The most important distribution of a continuous random variable is the normal or Gaussian distribution. The formula for the frequency distribution or probability density function is

$$y = \frac{1}{\sigma\sqrt{2\pi}} e^{-(x-\mu)^2/2\sigma^2}$$

where μ is the mean and σ^2 the variance of the distribution, e is the base of natural logarithms ($e = 2.71828$), and $\pi = 3.1416$, x ranges from $-\infty$ to ∞. In common sense terms, all normal distributions have the same shape. Any particular normal distribution is defined completely once we specify the numerical values of μ and σ^2, which are the parameters of that distribution.

The normal distribution is generally used in the standardized form in which $\mu = 0$ and $\sigma^2 = 1$. Thus

$$y = \frac{1}{\sqrt{2\pi}} e^{-(1/2)(x/\sigma)^2}$$

where x is a deviation from the mean $\mu = 0$; x/σ expresses the deviation in terms of standard deviation units.

$$\text{If}\quad x = 0,\quad y = \frac{1}{\sqrt{2\pi}} e^0 = \frac{1}{\sqrt{2\pi}} = \frac{1}{\sqrt{6.2832}},\quad y = \frac{1}{2.50663} = 0.3989$$

For some other values of x we have

$$\text{If}\quad x = \sigma,\quad y = 0.3989\, e^{-\frac{1}{2}} = \frac{0.3989}{\sqrt{2.71828}} = \frac{0.3989}{1.6487} = 0.2420$$

$$\text{If}\quad x = 2\sigma,\quad y = 0.3989\, e^{-(\frac{1}{2})(2)^2} = \frac{0.3989}{(2.71828)^2} = \frac{0.3989}{7.389} = 0.05399$$

$$\text{If } x = 3\sigma,\ y = 0.3989\, e^{-(\frac{1}{2})(3)^2} = \frac{0.3989}{(2.71828)^{4.5}} = \frac{0.3989}{90.013},\quad \text{or}\quad y = 0.004432$$

The values of y are, of course, the ordinates of the curve corresponding to the specified values of x.

It can be shown that the area under the standardized normal curve from $-\infty < x < \infty$ is 1, and that the curve reaches its maximum height, 0.3989, where $x = 0$ ($=\mu$, the arithmetic mean) and has points of inflection or "steepest descent" where $x = -\sigma$ and $x = \sigma$. (Since $\mu = 0$, these points may also be regarded as being at $x = \mu - \sigma$ and $x = \mu + \sigma$.)

We can get an intuitive appreciation that the total area under the curve is 1 if we consider that its area in any class interval of x/σ may be approximated in the following way:

Table 3.4

(1) Class Interval in Units of $\left(\frac{x}{\sigma}\right)$	(2) Heights of Curve at End Points of Interval	(3) Sum of End Points Divided by Two (Rounded)	(4) Actual Areas under the Normal Curve $N(0, 1)$
$-\infty - -3$	0 to 0.004432	$\cdots$	0.0014
$-3 - -2$	0.004432 and 0.05399	0.029	0.0214
$-2 - -1$	0.05399 and 0.2420	0.148	0.1359
$-1 - 0$	0.2420 and 0.3989	0.320	0.3413
$0 - 1$	0.3989 and 0.2420	0.320	0.3413
$1 - 2$	0.2420 and 0.05399	0.148	0.1359
$2 - 3$	0.05399 and 0.004432	0.029	0.0214
$3 - \infty$	0.004432 and 0	$\cdots$	0.0014
$-3 - 3$		0.994	0.9972
$-\infty - \infty$		$\cdots$	1.0000

The assumptions underlying Column (3) are, of course, very crude. The width of each class interval in units of (x/σ) is 1; averaging the height of the curve at the two end points and multiplying by the width, 1, gives us the area of a trapezoid as a rough approximation to the area under that segment of the smooth curve. The actual areas under the standardized normal curve $N(0, 1)$ are given in Column (4). These areas are mathematically precise except for rounding errors.

The areas under the normal curve $N(0, 1)$ are almost identical with the probabilities shown for corresponding standard deviation intervals of the binomial distribution for $n = 100$ and $p = q = \frac{1}{2}$, with the class intervals measured from the expected value or mean of that distribution. Evidently, the normal distribution can be approximated as closely as we like by means of a distribution of the "successes" obtained in sequences of n random events (each event analogous to the toss of a coin) when the probability of a "success" on each random event is $\frac{1}{2}$ and the number n is very large.

In connection with errors of measurement we may suppose that combinations of slight vibrations of the instrument, slight tremors in the hand or eye of the observer, slight variations in wind velocities, air temperatures, or air currents and the like are the sums of an almost infinite number of "microevents" each of which is equally likely. We suppose also that the occurrence or nonoccurrence of any one of the "microevents" is independent of the occurrence or nonoccurrence of each of the others, just as the probability of a head on the second toss of a coin is independent of the actual outcome (head or tail) on the first toss.

If these assumptions are correct, our actual errors of measurement may be regarded as random drawings from a normal distribution. If the measurements have no systematic bias, errors in the "too large" direction should balance errors in the "too small" direction, so the arithmetic mean of the errors should be zero or very close to it. The variance of these errors will be specific to the given experimental situation (what is being measured and what procedures and instruments are being used to measure it). However, if we know the variance σ^2 of the distribution of all possible measurement errors, we can say that 68% of these equally probable error outcomes lie within the range $-\sigma$ to σ around the mean of the distribution, $\mu = 0$. Similarly, we can say that slightly over 95% of these error outcomes lie within the range -2σ to 2σ. The probability of drawing a larger error than 2σ in the "too large" direction is 0.0228, or 2.28%; the probability of drawing an error of more than 2σ in the "too small" direction is also 0.0228, or 2.28%.

3.3 STATISTICAL INFERENCE IN NORMAL POPULATIONS

We recall that the mean of a binomial distribution is $\mu = np$ and the variance is $\sigma^2 = npq$. Under the special assumption that $p = q = \frac{1}{2}$, we obtain $\mu = n/2$ and $\sigma^2 = n(\frac{1}{2})(\frac{1}{2}) = n/4$; hence $\sigma = \sqrt{n}/2$.

As n increases, μ increases in direct proportion to n, whereas σ, the measure of dispersion, increases in proportion to the square root of n. The ratio of σ to μ is

$$\frac{\sigma}{\mu} = \frac{\sqrt{n}/2}{n/2} = \frac{\sqrt{n}}{n} = \frac{1}{\sqrt{n}}$$

Each equally probable sequence of n random events (such as tosses of a coin) in the binomial distribution with $p = \frac{1}{2}$ may be regarded as a random sample of n observations. The expected value, μ, is the expected value of the *sum* of the "successes" obtained in n "trials." The variance, $\sigma^2 = npq$, also refers to the *sums* obtained in n "trials" and so, of course, does $\sigma = \sqrt{npq}$.

As the arithmetic mean of a sample of n observations is equal to the sum divided by n, it appears that we can convert $\sigma = \sqrt{npq}$ into the standard deviation of a distribution of arithmetic means, rather than sums, by dividing by n as a "scale factor."

Table 3.5

X	$\dfrac{X}{100}$	$P\left(\dfrac{X}{100}\right)$
50	0.50	0.080
51	0.51	0.078
52	0.52	0.073
53	0.53	0.067
54	0.54	0.058
55	0.55	0.048
56	0.56	0.039
57	0.57	0.030
58	0.58	0.023
59	0.59	0.016
60	0.60	0.010
61	0.61	0.007
62	0.62	0.004
63	0.63	0.003
64	0.64	0.002
65	0.65	0.001
66	0.66	0.001

For example, consider what happens to the binomial distribution for $n = 100$ and $p = q = \frac{1}{2}$ when each value of X (the actual number of heads in 100 tosses of a coin) is divided by 100 to obtain the arithmetic mean number of heads per toss. We obtain Table 3.5.

The probability which applies to each value of X (per hundred tosses) will also apply to the corresponding value of X divided by 100, or $0.01X$. The standard deviation of the distribution of values of $0.01X$ is $0.01\sigma = 0.05$. If, as before, we divide the probabilities at the end points of intervals such as $(\mu/100 + \sigma/100)$ between the two adjacent intervals, we obtain the probability distribution shown in Column (2) of Table 3.6.

Table 3.6

(1) Class Interval of $\dfrac{X}{100}$	(2) Probability	(3) Analogous Probabilities in a Normal Distribution
Less than 0.35	0.0025	0.0014
0.35–0.40	0.0205	0.0214
0.40–0.45	0.1370	0.1359
0.45–0.50	0.3400	0.3413
0.50–0.55	0.3400	0.3413
0.55–0.60	0.1370	0.1359
0.60–0.65	0.0205	0.0214
Over 0.65	0.0025	0.0014
	1.0000	1.0000

Evidently, Column (2) gives us probabilities relating to means of samples of 100 random events, partitioned into class intervals of the standard deviation of the distribution of all such means. The number of equally probable samples of 100 (and hence of means) is 2^{100}, or approximately 1000^{10}, which would be a 1 followed by 30 zeros.

The normal curve probabilities in Column (3) are almost identical with those in the binomial distribution for $n = 100$ and $p = q = \frac{1}{2}$, so it appears that any statements which apply to one will apply to the other (if we can "smooth over" the discontinuous nature of the binomial distribution). We will talk in terms of the normal distribution.

Column (3) assumes that we know the mean of the "population" of 2^{100} random events and also the variance and standard deviation of the population: $\bar{p} = 0.50$, $\bar{\sigma}^2 = 0.25$; $\bar{\sigma} = 0.50$. If $n = 100$, the standard deviation of the distribution of $\bar{p}$ as estimated from samples of 100 is, as we have seen, 0.05.

What can we say of any particular random sample of 100 observations or "trials" from this population? We can say that in 68% of all equally probable samples, the sample mean will fall between 0.45 and 0.55 or $\bar{p} \pm \sigma_{\bar{p}}$, and that in 95% of all equally probable samples, the sample mean will fall between 0.40 and 0.60, or $\bar{p} \pm 2\sigma_{\bar{p}}$.

3.3.1 Sampling from a Population with Unknown Mean and Variance

In empirical research we are often interested in studying certain characteristics of a population. Sometimes the population is finite and the characteristics of every member of this population could *in principle* be measured. For example, the length of every passenger automobile in the United States on January 1, 1968, could be measured, and we could use every one of the 80,000,000 or so measurements in computing the mean and variance of this population of car lengths. Other populations may contain an infinite number of members, for example, the population of all possible errors of measurement in making repeated estimates of the speed of light with a particular experimental setup.

In the car-length example, the cost of making 80,000,000 measurements would far outweigh any utility of knowing the *exact* values of the population mean and variance. We know that the standard deviation of a distribution of means of random samples of n observations is $\sigma_{\bar{X}} = \sigma/\sqrt{n}$, where σ is the standard deviation of the population.

Suppose we take a random sample of 100 cars. Let X_i be the ith observation, $i = 1, 2, 3, \ldots, 100$. Then the mean of the 100 observations on car lengths is

$$\bar{X} = \frac{1}{100} \sum_{i=1}^{100} X_i$$

It can be shown that the sample mean $\bar{X}$ is an unbiased estimator of the unknown mean of the population. For that matter, each randomly drawn value X_i may be regarded as an estimate of the population mean μ. Our sample of $100 X_i$'s, then, contains 100 independent estimates of μ. When we divide $\sum_{i=1}^{100} X_i$ by 100, the resulting value, $\bar{X}$, is an unbiased estimate of μ.

Similarly, each $(X_i - \mu)^2$ would be an unbiased estimate of the unknown variance of the population σ^2. A random sample of $100 X_i$'s would yield 100 independent estimates of σ^2, each involving a different X_i in the expression $(X_i - \mu)^2$. The expression

$$\frac{1}{100} \sum_{i=1}^{100} (X_i - \mu)^2$$

would be an unbiased estimate of σ^2. But we do not know μ; we know only the sample mean $\bar{X}$. We have seen that the standard deviation of a distribution of means of random samples of n observations is

$$\sigma_{\bar{X}} = \frac{\sigma}{\sqrt{n}}$$

The variance of the distribution of sample means is

$$\sigma_{\bar{X}}^2 = \frac{\sigma^2}{n}$$

This is the variance of sample means of size n around the population mean μ. If $n = 100$, $100\sigma_{\bar{X}}^2$ is an unbiased estimate of σ^2.
   If

$$\frac{1}{100} \sum_{i=1}^{100} (X_i - \mu)^2$$

is an unbiased estimate of σ^2 and the variance of the sample mean $\sigma_{\bar{X}}^2$ is an unbiased estimate of $(1/100)\sigma^2$, we appear to have the following result:

$$\frac{1}{100} \sum_{i=1}^{100} [(X_i - \bar{X}) + (\bar{X} - \mu)]^2$$

is an unbiased estimate of σ^2. But

$$\frac{1}{100} \sum_{i=1}^{100} (\bar{X} - \mu)^2 = (\bar{X} - \mu)^2$$

is an unbiased estimate of $(1/100)\sigma^2$. Hence,

$$\frac{1}{100} \sum_{i=1}^{100} (X_i - \bar{X})^2$$

is an unbiased estimate of $\sigma^2 - (1/100)\sigma^2$, or $(99/100)\sigma^2$. [The value of the product term $2 \sum (X_i - \bar{X})(\bar{X} - \mu)$ is zero.]
   Evidently, to convert the expression

$$\frac{1}{100} \sum_{i=1}^{100} (X_i - \bar{X})^2$$

into an unbiased estimate of the population variance σ^2 we must adjust it as follows:

$$s^2 = \frac{100}{99} \left(\frac{1}{100}\right) \sum_{i=1}^{100} (X_i - \bar{X})^2, \quad \text{or} \quad s^2 = \frac{1}{99} \sum_{i=1}^{100} (X_i - \bar{X})^2$$

For samples of size n, we have

$$s^2 = \frac{1}{n-1} \sum_{i=1}^{n} (X_i - \bar{X})^2$$

as our unbiased estimate of σ^2. We sometimes speak of *degrees of freedom* in connection with adjustment factors such as $n/(n-1)$. A random sample of n observations has n degrees of freedom to vary around the population mean. But once we have calculated the arithmetic mean of the sample

$$\bar{X} = \frac{1}{n} \sum_{i=1}^{n} X_i$$

the variation of the n observations around the sample mean are subject to the constraint

$$\sum_{i=1}^{n} X_i = n\bar{X}$$

where $n\bar{X}$ is a fixed arithmetical value. If $n-1$ observations X_i are selected at random subject to this constraint, the value of the nth observation is rigidly determined as

$$X_n = n\bar{X} - \sum_{i=1}^{n-1} X_i$$

So we say that the variations of the individual observations around the mean of the sample have only $n-1$ degrees of freedom.

To estimate the variance of the mean of a sample, we use the formula $s_{\bar{X}}^2 = s^2/n$; the standard error of the mean is the square root of this expression $s_{\bar{X}} = s/\sqrt{n}$. But remember that s in the numerator has been "adjusted for degrees of freedom":

$$s^2 = \frac{\sum_{i=1}^{n} (X_i - \bar{X})^2}{n-1} \qquad \text{and} \qquad s = \left(\frac{\sum_{i=1}^{n} (X_i - \bar{X})^2}{n-1} \right)^{\frac{1}{2}}$$

To sum up: When we draw a random sample from a population, we are interested in *inferring* some characteristics of the population from those of the sample. In most problems encountered in this book, the inferences take the form of estimates of population parameters, such as means, variances, and the coefficients of lines or curves relating two or more economic variables.

To estimate lines or curves of relationship between (say) two variables, we will generally use the method of least squares. This method assumes that in the relevant *population*, deviations from the line of relationship are random and follow the normal distribution. The variance of primary interest is the variance of deviations of sample observations about a line or curve fitted to the sample observations. A straight line fitted to a sample requires the determination of two constants, a slope, and an intercept, and uses up two degrees of freedom. Hence, to obtain an unbiased estimate of the variance of deviations in the population, we must divide the sum of squared deviations in the sample by $n - 2$.

We will also need to estimate standard errors of points on a line of relationship and of the coefficients determining its slope and intercept. The theory underlying these standard error measures is a simple extension of that underlying the standard error of the mean.

We will state, without proving them, two characteristics of the arithmetic mean: (1) The positive and negative deviations of individual observations from the mean exactly offset one another in that their algebraic sum is zero; and (2) the sum of squared deviations of individual observations about the mean is smaller than the sum of their squared deviations about any other point. Thus the arithmetic mean is a least squares estimator.

When we infer from a sample mean to a population mean, we make such statements as the following:

1. The sample mean is $\bar{X}$ and its standard error is $s_{\bar{X}} = s/\sqrt{n}$.
2. What is the probability that a range centered on the sample mean, such as $\bar{X} \pm 2s_{\bar{X}}$, will include the population mean?

We know that under conditions of random sampling from a normal population, the means of 95 samples out of 100 (on the average) will lie within the range $\mu \pm 2\sigma$, where μ is the population mean and σ the square root of the population variance. If we say with respect to each of a large number of samples that "the population mean lies within the range $\bar{X} \pm 2s_{\bar{X}}$," we will be right 95% of the time and wrong 5% of the time. If we prefer to be right 99% of the time, we will choose (for large samples) the range $\bar{X} \pm 2.58s_{\bar{X}}$.

Sometimes we are interested in judging whether a sample mean is significantly different from a specified number, such as zero or 100. If the mean of a sample is 20 and its standard error is 5, is it likely that the sample has been randomly drawn from a population with mean zero? Given a normal population with $\mu = 0$ and $\sigma = 5$, only about 3 random samples per 100,000 would be expected to have means equal to or greater than $+20$. Hence given the sample mean of $+20$ and its standard error of 5, we reject the hypothesis that the population mean is zero or negative. In fact, we could reject the hypothesis that the population mean is equal to or less than $+10$ ($= \bar{X} - 2s_{\bar{X}}$), and we would be wrong in rejecting such hypotheses only about $2\frac{1}{2}\%$ of the time. Note that we are dealing here with the area under only one "tail" of the normal curve, the tail ranging from $\mu - 2\sigma$ down to $-\infty$. If we stated our hypothesis (given $\bar{X} = 20$ and $s_{\bar{X}} = 5$) in the form "the population mean is neither less than $+10$ nor more than $+30$," we would be wrong about 5% of the time, $2\frac{1}{2}\%$ at each tail of the normal distribution.

3.4 THE t-DISTRIBUTION

In small samples (conventionally, "small" in this context is taken as 30 observations or less) the ratio of a sample statistic to its standard error does not follow the normal distribution. The appropriate distribution is known as "*Student's distribution*" or the *t-distribution*. The intervals such as $\bar{X} \pm k s_{\bar{X}}$ must be made a little wider for small samples than for large ones to achieve the same relative frequency of correct statements.

In working with economic time series of annual data we sometimes have only 20 observations or less. A table of the values of t corresponding to 5% and 1% levels of significance (risks of being wrong) for samples of different sizes is a useful tool in appraising the significance of one's own results and facilitating their appraisal by other research workers. For a mean, $t_{\bar{X}} = \bar{X}/s_{\bar{X}}$; for a regression coefficient b, $t_b = b/s_b$. In the regression case, if the slope of the line of relationship between two variables is not significantly different from zero, we cannot reject the hypothesis that the two variables are unrelated, that is, have no correlation with or effects upon one another in the population from which our sample observations were drawn.

3.5 THE F-DISTRIBUTION

The F-distribution is used primarily in the analysis of variance (see Chapter 8). If we wish to test the hypothesis that two samples are random drawings from the same population, we can make one test on the basis of the means $\bar{X}_1$ and $\bar{X}_2$. The standard error of the difference between the means of two samples with variances

$$s_1^2 = \frac{\sum\limits_{i=1}^{n_1} (X_{1i} - \bar{X}_1)^2}{n_1 - 1}$$

and

$$s_2^2 = \frac{\sum\limits_{j=1}^{n_2} (X_{2j} - \bar{X}_2)^2}{n_2 - 1}$$

on the assumption that the hypothesis is correct, is

$$s_{(\bar{X}_1 - \bar{X}_2)} = \left(\frac{s_1^2}{n_1} + \frac{s_2^2}{n_2} \right)^{\frac{1}{2}} = (s_{\bar{X}_1}^2 + s_{\bar{X}_2}^2)^{\frac{1}{2}}$$

The relevant t-ratio is

$$t_{(\bar{X}_1 - \bar{X}_2)} = \frac{\bar{X}_1 - \bar{X}_2}{s_{(\bar{X}_1 - \bar{X}_2)}}$$

and probability statements can be based upon the t-table. The calculation of the standard error pools the two sample variances s_1^2 and s_2^2 as though they were both unbiased estimates of the variance of the same population.

The F-ratio is addressed to a different question: Can we reject the hypothesis that two variances are based on random drawings from the same population? Typically, we try to partition the sum of squares of deviations of individual observations from their mean into two or more components. Sometimes one component represents "experimental error" or "unexplained variation" and the other represents the effect of some systematic relationship with another variable. (There may be several systematic effects.) We compare the variance attributed to each systematic effect with the variance of the "error" or similar component in order to judge whether the systematic effect is significant or not.

Tables are available giving the 5% and 1% levels of significance for F-ratios with specified numbers of degrees of freedom in the numerator and in the denominator. Given two variances s_1^2 and s_2^2, where $s_1^2 > s_2^2$, the F-ratio is simply $F = s_1^2/s_2^2$ with $n_1 - 1$ and $n_2 - 1$ degrees of freedom. (Each variance has been properly adjusted for degrees of freedom.)

For example, suppose we have ascertained that $s_1^2 = 27$, with $n_1 - 1 = 20$ degrees of freedom, and that $s_2^2 = 5$, also with $n_2 - 1 = 20$ degrees of freedom. Entering Table 5 in Appendix II with $F = 27/5 = 5.40$, $n_1 - 1 = 20$, and $n_2 - 1 = 20$, we find that F-ratios larger than 2.94 would be expected only 1% of the time. We reject the hypothesis that the two variances are based on random samples from the same population; s_1^2 must be regarded as "significantly" larger than s_2^2 at the 1% level of significance.

3.6 SOME CONVENIENT TABLES

The following tables are included in Appendix II (at the end of the book): a table of random numbers, a table of areas under the standardized normal curve, a table of values of Student's t for several significance levels, and a table of the 1% and 5% points of the distribution of F, and 2 tables of four-place logarithms and antilogarithms.

For present purposes, all of these tables have been sufficiently explained except the table of random numbers. These numbers have been generated in such a way that the probabilities of drawing a 1, 2, 3, 4, 5, 6, 7, 8, 9, or 0 each equal 0.1 and are independent of the digits actually drawn in any previous "trials."

Random numbers can be used to generate the equivalent of random drawings from a normal population if we make an appropriate coding. For example, consider Table 3.7.

Table 3.7

(1) Random Numbers	(2) Corresponding Class Interval in Standard-ized Normal Curve		(3) Point Which Divides Area within the Class Interval	(4) Probability
90–99	∞–	1.29	1.64	0.10
80–89	1.28–	0.85	1.04	0.10
70–79	0.84–	0.53	0.67	0.10
60–69	0.52–	0.26	0.39	0.10
50–59	0.25–	0.00	0.13	0.10
40–49	0.00–	−0.25	−0.13	0.10
30–39	−0.26–	−0.52	−0.39	0.10
20–29	−0.53–	−0.84	−0.67	0.10
10–19	−0.85–	−1.28	−1.04	0.10
00–09	−1.29–	−∞	−1.64	0.10
				$P = 1.00$

The first random number in the Table of Random Digits is 10; we code this in Column (3) as −1.04 (that is, −1.04 standard deviations below the mean). The second random number in the top row of the table is 09; we code this in Column (3) as −1.64, and so on. In some of the later chapters we have occasionally used this approach to generate series of random variables or random and normally distributed errors.

We have paid no attention in this chapter to descriptive statistics. We assume that the student will have had an introductory course covering arrays, frequency tables, bar charts, or histograms, and methods of calculating means and standard deviations from individual observations and from grouped data. If the individual observations are recorded on cards or tapes, it seems best to base all calculations on the individual observations rather than upon mid-points of class intervals of grouped data.

For more systematic and rigorous treatments of probability theory, distributions, and inference the reader should consult the chapter references.

EXERCISES

1. The probability that an entering college student will graduate is 0.4. Determine the probability that out of five students (a) none, (b) one, (c) at least one will graduate. [*Hints:* Put $n = 5$, $p = 0.4$, $q = 0.6$, put $x = 0$ in (a), 1 in (b) in the binomial distribution; Prob (at least one will graduate) = 1 − Prob (none will graduate).]

2. (a) Find the ordinates of the normal curve at $z = (x - \mu)/\sigma = 0.65$, −1.38, −0.03.

(b) Find the area under the normal curve between (i) $z = -1.38$ and $z = 0.65$, (ii) $z = -1.38$ and -0.03.

(c) Determine the value of z where the area to the left of z is (i) 0.05, (ii) 0.95, and (iii) 0.90. (Use tables for the normal distribution.)

3. A fair coin is tossed 1000 times. Find the probability that the number of heads will not differ from 500 by more than 100. [*Hints:* Find the mean and standard deviation; consider the data as continuous. Compute the area under the normal curve between the two values of z.]

4. A sample of 10 television tubes produced by a company showed a mean lifetime of 1200 hours and a standard deviation of 100 hours. Estimate (a) the mean and (b) the standard deviation of the population of all television tubes produced by this company.

5. The mean lifetime of a sample of 100 fluorescent light bulbs produced by a company is computed to be 1570 hours with a standard deviation of 120 hours. If μ is the mean lifetime of all the bulbs produced by the company, test the hypothesis $\mu = 1600$ hours against the alternative hypothesis (i) $\mu \neq 1600$ hours and (ii) $\mu < 1600$, using a level of significance of 0.05 and assuming that the methods of large sampling theory are valid. [*Hints:* $\mu = 1600$; $\bar{X} = 1570$, $N = 100$, $\sigma_{\bar{X}} = 12$, $z = (\bar{X} - \mu)/\sigma = -2.50$. This is less than -1.96 for (i) a two-tailed test case and also less than -1.645 for (ii) a one-tailed test case; hence the null hypothesis is rejected in both cases.]

6. A sample of 8 measurements of the diameter of a sphere gave a mean $\bar{X} = 4.38$ inches and a standard deviation $s = 0.06$ inches. Find 95% confidence limits for the actual diameter (use small sampling theory).

7. Given $s_1^2 = 40$ and $s_2^2 = 10$, each based on 4 degrees of freedom, determine the probability that sample variances as divergent as these could be estimates of the same population variance against the alternative hypothesis that $\sigma_1^2 > \sigma_2^2$.

REFERENCES

1. Allen, R. G. D., *Statistics for Economists*, London: Hutchinson's University Library, 1949.
2. Anderson, R. L. and T. A. Bancroft, *Statistical Theory in Research*, New York: McGraw-Hill Book Co., 1952.
3. Brunk, H., *An Introduction to Mathematical Statistics*, Boston: Ginn and Company, 1960.
4. Hoel, P. G., *Introduction to Mathematical Statistics*, Second edition, New York: John Wiley and Sons, 1954.
5. Hogg, R. and A. Craig, *Introduction to Mathematical Statistics*, New York: The Macmillan Co., 1959.
6. Mood, A. M. and F. A. Graybill, *Introduction to the Theory of Statistics*, Second edition, New York: McGraw-Hill Book Co., 1963.
7. Spiegel, M. R., *Theory and Problems of Statistics*, New York: Schaum Publishing Co., 1961.
8. Wilks, S. S., *Mathematical Statistics*, New York: John Wiley and Sons, 1962.
9. Wilks, S. S., *Elementary Statistical Analysis*, Princeton, New Jersey: Princeton University Press, 1948.

CHAPTER 4

Simple Regression and the Measurement
of Economic Relationships

Regression analysis is a branch of statistical theory that is widely used in almost all the scientific disciplines. In economics it is the basic technique for measuring or estimating the relationships among economic variables that constitute the essence of economic theory and economic life. Simple regression will be our starting point, for it involves relationships between only two variables. Later chapters deal with multiple regression analysis and closely related estimation methods, which are necessary in the multitude of economic problems that involve relations among three or more variables.

4.1 INTRODUCTION

4.1.1 *Simple Regression as a Relationship Between Two Frequency Distributions*

From a *statistical* standpoint, simple regression can be presented as an extension of frequency distribution concepts to two variables. Suppose, for example, that from a sample of 10,000 urban households we obtain for each household estimates of its money income after taxes and its expenditures on clothing, each over a 12-month period.[1]

The distribution of income is of interest in itself. So is the frequency distribution of expenditures on clothing. But the *joint* frequency distribution of the two variables greatly advances our knowledge. At the extremes, we know

[1] The illustrations in this section are based partly on data from a very extensive family budget survey carried out in 1950 and tabulated by the U.S. Bureau of Labor Statistics for the Wharton School of Finance, University of Pennsylvania: *Study of Consumer Expenditures, Incomes and Savings*, Vols. 1 and 2, University of Pennsylvania Press, 1956.

that people with very low incomes simply cannot finance a mink coat; or, conversely, some very wealthy families spend more on clothing in a year than the total incomes of some less affluent families. But beyond these obvious and sensational points, what is the average or typical relationship between family income and clothing expenditures? This kind of information is of value in economic forecasting and policy.

The frequency distributions of (1) family money income after taxes and (2) expenditures on clothing are shown separately in Figure 4.1. Each of these

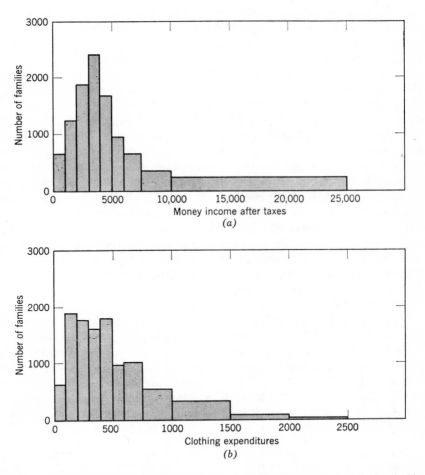

Figure 4.1 Separate frequency distributions of (*a*) family incomes and (*b*) clothing expenditures (partly hypothetical data).

distributions shows the number of families in the sample which had incomes or clothing expenditures within specified class intervals. Obviously, measures of central tendency, dispersion, and skewness or asymmetry could be calculated for each of these frequency distributions as indicated in preceding chapters.

Table 4.1 takes us further. The stub and first column of this table give us the frequency distribution of families by income class. But each line of the table shows for a particular income class the *frequency distribution* of their expenditures on clothing. For example, the first line shows that of 630 cases receiving incomes below $1000 a year, 587 spent less than $100 for clothing, and the remaining 43 families spent between $100 and $200.[2] As we look across the successive rows of Table 4.1, we see that each of them has a strong central tendency and tapers off to low frequencies and finally to zero. Each row is, in fact, a separate frequency distribution and could be analyzed as such. For example, we might ask: What is the frequency distribution of clothing expenditures among urban families with money incomes of $5000 to $6000 after taxes? If our interest were limited to these families, we could design a sampling procedure, interview the resulting sample of such families, and regard the associated frequency distribution of clothing expenditures as an estimate of the frequency distribution of clothing expenditures in the entire population of families having incomes of $5000 to $6000 after taxes.

Note, however, that each *column* is also a frequency distribution. For example, 1801 families had clothing expenditures of $400 to $500. Of these, 1039 had money incomes of $3000 to $4000, 577 had incomes of $4000 to $5000, 129 had incomes of $5000 to $6000, and so on. Thus, if as a practical matter we could define the population of all families spending between $400 and $500 a year for clothing, we could take a random sample of such families, determine their money incomes after taxes, and take the resulting frequency distribution as an estimate of the distribution of incomes in the population of $400 to $500 a year clothing purchasers.

Figure 4.2 expresses the formal symmetry of the relationship between the two frequency distributions. Each of the separate frequency distributions of 10,000 families is shown on a different axis. The dashed line connects points which represent the mean values of money income and clothing expenditures within each cell of Table 4.1. The numbers arranged vertically below the family income class bar for $6000 to $7500 incomes show the frequency distribution of clothing expenditures within this income class; the numbers arranged directly below for families having clothing expenditures of $750 to

---

[2] These data are partly hypothetical. The mean values of clothing expenditures for each family income class were taken from the Wharton School study. However, the dispersion of the individual families with respect to clothing expenditures were not given, so it was necessary to generate these distributions on a synthetic basis.

Table 4.1 Clothing Expenditure Class

Income Class	No. of Cases	Under $100	$100 to $200	$200 to $300	$300 to $400	$400 to $500	$500 to $600	$600 to $750	$750 to $1000	$1000 to $1500	$1500 to $2000	$2000 to $2500
Total	10,000	615	1189	1775	1602	1801	974	1029	556	339	104	16
Under $1000	630	587	43	–	–	–	–	–	–	–	–	–
1000–2000	1230	28	1007	195	–	–	–	–	–	–	–	–
2000–3000	1870	–	125	1167	535	43	–	–	–	–	–	–
3000–4000	2400	–	14	368	818	1039	161	–	–	–	–	–
4000–5000	1690	–	–	39	229	577	577	258	10	–	–	–
5000–6000	950	–	–	6	16	129	143	505	145	6	–	–
6000–7500	640	–	–	–	4	11	87	218	277	43	–	–
7500–10,000	350	–	–	–	–	2	6	47	120	175	–	–
10,000 and over	240	–	–	–	–	–	–	1	4	115	104	16

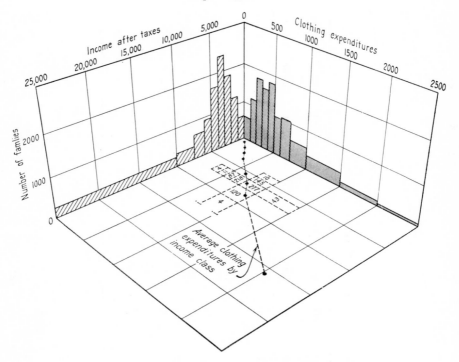

Figure 4.2 Clothing expenditures and money income after taxes.

$1000 show the frequency distribution of clothing expenditures among families of this income class.

Finally, Figure 4.3 shows another arrangement of the joint frequency distribution of Table 4.1, which indicates that the standard deviations or dispersions of clothing expenditures, *measured in dollars*, are substantially larger among the high-income families than among low-income families. Similar information is shown in Figure 4.4 for two family income classes, $4000 to $5000 and $6000 to $7500, respectively. It is clear that the frequency distribution of clothing expenditures for the higher family income class has a considerably higher mean value and a larger standard deviation than the lower one in terms of dollars.

The essence of simple regression is given by the dashed line in Figure 4.2 which for each family income class connects the average or expected value of clothing expenditures. As it stands this line simply describes certain properties of the particular sample. Clearly, if we had chosen a different set of class intervals for family income and clothing expenditures, we would have

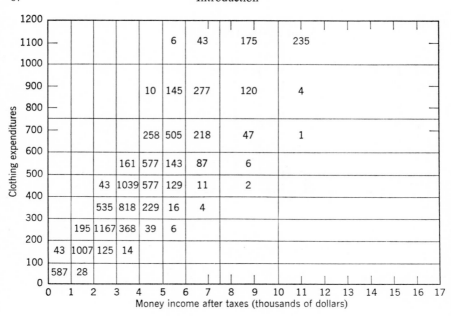

Figure 4.3 Joint frequency distribution of clothing expenditures and family incomes (partly hypothetical data).

obtained a somewhat different pattern of points, and the "bend" or change in slope which occurs in the three highest income groups would have occurred at a different income level.

The successive mean values of clothing expenditures for the first eight income classes fall very nearly on a straight line, and it seems unlikely that a revision of income class intervals would change this impression. Collectively, these eight income classes of our sample include 9760 families. Assuming that our sample was drawn randomly from a well-defined population, it would appear that this particular attribute of the sample should be a good estimate of the average relationship between family income and clothing expenditures in the population as a whole. In contrast, the mean value of clothing expenditures for families with incomes above $10,000 depends on only 240 cases. Recognizing that the 240 cases upon which this mean value is based constitute a frequency distribution with a standard deviation, we could in principle calculate a standard error of this mean and make some statement as to the probability that the "bend" which occurs within the three highest income groups is a property of the parent population or simply a vagary of

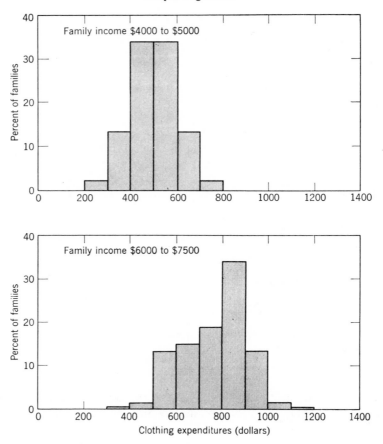

Figure 4.4 "Partial histograms" of clothing expenditures for two levels of family income (partly hypothetical data).

the particular sample. However, we will leave a more precise discussion of sampling aspects of regression analysis to a later chapter.

4.1.2 *The Measurement of Economic Relationships*

From the standpoint of economics, regression analysis is a technique for measuring or estimating relationships between economic variables. As noted in Chapter 2, virtually all economic concepts, forecasting problems, and policy issues involve relationships between two or more variables. Demand and supply curves, indifference curves, production functions, cost curves, and other kinds of relationships are quite central to both theoretical and applied economic analysis. Very frequently, economic problems involve the use of two curves—for example, a demand curve and a supply curve—to determine an equilibrium solution. A well-known introductory economics text contains more than 100 diagrams involving relationships between economic variables.

In the introductory economics texts and in Chapter 2, important consequences are said to flow from the shapes of demand and supply curves, from elasticities of demand and supply, from relations between consumer expenditures and income, and from the shapes of cost curves of individual firms and of the demand curves for their products. But, how do we measure these relationships—how do we come to grips with them in the real world? This is the primary job of regression analysis in economics.

4.2   EXAMPLES OF SIMPLE REGRESSION RELATIONSHIPS IN ECONOMICS

In Section 2.1 we reviewed a number of economic concepts in terms of exact functional relationships. Before pursuing the technical aspects of regression analysis, we will look at a few actual examples of economic relationships estimated from statistical data.

4.2.1 *Consumer Demand Curves*

Figures 4.5, 4.6, and 4.7 are taken from a 1961 article by B. F. Stanton. The statistical estimation of demand curves based on annual data has a history extending back to the early 1900s. Stanton, working with quarterly data, was interested in determining whether the aggregate United States demand curves for certain commodities had different slopes and levels in different seasons of the year. He consolidated the original quarterly data into two periods, summer, including the second and third quarters of the calendar year, and winter, including the fourth quarter of a given year and the first quarter of the succeeding one. He then estimated separate demand curves for the winter and summer seasons.

For beef there appears to be no significant difference in the demand curves for the two seasons. However, the demand for pork is much more elastic in winter than in summer and the winter demand curve stands at a higher level than the summer curve over most of its length. Thus it appears that during 1953–1959 consumers were willing to pay more than 50 cents a pound in the winter for a pork supply running at an annual rate of 65 pounds but only a little over 40 cents a pound for the same rate of supply in the summer.

The summer and winter observations for beef are closely intermingled,

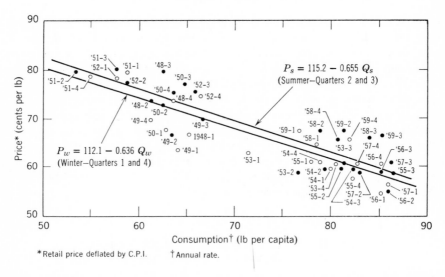

Figure 4.5 Beef: price-consumption relations—quarterly data, 1948–59. (From U.S. Department of Agriculture)

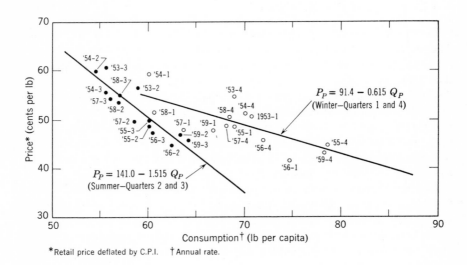

Figure 4.6 Pork: price-consumption relations—quarterly data, 1953–59. (From U.S. Department of Agriculture)

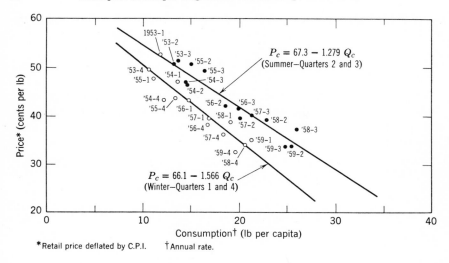

*Retail price deflated by C.P.I.   †Annual rate.

Figure 4.7 Broilers: price-consumption relations—quarterly data, 1953–59. (From U.S. Department of Agriculture)

much as though they might be two samples drawn from the same population. For pork there is little intermingling of the summer and winter observations and the general drift or "slope" of the two sets of observations looks quite different, as though they were samples drawn from distinctly different populations.

We will not attempt to make any formal test of the significance of these differences at this point. But in the pork instance we might consider trying to draw two straight lines such that one *reasonably* reflects the information provided by the black dots (summer) and the other the information conveyed by the hollow circles (winter), at the same time trying to give the two lines (1) the same slope and (2) the same level. It would take considerable imagination to draw two *reasonable* straight lines with the same slope, and if this were done, there would still be a striking difference in their levels.

The broiler case appears to be intermediate between those of beef and pork. Visually, the difference between slopes of the summer and winter demand curves does not appear large in relation to the scatter of the observations about the two regression lines, but it does appear that the levels of the curves over the range of annual consumption rates experienced during 1953–1959 are significantly different.

It will be recalled that price elasticity of consumer demand is a percentage relationship—the ratio of a percentage change in consumption to a percentage change in retail price. At a particular point (p_1, q_1) on the arithmetically linear demand curve $q = a + bp$ it can be calculated as

$Q = a - b P$ *(handwritten)*

(4.1) $\dfrac{\partial q}{\partial p} = -b$ $\beta = \left(b\dfrac{p_1}{q_1}\right)$

(handwritten annotations): $\eta = \dfrac{\partial q}{\partial p} \cdot \dfrac{P}{q}$ $\eta = \left(-b \cdot \dfrac{P}{q}\right)$

The pork demand curves in Figure 4.6 are written in the form $p = -(1/b)a + (1/b)q$. For the points on the demand curves at which $q_1 = 65$ pounds we can calculate the values of β as follows

Summer:

$$p_1 = 141.0 - 1.515q_1 = 141.0 - (1.515)65$$
$$= 141.0 - 98.475 = 43.525 \text{ cents}$$
$$\beta_S = \left(-\frac{1}{1.515}\right)\frac{43.525}{65.000} = -0.660(0.670) = -0.442$$

Winter:

$$p_1 = 91.4 - 0.615q_1 = 91.4 - (0.615)65$$
$$= 91.4 - 39.975 = 51.425 \text{ cents}$$
$$\beta_W = \left(-\frac{1}{0.615}\right)\frac{51.425}{65.000} = -1.626(0.791) = -1.286$$

If we calculate the elasticities at points nearer the centers of the respective sets of observations, say 60 pounds and 51.1 cents for summer and 70 pounds and 48.4 cents for winter, the results are as follows

Summer:

$$\beta_S = -0.562$$

Winter:

$$\beta_W = -1.137$$

For more than 40 years economists have had considerable success in demonstrating through regression analysis that different foods and agricultural commodities had significantly different elasticities of demand and that these differences in turn had important implications for policy and for price forecasting.

4.2.2 Engel Curves

Engel curves are named after a European economist who more than 100 years ago began collecting and interpreting information on family incomes and expenditures such as we discussed in the introductory section of this chapter. The name "Engel curves" is frequently used to indicate any kind of relationship between consumption expenditures and incomes derived from cross-section data for a sample of families. (By cross-sectional data we mean data relating to a single time period—a specified month, year, or other calendar period—as distinct from observations taken at different points in time. Time series data are of great importance in economics, and the demand curves just discussed are based on time series data.)

Figure 4.8 shows a number of family income and expenditure relationships based on the BLS-Wharton School survey previously mentioned. The relationship between income after taxes and income before taxes appears to be almost linear except for a slight bend somewhere between $5000 and $10,000. Total expenditures on goods and services for current consumption rise more slowly than does money income either before or after taxes. Food expenditures take up about 30% of money income after taxes when family income is $5000 but only 21% when family income is $10,000. Clothing expenditures, on the other hand, amount to slightly less than 12% at the lower income and slightly more than 10% at the higher income level. As a percent of total consumption expenditures, clothing expenditures are actually a trifle higher in the $10,000 consumption expenditure group than at the $5000 consumption expenditure level. Food accounts for 30% of total consumption expenditures

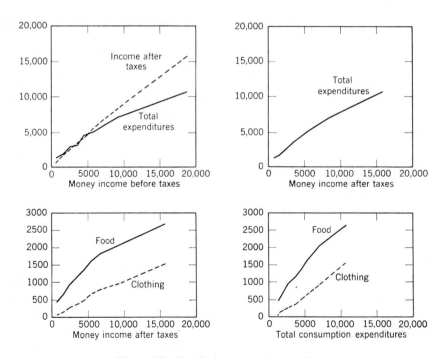

Figure 4.8 Family income and expenditures.

at the lower and for 25% of expenditures at the higher of the two total expenditure levels.

Engel curves are useful for several types of economic analysis and projections. For example, the effects of a change in a personal income tax rate schedule which is to be applied to money incomes before taxes will result in predictable changes in money incomes after taxes. Changes in the level or distribution of money incomes after taxes will (according to such relationships as those in Figure 4.8) lead to changes in expenditures for different categories of consumer goods and services. These impacts are of interest to business firms and public officials.

The counterpart of Engel curves for a single consumer in the theory of demand is the *standard of living line* or *consumption expansion path* of Figures 2.3 and 4.2.

4.2.3 *Aggregate Consumption Function (Time Series)*

Figure 4.9 represents simple regression relationships between personal consumption expenditures and disposable personal income (both in dollars of 1961 purchasing power) for 1929–1961 as a whole and for two subperiods, 1929–1941 and 1949–1961.

For any given period, the slope of the regression line is an estimate of the marginal propensity to consume. This concept figured prominently in Keynes' general theory of employment, interest, and money and is important in formulating policies for economic stability. Equation 2 in Table 4.2 implies a marginal propensity to consume of 0.74 during 1929–1941, whereas Equation 3 implies a marginal propensity of 0.91 during 1949–1961.

The observations from 1942 through 1948 were not used in the regressions because of the many unusual features of this period—direct price controls, consumer rationing, rationing of raw materials to manufacturers, and many other devices and situations. If we are interested in estimating a consumption function which is applicable to policy or forecasting problems in a peacetime economy, use of the 1942–1948 observations will "contaminate" the regression relationship. In terms of the discussions of frequency distributions and sampling in the preceding chapters, it is clear that a regression relationship based on all the years 1942 through 1961 is equivalent to combining samples drawn from two distinctly different populations.

The marginal propensities of 0.74 in 1929–1941 and 0.91 in 1949–1961 seem to differ rather widely considering the tightness with which the observations cluster about (2) and (3). There are statistical tests for appraising the significance of the difference between two regression slopes, but we will leave these for a later chapter.

Equation 4 is the regression of personal consumption expenditures on disposable personal income for the 1929–1941 and 1949–1961 observations

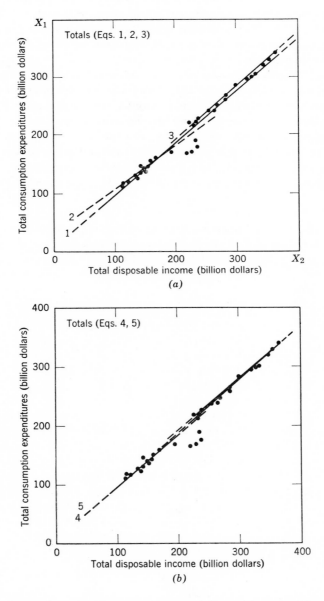

Figure 4.9 Personal consumption expenditures and disposable personal income in 1961 dollars, United States, 1929–61.

combined. Equation 5 includes the same observations but also includes a "shift variable" which allows the 1949–1961 segment to seek a different *level* than that for 1929–1941, although retaining the same slope and hence the same marginal propensity to consume. In this instance, the difference in levels between the two periods is very slight.

Figure 4.10 shows the results of converting both consumption expenditures and disposable income to a per capita basis and fitting regression equations to the same time periods and combinations as in the preceding figure. The equations for all ten regression lines are shown in Table 4.2.

In all cases the slopes or marginal propensities to consume are somewhat lower on the per capita basis. This is because total expenditures and total disposable income contain a common element, total population, which has shown a strong upward trend during the periods in question. The regression

Table 4.2 Regression Equations Expressing Personal Consumption Expenditures as a Function of Disposable Personal Income in Selected Periods, United States, 1929–1961[a]

Equation No.	Dependent Variable	n	Years	Regression Equation
		Total Expenditures and Income		
1	X_1	33	1929–61	$X_1 = 5.5490 + 0.8935X_2$
2	X_1	13	1929–41	$X_1 = 32.3380 + 0.7362X_2$
3	X_1	13	1949–61	$X_1 = 4.8819 + 0.9130X_2$
4	X_1	26	1929–41 plus 1949–61	$X_1 = 9.1725 + 0.8978X_2$
5	X_1	26	1929–41 plus 1949–61	$X_1 = 12.6146 + 0.8719X_2 + 4.7488X_6$
		Per Capita Expenditures and Income		
6	X_3	33	1929–61	$X_3 = 152.0856 + 0.8175X_4$
7	X_3	13	1929–41	$X_3 = 285.7055 + 0.7080X_4$
8	X_3	13	1949–61	$X_3 = 86.7016 + 0.8818X_4$
9	X_3	26	1929–41 plus 1949–61	$X_3 = 110.1962 + 0.8864X_4$
10	X_3	26	1929–41 plus 1949–61	$X_3 = 207.4444 + 0.7768X_4 + 70.7857X_6$

[a] Both variables are expressed in constant 1961 dollars.

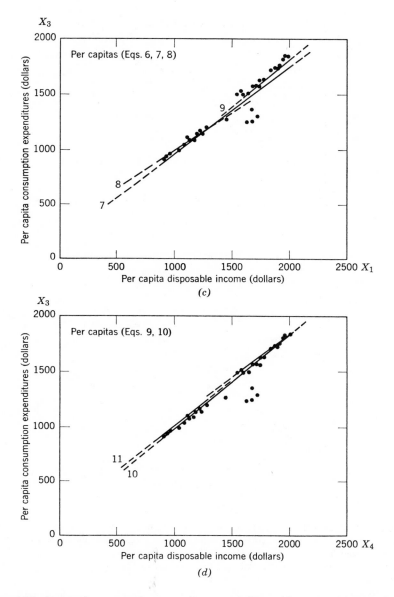

Figure 4.10 Personal consumption expenditures and disposable personal income in the United States, 1929–61.

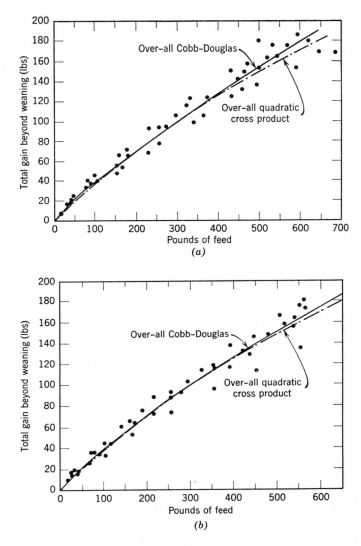

Figure 4.11 (a) Feed-gain relationships for a 16% protein ration derived from experiments 536 and 554 with aureomycin. (b) Feed-gain relationships for a 14% protein ration derived from experiments 536 and 554 with aureomycin. (c) Feed-gain relationships for a 14% protein ration derived from experiment 554 with aureomycin. (d) Feed-gain relationships for a 16% protein ration derived from experiment 554 with aureomycin.

Source: Heady, Earl O. and John L. Dillon, *Agricultural Production Functions*, Ames: Iowa State University Press, 1961, pp. 277–278.

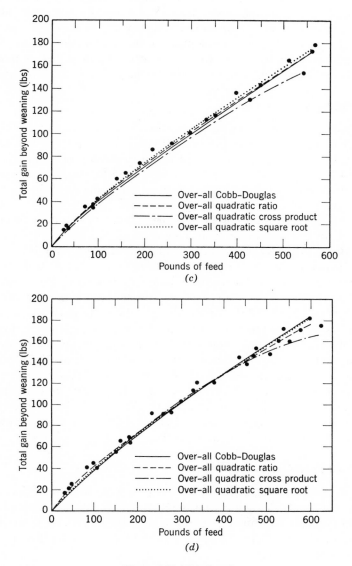

Figure 4.11 (*Continued*)

equation of a variable upon itself is $z = 0 + 1.0z$. If z is population and we denote per capita consumption and per capita income by y and x, respectively, then the regression of Y (total expenditures) upon X (total disposable income) gives us a multiplicative blend of $y = a + bx$ with the "identity equation" or regression of population upon itself, $z = 0 + 1.0z$. Since the slopes of the per capita regression equations are all less than 1.0, the regression of total expenditures upon total income results in slopes or marginal propensities which are closer to 1.0 than were the per capita regression slopes.

4.2.4 Production Functions

Production functions have wide application in economic analysis. Much of the theory of resource use within the individual firm revolves around production function concepts, as indicated in our discussion of Figures 2.5–2.9.

Figure 4.11 shows regression relationships fitted to experimental data on amounts of different kinds of protein rations fed to pigs and the associated gains in weight.

Two kinds of regression curves have been fitted to the data from each experiment. In the first experiment a number of pigs were fed on a 16% protein ration; in the second a number of pigs were fed on a 14% protein ration. (The two groups of pigs represented random drawings from the same population, which included a relatively homogeneous lot of pigs in terms of genetic characteristics.) From an economic standpoint, the investigators were interested in the shapes of the production functions for each group of pigs separately, as well as in possible differences between the production functions obtained with a 14% rather than a 16% protein ration. Assuming that the early increments of feed produced weight gains which were worth significantly more than the value of the feed, production theory indicates that profit from the feeding operation would be maximized if continued until the next $1 worth of feed would increase the value of the pig by only $1. The regression lines in Figure 4.11 do suggest a gradual tapering off of the marginal physical productivity of successive increments of feed.

4.2.5 Cost Functions

Figure 4.12 shows a regression relationship between the total expenses of a busline in the United Kingdom and the millions of car miles covered by its equipment in successive four-week periods. It corresponds to the total variable cost curve (TVC) of Figure 2.11 *plus* a positive constant term or intercept associated with fixed costs.

In principle, the constant term of the regression equation, £65,580, would be an estimate of the fixed or overhead costs of the company even if its buses were completely idle. The slope of the regression line indicates that each

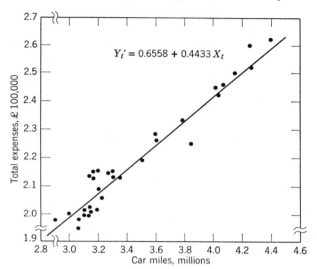

$$Y_t' = 0.6558 + 0.4433 X_t$$

Figure 4.12 Total expenses of a road passenger transport company as a function of total car miles driven, United Kingdom, 1949–1952, by four week periods. (Johnston, J., *Statistical Cost Analysis*, New York: McGraw-Hill Book Company, 1960, p. 79.)

additional million car miles traveled by the company's buses would increase its total expenses by £44,330. This amounts to roughly 23 miles per pound of expense or, as the pound was worth about $2.80 during the period indicated, to out-of-pocket costs of about 12 cents a mile. In effect, the slope of the regression line is an estimate of marginal cost. The form of the regression equation implies that the marginal cost curve of this company was horizontal (constant marginal costs) over the range of experience in which the company had actually operated during 1949–1952. This situation corresponds to that shown in Figure 2.13.

The examples presented here are a minute sampling of the tremendous volume of regression analysis, published and unpublished, that is constantly being done by economists and business analysts interested in estimating economic relationships and using them for purposes of policy, prediction, or control.

4.3   STRUCTURAL VERSUS EMPIRICAL REGRESSION RELATIONSHIPS

It should be clear even in advance of formal explanation that the various *arithmetic* operations involved in either separate frequency distributions or in the joint frequency distributions of regression analysis can be applied to any set of numbers regardless of whether these numbers make sense with respect to any practical or scientific purpose. For example, we could pick ten numbers out of our local telephone directory and compute their mean, their standard deviation, and the standard error of the mean. We could select these numbers arbitrarily or randomly—the arithmetic calculations would be the same in either case. From an analytical standpoint, however, this procedure is meaningless because the set of numbers has no relationship to any interesting question or hypothesis concerning the population from which it is derived. (If there is some lurking suspicion that a sample of actual telephone numbers *might* have some bearing upon an interesting question, we could simply think up the numbers or make up some *pot pourri* from calendars, automobile license plates, telephone directories, and patent numbers.)

By the same token, we could select any ten other numbers, tabulate them in a column parallel to the first ten, plot the observations, and draw some kind of line or curve representing the central tendency or drift of the observations.

In general, if there were no logical reason for expecting a systematic relationship between two sets of numbers, we would expect to find the observations so widely scattered that no systematic upward or downward drift or slope would appear. However, if the number of (logically unrelated) observations were small, we would not infrequently find scatter diagrams which *looked* as though there was a definite regression relationship.

At the extreme, it is clear that if each of two series contains only two observations, these define two points through which one and only one straight line can be drawn. It is quite unlikely that the slope of such a line will be exactly zero. Sets of three or four observations (logically unrelated) will also quite frequently suggest to the eye a definite relationship. But as the number of observations in two unrelated series increases, we expect that the great majority of samples will show a wide scatter and that no line will appear to be of much use for estimating values of one series from specified values of the other.

It is not always true, however, that a meaningless question gets a random answer. This is especially true in the case of economic time series, many of which show strong trends. In the United States since World War II, population has increased steadily. Output per man-hour and per man-year has also increased; so have prices of nonfarm goods and services. The numbers of workers in agriculture and in coal mining have persistently declined.

If a scatter diagram is made showing paired observations of two time series which have no known logical relationship but each of which contains a strong trend, the scatter will suggest a high degree of relationship between the two variables. The average value of one will increase (or decrease) steadily as the other increases over time.

In such a case, statistical tests routinely applied will suggest that the relationship could hardly be due to chance. If the two series are logically related, as with the consumption functions in Figures 4.9 and 4.10, we are inclined to take the regression relationship at its face value. Here we feel that Figure 4.10 can be used as a basis for estimating the increase in consumption expenditures that will be associated with a given increase in disposable income. But if there is no logical basis for expecting a permanently close association between two series, the relationship has no practical usefulness or safe interpretation. *Any two linear trends are perfectly correlated*—paired observations of the *trend* values of the two series would yield a linear regression equation with no residuals. = perfect correlation

Anyone who knows this elementary fact can generate misleading regression relationships to his heart's content. Many years ago a statistician wrote, "With statistics the unscrupulous deceive the unwary and the innocent deceive themselves." This appraisal is still widely applicable to the interpretation of regression relationships based on time series. There are many devices, tests, and safeguards that a competent economic statistician can use to avoid gross misinterpretation of regressions based on time trends. But the temptation to build causal explanations around the trend elements in possibly unrelated time series is very strong among the public.

So much for nonsense or spurious regressions. We shall turn now to "structural" relationships which grow directly out of economic theory and/or the technological facts of production. Figures 4.5 to 4.12 all involve structural relationships in our meaning of the term.

The structural relationships of interest to economists may be grouped into four categories: behavioral, technical, and institutional relations, and identities.

The *behavioral* relationships include demand curves, supply curves, and Engel curves which reflect the behavior of particular kinds of economic units. Consumers adjust their purchases to changes in commodity prices and in their own incomes; business firms adjust their outputs to changes in the prices of raw materials and factors of production and to the state of market demand for their products. Behavioral relationships were discussed in Chapter 2 in connection with Figures 2.1–2.4 and 2.10–2.19.

Technical relations include mainly production functions, which we discussed in connection with Figures 2.5–2.9. Some statistical production functions have already been shown in Figure 4.11. Table 4.3 shows two linear production functions or "activities" of the type which are basic to linear programming. They reflect two sets of farming operations, one of which (with average weather) would produce 40 bushels of corn and the other 20 bushels of wheat. The upper part of Table 4.3 shows inputs and expected output on a per acre basis; the lower part states requirements for land and labor per bushel of expected output. If the production process indicated for corn were replicated on one million acres of land of the appropriate quality, the production process in total would require 0.8 million hours of planting labor, 1.0 million hours of cultivating labor, and 0.8 million hours of harvesting labor. With average weather, these inputs would produce 40 million bushels of corn.

Table 4.3 also presents an example of input-output relationships for the entire United States transportation equipment industry in 1947. The column of input requirements per $10,000 of gross output is formally a *linear homogeneous production function* of the same type as the production activities for wheat and corn. The input categories in an input-output table are so broad that it is necessary to express them in terms of dollar values. These dollar figures implicitly include 1947 quantities of the many specific input commodities valued at their 1947 prices.

As indicated in Figure 2.21, input-output coefficients imply an exact linear relationship between the amount of total gross output of a given industry and the amount of inputs required from each of the industries which supply it. That is, input-output coefficients are usually manipulated as though they were exact numbers. In reality, of course, they are subject to various imperfections connected with the completeness and accuracy of the original data, with technological changes over time, and with aggregation problems.

Institutional relationships in economics are those specified by law or by regulatory agencies. A clear-cut example would be a schedule of personal income tax rates prescribed by the Congress. In principle, the effect of a change in the tax schedule upon the after-tax income of a specified individual or family is completely predictable, assuming that the size of money income before taxes does not change.

Figure 4.13 illustrates such a relationship based on the United States federal income tax forms for 1961. Curve *A* shows the tax which would be paid by a married taxpayer with a total of four exemptions, filing a joint return, under the actual tax rate schedule of 1961. Curve *B* shows the tax payments associated with each specified level of personal income before taxes if the tax rates were reduced by four percentage points in each bracket. Finally, curve *C* shows the effects of increasing personal exemptions by $400 for each family member. If curve *A* were a straight line, the tax change reflected in curve *B* would reduce its slope relative to curve *A*, but it would intersect the horizontal axis—that is, zero tax liability—at the same point. The tax change reflected in curve *C* would shift the zero tax point to the right by $1600 but would leave the slope of curve *C* identical with that of curve *A*.

In principle, the effect of a change in the tax rate schedule could be calculated for every actual and potential taxpayer. Hence tax rate schedule *A* would lead to a definite relationship between personal income tax revenues

Table 4.3 Examples of Technical Relationships

I. Microrelations: Production "Activities" on a Particular Farm

	Corn	Wheat
A. Outputs and Inputs per Acre:		
Yield (output)	40 bu.	20 bu.
Planting labor requirement	0.8 hr	0.8 hr
Cultivating labor requirement	1.0 hr	0 hr
Harvesting labor requirement	0.8 hr	2.0 hr
B. Inputs Required per Bushel of Output:[a]		
Land (acres)	0.025	0.05
Planting labor (hr)	0.02	0.04
Cultivating labor (hr)	0.025	0
Harvesting labor (hr)	0.02	0.10

II. Macrorelations: An Input-Output Production Function for Transport Equipment

Supplying Industry:	Direct Input Requirements per $10,000 Gross Output of Transport Equipment[b]
Transport equipment	$ 2128
Iron and steel	1389
Machinery	1069
Rubber products	319
Nonferrous metals	210
Transportation	170
Nonmetallic mineral products	125
Chemicals	92
Other industries	356
Subtotal	$ 5858
"Value added" in transport equipment industry	4042
Total inputs	$10,000

[a] Per acre figure divided by yield per acre.

[b] Direct requirements from specified industries to support $10,000 worth of total output from the transport equipment industry, United States, 1947 (assumes 1947 prices for outputs of all industries).

Sources: Microrelations from Earl O. Heady and Wilfred Candler, *Linear Programming Methods*, Iowa State University Press, 1958, p. 35, Table 2.1.

Macrorelations from Hollis B. Chenery and Paul G. Clark, *Interindustry Economics*, New York: John Wiley and Sons, 1959, pp. 222–223.

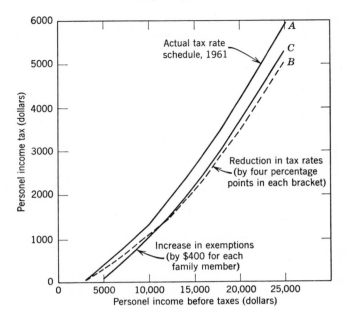

Figure 4.13 Personal income tax and personal income: effects of changes in exemptions and tax rate schedules. (Based on rates for married taxpayers with total of four exemptions, filing joint returns, U.S. *Federal Income Tax Forms for 1961*, p. 9, Schedule II.)

and personal income before taxes in terms of national aggregates. This would also imply a definite relationship at the national level between disposable personal income after taxes and personal income before taxes. Changes from schedule *A* to schedule *B* or *C* should influence these relationships among national aggregates approximately in the manner shown in Figure 4.13.

The fourth category of structural economic relationships consists of *identities* or *balance equations* of a bookkeeping nature. For example, the gross national product (GNP) is by definition equal to the sum of personal consumption expenditures, gross private capital formation, government purchases of goods and services, and net foreign trade. If each of the four components were to be estimated separately and independently of an estimate for total GNP, only by chance would the four estimated components add up to the estimated total. Other identities connect, for example, gross farm income, production expenses, and net farm income or retail food prices, equivalent farm prices, and food marketing margins.

The foregoing terminology was introduced into economics in the 1940s and has not yet found its way into the vocabularies of all economists and business analysts. Why are such relationships called "structural"? They reflect the way in which the variables are *actually* related. A demand curve implies that *if* the price of a given commodity were reduced 10% the quantity consumed would increase by the amount indicated by the demand curve.[3] A production function implies that if the quantity of nitrogen applied to an acre of corn is increased from one stipulated level to another, the yield of corn will increase by the amount indicated by the production function.[3] These are called structural changes because we have a theory which relates the two variables and which says that if one of them is moved the other will move with it in a specified way.[3]

A structural relationship is to be distinguished from a purely empirical relationship not supported by any theory. There is also a distinction between structural relationships and relationships which may be fitted for forecasting purposes to the same variables. In the latter instance, it is possible to show precise mathematical transformations from the structural relationships to the forecasting relationships or "reduced forms." If we recognize the connections between these two kinds of relationships we can pass back and forth between structural and prediction equations without logical inconsistency. However, unsophisticated people often use prediction equations as though they were structural relations and draw unwarranted inferences.

4.3.1 *Examples of Economic "Structures" or Models*

From a statistical viewpoint, simple regressions involve only two variables, and when we discuss regression mechanics in the following section we will confine ourselves to two-variable cases. However, most problems of importance in economic theory and in real economic behavior involve more than two simultaneously changing variables, and some involve several distinct equations operating simultaneously or with time lags. Hence it is particularly important that we see the mechanics and arithmetic of simple regression analysis against a realistic economic background.

Figure 4.14 expresses a hypothesis about the manner in which the production, consumption, retail price, and farm price of potatoes are related to one another and to certain other factors. The directions of the arrows express hypotheses about the direction of influence of one variable upon another, hypotheses often supported by the existence of time lags. The widths of the arrows express hypotheses concerning the relative importance of the various paths of influence. Each variable is measurable in the form of an economic time series except for "consumer preferences." "Weather" can be quantified in terms of joint distributions of rainfall, temperature, and humidity just

---

[3] Each of these three statements is predicated on the assumption that other important variables remain constant.

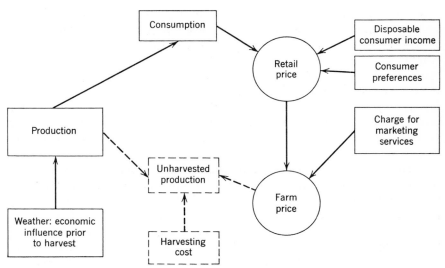

Figure 4.14 The demand and supply structure for potatoes. Arrows show direction of influence. Heavy arrows indicate major paths of influence which account for the bulk of the variation in current prices. Light solid arrows indicate definite but less important paths, dashed arrows indicate paths of negligible, doubtful, or occasional importance. (From U.S. Department of Agriculture)

before and during the growing season. "Economic influences prior to harvest" can also, in principle, be quantified in terms of the price of potatoes, prices of crops which compete for the same kind of land, prices of inputs used in potato production, and changes in employment and other factors affecting consumer demand.

In this model, we might state the following objectives for regression analysis:

1. Corresponding to each arrow in the diagram, we would like to estimate a coefficient (or a curvilinear relationship) stating the expected change in the variable to which the arrow leads that is associated with a one-unit increase in the variable from which it comes.

2. We should like to determine each of these coefficients, and hence the entire set of regression coefficients implicit in the diagram, in such a way that, given the time series values of disposable consumer income, weather, and preharvest economic influences actually experienced over a period of years, we could estimate time series values of consumption, retail price, farm price, and unharvested production that would correspond closely to the values of these variables actually observed.

3. If these estimated or "reconstructed" time series reproduce fairly accurately both the observed trends and the year-to-year changes in the original data, we may wish to use the regression results to predict future values of the dependent or *endogenous* variables.

The pattern of arrows in the diagram also expresses hypotheses as to which of the structural relationships and coefficients can be estimated appropriately by means of simple regression methods. For example, it appears from the diagram that consumption can be estimated solely on the basis of knowledge of changes in production; this implies a two-variable or simple regression relationship. On the other hand, there are at least two measurable variables plus "consumer preferences" affecting the retail price of potatoes. Thus an explanation of retail price requires multiple regression analysis, a method to be discussed in Chapter 7. We may (reluctantly) represent "consumer preferences" by a time trend, not necessarily linear.

Figure 4.15 expresses a hypothesis concerning the demand-supply-price structure for hogs and pork. It is on the same logical footing as the diagram for potatoes already discussed, and we will not elaborate on it here. A competent economist engaged in a serious investigation of the pork and hog economy would try to conceptualize this model in terms of consumption theory and theory of the firm; certain sequences of arrows would be recognized as technical relationships (number of hogs slaughtered as a function of the number of sows bred in the preceding year) and others as identities (pork production is the product of number of hogs slaughtered times pork yield per hog). The investigator could provide points of entry in his conceptual model for "institutional" changes such as an increase in sales taxes on retail pork (food) sales, the adoption of a federal subsidy to meat packers to reduce the margin between retail pork prices and the farm price of hogs, and other conceivable types of public intervention.

Although we have not yet defined closeness of relationship or "goodness of fit" for simple regression analysis, it is clear that this has something to do with the closeness with which the observations cluster about the regression line or curve. A number of elements condition the goodness of fit of a simple regression line or curve:

1. It must be recognized that most economic data are subject to some errors of measurement. A regression relationship is by definition a *systematic* relationship; hence (random) errors of measurement in one variable cannot be closely related to or explained by the second variable.

2. Frequently, there is some uncertainty as to whether the relationship between two economic variables is linear in terms of arithmetic numbers, linear in terms of logarithms, or nonlinear in one or the other of these forms. Nonlinearities stand out clearly in some of the diagrams presented earlier in

this chapter. However, Figure 4.11 illustrates the fact that, in general, two or more curves may describe a given set of data equally well.

3. If one variable, such as the retail price of pork, is in fact strongly influenced by two or more other variables (such as disposable consumer income, supplies of other meats and poultry, and pork consumption) it is unreasonable to expect that the simple regression of retail prices upon any one of the two or more associated variables will closely fit the observations. The scatter of observations around a simple regression between retail price of pork and pork consumption must leave room for the effects of variations in disposable income and supplies of competing meats, not to mention a possible time trend resulting from changes in consumer attitudes toward pork and competing foods.

Hence we should expect that a simple regression relationship between pork production and the farm price of hogs would be vulnerable to errors of measurement in pork consumption and the retail price of pork as well as in the two variables specifically included in the regression. The relationship between pork production and the farm price of hogs would be subject to disturbances resulting from variations in disposable consumer income and the supply of other meats and poultry; it would also be vulnerable to changes in unit costs of labor and in prices of intermediate goods and services used in the marketing process.

In the past, many business analysts and economists used simple regression relationships between variables such as these two because they had never learned how to run a multiple regression analysis or to conceptualize a complete set of relationships. In doing so, the business analysts and forecasters were behaving more naively than were the businessmen and production managers involved in the actual economic process.

It should be clear from Figure 4.15 that we cannot hope to use a simple regression between hog prices and pork production safely *unless* we are aware of the complete demand-supply-price structure into which these two variables fit. From a structural standpoint, this particular regression is equivalent to drawing a fictitious arrow from pork production to the farm price of hogs over a path where no real arrow exists.

In summary, the arrows in diagrams such as Figure 4.15 represent paths over which economic influences can be expected to travel. Regression analysis can be used appropriately to estimate or map out such paths of influence and relationship as exist in the real economy. Neither statistics nor economics can save us from the results of our folly if we treat nonstructural regression relationships as if they were real economic thoroughfares. In practical research applications, we must use economic theory, common sense, and knowledge of production and marketing processes to avoid the dead ends

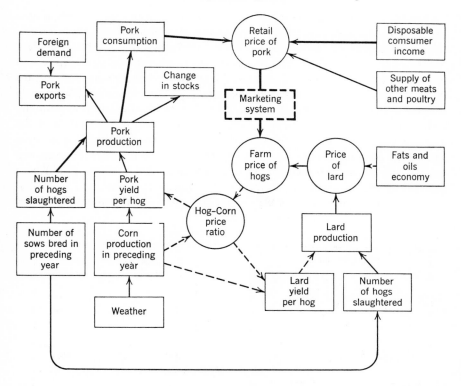

Figure 4.15 The demand and supply structure for pork. Arrows show direction of influence. Heavy arrows indicate major paths of influence which account for the bulk of the variation in current prices. Light solid arrows indicate definite but less important paths, dashed arrows indicate paths of negligible, doubtful, or occasional importance. (From U.S. Department of Agriculture)

that have characterized many earlier applications of regression analysis in economics and business.

Figure 4.16 portrays graphically a few of the variables involved in the demand-supply-price structure for pork during the 1949–1960 period.

First, it will be noted that there were some fairly sharp year-to-year changes in pork consumption per capita during the period. Usually, a sharp increase in consumption from one year to the next was associated with a sizable decrease in price, and vice versa. This inverse relationship between retail price and consumption is characteristic of a consumer demand curve (we have seen in Figure 4.6 how the quarterly data on pork price and consumption conform with the expected downward sloping demand curve).

Second, in most instances a change in retail price from one year to the next has been associated with a change in the same direction and of approximately the same magnitude in the farm price or net farm value of the equivalent weight of live hogs. Two other variables, disposable income per capita and marketing charges per pound of pork, are characterized primarily by upward trends. If two or more variables in the same regression equation have clearly defined trends, we run into the difficulties of interpretation and disentanglement previously discussed. Careful studies indicate a downward drift in the demand for pork since World War II that seems attributable to a gradual change in consumer preferences. Because the only quantitative representation we can give to declining consumer preferences in this instance would be a time trend, the influence of "time" will be difficult to disentangle from that of the upward trend in disposable income. It is also questionable whether the

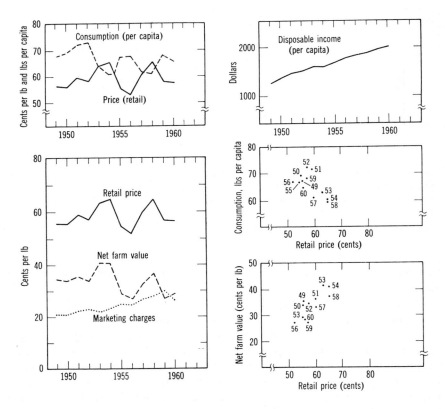

Figure 4.16 Pork: some variables involved in the demand-supply-price structure, 1949–60.

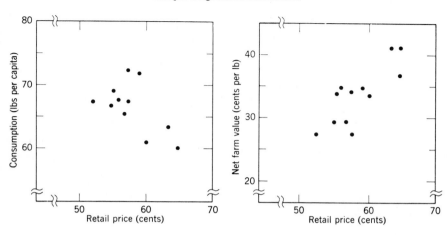

Figure 4.17 Pork: consumption and net farm value, related to retail price, 1949–60.

deviations of disposable income per capita around its upward trend are large enough to show a clear-cut effect upon year-to-year changes in the retail price of pork.

Figure 4.17 indicates that, although the scatter diagram between pork consumption and retail price shows a definite downward slope, the scatter of observations around any regression line or smooth curve is still quite substantial. Some of the scatter may result from one or both of the trend-like variables (consumer preferences and disposable income) just mentioned. On the basis of consumption theory and Figure 4.15, we should expect also that some of the scatter is attributable to fluctuations in supplies of competing meats and poultry.

4.4 SIMPLE REGRESSION MECHANICS

We have already pointed out that regression mechanics (computations) can be carried out for illogically paired variables as well as for variables which are logically related. There is no magic in the technique—nothing in the arithmetic can save us from the consequences of inaccurate data or illogical selection of variables.

4.4.1 *Simple Regression Methods*

The first two columns of Table 4.4 contain time series observations on per capita consumption of beef and the retail price of beef deflated by a consumer

Table 4.4   Beef Consumption and Price:
Straight Line Regression Equation, 1949–1960

Year	Consumption per Capita Q, lb	Retail Price[a] P, cents/lb	$\hat{Q} = 158.5183 - 1.2709P$		
			$\hat{Q}$ Estimated Consumption, lb/capita	$-1.2709P$	$z = (Q - \hat{Q})$ (residuals)
1949	63.9	67.2	73.1	−85.40	−9.2
1950	63.4	73.3	65.4	−93.16	−2.0
1951	56.1	79.5	57.5	−101.04	−1.4
1952	62.2	76.3	61.5	−96.97	0.7
1953	77.6	60.4	81.8	−76.76	−4.1
1954	80.1	59.7	82.6	−75.87	−2.5
1955	82.0	59.0	83.5	−74.98	−1.5
1956	85.4	56.8	86.3	−72.19	−0.9
1957	84.6	58.7	83.9	−74.60	0.7
1958	80.5	65.6	75.1	−83.37	5.4
1959	81.4	66.4	74.1	−84.39	7.3
1960	85.2	63.8	77.4	−81.08	7.8

[a] Deflated by the Consumer Price Index, 1957–1959 = 100.

price index. According to the theory of consumption, an equal percentage change in the prices of all commodities and in money income should not disturb the pattern of quantities demanded or consumed. Hence during a period such as 1949–1960 in which the Consumer Price Index rose more than 20%, we would expect that the actual price of beef would be less closely associated with changes in its per capita consumption than would the deflated price, which shows changes in the price of beef *relative to* the average price level for all consumer goods and services.

Figure 4.18a suggests a very close inverse relationship between changes in per capita consumption of beef and changes in its retail price. This close inverse relationship is also borne out by the scatter diagram in part c. The straight line in part b is the least squares simple regression line, the calculation of which will be described later. The equation of this regression line,

$$\hat{Q} = 158.5183 - 1.2709P$$

is shown at the top of Figure 4.18c.

$\hat{Q}$ is the value of per capita consumption computed from the regression equation for any specified value of P, the deflated retail price of beef. If we are willing to assume that the relationship (demand curve) connecting beef consumption and price is a straight line, the particular line shown is the one about which the sum of squared deviations of the individual observations about the regression line is a minimum. In an equation in which Q is the dependent variable, the deviations to be squared are measured vertically above and below the regression line, along the Q axis.

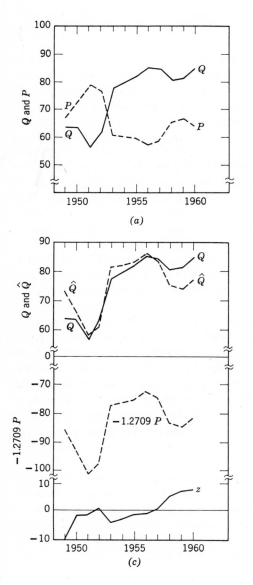

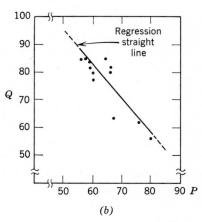

Figure 4.18 Beef consumption and price: straight line regression results, 1949–60.

The least squares regression line is not necessarily the "best" line in some ultimate sense. But if certain assumptions are met, this line does give us the best estimate that can be made of the expected value of Q associated with a stated value of P (retail price).[4]

If these assumptions are not met, the least squares regression line still has the advantage of definiteness and reproducibility. A set of arithmetic operations can be prescribed that should lead any two careful computing clerks, or any two electronic computers, to precisely the same numerical values for the constant term and slope of the least squares regression line.

We could, of course, try to approximate the least squares regression line by trial and error. Thus we could plot the observations in part b on a very large sheet of graph paper, using perhaps ten or twenty times as large a scale as in Figure 4.18. We could plot the points accurately with a sharp pencil, draw in by eye a thin straight line, measure the vertical distance of each dot from the line with a good ruler, square each of the deviations, and sum. Then we could draw in a second line by eye, measure, square, and sum, and see if the result were larger or smaller than for the first line. If the second sum were smaller than the first, we might try a third line a little further away from line 1. If the third sum were smaller than the second, we might move still a little further in the same direction away from line 1. If the third sum were larger than the second, we might try a fourth line somewhere in between lines 1 and 2.

This obviously would be a time-consuming and laborious procedure. Furthermore, if two investigators were asked to go through these operations independently, there is no guarantee that they would arrive at exactly the same line.

The trial-and-error process of approximating the least squares regression line could be expedited by taking advantage of one aspect of the mathematical method—the least squares regression straight line passes through the *point of means* of the two variables. Since this is a basic requirement of the method and every least squares regression straight line must pass through the point of means, it is clear that the regression analysis as such cannot claim to "explain" the level of the mean of one variable (Q) in terms of the level of the mean of the other variable (P). Rather, straight line regression analysis measures the relationship between *deviations from the arithmetic means* of the two variables.

Earlier it was pointed out that the arithmetic mean of a frequency distribution is the point about which the sum of squared deviations is a minimum. The least squares regression line extends this property of the arithmetic mean into the context of a two-variable joint frequency distribution. In Figure 4.2, it is clear that the frequency distribution of clothing expenditures within each

[4] These assumptions will be discussed in Chapters 6 and 7.

class interval of family income will have the least squares property with respect to the arithmetic mean of clothing expenditures for that income group. Table 4.4 shows how estimated values of $\hat{Q}$ are computed from the least squares regression equation for each observed value of P and how the deviations of residuals about the regression line are calculated by subtracting the estimated from the actual values of Q.

The figures in these four columns are also plotted in Figure 4.18c. The second or "slope" coefficient, -1.2709, implies that every change of one cent in retail price will be associated with an opposite change of 1.2709 lb in the expected or estimated value of per capita consumption $\hat{Q}$. The line labeled $-1.2709P$ in part c is clearly a mirror image of the line labeled P in Figure 4.18a, with the vertical scale accentuated by the factor of 1.2709. The time pattern of $\hat{Q}$ in part c is identical with that of P multiplied by the coefficient -1.2709. The deviations from the regression line $Q - \hat{Q} = z$ are shown in Column (5) of the table and in the lower portion of Figure 4.18c. There appears to be some upward trend in the residuals, but we will make no further comment on this for the present.

We shall state without proof another feature of simple straight line regression.

1. The sum of the squared deviations of Q from its arithmetic mean ($\bar{Q}$) is smaller than the sum of squared deviations of Q from any other point.

2. The sum of squared deviations of Q about the regression straight line ($\hat{Q} = a + bP$) is smaller than the sum of squared deviations of Q from any other straight line.

3. The regression procedure, then, may be regarded as dividing the sum of squared deviations of Q around $\bar{Q}$ into two portions, the sum of squared deviations which is "unexplained" by variations of P around its own mean ($\bar{P}$) and the remaining sum of squares which is in some sense "explained" by variations in P. The three sums of squares mentioned may be written as

(1) Total: $\sum\limits_{i=1}^{n} (Q - \bar{Q})^2$

(2) "Explained" by the regression straight line:

$$\sum\limits_{i=1}^{n} (\hat{Q} - \bar{Q})^2$$

(3) "Unexplained" by the regression straight line:

$$\sum\limits_{i=1}^{n} (Q - \hat{Q})^2 = \sum\limits_{i=1}^{n} z^2$$

The three sums of squares are then related by the following equality:

(4) $\sum\limits_{i=1}^{n} (Q - \bar{Q})^2 = \sum\limits_{i=1}^{n} (\hat{Q} - \bar{Q})^2 + \sum\limits_{i=1}^{n} (Q - \hat{Q})^2$

The ratio of the unexplained variation in Q to the total variation about its mean would evidently have some value in characterizing the "goodness of fit" of the regression line to the observed data. Or, perhaps, this particular ratio might be regarded as a measure of the *badness* of fit. Its complement, the ratio of explained variation to the total variation about the mean, would appear to be a useful measure of the degree of association between Q and P—the extent to which changes in P are useful in predicting changes in Q by means of the regression line $\hat{Q} = a + bP$. The ratio of explained variation to total variation has a name, *the coefficient of determination*, and a symbol, r^2.

The unexplained variation has a more useful meaning in simple regression analysis if it is transformed in the following way:

1. Divide the sum of the squared deviations from the regression line by $n - 2$, where n is the number of observations to which the line was fitted.

2. The square root of this result

$$(4.2) \qquad \bar{S} = \left(\frac{\sum\limits_{i=1}^{n} z_i^2}{n - 2} \right)^{1/2}$$

is called *the standard error of estimate*. If the frequency distribution of deviations about the regression line has a fairly marked central tendency, roughly two-thirds of the observations will lie within the range of plus or minus $\bar{S}$ of the regression line.

Having gone this far, we define one or two other measures explicitly. First, from the earlier chapters we have seen that *the standard deviation* of Q may be defined as

$$(4.3) \qquad s_Q = \left(\frac{\sum\limits_{i=1}^{n} (Q_i - \bar{Q})^2}{n - 1} \right)^{1/2}$$

The adjustment factor in the denominator reflects the fact that one degree of freedom is used in determining the sample mean $\bar{Q}$ so that only $n - 1$ degrees of freedom are available for variations about the sample mean.

We have noted that the least squares regression straight line passes through the point of means. If we specify one additional point, this point together with the point of means completely and uniquely determines a straight line. In practice, the least squares method leads to the unique determination of the *slope* of the regression line, and only one straight line can be drawn through the point of means with the required slope. Hence unique determination of the regression straight line involves two restrictions and uses up two of the n degrees of freedom. There remain $n - 2$ degrees of freedom for variations about the regression line, and this consideration accounts for the factor $n - 2$ which appears in the formula for the standard error of estimate.

The standard error of estimate is always adjusted for degrees of freedom, as indicated in Eq. (4.3). There is some variation in practice among economists in adjusting r^2 for degrees of freedom. When the adjustment is used, the formula for adjusted r^2 is

$$(4.4) \qquad \bar{r}^2 = 1 - (1 - r^2)\left(\frac{n-1}{n-2}\right)$$

When degrees of freedom are disregarded, $(1 - r^2)$ is equal to $\sum_1^n z^2 / \sum_1^n (Q - \bar{Q})^2$. If the numerator is divided by $n - 2$ and the denominator by $n - 1$, as is done in calculating $\bar{S}^2$ and s_Q^2, respectively, we obtain the adjustment factor $(n - 1)/(n - 2)$ as indicated.

In most economic applications of regression analysis, this adjustment is a needless refinement. It tends to place undue emphasis upon the value of r^2 when, as we shall see in Chapter 6, this coefficient is usually less stable and less meaningful than the regression equation and the standard error of estimate. It is sometimes argued that the adjustment factor applied to r^2 helps us to avoid overestimating the closeness of the regression relationship. However, this warning is given efficiently and in readily interpretable form by the adjusted standard error of estimate $\bar{S}$.

4.4.2 *Further Regression Algebra and Arithmetic*

We have noted that straight line regression analysis involves deviations from the point of means. Let us write $q_i = Q_i - \bar{Q}$ and $p_i = P_i - \bar{P}$, where i denotes the ith individual observation $(i = 1, 2, 3, \ldots, n)$. Then the slope of the regression line b can be computed from the formula

$$(4.5) \qquad b = \frac{\sum\limits_{i=1}^{n} q_i p_i}{\sum\limits_{i=1}^{n} p_i^2}$$

The constant term a in the regression equation can be calculated from the following formula:

$$a = \bar{Q} - b\bar{P}$$

These calculations complete the formula for the regression line $\hat{Q} = a + bP$.
The coefficient of determination r^2 can be calculated from the formula

$$(4.6) \qquad r^2 = \frac{\left(\sum\limits_{i=1}^{n} q_i p_i\right)^2}{\sum\limits_{i=1}^{n} q_i^2 \cdot \sum\limits_{i=1}^{n} p_i^2}$$

The expressions $(1/n) \sum_{i=1}^{n} q_i^2$ and $(1/n) \sum_{i=1}^{n} p_i^2$ are called, respectively, the (unadjusted) variances of Q and P; the expression $(1/n) \sum_{i=1}^{n} q_i p_i$ is called the *covariance* of Q and P.

In regard to regression arithmetic, we could exchange the positions of the two variables and fit the regression equation $\hat{P} = \alpha + \beta \cdot Q$. In this instance,

(4.7)
$$\beta = \frac{\sum\limits_{i=1}^{n} p_i q_i}{\sum\limits_{i=1}^{n} q_i^2}$$

Comparing (4.5), (4.7), and (4.6), we see that $r^2 = b\beta$. If $\beta = 1/b$, $r^2 = 1$. Since r^2 is the ratio of explained to total variation, an r^2 of 1.0 can only mean that all of the observations lie precisely on the regression line. Furthermore, r^2 cannot exceed 1; hence whenever r^2 is less than 1, β is less (in absolute value) than $1/b$ and the regression line in which $\hat{P}$ is estimated from Q will not coincide with the regression line in which $\hat{Q}$ is estimated from P. Further discussion of this somewhat surprising asymmetry will be deferred until Chapter 6.

The foregoing formulas give a fairly good indication of "what goes on" in simple straight line regression analysis. They are not the most convenient formulas from which to compute regression equations and other measures when desk calculators are employed. For such purposes we may use the following formulas:

(4.8)
$$\sum_{i=1}^{n} q_i^2 = \sum_{i=1}^{n} Q_i^2 - n \cdot \bar{Q}^2$$

(4.9)
$$\sum_{i=1}^{n} p_i^2 = \sum_{i=1}^{n} P_i^2 - n \cdot \bar{P}^2$$

and

(4.10)
$$\sum_{i=1}^{n} q_i p_i = \sum_{i=1}^{n} Q_i P_i - n \cdot \bar{Q}\bar{P}$$

Further, if we write $\hat{q}_i = b \cdot p_i$, we may also write

$$\sum_{i=1}^{n} \hat{q}_i^2 = b^2 \cdot \sum_{i=1}^{n} p_i^2$$

Then,

(4.11)
$$r^2 = \frac{b^2 \cdot \sum\limits_{i=1}^{n} p_i^2}{\sum\limits_{i=1}^{n} q_i^2}$$

If we denote the deviation of a particular observation from the regression line as z_i,

(4.12)
$$\sum_{i=1}^{n} z_i^2 = \sum_{i=1}^{n} q_i^2 - b^2 \sum_{i=1}^{n} p_i^2$$

The adjusted standard error of estimate $\bar{S}$ can then be computed from the formula

(4.13)
$$\bar{S} = \left(\frac{\sum\limits_{i=1}^{n} z_i^2}{n-2}\right)^{1/2}$$

as before.

In the past, many textbooks in economic and business statistics have stressed the clerical and computational aspects of simple regression analysis. In well-run research organizations even a generation ago, the actual calculations were turned over to clerks, with enough supervision from a statistician to maintain an adequate check upon the accuracy of the calculations. Various devices such as "check sums" were built into the routine instructions for such clerical operations and were important in assuring numerical accuracy.

By the early 1960s, electronic computers had become widely available, and standard regression programs were developed for virtually all such computers. Once the individual observations were recorded on punched cards, the previous drudgery of grinding out sums of squares and cross products was taken over by the computer and handled at incredible speeds. As a student in the early 1940s, the author was required to carry out on a desk calculator a four-variable multiple regression analysis (see Chapter 7) involving some 50 observations. The operation took two days; even an experienced computing clerk would have needed several hours. In a well-run computing service in the early 1960s, only the copying of the original observations onto punched cards—translating them into language a machine can understand—would involve significant amounts of human labor of a clerical type if a standard regression program were used.

Hence we propose to emphasize here the basic logic of regression methods and the economic settings in which they can be appropriately applied and interpreted. It appears that an increasing number of students in all disciplines will be learning at least the rudiments of "programming" sequences of calculations to be performed by electronic computers. A "program" for simple straight line regression analysis is essentially a set of instructions telling the computer to carry out the various summations, multiplications, subtractions, and divisions implied in equations such as (4.2)–(4.13) in a prescribed sequence. A student or research worker who writes his own programs must know his subject well enough to "teach" it to the computer. And the authors can vouch for the fact that a highly important byproduct of trying to teach a subject to others is that you are thereby forced to learn it quite well yourself.

Although computers take most of the drudgery out of regression analysis, it is important that the economist does not get too far away from his data. Even if he relies on standard "canned" regression programs prepared by a specialized computing service, he should know enough about the arithmetic of regression analysis to recognize a major error on the part of the punch card operator or the programmer. Stupid errors usually leave tracks and can often be detected if the investigator has carefully studied his original observations and the manner in which they appear to have been generated in the real world. Serious errors at the card-punching stage are likely to result in mean values which look improbably high or low, or in standard deviations which look improbably large in relation to the variability in the original series as appraised by visual inspection.

4.4.3 Data Transformations

The arithmetic operations involved in simple straight line regression analysis can be applied to any set of paired observations. Hence no new problems are encountered if, for example, our basic series on beef consumption and retail price is transformed into logarithms, into arithmetic first differences (year-to-year changes), or into first differences (year-to-year changes) of logarithms. Or one variable could be transformed into logarithms and the other remain in arithmetic numbers.

Note that the observed retail prices of beef have already undergone one transformation, namely division or "deflation" by a consumer price index. In each case, a least squares regression straight line is fitted to *transformed* values of the variables.[5] In most instances, except for the first difference transformation, a straight line relationship between the transformed variables implies a nonlinear relationship between the original arithmetic values.

In general, the desirability or permissibility of data transformations should be determined on the basis of economic theory and the facts of production, marketing, or other processes relevant to the problem at hand. Such considerations will not always lead to a single best set of data transformations, but they will usually eliminate some of the more complicated transformations which might lead to spurious "improvements" in the closeness of fit to the data.

A freehand regression curve may be regarded as a data transformation corresponding to an unknown mathematical formula. There is no compelling reason why estimates from such curves should not be used as data transformations. The principal danger is a strong propensity to "explain" relationships in a particular sample without sufficient concern for the likelihood that such relationships exist in the parent population to which inferences are to be

[5] We have been careful in the text to emphasize that only *an arithmetic straight line* regression passes through the point of arithmetic means of the *original* variables. If the original variables Q and P were, for example, transformed into $\log Q$ and $\log P$, the regression equation $(\widehat{\log Q}) = c + d(\log P)$ would pass through the point of means of $\log Q$ and $\log P$, namely $(\overline{\log Q})$ and $(\overline{\log P})$.

made. Mathematical regression methods automatically yield estimates of the sampling errors associated with each coefficient of the regression equation; graphic methods do not.

4.4.4 *Simple Curvilinear Regression*

It should be clear from the figures and examples presented in this chapter and in Chapter 2 that many important relationships among economic variables are curvilinear. The *idea* of a smooth curve relating Q and P is no more complicated than the idea of a straight line relationship. The formulas and calculations required to fit simple curvilinear regressions involve only slight extensions of those for the straight line situation.

One of the simplest two-variable curves is the *second-degree parabola*. The equation of a straight line may be written $Q = a + bP$, whereas the equation of a parabola may be written $Q = a + bP + cP^2$. The curvature clearly comes from the term in P^2 as can be readily seen if the value of Q is calculated from the equation using, successively, values of 1, 2, 3, and 4 for P and values of 1 for the coefficients a, b, and c. (Note that these coefficients may be either positive or negative.)

Two points uniquely determine a straight line, and three points uniquely determine a second-degree parabola. In fitting the three constants of a second-degree parabola by least squares, we use up three degrees of freedom just as though we had required the parabola to pass through three designated points. As in the straight line case, the parabolic regression curve divides the total variation in Q into a portion "explained" by regression and an unexplained remainder, which has $n - 3$ degrees of freedom.

The following formulas associated with the second-degree parabola may be compared with the corresponding formulas in the linear case:

$$(4.14) \qquad \bar{S} = \left(\frac{\sum_{i=1}^{n} z_i^2}{n - 3} \right)^{1/2}$$

$$(4.15) \qquad s_Q = \left(\frac{\sum_{i=1}^{n} (Q_i - \bar{Q})^2}{n - 1} \right)^{1/2}$$

Equation (4.14) differs from (4.2) only in the use of $n - 3$ in the denominator. Equation (4.15) is identical with (4.3); the standard deviation of the dependent variable is, of course, not affected by a change in the form of the regression equation.

Whenever three or more constants are to be determined in a regression equation, it is customary to designate the ratio of "explained" variation to total variation in the dependent variable by the symbol R^2; r^2 is reserved for the two constant case. The formula for $\bar{R}^2$ in (4.16), which follows, differs from that for $\bar{r}^2$ in (4.4) only in that the factor $n - 3$ rather than $n - 2$ appears in the denominator.

$$(4.16) \qquad\qquad \bar{R}^2 = 1 - (1 - R^2)\left(\frac{n - 1}{n - 3}\right)$$

In using $n - 3$, we imply that three constants are to be determined; if four constants are to be determined, we use $n - 4$, and so on.

To simplify the notation in the next two equations, we shall omit the subscript index i and substitute U for P^2. We let q equal $Q - \bar{Q}$, $p = P - \bar{P}$, and $u = U - \bar{U}$. Then the three constants of the second-degree parabola may be calculated from any given set of observations as follows:

$$(4.17) \qquad\qquad b = \frac{\sum pq \cdot \sum u^2 - \sum uq \sum pu}{\sum p^2 \sum u^2 - (\sum pu)^2}$$

$$(4.18) \qquad\qquad c = \frac{\sum uq \cdot \sum p^2 - \sum pq \sum pu}{\sum p^2 \sum u^2 - (\sum pu)^2}$$

$$(4.19) \qquad\qquad a = \bar{Q} - b\bar{P} - c\bar{U}$$

The derivation of the last three formulas will be given in Appendix A and a more compact presentation of the algebra will be given in Appendix B at the end of this chapter.[6]

The parabolic regression which results from applying the method of least squares to observations on beef consumption and retail prices during 1949–1960 is shown in Table 4.5 and Figure 4.19. In Figure 4.20 both the parabolic and the straight line regressions are plotted on the scatter diagram of the original observations.

The parabola lies so close to the straight line over the range covered by the 1949–1960 observations that its "goodness of fit" appears to be about the same as that of the straight line. For the parabola, $R^2 = 0.8025$; for the straight line, $r^2 = 0.789$—both coefficients unadjusted for degrees of freedom. The standard error of estimate $\bar{S}$ is 5.207 for the parabola compared with 5.102 for the straight line. According to this criterion, the parabola fits the observations less closely than does the straight line.

---

[6] Note that these formulas treat the transformed variable U as if it corresponded to a third variable distinct from P. Geometrically, it is as though the original observations were plotted in a three-dimensional diagram with Q, P, and U axes. The ith observation would have the three coordinates (Q_i, P_i and U_i). The regression equation $\hat{Q} = a + bP + cU$ is the equation of the "*plane* of best fit" to the three-dimensional scatter and it minimizes the sum of the squared deviations, measured along the Q axis, of the actual observations Q_i from the corresponding values of $\hat{Q}_i = a + bP_i + cU_i$, which are points on the regression plane. The regression plane passes through the point of means of the three-dimensional scatter, namely ($\bar{Q}$, $\bar{P}$, and $\bar{U}$).

Table 4.5 Beef Consumption and Price: Parabolic Regression Equation, 1949–1960

| | Original Data | | | $\hat{Q} = 37.8569 + 2.3278P - 0.026509P^2$ | | | |
Year	Q Consumption per Capita, lb	P Retail Price (deflated), cents/lb	U ($= P^2$), cents/lb²	$\hat{Q}$ Estimated Consumption, lb/cap	$2.3278P$	$-0.026509P^2$	$z = (Q - \hat{Q})$ (residuals)
1949	63.9	67.2	4515.84	74.6	156.43	−119.71	−10.7
1950	63.4	73.3	5372.89	66.1	170.63	−142.43	−2.7
1951	56.1	79.5	6320.25	55.4	185.06	−167.54	0.7
1952	62.2	76.3	5821.69	61.1	177.61	−134.34	1.1
1953	77.6	60.4	3648.16	81.8	140.60	−96.70	−4.2
1954	80.1	59.7	3564.09	82.4	138.97	−94.48	−2.2
1955	82.0	59.0	3481.00	82.9	137.34	−92.28	−0.9
1956	85.4	56.8	3226.24	84.6	132.22	−85.52	0.8
1957	84.6	58.7	3445.69	83.2	136.64	−91.35	1.4
1958	80.5	65.6	4303.36	76.5	152.70	−114.07	4.0
1959	81.4	66.4	4408.96	75.6	154.57	−116.88	5.9
1960	85.2	63.8	4070.44	78.5	148.51	−107.89	6.7

105

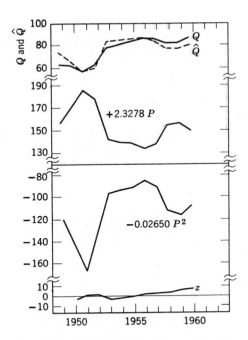

Figure 4.19 Parabolic regression ($\hat{Q} = 37.8569 + 2.3278P - 0.026509P^2$).

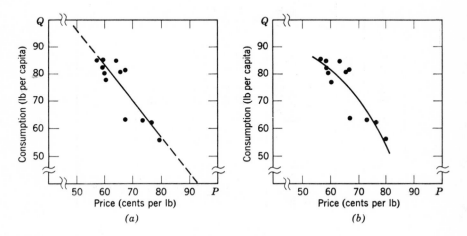

Figure 4.20 Beef consumption and price: comparison of (a) straight line and (b) parabolic regressions with the scatter diagram of the original data, United States, 1949–60.

Hence the parabola is very similar to the straight line in its capacity to "track" the 1949–1960 time path of beef consumption Q. The time path of P^2 is very much like that of P and, since the coefficient of P^2 is negative and that of P is positive, the two terms tend to offset one another. The time paths of the residuals from the two equations are quite similar.

On economic grounds, we know that consumers' purchases of beef are influenced by other factors in addition to its retail price. One of the important factors is consumer income. If the straight line in Figure 4.18b is regarded as the demand curve when income is at its average value for 1949–1960, we would expect an increase in consumer income to raise the demand curve (or, what is the same thing, shift it to the right); similarly, a consumer income below the 1949–1960 average should be associated with a lower position of the demand curve. If consumer income per capita trended upward steadily during 1949–1960, we would expect to find that the position of the demand curve in each successive year would be slightly higher than in the preceding year.

It turns out that the arithmetic involved in fitting a three-variable (multiple) linear regression equation is identical with that involved in fitting a second-degree parabola. Letting Y stand for consumer income, we write $Q = a + bP + cY$. If we simply substitute $y = Y - \bar{Y}$ for u in (4.17) and (4.18), we will have the calculations required to determine the three coefficients of our multiple regression equation.[7]

The results of such a three-variable regression analysis for beef during 1949–1960 are as follows:

$$\hat{Q} = 49.9144 - 0.8631P + 0.05771\,Y; \quad R^2 = 0.9846; \quad \text{and} \quad \bar{S} = 1.4529$$

Adding the consumer income variable Y evidently improves the "goodness of fit" of the regression equation to the data very markedly as compared with the simple two-variable relationship. Correspondingly, the standard error of estimate is less than one-third as large as it was in the two-variable case.

---

[7] As indicated in footnote 6, the regression equation here is that of a plane passing through the three-dimensional scatter of the original observations. The ith observation has the three coordinates (Q_i, P_i, Y_i). The regression plane passes through the point of means $(\bar{Q}, \bar{P}, \bar{Y})$ in such a way that the sum of the squared deviations $(Q_i - \hat{Q}_i)^2$ is smaller than it would be from any other plane. In the foregoing expression, $\hat{Q}_i = a + bP_i + cY_i$, a point on the regression plane having the P and Y values of the ith observation.

APPENDIX A

DERIVATION OF THE NORMAL EQUATIONS USED IN SOLVING FOR LEAST SQUARES REGRESSION COEFFICIENTS

When we fit a straight line by the method of least squares, we require that the sum of the squared deviations be a minimum. Each observation on Y and X satisfies the equation

(A.1) $$Y = a + bX + z$$

Hence,

(A.2) $$z = Y - (a + bX)$$

Squaring each side of (A.2) and summing, we obtain

(A.3) $$\sum z^2 = \sum Y^2 - 2 \sum Y(a + bX) + \sum (a + bX)^2$$

Now we must choose a and b in such a way as to minimize $\sum z^2$. The necessary condition for such a minimum is that $\partial \sum z^2 / \partial a = 0$ and $\partial \sum z^2 / \partial b = 0$.

Differentiating (A.3) with respect to a we obtain

(A.4) $$\frac{\partial \sum z^2}{\partial a} = -2 \sum Y + 2 \sum (a + bX) = 0$$

or

(A.4a) $$na + b \sum X = \sum Y$$

Differentiating (A.3) with respect to b yields

(A.5) $$\frac{\partial \sum z^2}{\partial b} = -2 \sum YX + 2 \sum (a + bX)X = 0$$

or

(A.5a) $$a \sum X + b \sum X^2 = \sum YX$$

Equations (A.4a) and (A.5a) are referred to as the *normal equations*. All the terms in these equations are given numbers, calculated from the data, except a and b.

Solving for b by simple algebra, we obtain

(A.4b) $$na \sum X + b(\sum X)^2 = \sum Y \cdot \sum X$$

(A.5b) $$na \sum X + nb \sum X^2 = n \sum YX$$

and

(A.6) $$b = \frac{\sum Y \cdot \sum X - n \sum YX}{(\sum X)^2 - n \sum X^2}$$

Since $\bar{X} = 1/n \sum X$ and $\bar{Y} = 1/n \sum Y$, we can rewrite (A.6) as

(A.6a) $$b = \frac{\sum YX - n\bar{Y}\cdot\bar{X}}{\sum X^2 - n\bar{X}^2}$$

Similarly, solving for a yields

(A.4c) $$na \sum X^2 + b \sum X \cdot \sum X^2 = \sum Y \cdot \sum X^2$$

(A.5c) $$a(\sum X)^2 + b \sum X \cdot \sum X^2 = \sum YX \cdot \sum X$$

and

(A.7) $$a = \frac{\sum Y \cdot \sum X^2 - \sum YX \cdot \sum X}{n \sum X^2 - (\sum X)^2}$$

This can be rewritten as

(A.7a) $$a = \frac{\bar{Y}\cdot\sum X^2 - \bar{X}\sum YX}{\sum X^2 - n\bar{X}^2}$$

which has the same denominator as (A.6a). We can arrive at a simpler expression by simultaneously adding and subtracting the term $-n\bar{X}^2\cdot\bar{Y}$ in the numerator as follows:

(A.7b) $$a = \left[\frac{(\bar{Y}\cdot\sum X^2 - \bar{Y}n\bar{X}^2) - (\bar{X}\cdot\sum YX - n\bar{X}^2\cdot Y)}{\sum X^2 - n\bar{X}^2}\right]$$

Hence,

(A.7c) $$a = \bar{Y} - \frac{\bar{X}(\sum YX - n\bar{Y}\cdot\bar{X})}{\sum X^2 - n\sum X^2}$$

or

(A.7d) $$a = \bar{Y} - b\bar{X}$$

In the text we noted that the regression line passes through the point of means $(\bar{Y}, \bar{X})$. It is sometimes convenient to express all variables as deviations from their respective means.

If we let $y = Y - \bar{Y}$, we find that

(A.8) $$\sum y^2 = \sum (Y - \bar{Y})^2 = \sum Y^2 - 2 \sum Y \cdot \bar{Y} + \sum \bar{Y}^2$$

As $\sum Y = n\bar{Y}$ and $\sum \bar{Y}^2 = n\bar{Y}^2$, (A.8) simplifies to

(A.8a) $$\sum y^2 = \sum Y^2 - n\bar{Y}^2$$

similarly,

(A.9) $$\sum x^2 = \sum X^2 - n\bar{X}^2$$

where $x = X - \bar{X}$.

We also find that

(A.10) $\sum yx = \sum (Y - \bar{Y})(X - \bar{X}) = \sum YX - \bar{Y} \cdot \sum X - \bar{X} \sum Y + \sum \bar{Y} \cdot \bar{X}$

or

$$\sum yx = \sum YX - n\bar{Y} \cdot \bar{X} - n\bar{Y} \cdot \bar{X} + n\bar{Y} \cdot \bar{X}$$

and

(A.10a) $$\sum yx = \sum YX - n\bar{Y} \cdot \bar{X}.$$

Using the foregoing relationships, we see at once in (A.6) that

(A.6b) $$b = \frac{\sum yx}{\sum x^2}$$

and in (A.7b) that

(A.7d) $$a = \bar{Y} - b\bar{X}$$

The three-variable regression equation

(A.11) $$Y = a + b_1 X_1 + b_2 X_2 + z$$

passes through the point of means or *centroid* of the n observations in three-dimensional space ($\bar{Y}$, $\bar{X}_1$, $\bar{X}_2$). This condition enables us to calculate a from the expression

(A.12) $$a = \bar{Y} - b_1 \bar{X}_1 - b_2 \bar{X}_2$$

So, our problem reduces to that of finding the values of b_1 and b_2 which minimize $\sum z^2$.

Rewriting (A.11) in deviation form, letting $x_1 = X_1 - \bar{X}_1$ and $x_2 = X_2 - \bar{X}_2$, we have

(A.11a) $$y = b_1 x_1 + b_2 x_2 + z$$

or

$$z = y - (b_1 x_1 + b_2 x_2)$$

and

$$\sum z^2 = \sum y^2 - 2 \sum y(b_1 x_1 + b_2 x_2) + \sum (b_1 x_1 + b_2 x_2)^2$$

Differentiating with respect to b_1, we obtain

(A.13) $$\frac{\partial \sum z^2}{\partial b_1} = -2 \sum yx_1 + 2 \sum x_1(b_1 x_1 + b_2 x_2) = 0$$

or

(A.13a) $$b_1 \sum x_1^2 + b_2 \sum x_1 x_2 = \sum yx_1$$

Differentiating with respect to b_2 yields

(A.14) $\dfrac{\partial \sum z^2}{\partial b_2} = -2 \sum yx_2 + 2 \sum x_2(b_1x_1 + b_2x_2) = 0$

or

(A.14a) $b_1 \sum x_1x_2 + b_2 \sum x_2{}^2 = \sum yx_2$

Solving (A.13a) and (A.14a) simultaneously by simple algebra gives us

(A.15) $b_1 = \dfrac{\sum yx_1 \cdot \sum x_2{}^2 - \sum yx_2 \cdot \sum x_1x_2}{\sum x_1{}^2 \cdot \sum x_2{}^2 - (\sum x_1x_2)^2}$

and

$b_2 = \dfrac{\sum yx_1 \cdot \sum x_1x_2 - \sum yx_2 \cdot \sum x_1{}^2}{(\sum x_1x_2)^2 - \sum x_1{}^2 \cdot \sum x_2{}^2}$

or

(A.16) $b_2 = \dfrac{\sum yx_2 \cdot \sum x_1{}^2 - \sum yx_1 \cdot \sum x_1x_2}{\sum x_1{}^2 \cdot \sum x_2{}^2 - (\sum x_1x_2)^2}$

It will be noted again that the denominators of (A.15) and (A.16) are identical and that the numerators differ only in the exchange of x_2 for x_1 in certain terms.

The essential symmetry shown by (A.13a) and (A.14a) extends to multiple regression equations in any number of variables, as will be shown in Chapter 7.

APPENDIX B

MATRIX NOTATION APPLIED TO A SECOND-DEGREE PARABOLIC OR A THREE-VARIABLE MULTIPLE REGRESSION EQUATION

Many aspects of regression analysis can be expressed more compactly and generalized more readily in terms of matrix algebra. Some knowledge of matrix algebra is almost indispensable today for economists and students of economics.

Most students will have had some contact in high school algebra with the use of *determinants* in solving simultaneous equations. Thus we can apply *Cramer's rule* to (A.13a) and (A.14a) of Appendix A, as follows, remembering that in this context b_1 and b_2 are the unknowns and all other terms are known numbers.

(A.13a) $\qquad (\sum x_1{}^2)b_1 + (\sum x_1 x_2)b_2 = \sum y x_1$

(A.14a) $\qquad (\sum x_1 x_2)b_1 + (\sum x_2{}^2)b_2 = \sum y x_2$

To solve for b_1, Cramer's rule tells us to form the coefficients of b_1 and b_2 into a determinant

$$\begin{vmatrix} \sum x_1{}^2 & \sum x_1 x_2 \\ \sum x_1 x_2 & \sum x_2{}^2 \end{vmatrix}$$

and to form a second determinant by substituting in the first one the constant terms on the right-hand sides of the equations in place of the coefficients of b_1

$$\begin{vmatrix} \sum y x_1 & \sum x_1 x_2 \\ \sum y x_2 & \sum x_2{}^2 \end{vmatrix}$$

Then

(B.1) $\qquad b_1 = \dfrac{\begin{vmatrix} \sum y x_1 & \sum x_1 x_2 \\ \sum y x_2 & \sum x_2{}^2 \end{vmatrix}}{\begin{vmatrix} \sum x_1{}^2 & \sum x_1 x_2 \\ \sum x_1 x_2 & \sum x_2{}^2 \end{vmatrix}}$

Expanding (B.1) we obtain

(B.1a) $\qquad b_1 = \dfrac{\sum y x_1 \cdot \sum x_2{}^2 - \sum y x_2 \cdot \sum x_1 x_2}{\sum x_1{}^2 \cdot \sum x_2{}^2 - (\sum x_1 x_2)^2}$

This is identical with (A.15).

In solving for b_2, we again use the determinant of coefficients of b_1 and b_2 as a denominator; we then replace the coefficients of b_2 in this determinant with the constant terms on the right-hand sides of (A.13a) and (A.14a)

$$\begin{vmatrix} \sum x_1{}^2 & \sum y x_1 \\ \sum x_1 x_2 & \sum y x_2 \end{vmatrix}$$

Hence

(B.2) $\qquad b_2 = \dfrac{\begin{vmatrix} \sum x_1{}^2 & \sum y x_1 \\ \sum x_1 x_2 & \sum y x_2 \end{vmatrix}}{\begin{vmatrix} \sum x_1{}^2 & \sum x_1 x_2 \\ \sum x_1 x_2 & \sum x_2{}^2 \end{vmatrix}}$

and

(B.2a) $\qquad b_2 = \dfrac{\sum y x_2 \cdot \sum x_1{}^2 - \sum y x_1 \cdot \sum x_1 x_2}{\sum x_1{}^2 \cdot \sum x_2{}^2 - (\sum x_1 x_2)^2}$

which is identical with (A.16).

Cramer's rule can be extended to sets of three or more simultaneous equations, although the notation and the calculations become tedious as the number of equations increases. Determinants are always square—that is, they have the same number of rows and columns—and their numerical values can be determined.

A *matrix* is simply a rectangular array of numbers or elements with respect to which certain operations are defined. The generalized matrix A, with m rows and n columns, may be written as

(B.3)
$$A = \begin{bmatrix} a_{11} & a_{12} & a_{13} & \cdots & a_{1n} \\ a_{21} & a_{22} & a_{23} & \cdots & a_{2n} \\ \vdots & \vdots & \vdots & & \vdots \\ a_{m1} & a_{m2} & a_{m3} & \cdots & a_{mn} \end{bmatrix}$$

A simple example would be the matrix

(B.4)
$$A = \begin{bmatrix} 1 & 3 & 1 \\ 2 & 2 & 4 \end{bmatrix}$$

A matrix consisting of a single row or column is called a *vector*. For example, $\begin{bmatrix} 1 \\ 2 \end{bmatrix}$, $\begin{bmatrix} 3 \\ 2 \end{bmatrix}$, and $\begin{bmatrix} 1 \\ 4 \end{bmatrix}$ are column vectors and $[1 \quad 3 \quad 1]$ and $[2 \quad 2 \quad 4]$ are row vectors.

Certain special matrices may be mentioned such as the *null matrix*, in which all elements are zero, and the *unit matrix* or *identity matrix* which has ones on the principal diagonal and zeros everywhere else:

(B.5)
$$I = \begin{bmatrix} 1 & 0 & 0 & \cdots & 0 \\ 0 & 1 & 0 & \cdots & 0 \\ 0 & 0 & 1 & \cdots & 0 \\ \vdots & \vdots & \vdots & & \vdots \\ 0 & 0 & 0 & \cdots & 1 \end{bmatrix}$$

Two (or more) matrices with the same number of rows and the same number of columns may be *added*. For example,

(B.6)
$$\begin{bmatrix} 3 & 4 & 5 \\ 2 & 2 & 2 \end{bmatrix} + \begin{bmatrix} 1 & 1 & 2 \\ 2 & 1 & 1 \end{bmatrix} = \begin{bmatrix} 4 & 5 & 7 \\ 4 & 3 & 3 \end{bmatrix}, \quad \text{or} \quad A + B = C$$

Each element of the second matrix is added to the element which occupies the corresponding row and column position in the first to form the matrix sum at the right of the equality sign.

A matrix may be *multiplied* by a scalar, or simple arithmetic number; for example, if

$$A = \begin{bmatrix} 1 & 2 \\ 4 & 3 \\ 1 & 2 \end{bmatrix} \quad \text{we may write} \quad 2A = \begin{bmatrix} 1 & 2 \\ 4 & 3 \\ 1 & 2 \end{bmatrix} = \begin{bmatrix} 2 & 4 \\ 8 & 6 \\ 2 & 4 \end{bmatrix}$$

Each element of the matrix is multiplied by the scalar in forming the *product matrix*. (We may note that multiplication is simply "repeated addition.")

A matrix may be *postmultiplied* by a column vector *if* the number of elements in the vector is equal to the number of columns in the matrix. Thus

(B.7)
$$\begin{bmatrix} 2 & 1 \\ 1 & 0 \end{bmatrix} \times \begin{bmatrix} 3 \\ 1 \end{bmatrix} = \begin{bmatrix} (3 \times 2 + 1 \times 1) \\ (3 \times 1 + 1 \times 0) \end{bmatrix} = \begin{bmatrix} 7 \\ 3 \end{bmatrix}$$

The element in the first row of the product matrix is obtained by multiplying the elements in the first row of the original matrix by the corresponding elements of the vector:

$$\begin{bmatrix} 2 & 1 \end{bmatrix} \begin{bmatrix} 3 \\ 1 \end{bmatrix} = (3 \times 2 + 1 \times 1) = 7$$

The element in the second row of the product matrix is obtained by multiplying the elements in the second row of the original matrix by the corresponding elements of the vector:

$$\begin{bmatrix} 1 & 0 \end{bmatrix} \begin{bmatrix} 3 \\ 1 \end{bmatrix} = (3 \times 1 + 1 \times 0) = 3$$

Similarly, a matrix may be *postmultiplied* by a second matrix *if* the number of rows in the second matrix is equal to the number of columns in the first. Thus

(B.8)
$$\begin{bmatrix} 2 & 1 \\ 2 & 3 \\ 0 & 1 \end{bmatrix} \begin{bmatrix} 1 & 1 & 2 \\ 2 & 0 & 2 \end{bmatrix} = \begin{bmatrix} 4 & 2 & 6 \\ 8 & 2 & 10 \\ 2 & 0 & 2 \end{bmatrix}$$

where the elements in the first column of the product matrix are formed by using the first column of the two-rowed matrix; the second column of the product matrix involves multiplications by the second column of the two-rowed matrix; and so on.

A column vector may be *transposed* into a row vector. Thus the row vector $y' = \begin{bmatrix} 5 & 8 & 2 \end{bmatrix}$ is called the transpose of the column vector $y = \begin{bmatrix} 5 \\ 8 \\ 2 \end{bmatrix}$.

The *transpose* of a matrix is obtained by rewriting each *column* of the original matrix as the corresponding *row* of a new matrix. For example,

$$A' = \begin{bmatrix} 2 & 2 & 0 \\ 1 & 3 & 1 \end{bmatrix} \quad \text{is the transpose of} \quad A = \begin{bmatrix} 2 & 1 \\ 2 & 3 \\ 0 & 1 \end{bmatrix}$$

$$A' = \begin{bmatrix} 2 & 1 & 0 \\ 3 & 4 & 2 \\ 1 & 6 & 1 \end{bmatrix} \quad \text{is the transpose of} \quad A = \begin{bmatrix} 2 & 3 & 1 \\ 1 & 4 & 6 \\ 0 & 2 & 1 \end{bmatrix}$$

The transpose of a matrix symmetrical about its principal diagonal is identical with the original matrix; thus

$$A' = \begin{bmatrix} 1 & 3 & 0 \\ 3 & 2 & 4 \\ 0 & 4 & 7 \end{bmatrix} \quad \text{is the transpose of} \quad A = \begin{bmatrix} 1 & 3 & 0 \\ 3 & 2 & 4 \\ 0 & 4 & 7 \end{bmatrix}$$

The product of an ordinary arithmetic number by its reciprocal is unity; for example, $4 \times \frac{1}{4} = 1$. There is an analogous concept in matrix algebra—the product of a matrix by its *inverse* is equal to the unit matrix

$$\begin{bmatrix} 1 & 0 & \cdots & 0 \\ 0 & 1 & \cdots & 0 \\ \vdots & \vdots & & \vdots \\ 0 & 0 & \cdots & 1 \end{bmatrix}$$

Only a square matrix may have an inverse; the unit matrix is, of course, also a square matrix. The determinant of any square matrix can be evaluated by methods described in high school algebra texts.

A determinant can be evaluated by multiplying each element in a given column by its *cofactor* or "signed" minor, a square array consisting of those elements of the determinant which are not included in either the row or the column which intersect in the given element. Thus in the determinant $A = \begin{vmatrix} 3 & 2 \\ 4 & 7 \end{vmatrix}$, the *minor* corresponding to 3 is 7, and the minor corresponding to 4 is 2. The products of 3 and 4 by their respective minors are 21 and 8.

We know, however, that the value of A is equal to $(3 \times 7) - (4 \times 2) = 21 - 8 = 13$. The rule for determining the proper sign of such a product is to add the row and column indexes of the given element—if the sum is even, its corresponding minor is given a positive sign; if the sum is odd, its minor is given a negative sign. For example, the number 3 is in row 1, column 1; the sum of these indexes (2) is even, so the cofactor 7 receives the positive sign. The number 4 is in row 2, column 1; the sum of the indexes (3) is odd, so the cofactor, -2, receives the negative sign.

A matrix in which each element of the original (square) matrix is replaced by its cofactor is called the *adjugate* of the original matrix. If the original matrix is $A = \begin{bmatrix} 3 & 2 \\ 4 & 7 \end{bmatrix}$, the adjugate is adj $A = \begin{bmatrix} 7 & -4 \\ -2 & 3 \end{bmatrix}$. The transpose of this matrix is called *adjoint* of the original: adj $A' = \begin{bmatrix} 7 & -2 \\ -4 & 3 \end{bmatrix}$.

The *inverse* A^{-1} of the matrix A is formed by dividing each element of the adjoint by the determinant of A, which we call Δ. In the present example, $\Delta = 13$. Thus $A^{-1} = $ adj $A'/\Delta = \dfrac{1}{13} \begin{bmatrix} 7 & -2 \\ -4 & 3 \end{bmatrix}$ the product of a matrix by a scalar; hence

$$A^{-1} = \begin{bmatrix} \dfrac{7}{13} & \dfrac{-2}{13} \\ \dfrac{-4}{13} & \dfrac{3}{13} \end{bmatrix}$$

To demonstrate that the product of A^{-1} times A is a unit matrix, we carry out the matrix multiplication

$$A^{-1}A = \begin{bmatrix} \dfrac{7}{13} & \dfrac{-2}{13} \\ \dfrac{-4}{13} & \dfrac{3}{13} \end{bmatrix} \begin{bmatrix} 3 & 2 \\ 4 & 7 \end{bmatrix}$$

$$A^{-1}A = \begin{bmatrix} \dfrac{21-8}{13} & \dfrac{\cdot 14-14}{13} \\ \dfrac{-12+12}{13} & \dfrac{-8+21}{13} \end{bmatrix} = \begin{bmatrix} 1 & 0 \\ 0 & 1 \end{bmatrix}$$

The relevance of matrix algebra to the solution of the normal equations in either parabolic or multiple regression analysis may be indicated as follows.

Write, from (A.13a) and (A.14a),

$$\begin{bmatrix} \sum x_1^2 & \sum x_1 x_2 \\ \sum x_1 x_2 & \sum x_2^2 \end{bmatrix} \begin{bmatrix} b_1 \\ b_2 \end{bmatrix} = \begin{bmatrix} \sum y x_1 \\ \sum y x_2 \end{bmatrix}, \quad \text{or} \quad Xb = y$$

Note that by multiplying each row of the square matrix by the column vector $\begin{bmatrix} b_1 \\ b_2 \end{bmatrix}$ we can immediately reconstruct the original equations.

The inverse of the square matrix equals

$$X^{-1} = \dfrac{1}{\Delta} \begin{bmatrix} \sum x_2^2 & -\sum x_1 x_2 \\ -\sum x_1 x_2 & \sum x_1^2 \end{bmatrix}$$

where

$$\frac{1}{\Delta} = \frac{1}{\sum x_1{}^2 \cdot \sum x_2{}^2 - (\sum x_1 x_2)^2}$$

The product $X^{-1}X$ is

$$\begin{bmatrix} 1 & 0 \\ 0 & 1 \end{bmatrix} = \frac{1}{\Delta} \begin{bmatrix} [\sum x_1{}^2 \cdot \sum x_2{}^2 - (\sum x_1 x_2)^2] & (\sum x_2{}^2 \cdot \sum x_1 x_2 \\ & \quad - \sum x_2{}^2 \cdot \sum x_1 x_2) \\ (-\sum x_1{}^2 \cdot \sum x_1 x_2 & [-(\sum x_1 x_2)^2 + \sum x_1{}^2 \cdot \sum x_2{}^2] \\ \quad + \sum x_1{}^2 \cdot \sum x_1 x_2) & \end{bmatrix}$$

which indeed yields the result $\begin{bmatrix} 1 & 0 \\ 0 & 1 \end{bmatrix} = \begin{bmatrix} 1 & 0 \\ 0 & 1 \end{bmatrix}$.

If we premultiply both sides of the matrix equation $Xb = y$ by the inverse X^{-1} we obtain $X^{-1}Xb = X^{-1}y$, or $Ib = X^{-1}y$. In the expanded notation the left-hand side may be written

$$\begin{bmatrix} 1 & 0 \\ 0 & 1 \end{bmatrix} \begin{bmatrix} b_1 \\ b_2 \end{bmatrix} = \begin{bmatrix} b_1 + 0b_2 \\ 0b_1 + b_2 \end{bmatrix} = \begin{bmatrix} b_1 \\ b_2 \end{bmatrix}$$

That is, the product of any matrix by the unit or identity matrix is the matrix itself. The I may be deleted from the equation $Ib = X^{-1}y$ leaving $b = X^{-1}y$.

The significance of this expression can be seen in terms of expanded notation:

$$\begin{bmatrix} b_1 \\ b_2 \end{bmatrix} = \frac{1}{\Delta} \begin{bmatrix} \sum x_2{}^2 & -\sum x_1 x_2 \\ -\sum x_1 x_2 & \sum x_1{}^2 \end{bmatrix} \begin{bmatrix} \sum y x_1 \\ \sum y x_2 \end{bmatrix}$$

Multiplying the right-hand vector by the inverse we obtain

$$\begin{bmatrix} b_1 \\ b_2 \end{bmatrix} = \frac{1}{\Delta} \begin{bmatrix} (\sum x_2{}^2 \cdot \sum y x_1 - \sum x_1 x_2 \cdot \sum y x_2) \\ (-\sum x_1 x_2 \cdot \sum y x_1 + \sum x_1{}^2 \cdot \sum y x_2) \end{bmatrix}$$

or

$$\begin{bmatrix} b_1 \\ b_2 \end{bmatrix} = \begin{bmatrix} \dfrac{\sum x_2{}^2 \cdot \sum y x_1 - \sum x_1 x_2 \cdot \sum y x_2}{\sum x_1{}^2 \cdot \sum x_2{}^2 - (\sum x_1 x_2)^2} \\[2mm] \dfrac{-\sum x_1 x_2 \cdot \sum y x_1 + \sum x_1{}^2 \cdot \sum y x_2}{\sum x_1{}^2 \cdot \sum x_2{}^2 - (\sum x_1 x_2)^2} \end{bmatrix}$$

The two elements in the right-hand vector are the desired values of b_1 and b_2; they reproduce (A.15) and (A.16).

Example 1: Simple parabola

$Y = a + b_1X_1 + b_2X_2$, where $X_2 = X_1^2$.

Given the following values:

$\bar{Y} = \quad 75.2 \quad ; \quad \sum x_1^2 = \quad\quad 603.8692; \quad \sum xy_1 = \quad\quad -767.4600;$
$\bar{X}_1 = \quad 65.5583; \quad \sum x_2^2 = 11,151,338.6409; \quad \sum yx_2 = -104,792.5200;$
$\bar{X}_2 = 4,348.2175; \quad \sum x_1x_2 = \quad\quad 81,975.3038; \quad \sum y^2 = \quad\quad 1,235.6800;$

solve for a, b_1, and b_2 using matrix notation and operations.

Example 2: Three-variable linear regression

$Y = a + b_1X_1 + b_2X_2$.

Given the following values:

$\bar{Y} = \quad 20.6506; \quad \sum x_1^2 = \quad\quad 25.2134; \quad \sum yx_1 = \quad\quad -22.6093;$
$\bar{X}_1 = \quad 31.2333; \quad \sum x_2^2 = 88,873.600\ ; \quad \sum yx_2 = -4,143.3040;$
$\bar{X}_2 = 703.40 \quad ; \quad \sum x_1x_2 = \quad\quad 539.7000; \quad \sum y^2 = \quad\quad 205.3511;$

solve for a, b_1, and b_2 using matrix notation and operations.

EXERCISES

1. Explain carefully the relationship between the *joint* frequency distribution of two variables and a simple regression analysis showing the interdependence between the same two variables.

2. From Table 4.1, compute each of the points on the "regression line" which is illustrated in Figure 4.2.

3. In each of the regression analyses of consumption functions, production functions, and cost functions, explain carefully the economic significance of the intercept coefficient and the slope coefficient.

4. Using the data given in Table 4.4, compute the Total, "Explained," and "Unexplained" sums of squares. Explain the significance of the ratio of explained to the total sum of squares, that is, *the coefficient of determination*.

5. Assume that the regression equation is $Y = a + bX + z$. Show that the fitted least squares regression line passes through the point $(\bar{X}, \bar{Y})$.

6. Using the data in the following table, carry out the following computations:
(a) Compute the least squares estimators, a and b, for α and β, if our model is

$$C = \alpha + \beta Y_d + z$$

(b) Compute the standard errors of the least squares estimators, a and b.

Disposable Personal Income and Personal Consumption Expenditures, in 1964 Prices (Billions of Dollars)

Year	Total Disposable Personal Income, Y_d	Total Personal Consumption Expenditures, C
1955	313.3	293.3
1956	329.0	303.2
1957	337.1	311.3
1958	340.8	314.2
1959	356.9	331.9
1960	365.3	342.7
1961	377.9	349.5
1962	394.9	366.4
1963	408.1	380.2

Source: Economic Report of the President, 1965, Table B-16, p. 209.

(c) Compute r^2, the *coefficient of determination*. Then compute $\bar{r}^2$, which is done by adjusting r^2 for degrees of freedom.

(d) Carry out the same computations as in (a)–(c), only this time fit a simple curvilinear regression. Compare the results obtained with those for simple linear regression.

REFERENCES

1. Dwyer, P. S., *Linear Computations,* New York: John Wiley and Sons, 1951.
2. Ezekiel, Mordecai and Karl A. Fox, *Methods of Correlation and Regression Analysis,* Third edition, New York: John Wiley and Sons, 1959.
3. Ferber, R. and P. J. Verdoorn, *Research Methods in Economics and Business,* New York: The Macmillan Co., 1962.
4. Foote, R. J., "Analytical Tools for Studying Demand and Price Structures," Washington: United States Department of Agriculture, *Agriculture Handbook* No. 146, 1958.
5. Fox, Karl A., *Econometric Analysis for Public Policy,* Ames: Iowa State University Press, 1958.
6. Plackett, R. L., *Principles of Regression Analysis,* Oxford: Clarendon Press, 1960.
7. Theil, H., *Applied Economic Forecasting,* Chicago: Rand McNally and Co., 1966.
8. Williams, E. J., *Regression Analysis,* New York: John Wiley and Sons, 1959.

CHAPTER 5

Index Numbers and Time Series

This chapter consists of two major sections, one on index numbers and the other on time series. Both topics will be treated primarily as descriptive statistics involving special kinds of frequency distributions. An index number of prices may be regarded as the (weighted) average of a frequency distribution of *price relatives*, a concept to be defined shortly. An economic time series may be regarded as a frequency distribution in which "time" is a logical and usually essential classifying variable. For example, a large percentage of the variance in a frequency distribution of monthly sales of men's overcoats over a period of years can be "explained" simply by the calendar months to which the different observations relate. The variance of overcoat sales within a subgroup, such as "all Januarys" or "all Julys," is much smaller than the variance of sales for all months combined.

5.1 INDEX NUMBERS

We have all had some contact through newspapers and other media with index numbers of wholesale prices, consumer prices, farm prices, and industrial production.

Historically, the development of each major kind of index number was stimulated by the emergence of problems of political and economic importance which required some type of aggregative measurement. In the United States from the early 1870s until the 1890s declining prices of primary products put debtors (particularly farmers) at a disadvantage in paying off mortgages and other long-term obligations stated in fixed dollar amounts. In effect, a farmer who had borrowed a sum which was then the money equivalent of

1000 bushels of wheat was obligated to pay back the equivalent of 2000 bushels if the price of wheat declined 50% by the time the mortgage was due. In addition to spectacular political fireworks, this situation spurred interest in a "commodity dollar" and brought forth attempts to measure changes in the *purchasing power of money*. These found expression in index numbers of wholesale prices.

The growth of industry, wage labor, and labor unions during the early 1900s, plus rapid increases in both prices and wages during World War I, created interest in measuring changes in the *cost of living* and in the real wages or purchasing power of urban workers. The U.S. Bureau of Labor Statistics' Cost of Living Index (now called the Consumer Price Index), first published in 1919, resulted from this interest.

The agricultural depression of the 1920s found many farmers in serious financial straits at a time when most nonfarm people in the United States were prospering. This created a special interest in measuring changes in the economic well-being of farmers over time and comparing them with changes in the economic well-being of other groups. This led to the construction of official index numbers of Prices Received by Farmers and Prices Paid by Farmers. The ratio between these indexes, the "parity ratio," has played an important role in farm price support legislation since the early 1930s.

Index numbers of physical output developed much later than index numbers of prices. It was a relatively easy matter to collect wholesale prices at a few commodity exchanges and central markets, and these prices had at least a barometric significance to buyers and sellers throughout the nation. It is a much more arduous and expensive undertaking to collect information about production, which may be accurately known for a given firm only by the proprietor of that firm. In the United States a few quantity indexes of limited scope were published in the early and middle 1920s. The first comprehensive index of output for the manufacturing sector, the Federal Reserve Board's Index of Industrial Production, was published in 1927.

The implementation in the 1930s of national income and product accounts for the United States opened the way for a broader view of the role of price and quantity indexes. The changed conception of business cycles which followed the publication of J. M. Keynes' *General Theory of Employment, Interest and Money* (1936) brought a new level of need, and hence of aspiration, for comprehensive and consistent measurements of all of the major macroeconomic variables.

As a consequence of further developments since World War II, it appears that index numbers should be viewed as a subdivision of the broader subject of measuring economic aggregates of all sorts. We will have something to say about modern approaches to aggregation in Chapter 14, but in this chapter we will confine ourselves to index numbers in the customary sense.

A major index number such as the Consumer Price Index is an expensive undertaking. A tremendous number of detailed procedures is developed which are specific to that particular index and which must be modified as business practices or consumers' shopping habits change. We cannot take up these highly specialized matters here. However, the annotated references at the end of the chapter will direct the interested reader to basic descriptions of the more important official index numbers in the United States.

5.1.1 Sampling Considerations in Index Number Construction

Let us consider the specific problem of measuring changes over time in prices paid by consumers. The Consumer Price Index is one of the most important official index numbers in the United States. From 1919 until 1945 it was known as the Cost of Living Index. This name indicated an intent to measure changes in the cost to *someone* of acquiring those goods and services deemed necessary for a socially acceptable material standard of living. The present name has less of a normative or welfare connotation and could be construed to mean simply an index of retail prices of goods and services bought and used by consumers as distinguished from business firms or institutions.

In earlier chapters, considerable attention was paid to the distinction between populations and samples. In the present context, we might specify the population as "every purchase made by any resident of the United States during the calendar year 1964 for purposes of consumption." This seemingly comprehensive definition leaves out important items such as the net rental values of owner-occupied dwellings and the values of home-grown fruits and vegetables, so let us expand our population to include imputed items. This population can be assigned an approximate monetary value. In 1964, personal consumption expenditures in the United States were estimated at 399.2 billion dollars. The goods and services included in this aggregate were consumed by 192.072 million people. Thus personal consumption expenditures per capita in 1964 averaged $2079.

Some individuals consumed much less than this and others consumed much more. But let us ignore this for the moment. If we had complete, detailed information about the total physical quantities of various commodities which had moved into consumption and the prices at which they were bought, we would be able to say that "consumers spent an average of $2079 per person in 1964, receiving for this X pounds of butter, Y pairs of shoes, Z gallons of gasoline," and so on.

If this collection of commodities were compared with another collection reflecting the same average concept for another country, we would learn a great deal about the material differences in the two 1964 ways of life. But let us concentrate instead on the problem of measuring changes in consumer prices in the United States from one year to the next.

In 1963 personal consumption expenditures were estimated at 375.0 billion dollars. There were 189.375 million consumers and consumption expenditures per capita averaged $1980. Given complete information, we could list the average number of units of each commodity that was purchased in 1963. It would indeed be instructive if we could lay out the 1963 and 1964 collections of commodities (and pictures or tokens standing for services) on one side of a huge exhibition hall and spend as much time as we liked walking back and forth to compare the numbers of units and kinds of commodities in each. Of course, the average consumer would have bought a very small fraction of a Cadillac, so we might have to lay out on either side of the exhibition hall the goods and services purchased by (say) 1000 average consumers in order to get recognizable amounts of the less common items. Each item would be tagged with the average annual price paid for it.

Our immediate problem is to measure the change in "consumer prices" from 1963 to 1964. How would we go about this? We could spend a great deal of time looking at the $1980 worth of commodities bought in 1963 and the $2079 worth of commodities bought in 1964 without coming to any completely satisfactory answer. Painstaking study might ultimately disclose that, where *identical* commodities were available in both years, an average of from 2 to 4% more units per capita were purchased in 1964 than in 1963. There would be many perplexing cases in which the number of units of a commodity purchased in the two years was identical, but the commodity itself was a little different. If a "new process" shirt sold for $5.25 in 1964 and an "old process" shirt sold for $4.95 in 1963, has the price of shirts gone up? Does the "new process" shirt wear longer, feel better, or look better? Was the consumer getting "more shirts per shirt" in 1964 than in 1963?

Finally, we would notice a few interesting commodities in the 1964 collection which simply did not exist on the 1963 side of the hall. On the 1964 side we would look in vain for a few shopworn articles that we found in small quantities in the 1963 collection.

By hypothesis, each collection is a perfectly accurate representation of the population from which it was drawn. But the two populations are a little different. We want to make a quantitative statement as to how much the average level of consumer prices has changed from 1963 to 1964, but there is some ambiguity about *what* it is that has undergone the price change.

The 1963 collection of commodities, worth $1980 at 1963 prices, is a faithful reflection of the 1963 population. A pragmatic approach to measuring the change in consumer prices from 1963 to 1964 might be the following:

1. Form a special subcollection of those 1963 commodities which also appear in identical form and style in the 1964 collection.

2. As measures of the relative importance of the different commodities in the subcollection *in 1963*, we take the numbers of units of these commodities consumed in 1963.

3. Next we multiply the 1963 number of units of each of the identical commodities first by its average price in 1963 and second by its average price in 1964.

4. We then determine the total value of this collection of identical commodities in 1964 and divide it by the total value of the same collection in 1963. The resulting ratio may be taken as *one* measure of the change in consumer prices from 1963 to 1964. A ratio of, for example, 1.013 would be taken to mean that the consumer price level had risen 1.3% between the two years.

However, restricting our subcollection to commodities which existed in identical forms in both years limits the importance of this figure. The 1963 subcollection might include all of the more humdrum staple commodities and exclude all style goods and the consumer durables which undergo frequent model changes. To get a more representative subcollection of the commodities people actually bought in 1963, we would have to include some style goods. But this once again brings us to the dilemma of valuing "new process" and "old process" shirts, not to mention the widening or narrowing of decorative trimp strips on automobiles.

In spite of these difficulties, one plausible approach to the measurement of price change is to take a collection of commodities which is as nearly representative of the 1963 population as feasible and then determine how much it would have cost a consumer in 1964 to live the same way the average consumer had lived in 1963. We could adhere as closely as possible to this 1963 collection for a number of years. Each year would bring a larger number of ambiguities in the form of style goods or models which look quite different from their 1963 counterparts. Each passing year would find us a little less interested in knowing how much it would have cost a person (in 1968, 1969, or 1970) to live the way an average consumer lived in 1963.

Clearly, then, attempts to measure changes in the cost of a fixed collection of commodities are most nearly successful over relatively short spans of years. As a practical matter, agencies responsible for constructing index numbers substitute a new collection of commodities and weights every few years so that current policymakers will receive estimates of price changes which are reasonably indicative of what consumers are actually experiencing.

In the preceding discussion we have defined the 1963 way of life in terms of a collection of consumer goods which cost $1980 in that year. This array of commodities is a composite of the 1963 consumption patterns of people of all income groups, living on farms, in small towns, or in big cities and in states as climatically diverse as Alaska and Hawaii. This suggests that the 1963 population of 189.375 million consumers and the 1963 total of 375.0 billion dollars of personal consumption expenditures should be partitioned and related to one another in more illuminating ways.

One meaningful partitioning would be by metropolitan areas or similar compact and contiguous population clusters, each of which has a well-integrated retail price system and constitutes a relatively self-contained labor market and retail trade area. For example, if we had complete information on the several billion dollars worth of goods and services bought by consumers in (say) Los Angeles in 1963 and could identify them with a stipulated number of consumers living in the Los Angeles area, we would define an array of goods and services consisting of the average quantities bought by these consumers. We could then price this 1963 array of commodities for several successive years to measure how much it would cost residents of Los Angeles in 1968 or 1969 to live the way the average Los Angeles consumer had lived in 1963. Similar collections of commodities could be determined and priced for any other city or small geographic area.

However, the average 1963 expenditures per capita in different metropolitan areas might reflect different average income levels, different age distributions, different distributions of family sizes, and different ratios of families to single individuals. In theory, within any given metropolitan area we could sort all the commodities sold in 1963 into separate collections bought by each subgroup of residents classified by income level, family size, and such other characteristics as seem relevant to us. We would identify each subgroup of consumers with the appropriate collection of goods and determine the average 1963 pattern of consumption for that subgroup. We would then move forward in time, pricing the 1963 collection of commodities for each subgroup in each successive year.

We would find that in any given year the canned baby foods were being bought by a limited number of families. We would find that "automobile" is a different commodity for a family man with a $6000 income than for a bachelor with a $20,000 income. The suits, shirts, and shoes would also tend to be sorted out into different price lines and brand names for consumers in the various income and family composition categories. Finally, if we could scrutinize the arrays of things bought by individual households we might find that no two of them had selected truly identical collections.

At one extreme, we could envisage 192 million price index numbers, one for each consumer, or at least 60 million, one for each "spending unit" (family or single individual). The practical level of aggregation actually chosen would depend on the extent of consumption differences existing between areas and between family income and size groups and on how small a difference in the average price changes affecting two groups is regarded as of interest in relation to policy or analysis.

If there is not much geographical variation in the consumer prices of identical commodities it might be sufficient to divide the United States into a limited number of areas. Furthermore, if the major policy questions associated with consumer price changes had to do with (1) wage negotiations for blue-collar and clerical workers, (2) adjustments in minimum wage levels, and (3) adjustments in pensions for retired or disabled persons, consumer price indexes might be calculated only for these groups. Primary attention might be given to achieving quite an accurate measure of price changes affecting wage and clerical worker families with two children under the age of 18. We might put an upper and a lower income limit on the families whose 1963 purchases would be used in the determination of index number weights. The implicit assumption would be that single individuals and families of two or three persons in the specified income range are living well enough to be of little policy concern and that families of any size earning more than the upper limit of that range need no special public attention.

There are, of course, other sampling considerations in constructing a consumer price index. As a practical matter, current prices are collected from stores rather than from individual consumers. In a large city, we visit a small percentage of the total number of stores. Within the line of goods covered by (say) clothing stores, we specify a limited number of items. If exact information is available on a homogeneous commodity (for example, electric power) accounting for a significant percentage of total consumption expenditures, this commodity should be included in the index number by analogy with the "$(N - n)/N$" principle in sampling without replacement. An item of this sort is itself a significant part of the population; its inclusion in the sample reduces our uncertainty concerning the "true" average price change which would be observed if every commodity were included in the price index. This part of index number construction is simply an aspect of the broader topic of survey sampling and its principles will be left to a later chapter.

5.1.2 Price Index Numbers

The raw data from which price index numbers are made are prices in dollars and cents per unit—pounds, cans, pairs, dozens, units, or whatever the customary basis of quotation may be. It is difficult to give any useful meaning to the concept of the average actual price of a collection of dissimilar commodities. What we *can* do is to measure *percentage changes* in the price of each commodity from some base period to specified subsequent periods.

The price of a commodity in a given year divided by the price of the same commodity in a specified base year is called a *price relative*. For example, the United States average retail price of beef in 1951 was 79.4 cents a pound; in 1950 it was 67.9 cents a pound. The *price relative* for 1951, using 1950 as the base, was 79.4 cents/67.9 cents or 1.169.

A price relative is a pure number, free of any unit of measure. The 1951 price relatives for three other meats—lamb, pork, and chicken—were 1.112, 1.075, and 1.047, respectively, on a 1950 base. These four pure numbers, the price relatives, form a frequency distribution. Suppose that we wish to measure the average percentage change in prices of the four meats from 1950 to 1951. The answer is a measure of central tendency for the distribution of price relatives. In practice, the measure of central tendency usually chosen is a weighted arithmetic mean.

Although a great many different weighting patterns or "formulas" for index numbers are possible and many have actually been used, most published index numbers are of either the Laspeyres or the Paasche type. The Laspeyres formula assigns to each price relative a weight which is appropriate for the base year. The weight for each commodity is then held constant for a number of years.

The Paasche formula, in contrast, would apply to each price relative in a given year a weight appropriate to that specific year. Since each price relative is the ratio of a given year's price to the price in the specified base year, the Paasche formula measures *pure* price change only between the base year and that given year to which a particular set of weights applies.

More specifically, the Laspeyres formula would apply the same weights to price relatives for 1951, 1952, 1953, and so on. The Paasche formula would apply one set of weights to the price relatives for 1951, a second set of weights to price relatives for 1952, and a third set to price relatives for 1953. In each formula we assume that the price relative for each commodity expresses its given year price as a ratio to its 1950 price.

Table 5.1 shows the retail prices of each of four kinds of meat in each year from 1950 through 1960. Table 5.2 shows the corresponding series of price relatives on the base 1950 = 1.

How should we average these relatives to measure the average price change? We *could* add up the four price relatives in each year and divide by four. Our index number would then be simply an unweighted arithmetic mean.

But the foregoing procedure implies that the four price relatives are of equal importance. However, from Table 5.3 we see that the per capita consumption of beef in 1950 was 57.1 pounds, whereas the per capita consumption of lamb was only 3.6 pounds. The retail prices of the two meats were of the same order of magnitude (around 70 cents a pound during most of the

Table 5.1 Meats: Basic Series on Retail Prices, United States, 1950–1960

Year	P_1, Beef and Veal	P_2, Lamb and Mutton	P_3, Pork	P_4, Chicken and Turkey
	Retail Price			
	Cents per Pound			
1950	67.9	67.1	49.6	57.0
1951	79.4	74.6	53.3	59.7
1952	77.9	72.6	51.8	60.0
1953	62.2	61.9	57.2	58.5
1954	61.6	63.2	58.3	52.8
1955	60.8	61.2	49.3	54.8
1956	59.4	61.5	46.9	47.8
1957	63.5	65.1	54.2	46.7
1958	72.9	70.9	58.3	46.1
1959	74.4	67.0	51.5	42.3
1960	72.6	66.3	50.8	42.7

Source: United States Department of Agriculture, Economic Research Service.

Table 5.2 Meats: Retail Price Relatives to the Base 1950 = 1, United States, 1950–1960

Year	Beef and Veal	Lamb and Mutton	Pork	Chicken and Turkey
	Price Relatives, 1950 = 1.000			
1950	1.000	1.000	1.000	1.000
1951	1.169	1.112	1.075	1.047
1952	1.147	1.082	1.044	1.053
1953	0.916	0.923	1.153	1.026
1954	0.907	0.942	1.175	0.926
1955	0.895	0.912	0.994	0.961
1956	0.875	0.917	0.946	0.839
1957	0.935	0.970	1.093	0.819
1958	1.074	1.057	1.175	0.809
1959	1.096	0.999	1.038	0.742
1960	1.069	0.988	1.024	0.749

Source: Computed from prices in Table 4.1.

Table 5.3 Meats: Basic Series on Quantities Consumed per Capita, United States, 1950–1960

	Per Capita Consumption			
Year	q_1, Beef and Veal	q_2, Lamb and Mutton	q_3, Pork	q_4, Chicken and Turkey
	Pounds			
1950	57.1	3.6	64.4	24.7
1951	50.2	3.0	66.9	26.1
1952	55.5	3.7	67.3	26.8
1953	69.7	4.2	59.1	26.7
1954	72.1	4.1	55.8	28.1
1955	73.1	4.1	62.1	26.4
1956	75.9	4.0	62.6	29.8
1957	74.7	3.7	56.8	31.4
1958	69.8	3.6	56.0	34.1
1959	69.7	4.0	62.9	35.2
1960	73.1	4.1	60.7	34.6

Source: United States Department of Agriculture, Economic Research Service.

Table 5.4 Meats: Consumer Expenditures per Capita, United States, 1950–1960

Year	Beef and Veal	Lamb and Mutton	Pork	Chicken and Turkey	Total
1950	$38.77	$2.42	$31.94	$14.08	$87.21
1951	39.86	2.24	35.66	15.58	93.34
1952	43.00	2.69	34.86	16.08	96.63
1953	43.35	2.60	33.81	15.62	95.38
1954	44.41	2.59	32.53	14.84	94.37
1955	44.44	2.51	30.62	14.47	92.04
1956	45.08	2.46	29.36	14.24	91.14
1957	47.43	2.41	30.79	14.66	95.29
1958	50.88	2.55	32.65	15.72	101.80
1959	51.86	2.68	32.39	14.89	101.82
1960	53.07	2.72	30.84	14.77	101.40

Source: Computed from prices in Table 5.1 and quantities in Table 5.3.

1950–1960 period). A simple arithmetic mean of price relatives implicitly assumes that 3.6 pounds of lamb are as important as 57.1 pounds of beef.

A measure of importance which appeals very strongly to common sense is the amount of money that an average consumer spent on each of the four meats in the base year chosen for the price relatives, 1950. Table 5.4 shows the number of dollars spent in each year from 1950 through 1960 for the quantity of each meat actually consumed in the specified years.

In 1950, the per capita expenditure for the four meats was $87.21. The amount spent for beef in 1950 was $38.77. Hence the value of beef consumption constituted $38.77/$87.21 or 0.44456 of the total. The 1950 proportions of expenditures for the other three meats were lamb, 0.02775; pork, 0.36624; and chicken, 0.16145. These four weights add up to 1.00000. These are the weights which are called for by the Laspeyres formula, assuming that we wish to use 1950 as our base period.

Table 5.5 shows the results of multiplying each of the price relatives in Table 5.2 by the corresponding 1950 expenditure weight. In each year from 1950 through 1960, the four weights remain constant and their sum is unity. The Laspeyres price index can be obtained by simply adding up the four figures in the first four columns of Table 5.5, with the results shown in Column 5. Since the weights do not change, the variations in the Laspeyres price index from year to year must be attributed exclusively to variations in the price relatives and hence in the actual prices from which they are derived.

Table 5.5   Meats: Price Relatives (1950 = 1.000) Multiplied by
Laspeyres Weights, United States, 1950–1960   P. I

Year	Beef and Veal	Lamb and Mutton	Pork	Chicken and Turkey	Total
1950	0.44456	0.02775	0.36624	0.16145	1.00000
1951	0.51969	0.03086	0.39371	0.16904	1.11329
1952	0.50991	0.03003	0.38235	0.17001	1.09230
1953	0.40722	0.02561	0.42227	0.16565	1.02075
1954	0.40322	0.02614	0.43033	0.14950	1.00919
1955	0.39788	0.02531	0.36404	0.15515	0.94239
1956	0.38899	0.02545	0.34646	0.13546	0.89636
1957	0.41566	0.02692	0.40030	0.13223	0.97511
1958	0.47746	0.02933	0.43033	0.13061	1.06773
1959	0.48724	0.02772	0.38016	0.11980	1.01491
1960	0.47523	0.02742	0.37503	0.12093	0.99861

Source: Computed from price relatives in Table 5.2 and weights derived from 1950 values in Table 5.4.

5.1.3 *Price Index Number as a Ratio of Aggregates*

To make clear the relationship of index numbers to frequency distributions and weighted arithmetic means, we have approached the Laspeyres price index formula as an average of price relatives. However, the Laspeyres formula can also be calculated in a different way.

Suppose we look upon the quantities of the four meats consumed in 1950 as constituting a "market basket." This market basket consists of 57.1 pounds of beef, 3.6 pounds of lamb, 64.4 pounds of pork, and 24.7 pounds of chicken. The value of the market basket in 1950 (that is, at the prices actually prevailing in that year) is $87.2079. What would it cost to buy this same market basket in 1951? The answer, of course, involves multiplying 57.1 pounds of beef, 3.6 pounds of lamb, 64.4 pounds of pork, and 24.7 pounds of chicken by their respective 1951 prices. The cost of the 1950 market basket at 1951 prices proves to be $97.0941.

It is clear that the increase in the cost of the market basket has resulted exclusively from price changes, as the quantities of each meat have not changed. The ratio of the 1951 cost to that of 1950 is 1.11336, precisely the same result we obtained when we applied 1950 expenditure weights to the respective price relatives for each meat (except for rounding errors). Evidently, we have arrived at the same place by different roads. Some algebra will clarify the situation.

The Laspeyres price index formula for two commodities may be written as

$$(5.1) \qquad P_L = w_{10}p_1 + w_{20}p_2; \qquad w_{10} + w_{20} = 1$$

In (5.1), p_1 and p_2 are price relatives. The weights are defined as

$$(5.2) \qquad w_{10} = \frac{p_{10}q_{10}}{p_{10}q_{10} + p_{20}q_{20}}$$

$$(5.3) \qquad w_{20} = \frac{p_{20}q_{20}}{p_{10}q_{10} + p_{20}q_{20}}$$

In (5.2) and (5.3), p_{10} and p_{20} are *prices* in cents per pound. In these subscripts, the first digit, 1 and 2, identifies commodities 1 and 2; the second digit, 0, identifies each of these prices as belonging to the base year (in our specific illustration here, 1950). The subscripts of q_{10} and q_{20} have the same significance; q_{10} and q_{20} are measured in pounds.

We now rewrite (5.1) in terms of prices and quantities:

$$(5.4) \qquad P_{L(t)} = w_{10}\left(\frac{p_{1t}}{p_{10}}\right) + w_{20}\left(\frac{p_{2t}}{p_{20}}\right)$$

$$= \frac{p_{10}q_{10}(p_{1t})}{(p_{10}q_{10} + p_{20}q_{20})(p_{10})} + \frac{p_{20}q_{20}(p_{2t})}{(p_{10}q_{10} + p_{20}q_{20})(p_{20})} = \frac{P_{1t}Q_{10} + P_{2t}Q_{20}}{P_{10}Q_{10} + P_{20}Q_{20}}$$

$$= \frac{\sum P_{1t}Q_{10}}{\sum P_{10}Q_{10}}$$

In (5.4), p_{1t} and p_{2t} refer to the prices in cents per pound of commodities 1 and 2, respectively, in some given year t other than the base year (1950). The price relatives p_1 and p_2 are equal to (p_{1t}/p_{10}) and (p_{2t}/p_{20}), respectively.

We can divide both the numerator and the denominator of the first term in (5.4) by p_{10} and we can divide both numerator and denominator of the second term by p_{20}. The denominators of the two terms are now identical, so we can add up the two numerators and place them over the common denominator. Finally, simplifying the notation, we may write the formula for the Laspeyres price index in year t as $\sum p_t q_0 / \sum p_0 q_0$, as shown in (5.5):

$$(5.5) \qquad P_{L(t)} = \frac{p_{1t}q_{10}}{(p_{10}q_{10} + p_{20}q_{20})} + \frac{p_{2t}q_{20}}{(p_{10}q_{10} + p_{20}q_{20})} = \frac{\sum p_t q_0}{\sum p_0 q_0}$$

The last formula is indeed that of a market basket in which the base year quantity of each commodity is multiplied in the numerator by its price in year t and in the denominator by its price in year 0. The ratio of aggregates is identical with the (weighted) average of ratios or price relatives.

The difference between the Paasche price index formula and the Laspeyres formula is more readily shown in terms of ratios of aggregates than of averages of price relatives. Thus looking ahead to (5.10), we see the Paasche formula written in the customary manner as the ratio $\sum p_t q_t / \sum p_0 q_t$. Comparing this with the Laspeyres formula in (5.5), we find that the *prices* in the numerator and denominator, respectively, are the same, but the quantity weights of the *given year* q_t are substituted in both numerator and denominator of the Paasche formula for the *base year* weights q_0 of the Laspeyres formula.

We may write the Paasche formula alternatively as

$$(5.6) \qquad P_{p(t)} = w_{1t}p_1 + w_{2t}p_2; \qquad w_{1t} + w_{2t} = 1$$

Equation (5.6) expresses the Paasche formula as a weighted average of price relatives. However, the weights are hybrids, obtained by multiplying the prices in the base year by the respective quantities in the given year t. The pseudovalues shown in (5.7) and (5.8) did not really exist in either year t or year 0. They are a combination of base year prices and given year quantities, but the unit of measure of this combination is dollars, just as in the weights for the Laspeyres price index. The Paasche formula weights are defined as

$$(5.7) \qquad w_{1t} = \frac{p_{10}q_{1t}}{(p_{10}q_{1t} + p_{20}q_{2t})}$$

and

$$(5.8) \qquad w_{2t} = \frac{p_{20}q_{2t}}{(p_{10}q_{1t} + p_{20}q_{2t})}$$

Equation (5.9) states the Paasche formula in terms of prices and quantities:

(5.9) $$P_{p(t)} = w_{1t}\left(\frac{p_{1t}}{p_{10}}\right) + w_{2t}\left(\frac{p_{2t}}{p_{20}}\right)$$

$$= \frac{p_{10}q_{1t}(p_{1t})}{(p_{10}q_{1t} + p_{20}q_{2t})(p_{10})} + \frac{p_{20}q_{2t}(p_{2t})}{(p_{10}q_{1t} + p_{20}q_{2t})(p_{20})}$$

The numerator and denominator of the first term can both be divided by p_{10}; the numerator and denominator of the second term can both be divided by p_{20}. The denominators of the two terms are identical, so we can combine their numerators also in the simplified notational form of (5.10):

(5.10) $$P_{p(t)} = \frac{p_{1t}q_{1t}}{(p_{10}q_{1t} + p_{20}q_{2t})} + \frac{p_{2t}q_{2t}}{(p_{10}q_{1t} + p_{20}q_{2t})} = \frac{\sum p_t q_t}{\sum p_0 q_t}$$

The Laspeyres and Paasche price index numbers for the four meats of our example are shown in Columns (3) and (4) of Table 5.6. Although the movements of the two indices during 1950–1960 are quite similar, they are by no means identical. We shall return to this comparison shortly, but first we shall consider the question of formulas for index numbers of quantities.

5.1.4 *Index Numbers of Quantities*

The outputs of different manufactured products vary from year to year. If we wish to make a statement about the average percentage increase in industrial production from 1960 to 1965, it seems quite reasonable to calculate a *quantity relative* for the output of each industry in which we are interested. If output of steel is measured in tons, the quantity relative for steel in 1965 using 1960 as a base is a pure number, just as in the case of a price relative. Depending upon our purpose, we can then apply a set of value weights to the quantity relatives for steel and for other industrial products. The options available to us in constructing quantity index numbers are essentially the same as for price index numbers.[1]

The real income of the people of a country consists of *quantities* of goods and services, regardless of whatever changes may occur in their prices. The theory of consumer demand expresses a consumer's satisfaction or "utility" as a function strictly of the quantities of goods and services he consumes. The particular set of quantities of goods and services the consumer will buy in a given year depends upon the prices of the commodities and upon his money income, but these are regarded as affecting the consumer's

---

[1] There is the additional possibility of using "value added" weights rather than "value of gross output" weights to avoid double counting of (for example) steel as steel and steel in the form of automobiles.

welfare only *indirectly*; the welfare, satisfaction, or utility is a matter exclusively of quantities.

The data of our numerical example lend themselves to the construction of an index number of per capita consumption of meats. Meats account for a small but significant portion (around 5%) of total consumer expenditures in the United States. An increase in per capita meat consumption from 1950 to some subsequent year evidently reflects an increase in the satisfaction or utility of the average consumer so far as meats can contribute to it.

The Laspeyres formula for calculating an index of per capita consumption would use precisely the same 1950 expenditure weights that are called for by the Laspeyres price index number:

$$(5.11) \qquad Q_L = w_{10}q_1 + w_{20}q_2; \qquad w_{10} + w_{20} = 1$$

Equation (5.11) expresses the Laspeyres quantity index number as a weighted average of quantity relatives. Equation (5.12) expresses the same index number in terms of actual quantities and prices in year t and year 0; it should be compared term by term with (5.4).

$$(5.12) \qquad Q_{L(t)} = \frac{p_{10}q_{10}(q_{1t})}{(p_{10}q_{10} + p_{20}q_{20})(q_{10})} + \frac{p_{20}q_{20}(q_{2t})}{(p_{10}q_{10} + p_{20}q_{20})(q_{20})}$$

$$= \frac{q_{1t}p_{10} + q_{2t}p_{20}}{(p_{10}q_{10} + p_{20}q_{20})} = \frac{\sum q_t p_0}{\sum q_0 p_0}$$

In the first term of (5.12) we can divide both numerator and denominator by q_{10}; we can divide both numerator and denominator of the second term by q_{20}. In simplified notation, we obtain the customary formula for a Laspeyres quantity index as the ratio of two value aggregates $\sum q_t p_0 / \sum q_0 p_0$.

The Paasche quantity index number is expressed as an average of relatives in (5.13) and as a ratio of value aggregates in (5.14):

$$(5.13) \qquad Q_{P(t)} = w_{1t}q_1 + w_{2t}q_2; \qquad w_{1t} + w_{2t} = 1$$

$$(5.14) \qquad Q_{P(t)} = \frac{q_{10}p_{1t}(q_{1t})}{(q_{10}p_{1t} + q_{20}p_{2t})(q_{10})} + \frac{q_{20}p_{2t}(q_{2t})}{(q_{10}p_{1t} + q_{20}p_{2t})(q_{20})}$$

$$= \frac{q_{1t}p_{1t} + q_{2t}p_{2t}}{(q_{10}p_{1t} + q_{20}p_{2t})} = \frac{\sum q_t p_t}{\sum q_0 p_t}$$

Comparing the simplified notational version of (5.14) with that of (5.12), we find that the quantities appearing in the numerators and denominators of both formulas are the same, but the Paasche formula includes p_t in both numerator and denominator instead of p_0.

It should be noted that the weights in (5.14) are not identical with those in (5.9); rather, the time subscripts of the q's and p's are reversed. The weights for the Paasche quantity index number are computed using base year quantities and given year prices. Only by rare coincidence would the weights prove to be identical for the Paasche price index formula and the Paasche quantity formula. This is in sharp contrast with the Laspeyres formulas, in which the weights for both price and quantity relatives are identical.

5.1.5 *Relationships between Price and Quantity Index Numbers*

The weights in a Laspeyres quantity index remain constant over a period of several (or many) years. Hence changes in a Laspeyres quantity index over a period of years must be attributed exclusively to changes in the quantities or quantity relatives. Similarly, the Laspeyres price index is a measure of pure price change.

Intuitively, it would seem that an index of pure price change from (say) 1950 to 1960 could be multiplied by an index of pure quantity change to obtain an exact measure of the change in *value* or expenditures between the two years. Let us see if the Laspeyres price and quantity index numbers will indeed give us this result.

First, we write

$$(5.15) \qquad \frac{V_t}{V_0} = \frac{p_{1t}q_{1t} + p_{2t}q_{2t}}{p_{10}q_{10} + p_{20}q_{20}}$$

Equation (5.15) defines the ratio of two value aggregates. The numerator contains the quantities of two commodities in year t multiplied by their actual prices in year t. The denominator contains the quantities of each commodity in the base year multiplied by their respective prices in the base year. The ratio should be an exact "value relative" from which we can derive a precise measure of the percentage change in value from year 0 to year t.

In (5.16) we multiply the Laspeyres price index for year t by the Laspeyres quantity index for the same year:

$$(5.16) \qquad P_{\mathrm{L}(t)}Q_{\mathrm{L}(t)} = \frac{(p_{1t}q_{10} + p_{2t}q_{20})(q_{1t}p_{10} + q_{2t}p_{20})}{(p_{10}q_{10} + p_{20}q_{20})^2}$$

The two indices have the same denominator, so the denominator of their product is simply the square of the total base year value of the two commodities. The terms in the numerator, however, in every instance involve a combination of price in one year and quantity in another. There is no way to simplify this expression, and the ratio of numerator to denominator is not equal to the value ratio in (5.15).

Equation (5.17) presents the product of the price and quantity indices computed by the Paasche formula:

$$(5.17) \qquad P_{P(t)}Q_{P(t)} = \frac{(p_{1t}q_{1t} + p_{2t}q_{2t})^2}{(p_{10}q_{1t} + p_{20}q_{2t})(q_{10}p_{1t} + q_{20}p_{2t})}$$

Here, the numerators of the two indices are the same, so the numerator of the product is simply the square of the value of expenditures in year t. Each term in the denominator combines a quantity from one year with a price from a different year. As in (5.16), we cannot simplify the expression further, and the ratio of numerator to denominator is not equal to the value ratio in (5.15).

Evidently, although we think of our index numbers as expressing either pure price change or pure quantity change, neither the two Laspeyres formulas nor the two Paasche formulas are "pure" enough to yield, in combination, a precise measure of changes in value. But consider the hybrid product

$$(5.18) \qquad P_{P(t)}Q_{L(t)} = \frac{(p_{1t}q_{1t} + p_{2t}q_{2t})(q_{1t}p_{10} + q_{2t}p_{20})}{(p_{10}q_{1t} + p_{20}q_{2t})(p_{10}q_{10} + p_{20}q_{20})}$$

$$= \frac{(p_{1t}q_{1t} + p_{2t}q_{2t})}{(p_{10}q_{10} + p_{20}q_{20})} = \frac{V_t}{V_0}$$

Equation (5.18) multiplies a Paasche index number of price change by a Laspeyres index of quantity change, with a very interesting result—the denominator of the Paasche price index proves to be identical with the numerator of the Laspeyres quantity index. This term can be cancelled out in both numerator and denominator; the remaining terms give us precisely the value ratio of (5.15).

Finally, consider the hybrid product

$$(5.19) \qquad P_{L(t)}Q_{P(t)} = \frac{(p_{1t}q_{10} + p_{2t}q_{20})(q_{1t}p_{1t} + q_{2t}p_{2t})}{(p_{10}q_{10} + p_{20}q_{20})(q_{10}p_{1t} + q_{20}p_{2t})}$$

$$= \frac{(q_{1t}p_{1t} + q_{2t}p_{2t})}{(p_{10}q_{10} + p_{20}q_{20})} = \frac{V_t}{V_0}$$

Equation (5.19) indicates that the same result can be accomplished if we multiply a Laspeyres price index by a Paasche quantity index. The product shows that the numerator of the Laspeyres price index is identical with the denominator of the Paasche quantity index. When this term is cancelled out in both numerator and denominator, the remaining terms again give us precisely the value ratio of (5.15).

The relationships in (5.18) and (5.19) are very useful when we wish to have measures of price and quantity change which are precisely consistent with changes in values. We shall refer to this once again later in this section.

5.1.6 Comparison between Paasche and Laspeyres' Indices Over a Period of Years: A Concrete Example

Table 5.6 shows price indices and quantity indices for meats calculated by the Laspeyres and Paasche formulas, respectively. We show the indices

Table 5.6 Meats: Comparisons of Price and Per Capita Consumption Indices Using Laspeyres and Paasche Formulas, United States 1950 = 100

Year	(1) Expenditures in Current Dollars $\sum p_t q_t$, Dollars	(2) Value Index, 1950 = 100[a]	(3) Price Indices Laspeyres, 1950 = 100	(4) Paasche, 1950 = 100	(5) Quantity Indices Laspeyres, 1950 = 100	(6) Paasche, 1950 = 100	(7) Work Columns $\sum p_0 q_t$, Dollars	(8) $\sum q_0 p_t$, Dollars
1950	$87.2079	100.000	100.000	100.000	100.000	100.000	$87.2079	$87.2079
1951	93.3362	107.027	111.336	110.906	96.503	96.130	84.1582	97.0941
1952	96.8621	111.070	109.249	109.049	101.853	101.667	88.8240	95.2737
1953	95.3779	109.368	102.090	100.740	108.565	107.129	94.6771	89.0309
1954	94.3730	108.216	100.949	98.923	109.395	107.199	95.4008	88.0356
1955	92.0365	105.537	94.263	93.690	112.645	111.960	98.2356	82.2048
1956	91.1484	104.519	89.604	89.138	117.255	116.645	102.2557	78.1416
1957	95.2926	109.271	97.516	95.989	113.837	112.054	99.2748	85.0418
1958	101.8047	116.738	106.768	104.929	111.255	109.338	97.0228	93.1102
1959	101.8199	116.755	101.491	100.540	116.128	115.040	101.2727	88.5085
1960	101.3987	116.272	99.880	99.201	117.209	116.412	102.2152	87.1035

[a] Column (1) divided by $87.2079 and multiplied by 100. Formula is $\left(\dfrac{\sum p_t q_t}{\sum p_0 q_0}\right)$ times 100.

137

on the base 1950 = 100 because 100 rather than 1 is used as the base in most published index numbers. Table 5.6 also contains some work columns showing the value aggregates which are used in computing the respective formulas.

Let us first compare the two price index numbers in Columns (3) and (4). The computations in Table 5.6 are carried out as ratios of aggregates. Thus we write the Laspeyres indices as

$$(5.20) \qquad P_L = \frac{\sum p_t q_0}{\sum p_0 q_0} \qquad \text{(Price)}$$

$$(5.21) \qquad Q_L = \frac{\sum q_t p_0}{\sum q_0 p_0} \qquad \text{(Quantity)}$$

and the corresponding Paasche indices as

$$(5.22) \qquad P_P = \frac{\sum p_t q_t}{\sum p_0 q_t} \qquad \text{(Price)}$$

$$(5.23) \qquad Q_P = \frac{\sum q_t p_t}{\sum q_0 p_t} \qquad \text{(Quantity)}$$

The expenditures in 1950 were \$87.2079. We divide this figure by itself and multiply by 100 to establish the base value for 1950 at the convenient figure of 100. Then, the 1951 value of the Laspeyres price index is obtained by dividing \$97.0941 by \$87.2079 which (times 100) equals 111.336. The 1951 value of the Paasche index is obtained by dividing \$93.3362 by \$84.1582 which (times 100) equals 110.906. The difference is about 0.4 index points.

The maximum difference between the two price indices occurs in 1958 at 1.839 index points. The Laspeyres index indicates that meat prices were 6.8% higher in 1958 than in 1950; the Paasche index indicates a price difference of only 4.9%. The Laspeyres and Paasche quantity indices show a maximum difference of 2.2 index points in 1954.

Table 5.7 shows the results of multiplying various pairs of price and quantity indices. Our standard of comparison is Column (3), which is actual expenditures in each year divided by \$87.2079 and multiplied by 100 to turn it into an expenditure or value index.

The product (divided by 100) of Laspeyres quantity and Laspeyres price [Column (1)] shows discrepancies from Column (3) of about 2 index points in 1954, 1957, and 1958. The discrepancies between the product of Paasche price and Paasche quantity indices [Column (2)] and Column (3) also amount to about 2 index points in those years, but they are in the opposite direction. In 1954, the Laspeyres price-quantity product of 110.433 is 4.4 index points higher than the corresponding Paasche product. The Paasche product implies that expenditures for meat were 6% higher in 1954 than in 1950,

Table 5.7 Meats: Products of Various Pairs of Price and Consumption Indices
Compared with Value of Expenditures in Current Dollars,
United States, 1950–1960
1950 = 100

Year	(1) Laspeyres Price and Laspeyres Quantity	(2) Paasche Price and Paasche Quantity	(3) Expenditures in Current Dollars	(4) Laspeyres Quantity and Paasche Price	(5) Paasche Quantity and Laspeyres Price
1950	100.000	100.000	100.000	100.000	100.000
1951	107.443	106.614	107.027	107.027	107.027
1952	111.273	110.867	111.070	111.070	111.070
1953	110.834	107.922	109.368	109.368	109.368
1954	110.433	106.044	108.216	108.216	108.216
1955	106.183	104.895	105.537	105.537	105.537
1956	105.065	103.975	104.519	104.519	104.519
1957	111.009	107.560	109.271	109.271	109.271
1958	118.785	114.727	116.738	116.738	116.738
1959	117.859	115.661	116.755	116.755	116.755
1960	117.068	115.482	116.272	116.272	116.272

whereas the Laspeyres product implies that 1954 expenditures were 10.4%
higher than in 1950. The Laspeyres product is consistently higher than the
index of current dollar expenditures, and the Paasche product is consistently
lower.

As noted earlier, if we want a quantity and a price index number that are
perfectly consistent with the current value index in Column (3) we may (1)
multiply a Laspeyres quantity and a Paasche price index or (2) multiply
a Paasche quantity index and a Laspeyres price index. These products are
shown in Columns (4) and (5); both of them are identical with the expenditure
series in Column (3).

In recent years, economists responsible for the United States national
income and product accounts have settled on the combination of Laspeyres
quantity and Paasche price measures. First, they make a direct effort to
measure quantity change by valuing the current year quantities at constant
base year prices for each major component of the gross national product.
The corresponding expenditure estimate in current dollars is divided by the
estimate of expenditures at base year prices to obtain an *implicit price
deflator*. Since the current value has the formula $\sum p_t q_t$ and the value in
fixed prices has the formula $\sum p_0 q_t$, the price deflator has the implicit formula
$\sum p_t q_t / \sum p_0 q_t$.

We have seen that different weighting patterns give us different estimates of the amount of either price or quantity change. This basic fact is not altered if we include 5000 commodities in an index number rather than 2, or 4, or 100. If we wish to partition a change in money values *exactly* into a quantity component and a price component, we must *either* make a direct estimate of the quantity component and derive the price component by dividing the quantity index into the dollar value series *or* we must make a direct estimate of the price component and derive the quantity component by dividing the price index into the dollar value series.

Whichever component is estimated directly may be measured with various degrees of accuracy. However, its precision will affect not only its own usefulness but also the usefulness of the derived estimate of the other component.

In the United States, implicit price deflators are an integral part of the gross national product and income tables. As of 1964, for example, direct estimates were made of the 1963 gross national product and its quantity component in constant (1954) dollars. Corresponding estimates were, of course, made in current dollars—that is, in the prices actually existing in each quarter or year. Then implicit price deflators for the gross national product and its major components were calculated by dividing the constant (1954) dollar series into the current dollar series.

These calculations may be illustrated for the total gross national product for the years 1954 and 1963:

	1954 (Billions of Dollars)	1963 (Billions of Dollars)
1. Gross national product in current dollars	363.1	583.9
2. Gross national product in constant (1954) dollars	363.1	492.6
3. Implicit price deflator for the gross national product	1.000	1.185

Implicit price deflators are also published for the following components of the gross national product: (1) total personal consumption expenditures as well as separate components for durable goods, nondurable goods, and services; (2) total construction and separate components for residential nonfarm construction and other construction; (3) producers' durable equipment; (4) gross exports and gross imports of goods and services; and (5) total government purchases of goods and services and separate components for (*a*) federal and (*b*) state and local governments.

Given the existence of discretionary elements in the choice of any standard index number formula, the consistency aspect of implicit price deflators and the two related series is a telling argument in their favor. In 1922 Irving Fisher, after studying some 200 or more possible index number formulas, selected as his "ideal index number" the geometric mean of a Laspeyres index and a Paasche index. Operationally, an "ideal" price index would be obtained by calculating the price change between two years according to the Laspeyres formula and the Paasche formula, multiplying the two indices together, and extracting the square root of the product. If an "ideal" quantity index is calculated in the same fashion, and multiplied by the corresponding "ideal" price index, the product proves to be $\sum p_1 q_1 / \sum p_0 q_0$, a true index of the change in money value between year 0 and year 1. According to Fisher's terminology, the price and quantity indices in this form satisfied the *factor reversal test* in that they were precisely consistent with the corresponding value index.[2]

In Chapter 14 we will find that the concept of an implicit price deflator and the concept of Fisher's "ideal index" both have affinities with Theil's approach to "perfect aggregation."

5.1.7 *Descriptive Indices and Economic Relationships*

It is customary to regard an index number of (say) prices as a summary statistic for a frequency distribution of price relatives. The frequency distribution of price relatives in 1960 is regarded as independent of the distribution in 1959. We seldom bother to note that the price relative for a particular commodity has changed its rank in the array from one year to the next. Instead we concentrate only on changes in the index number itself as the (weighted) arithmetic mean of the successive years' distributions.

Similarly, a quantity index is treated as a summary statistic for successive years' frequency distributions of "anonymous" quantity relatives. And it is rare indeed that we regard the prices and quantities of commodities included in two different index numbers as functionally related.

The traditional attitude, however, is very shortsighted. There is a great deal of economic meaning just beneath the surface of our price and quantity index numbers for meats.

[2] The calculations are

1. "Ideal" Price Index $\quad = \left(\dfrac{\sum p_1 q_0}{\sum p_0 q_0} \dfrac{\sum p_1 q_1}{\sum p_0 q_1} \right)^{1/2}$

2. "Ideal" Quantity Index $= \left(\dfrac{\sum q_1 p_0}{\sum q_0 p_0} \dfrac{\sum q_1 p_1}{\sum q_0 p_1} \right)^{1/2}$

3. Item 1 times Item 2 $\quad = \left[\left(\dfrac{^{*}\sum p_1 q_0}{\sum p_0 q_0} \dfrac{\sum p_1 q_1}{^{\dagger}\sum p_0 q_1} \right) \left(\dfrac{^{\dagger}\sum p_0 q_1}{\sum p_0 q_0} \dfrac{\sum p_1 q_1}{^{*}\sum p_1 q_0} \right) \right]^{1/2}$

$\qquad\qquad\qquad\qquad = \left[\left(\dfrac{\sum p_1 q_1}{\sum p_0 q_0} \right) \left(\dfrac{\sum p_1 q_1}{\sum p_0 q_0} \right) \right]^{1/2} = \dfrac{\sum p_1 q_1}{\sum p_0 q_0}$

(The four terms marked with * and † cancel out.)

The prices and quantities of these four commodities should be related to one another in a set of consumer demand curves. Since the own-price elasticities of demand for each meat should have a negative sign for every consumer, we should expect that a true aggregate of the demand functions for all consumers in the United States should at least reflect this negative sign, unless the effects of other variables seriously obscure the price-quantity relationships for the individual commodities.

If in Table 5.8 we compare the first differences of the quantity relatives and the price relatives for beef and veal we find that all ten of the year-to-

Table 5.8 Meats: Year-to-Year Changes in Retail Price and per Capita Consumption Relatives, United States, 1950–1960
(1950 = 100)

Year	Beef and Veal	Lamb and Mutton	Pork	Chicken and Turkey
Year-to-Year Changes (First Differences) in Quantity Relatives (times 100)				
1950	–	–	–	–
1951	− 12.1	− 16.7	3.9	5.7
1952	9.3	19.5	0.6	2.8
1953	24.9	13.9	− 12.7	− 0.4
1954	4.2	− 2.8	− 5.2	5.7
1955	1.7	0.0	9.8	− 6.9
1956	4.9	− 2.8	0.8	13.7
1957	− 2.1	− 8.3	− 9.0	6.5
1958	− 8.6	− 2.8	− 1.2	11.0
1959	− 0.1	11.1	10.7	4.4
1960	5.9	2.8	− 3.4	− 2.4
Year-to-Year Changes (First Differences) in Price Relatives (times 100)				
1950	–	–	–	–
1951	16.9	11.2	7.5	4.7
1952	− 2.2	− 3.0	− 3.1	0.6
1953	− 23.1	− 15.9	10.9	− 2.7
1954	− 0.9	1.9	2.2	− 10.0
1955	− 1.2	− 3.0	− 18.1	3.5
1956	− 2.0	0.5	− 4.8	− 12.2
1957	6.0	5.3	14.7	− 2.0
1958	13.9	8.7	8.2	− 1.0
1959	2.2	− 5.8	− 13.7	− 6.7
1960	− 2.7	− 1.1	− 1.4	0.7

year quantity and price changes have the inverse relationship or negative sign which the theory of consumption leads us to expect. The year-to-year changes in consumption and prices of lamb and mutton also show opposite signs in nine years, and the tenth observation is inconclusive because the quantity relative showed no change. The price and quantity changes for pork show opposite signs in eight cases and the same sign in two. Finally, the year-to-year changes in price and consumption of chicken and turkey show opposite signs in seven instances and the same sign in three. Thus 34 out of 39 usable observations for the four commodities suggest that the quantities and prices are linked in some functional manner.

We may note further that in Table 5.6 the Laspeyres price and Laspeyres quantity indices change in opposite directions in all ten instances. The same perfect record is shown by the Paasche price and Paasche quantity indices, although the price change between 1953 and 1954 was only 0.1 index points.

These observations suggest that new and unconventional methods of aggregation may well be called for when aggregative economic variables are treated as components of a complex and interrelated economic system. The fact that perfect consistency among quantity, price and value aggregates requires us to construct an aggregative quantity variable by the Laspeyres formula and an aggregative price variable by the Paasche formula suggests that "custom aggregation" may be justified for sets of variables which must meet tests of consistency in national income accounts or in macroeconomic models.

5.2   THE ANALYSIS OF ECONOMIC TIME SERIES

Most sciences are concerned in part with phenomena which show quantitative variations over time. Some scientists have had considerable success with time series problems and economists have experimented with their methods. Some of these adaptations have been of little value; others have at least provided valuable insights to the experimenters.

It may be that some other scientists have been more specific than economists as to why they expect particular variables to move in particular ways, the reasons for expecting cycles of certain lengths, and the nature of the other variables, if any, that determine or influence the time path of the variable of primary concern.

During the 1920s and 1930s, textbooks on economic and business statistics seemed to reflect an implicit unanimity concerning the subject matter of economic time series analysis. There was virtual unanimity concerning the best method for analyzing all economic time series that fell within the prescribed subject matter area. The time series were usually national aggregates or averages; collectively, they included most of the publicly available records which might conceivably throw some light on that formidable and complex phenomenon known as "the business cycle."

The late 1930s witnessed a major revolution in the field of macroeconomics, sparked by J. M. Keynes' *General Theory of Employment, Interest and Money* (1936). The disruption of normal research and other professional activities during World War II meant that the follow-through on this "macroeconomic revolution" in terms of empirical testing and the synthesis of theory and methods was delayed for several years.[3]

It appears that the subject known in the 1920s and 1930s as "business cycles" or "business cycle analysis" is being absorbed into the newer subject matter division of *macroeconomics*. The subject of "economic time series analysis" must also be drastically realigned to meet the requirements of the new macroeconomic synthesis.

The traditional method of analysis of economic time series has been to attempt to separate any series of monthly, weekly, or quarterly observations into four logically distinct components—seasonal, trend, cyclical, and erratic. Assuming the original data to be on a monthly basis, the procedure, with minor variations, has been as follows:

1. Estimate the *seasonal* component with the aid of a 12-month moving average (centered), and eliminate this component from the orignal observations.

2. Estimate the *trend* of the seasonally adjusted series by means of (a) a least-squares straight line or some other function fitted by least squares or (b) a moving average of a relatively long period such as nine years, and eliminate this component from the seasonally adjusted observations.

3. Record and plot graphically the residuals which remain after the elimination of seasonal and trend components from the original time series. *This residual variation is compared visually or otherwise with the residual variation (after elimination of seasonal and trend) in other economic time series.*

The logic of this procedure was that there were tremendous individual differences among economic time series with respect to trends and seasonal patterns, but if these peculiarities were cleared away the remaining variation in *every* series should shed some light on the factor common to all of them, "the business cycle."

[3] However, Tinbergen published an econometric model of the United States in 1939, using then-recent estimates by Simon Kuznets of the national income and its components. Leontief's first applications of input-output analysis to "interindustry relations" in the United States were also published in 1939 or earlier.

In the late 1940s, sharp methodological arguments broke out between business cycle analysts who had processed, studied, and reflected upon many hundreds of economic time series and proponents of the new macroeconomic synthesis, some of whom had served very little apprenticeship in the analysis of empirical data. In part, the business cycle analysts were shocked by the small number of variables and equations with which the pioneer macroeconomic models were supposed to explain the business cycle and with the grossness and rigidity of the time units used—for the most part, annual observations. The advocates of macroeconomic models, although fired with a conviction that their basic concepts were correct, would also have conceded that their first, highly aggregative models left much to be desired.

Time and computer technology had, by the mid-1960s, brought economists who were primarily interested in economic and statistical theory into constructive collaboration with economists who had knowledge in depth concerning data, technology, and institutional factors in particular sectors of the economy.[4]

In view of their objectives, the economic statisticians of the 1920s and 1930s cannot fairly be accused of thinking that each economic time series should be studied in isolation from all others or that its movements were essentially self-generated. However, the techniques which they applied to the individual series encouraged some mathematical economists to import genuinely univariate methods of time series analysis from other sciences.

This section will be concerned with what might be called "univariate analysis" of time series. A multivariate approach will be outlined in Chapter 9.

5.2.1 Time Series and Frequency Distributions

Time is an essential attribute of many economic series. However, for so-called *random time series*, time is in a sense irrelevant even though the observations have been recorded for successive equally spaced time intervals. For example, consider the following series of 24 monthly observations: -5, -5, 3, -3, -1, 3, 1, -9, -1, 5, -1, 1, -1, -1, 3, 3, 7, 5, 5, -3, -1, -3, -3, and -1.

We can form these observations into a frequency distribution in Table 5.9.

This frequency distribution can be treated like any sample from a specified population. The sample of 24 observations has a mean, -0.167, and a standard deviation, 3.864. Seventeen of the 24 observations, or slightly more than two-thirds, lie within one standard deviation of the mean.

We can regard the next 24 observations from the same monthly time series

---

[4] See, for example, Chapter 10.

Table 5.9

Value	Frequency	Value × Frequency	Value²	Value² × Frequency
9	0	0	81	0
7	1	7	49	49
5	3	15	25	75
3	4	12	9	36
1	2	2	1	2
−1	6	−6	1	6
−3	5	−15	9	45
−5	2	−10	25	50
−7	0	0	49	0
−9	1	−9	81	81
	24	−4		344

as another random sample. The second sample yields an arithmetic mean of −1.083 and a standard deviation of 3.987. Sixteen of the 24 observations, or two-thirds, lie within one standard deviation of the mean. The two standard deviations are very nearly the same. The means differ by 0.916. This is less than the standard error of the difference between the means, so we cannot reject the hypothesis that the two samples of 24 have been drawn randomly from the same population.

There are additional tests of the randomness of sequences of observations in successive time periods, but we will not discuss these here. The two samples just described were generated with the aid of a table of random numbers. Although the rather long sequences of negative and positive numbers in the first sample are somewhat unusual, they were indeed generated by a random sampling process.

Consider the time series of 240 monthly observations in Table 5.10. In displaying the 240 monthly observations in a format with one column for each of the 12 months and one row for each of the 20 years, as is quite usual in recording economic time series, we are partitioning the original frequency distribution with respect to time in two alternative ways.

We have only to compare the column of figures for January with the corresponding column for July to see that the frequency distribution for January is drawn from a very different population than the frequency distribution for July. The arithmetic mean of the 20 January observations is 29.0, and that of the 20 July observations is 76.6, a difference of 47.6. The highest figure for any January is 47, whereas the lowest figure for any July is 59. The two populations are so distinct as to constitute disjoint sets.

The general mean of the 240 observations is 53.4. No January observation is as high as the general mean and no July observation is as low as the general mean. If we set ourselves the task of "explaining" the variance of the 240 observations around the general mean, it is clear that a partitioning of the observations into different months will account for a large proportion of the total variance. The expected value of the variable in July is very different from the expected value in January, so knowledge that some future value of the series is to occur in January rather than July greatly reduces our uncertainty and increases the accuracy of our prediction as compared with the alternative of taking the general mean as our expected value regardless of the month.

We can also make a preliminary examination of our data to see whether a significant part of the variance could be explained by partitioning the observations into years. We might explore this in various ways. For example, if we classify the 20 January observations into four 5-year periods, the

Table 5.10 Time Series: Original Monthly Observations, Years 1 through 20[a]

Year	Jan.	Feb.	Mar.	Apr.	May	June	July	Aug.	Sept.	Oct.	Nov.	Dec.
1	17	23	43	48	61	71	76	61	65	61	45	36
2	29	33	46	55	68	69	74	59	54	41	29	20
3	14	18	29	35	46	45	59	59	48	39	38	19
4	21	26	35	47	57	67	75	63	59	48	51	35
5	31	40	44	57	65	77	78	68	66	54	49	23
6	20	24	40	41	54	52	69	56	50	42	30	17
7	10	22	27	54	47	68	67	64	59	54	48	33
8	29	39	50	56	67	78	88	78	73	60	57	32
9	32	37	48	54	56	68	72	72	60	49	30	28
10	20	23	35	38	52	62	69	73	67	47	44	38
11	27	35	47	62	71	79	78	81	75	63	55	40
12	37	45	54	61	74	77	80	75	66	57	41	40
13	30	24	35	53	62	65	67	57	50	45	34	31
14	29	32	43	51	69	73	83	77	71	72	61	53
15	47	48	56	67	75	89	86	86	72	70	55	33
16	26	30	42	55	68	68	73	68	60	48	44	25
17	26	34	43	52	67	72	85	80	75	66	56	45
18	43	43	60	72	85	86	98	88	81	74	59	46
19	42	49	60	58	74	74	74	74	64	59	48	36
20	30	35	37	56	72	70	81	73	73	65	52	48

[a] Hypothetical data.

arithmetic means are 22.4 for years 1–5, 26.2 for years 6–10, 34.0 for years 11–15, and 33.4 for years 16–20. Similarly, if the July observations are classified into 5-year intervals, the arithmetic means are 72.4 for years 1–5, 73.0 for years 6–10, 78.8 for years 11–15, and 82.2 for years 16–20.

The observations for each of the two months suggest a significant upward trend during the 20-year period. The average of the first ten January observations is 24.3, centered between years 5 and 6; the mean of the January observations for years 11–20 is 33.7, centered between years 15 and 16. The difference is 9.4, spread over a ten-year period. Similarly, the mean of the first ten Julys is 72.7 and that of the Julys for years 11–20 is 80.5, a difference of 7.8. If we pool the January and July evidences of trend, we find an average increase of 8.6 over a ten-year period, or 0.86 per year. This would imply a difference of 16.34 between year 20 and year 1 (19 years) attributable to a trend, for the moment presumed linear.

An interesting feature of the foregoing search for trend is that it was conducted within two relatively homogeneous subsets of observations from which the very strong influence of seasonal variations had been eliminated. Evidently the amplitude of the seasonal effect, a difference of 47.6 between the average level for July and the average level for January, is almost three times as great as the amplitude of the estimated trend effect from years 1 to 20.

Another approach to determining the presence of a trend effect is to compare the 12 original monthly observations for year 1 and year 20. These observations are shown in the first two columns of Table 5.11.

We see that 10 of the 12 observations for individual months in year 20 are higher than those for the corresponding months in year 1. However, the difference between the means of the 12 observations for years 1 and 20 is only 7.1, whereas our examination of the January and July observations for all 20 years yielded an estimate of 16.34. This suggests that there may be some additional process underlying our time series which causes particular years to depart very substantially from the basic upward trend. It would, of course, be helpful to have the time series plotted on a chart. However, simply scanning the basic data in Table 5.10 suggests that a comparison between year 20 and year 18 may be instructive.

Eleven of the 12 monthly observations in year 18 proved to be *higher* than the corresponding monthly observations in year 20. The arithmetic mean of the monthly observations for year 18 is 11.9 *higher* than for year 20. Furthermore, if our first estimate of the trend effect based on the January and July observations were correct, the observations for year 18 should have averaged about 1.7 *below* those for year 20. Apparently, our time series reflects a third process, not seasonal and not trend, which has an estimated amplitude of 11.9 + 1.7 = 13.6 over the 24-month period centered on July 1st of years 18 and 20.

Table 5.11   Time Series: Comparisons of Monthly Observations for
Years, 1, 20, 18, and 19[a]

Month	Year 1	Year 20	Year 18	Year 19	Year 19 − Year 18	Year 20 − Year 19
January	17	30	43	42	− 1	− 12
February	23	35	43	49	6	− 14
March	43	37	60	60	0	− 23
April	48	56	72	58	− 14	− 2
May	61	72	85	74	− 11	− 2
June	71	70	86	74	− 12	− 4
July	76	81	98	74	− 24	7
August	61	73	88	74	− 14	− 1
September	65	73	81	64	− 17	9
October	61	65	74	59	− 15	6
November	45	52	59	48	− 11	4
December	36	48	46	36	− 10	12
	607	692	835	712		
Mean	50.6	57.7	69.6	59.3		

[a] Hypothetical data, from Table 5.10.

A comparison of year 19 with year 18 shows an arithmetic mean of 59.3 for year 19, 10.3 *below* year 18. Also, the arithmetic mean for year 19 is 1.6 higher than the arithmetic mean for year 20.

If we subtract the January observation for year 18 from the January observation for year 19, February of year 18 from February of year 19, and so on, ending our series by subtracting December of year 19 from December of year 20, we obtain the following series of differences: − 1, 6, 0, − 14, − 11, − 12, − 24, − 14, − 17, − 15, − 11, − 10, − 12, − 14, − 23, − 2, − 2, − 4, 7, − 1, 9, 6, 4, and 12 (Table 5.11). Although there are some erratic jumps from one month to the next, we have 15 consecutive negative differences, which clearly suggests a cyclical process with a duration of 15 months or more from the time it starts falling below trend until the time when it once again crosses the trend of the series on a cyclical upswing. Allowing for the erratic variation and alternation of signs just before and just after the run of negative differences, it appears that the cyclical process may have a half-period of something like 17 to 19 months rather than 15. By comparing observations 12 months apart, we hold the seasonal aspect constant; and the trend effect must be relatively small, being the expected increment over only a 12-month period. The series of 24 differences, then, consists almost exclusively of cyclical and erratic (or possible random) components.

5.2.2 *Formal Partitioning of the Variance of a Time Series*

Evidently the time series of our example fits the traditional assumptions about the nature of economic time series. Our series includes seasonal, trend, and cyclical components plus an erratic or random residual.

We can express this hypothesis by writing the formula

$$A = R + S + T + C$$

where A stands for actual, R for random, S for seasonal, T for trend, and C for cycle.[5] If each of these five symbols were represented by a series of numbers, implying that we had successfully separated out the four components of the actual series, we could express the relationship by means of a standard formula of variance analysis. Using small letters to represent deviations from the arithmetic mean of each series, we may write

$$a = r + s + t + c$$

Squaring both sides and summing we have

$$\sum a^2 = \sum r^2 + \sum s^2 + \sum t^2 + \sum c^2 + 2 \sum rs + 2 \sum rt \\ + 2 \sum rc + 2 \sum st + 2 \sum sc + 2 \sum tc$$

Actually, the present time series was constructed in such a way that we have numerical representations of each symbol called for in the foregoing equations. If we divide each sum of squares by 239, we obtain the mean squares or variances of the five series. We may express the first cross-product term as $2r_{rs}s_r s_s$ (that is, two times the coefficient of correlation times the standard deviation of R times the standard deviation of S). The other five cross-product terms can be written in similar fashion.

We may list the numerical values of each of the 11 terms as follows:

$$\frac{\sum a^2}{239} = 336.5255 \qquad \frac{\sum r^2}{239} = 15.0736$$

$$\frac{\sum s^2}{239} = 222.2803 \qquad \frac{\sum t^2}{239} = 33.6402$$

$$\frac{\sum c^2}{239} = 50.1088 \qquad 2r_{rs}s_r s_s = 20.3754$$

$$2r_{rt}s_r s_t = 3.3282 \qquad 2r_{rc}s_r s_c = -1.0944$$

$$2r_{st}s_s s_t = 3.7529 \qquad 2r_{sc}s_s s_c = 0$$

$$2r_{tc}s_t s_c = -10.7077$$

[5] This formula implies that the four basic components are additive in arithmetic form. Other relationships are possible; for example, the seasonal component might tend to be a constant percentage of the trend values year by year rather than a constant arithmetic amount. It is enough for our present expository purposes if we simply assume the general function $A = f(R, S, T, C)$.

The variance of the actual series is 336.5. The seasonal component accounts for about two-thirds of the total variance, or 222.3. If we successfully eliminated seasonal variation from the original series, the variance of the adjusted series would be about 114.

The variance of the trend component is 33.6; subtracting this from the seasonally adjusted series would leave a remaining variance of 80. The variance of the cyclical component is 50.1; if this is successfully eliminated, the remaining series should have a variance of 30. Finally, the random component, generated with the aid of a table of random numbers, has a variance of 15.1. Subtracting this from the residual variance, we have a remainder of about 15 which represents the net effect of interactions (intercorrelations) among the four basic components of the time series.

5.2.3 *Estimating Seasonal Patterns and Trends by Regression Techniques*

In Chapter 4 we noted that a least squares regression equation separates the total variance of the dependent variable into an unexplained portion and a portion explained by the equation. This suggests that we might try estimating at least the seasonal and trend components of our original time series by using it as the dependent variable in a regression equation. Clearly, we can regress the original series upon "time" and estimate a least squares linear trend. For example, t can be assigned a value of 1 in January of year 1, 2 in February of year 1, and so on, up to a value of 240 in December of year 20.

To estimate the seasonal pattern by regression techniques involves a technical device. Suppose we list our 240 original observations in a vertical column. We then add 13 columns to the right of the original series. The first column contains our trend variable, $t = 1, 2, 3, \ldots, 240$. The next column represents January. In this column we enter a 1 for observations 1, 13, 25, 37, and so on, the January observations; for all non-January observations we enter a 0 in the January column. Similarly, in the February column we enter a 1 for observations 2, 14, 26, etc.; in the March column we enter a 1 for observations 3, 15, 27; and we use the same method for the other nine months.

The resulting regression equation includes 13 independent variables which would be difficult to handle with a desk calculator. However, it is very light work for an electronic computer, using a standard regression program.

The regression equation gives us an estimate of 0.075 for the *monthly* trend effect. This would amount to 0.90 per year or about 20 points from January of year 1 through December of year 20. This is quite close to our estimate of 0.86 per year obtained earlier from the January and July observations. If we set $t = 0$, the appropriate value for December of "year 0," our regression equation consists in round numbers of a constant term, $b_0 = 18$, and the regression coefficients, $b_{a.i}$, for the individual months shown in the first column of Table 5.12.

To obtain an estimate of the expected value of $A(= \hat{A}_i)$ for each month, with the trend term somewhat artificially held constant at $t = 0$, we simply multiply 1 by the appropriate regression coefficient and add the result to the constant term (Table 5.12, second column).

The combination of linear trend and seasonal pattern accounts for about 80% of the total variance of the time series. The variance of residuals from the regression equation is 65.724. This is almost exactly the sum of the variance of the cyclical component (50.109) and the variance of the random component (15.074).

To obtain the expected trend-plus-seasonal value for $t = 120$, we simply add nine points (0.075 times 120) to each of the monthly values previously listed for $t = 0$. The expected values for $t = 120$ are shown in the third column of Table 5.12. In all instances, these values come within two points of the true trend-plus-seasonal component which was used in constructing the synthetic time series, starting from a general mean of 53.75 when $t = 120.5$.

Table 5.12 Time Series: Seasonal Component Estimated by Least Squares Regression Equation, Simultaneously with a Linear Trend [a]

Month	Seasonal Regression Coefficients, Rounded $b_{a.i}$	Regression Estimate of A When $t = 0$ $(b_0 + b_{a.i}) = \hat{A}_i$	Regression Estimate of A When $t = 120$ $(b_0 + b_{a.i} + 120 b_{a.i}) = \hat{A}_i$
January	1	19	28
February	6	24	33
March	17	35	44
April	27	45	54
May	38	56	65
June	44	62	71
July	50	68	77
August	44	62	71
September	37	55	64
October	28	46	55
November	19	37	46
December	7	25	34

[a] Based on the hypothetical data in Table 5.10. The constant term is $b_0 = 18$ and the monthly trend increment is $b_{a.i} = 0.075$, both slightly rounded.

5.2.4 *Cyclical Variations in Economic Time Series*

The residuals from the regression equation just described may be regarded as our best estimates of the cyclical plus random components. The time series involved (for example) in telephone and radio transmission have extremely regular periodicities which can be represented by exact mathematical functions. *Spectral analysis* has been highly successful in such sciences in estimating the lengths and amplitudes of the basic cycle or cycles involved in particular time series. The simplest cycle is a sine wave not unlike the seasonal pattern of our present example. In addition to its seasonal component, our time series includes a cyclical process which is approximately a sine wave with a period of 40 months and an amplitude from peak to trough of 20. This cycle could be approximately reproduced by an expression involving two constants, one for amplitude and the other for "radians per month." A circle of 360 degrees includes 6.2832 radians. A sine wave with a period of 40 months involves an angular change of 0.157 radian per month.

It would be possible to arrive at estimates of the amplitude and period of the cyclical component of our series simultaneously with estimates of the trend and seasonal components. However, the relevance of this operation for economic time series in general would depend upon the regularity of economic cycles. There have been some approximate regularities in the downswings of business cycles in the United States since World War II. However, the numbers of months between successive downturns have varied considerably. Moreover, the Federal government is obligated under the Employment Act of 1946 to apply whatever instruments it reasonably can to influence the level of employment and production, to prolong the upswings of business cycles, to avert or postpone the next downturn, and, if a recession begins, to moderate its amplitude and shorten its duration.

In this context of an active and self-conscious economic stabilization policy, it seems unwise to place great emphasis on techniques of time series analysis which assume cycles of constant amplitude and duration. Nevertheless, the idea of simultaneously estimating all the systematic components of an economic time series is an intriguing one and justifies some methodological study and experimentation. Another feature which could be added to a simultaneous estimating procedure might be an allowance for a linearly changing seasonal pattern—for example, representing a gradual (linear) reduction in the amplitude of seasonal price variations over a period of years. As an isolated problem, this is mentioned in Appendix B to this chapter.

In the time series of our present example, it would be possible to obtain quite a good estimate of the average duration and amplitude of the cyclical component by using the 240 residuals from the trend-plus-seasonal regression equation. These residuals from regression will have an arithmetic mean of 0. However, they include a random as well as a cyclical component.

Inspection of the last 36 months of our time series suggested a cycle with a half-period of something like 17 to 19 months or a complete period of 34 to 38 months. One approach is simply to try out the effects of assuming different periods for the cyclical process. Thus suppose we enter the first 30 residuals on the first row of a large worksheet. Then Residual 31 is entered directly below Residual 1, Residual 32 below Residual 2, and so on. We then compute the arithmetic mean of the eight residuals in each of the 30 columns.

We can make similar tabulations for (say) 34 months, 38 months, and 42 months, in each instance calculating averages for an integral number of cycles. If the cycle is extremely regular in length, the difference between the highest and lowest of the column means will increase quite significantly as we increase the trial periods from 30 months to the length of the true cycle; then, as we increase the trial periods beyond this length, the amplitude or difference between the highest and lowest column means should diminish. If the random component in the residuals is large, there may be some ambiguity as to the exact length (or true average length) of the cycle period. If the cycle has actually varied from (say) 30 months to 50 months during the 20-year period, our "periodogram" approach will not lead to a sharp focus on a particular period but rather to a range of plausible average periods from perhaps 35 to 45 months.

If the cyclical period and amplitude are indeed quite regular, we could fit a sine wave pattern to the 240 time series residuals by means of least squares. The residuals from the resulting regression equation could then be tested for randomness, using the von Neumann ratio (see Chapter 6 or 7). The standard error of estimate from the regression equation would be an estimate of the square root of the variance of the random component.

Many economists prefer the word *erratic* to *random* in describing the residual component of economic time series. A strike in the steel industry or automobile industry may very suddenly reduce the level of output by 50% or even more. A glance at a time series chart of steel production will indicate that these episodes can hardly be regarded as "random."

Brief mention may be made of two other methods of separating the random from the systematic components of a time series. These are the variate difference method and the autoregressive method.

5.2.5 *Variate Difference Method*

It can be shown that if a series of observations satisfies certain criteria of random ordering over time, the expected value of the variance of the *first differences* of such a series is twice as large as that of the original series. This relationship is, in fact, the basis for *von Neumann's ratio*, which is used routinely as a test of the randomness of residuals from regression equations involving economic time series (see Chapters 6 and 7).

Obviously, it is arithmetically possible to take first differences of the series of first differences—these are called *second differences* of the original series. The series of variances of second differences, third differences, and differences of higher orders, when divided by an appropriate series of numbers, should at some point stabilize except for random fluctuations. If this happens in comparing the variance of (say) the fourth differences with that of the third differences, it is assumed that a fourth-degree parabola, when fitted to the original series by least squares, would leave residuals which were randomly ordered over time.

Here again, there is no theoretical basis in economics for expecting a time series to follow the path indicated by a high-order parabola. Also, even if a parabola meets the criteria for goodness of fit *in the particular time period for which it is fitted*, parabolas are notoriously poor forecasters in economic time series. A hint of this may be seen in the fact that a second-order parabola which is convex upward, after reaching its maximum value, decreases at an increasing rate for all successive future values of time. If the parabola is concave from above it will, after reaching its minimum value, increase at an increasing rate for all successive future values of time.

It is perhaps more realistic to think of a high-order parabola arrived at by the variate-difference method as a complex *trend* having empirical application only to the particular time period for which it was fitted. Although one may wish to interpret some of the undulations in this trend as "cycles," the parabolic trend cannot be counted on to produce "cycles" of comparable amplitude and duration in subsequent time periods. It is more likely that on extrapolation a few years beyond the original time period the term involving the highest power of time (t) will take over and the parabola may shoot completely off the time series chart.

5.2.6 *Autoregressive Models*

If a time series shows "runs" of several consecutive positive or several consecutive negative values, and the distribution of such runs departs significantly from randomness (see Chapter 6, perhaps the least pretentious way of taking advantage of this property is by means of a simple autoregressive scheme. The word "autoregressive" implies that the present value of a series is regressed upon previous values of the same series.

The simplest autoregressive model is

$$u_t = a + bu_{t-1} + v_t$$

If u_t is the original series, with $t = 1$ in January 1966 and $t = 2$ in February 1966, then u_{t-1} represents the original time series shifted backward by one month, so that the value of *u* for February 1966 is regressed upon its value for January 1966, and so on.

If the residuals from this simple or *first-order autoregressive scheme*, v_t, are random, the simple or *first-order* autoregressive equation evidently takes advantage of all of the inertia in the time series which is genuinely helpful in improving forecasts of its successive future values. However, if the residuals v_t still appear to contain substantially more and longer runs of positive and negative values than can reasonably be expected in a random series, one or more additional terms can be added to the autoregressive scheme. Thus a second-order autoregressive scheme would be

$$u_t = a + b_1 u_{t-1} + b_2 u_{t-2} + v'_t$$

If they proved helpful, additional terms involving u_{t-3}, u_{t-4}, and even longer time lags could be added.

Autoregressive schemes may imply that certain factors impinging on the times series affect it directly for two or more time periods or that the *reaction* of the time series to some impact of relatively brief duration takes two or more time periods to work itself out.

If autoregressive patterns exist, there may be a plausible explanation for them in terms of the theory of the particular discipline concerned. If there is no plausible theory, some wariness is justified in applying the autoregressive scheme in time periods subsequent to that for which the autoregressive scheme itself was determined.

APPENDIX A

SELECTED REFERENCES ON INDEX NUMBERS

1. Fisher, Irving, *The Making of Index Numbers: A Study of Their Varieties, Tests, and Reliability*, third edition (Boston: Houghton Mifflin Co.), 1927, 538 pp.

The first edition was published in 1922. The third edition, revised, contains interesting supplementary materials connected with the many book reviews and widespread controversy elicited by the 1922 edition. The book contains discussions and calculations involving a total of more than 100 alternative index number formulas. In addition to extensive technical appendices, his brief appendix (pp. 458–460) on "landmarks in the history of index numbers" and his selected bibliography (pp. 519–520) provide an entry into the classical literature on index numbers from 1863 to 1921.

Fisher's book marked the culmination of the first 60 years of interest in index number formulas by professional economic statisticians.

2. Haberler, Gottfried, *Der Sinn Der Indexzahlen* [Tubingen: Verlag von J. C. D. Mohr (Paul Siebeck)], 1927, 134 pp.

A selected bibliography (pp. 129–132) contains many references to the early literature on index numbers in addition to those mentioned in Fisher's bibliography. For example, references are given to the original papers by Laspeyres (1864 and 1871) and by Paasche (1874) describing and justifying the two index number formulas that are still in almost universal use. The fact that the cross product of a Laspeyres price index and a Paasche quantity index or of a Paasche price index and a Laspeyres quantity index gives a mathematically exact measure of changes in the current dollar value of the "composite commodity" involved is likely to insure the survival of the Laspeyres and Paasche formulas for a long time to come. Although the phrase *perfect aggregation* entered the economic literature only in the 1950s, the preoccupation of Irving Fisher and others with the mathematical consistency of index numbers of price, quantity, and value may be regarded as a concern with "perfect aggregation." The relevant aspects of index number theory may well be assimilated into the broader topic of measurement of economic aggregates during the 1960s.

3. Joint Economic Committee, United States Congress, *1964 Supplement to Economic Indicators: Historical and Descriptive Background,* prepared for the Joint Economic Committee by the Committee Staff and the Office of Statistical Standards, Bureau of the Budget (Washington: United States Government Printing Office), 1964, 130 pp.

This supplement gives brief but accurate descriptions of the principal index numbers and economic aggregates which are published monthly in *Economic Indicators* by the Joint Economic Committee of the United States Congress. The monthly publication *Economic Indicators* is prepared by the staff of the President's Council of Economic Advisers. The *Supplement* also contains references to the basic official descriptions of the major aggregates and index numbers—descriptions published by the agencies directly responsible for the series.

4. U.S. Department of Commerce, Office of Business Economics, *Survey of Current Business.* July 1966, pp. 7–40.

These pages contain a complete set of estimates of components of the national income and product accounts in 1965 and for a number of earlier years. Page 7 also refers to the official description of the most recent major revision in the United States social accounts, U.S. National Income and Product Accounts (1962–65).

The same tables are published each year in the July issue of the *Survey of Current Business.*

5. *Economic Report of the President: together with the Annual Report of the Council of Economic Advisers*. January 1967.

Each annual issue of the *President's Economic Report* includes an appendix on "statistical tables relating to income, employment, and production." In the January 1967 issue this appendix covers more than 100 pages (pp. 207–314). It includes most of the official measures of economic aggregates in the United States which are used by policymakers and their economic advisers for appraising the current state of the economy. The major categories of tables include national income or expenditure; population, employment, wages, and productivity; production and business activity; prices; money supply, credit, and finance; government finance; corporate profits and finance; agriculture; and international statistics. Many of the annual series extend back to 1929.

This annual appendix is an extremely useful, compact, and well-selected handbook for professional economists and students.

6. Allen, R. G. D., *Mathematical Economics*, second edition (New York: Macmillan and Co.), 1959, 812 pp.

Chapter 20 (pp. 694–724) outlines the principle of "perfect aggregation" based on the pioneering work by H. Theil (1954). Allen's references on pages 723–724 are a good introduction to the literature on *aggregation* as distinct from the narrower topic of *index numbers*. The aggregation literature was largely stimulated by problems encountered in constructing econometric models of national economies. Allen's earliest reference is to Tinbergen (1939).

7. Theil, H., *Linear Aggregation of Economic Relations* (Amsterdam: North-Holland Publishing Co.), 1954, 205 pp.

This is the first systematic treatment of aggregation problems in the modern sense. The text treatment in our own Chapter 14 is based on Theil and on Allen's exposition of Theil's concepts.

APPENDIX B

A METHOD OF ESTIMATING SEASONAL PATTERNS, INCLUDING PATTERNS WHICH ARE CHANGING OVER TIME

Constant Seasonal Pattern over the Entire Period Analyzed

Figure 5.1 is based on monthly average prices of hogs of a particular grade and weight class at Chicago from January 1947 through May 1962. The series shown in Figure 5.1 does not represent the actual prices but rather ratios of the actual prices to their 12-month moving average centered.

The calculations underlying Figure 5.1 are as follows:

1. We assume that the average price for a month is most accurately represented on a time scale by plotting it at the middle of the month. Roughly speaking, we may say that each monthly figure centers on the fifteenth day of the month.

Our first step is to calculate the sum of the first 12 monthly prices in the series and tabulate it at a level intermediate between the sixth and seventh month of the original series. An average of the 12 months, January through December, logically centers on July 1st; the average for the 12 months, February through January, centers on August 1st and so on.

2. We next calculate the 12-month total for month 2 through month 13 and record it between the seventh and eighth month of the original series.

3. We sum these two 12-month totals and divide by 24, obtaining an average which is logically centered on the fifteenth day of the seventh month. Thus, if month 1 in our original series is January, the first entry in the 12-month moving average (centered) series is entered opposite July (presumably July 15th) of the original series.

These calculations are repeated until the last month of the original series has been brought into a moving average calculation. The last 12-month moving average (centered) will be recorded opposite the seventh month from the end of the original series.

4. We now compute the ratio of the actual price to the corresponding 12-month moving average (centered) and multiply this ratio by 100. These are the "seasonally adjusted" figures which are charted in Fig. 5.1.

The logic of this adjustment process may be stated as follows: By definition, the *seasonal* forces operating in a time series should be identical in their effects on successive Januarys or successive Februarys but different in their effects between any January and any February. If we assign some arbitrary number (say 100) to the average of 12 actual monthly observations, the average of any 12 consecutive seasonal adjustment factors, positive and negative together, should be zero and the average of any 12 consecutive figures including only the annual figure of 100 *and* the effects of seasonal factors should be 100. Hence the *averages* of months 1–12 and 2–13 should each be free of seasonal influences. The centering process is a logical refinement because the original 12-month totals center on July 1st and August 1st— out of step with the July observation which centers on July 15th.

The ratios of actual observations to the 12-month moving averages (centered) may be inspected visually before taking the next step. The ratios for January and February fluctuate from year to year but show no definite trend. Their average levels are well below 100. If the series for each of the 12 months showed patterns such as these, we could proceed to calculate the

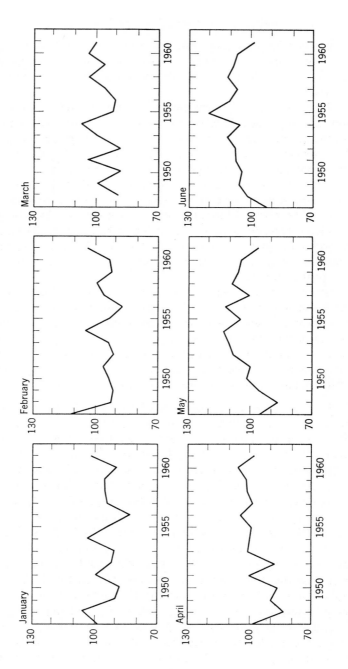

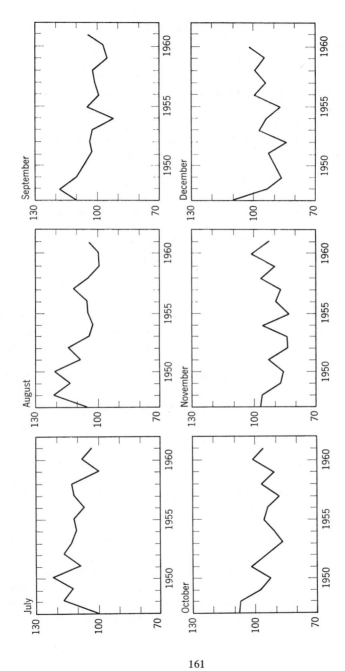

Figure 5.1 Hogs, monthly average price per 100 pounds (ratios of the actual prices to their 12-month moving average centered), Chicago, 1947–62.

161

arithmetic mean or perhaps the median of the January ratios and take this as our best estimate of the true seasonal factor for that month. If one or two of the January observations had been affected by special circumstances, such as strikes in the meat packing industry, these observations could be eliminated before taking either the arithmetic mean or the median of the others. If no special reasons are known for excluding one or two extreme observations, the median may be a more representative average than the mean.

For example, from a set of ratios of actual hog prices to 12-month moving average (centered) extending from January 1947 through June 1959, the seventh highest ratio for each month yields the following pattern:

January	94.0	July	112.2
February	93.3	August	105.2
March	96.6	September	102.4
April	99.1	October	95.5
May	104.8	November	87.4
June	106.4	December	93.7

If these 12 numbers summed exactly to 1200, they would be taken as our seasonal index. If they summed to somewhat more or less than 1200, then each of the 12 medians (or means) would be multiplied·by an adjustment factor to bring their total up to 1200 and their average to 100. The original observation for each month would then be divided by the seasonal index for the same month. This adjusts the data for "normal" seasonal variation. The same set of seasonal indices would be used for the entire period under our special assumption that none of the monthly indices showed cumulative changes or trends from 1947 to 1960.

Linearly Changing Seasonal Variation

Actually, the ratios for certain months, including March, April, July, August, and December, show movements that *might* be represented by straight line trends. When the late M. A. Girshick was on the staff of the United States Bureau of Agricultural Economics, he devised a simple procedure for calculating indices of *linearly changing seasonal variation*. There would be an equation of the type $S_{ij} = a_i + b_i t_j$ for each month, $i = 1$, $2, \ldots, 12$. The 12 equations would be constrained in such a way that the sum of the a_i's for the 12 months must equal 1200 and the sum of the b_i's must equal zero. The subscript j in the foregoing equations stands for time in years from the beginning to the end of the series. Thus for year 0, the 12 seasonal indices would be given exclusively by the 12 a_i's. For year 1, each seasonal index would be increased or decreased by the appropriate b_i; in year 2 each seasonal index would be increased or decreased by two b_i, and so on, as long as the pattern of linearly changing seasonal variation was assumed to continue. (The value of b_i for one or more months could be zero if, as in the January and February series of Figure 5.1, these months showed no discernible trends. The only restriction is that the sum of the 12 b_i's should be zero.)

But the real world reflected in Figure 5.1 is evidently neither fixed nor linearly changing. The ratios for May and June appear to follow a trend which is convex from above; the ratios for April could also be represented as well or better by a convex curve as by a straight line. Conversely, the ratios for September, October, and November seem to follow trends which are concave from above and this interpretation would fit the August ratios as well as the linear trend previously assumed.

Logically, it would seem that Girshick's method could be extended to particular types of *nonlinear* change in seasonal patterns. For example, could the seasonal index for each month be calculated from an equation of the type $S_{ij} = a_i + b_i t_j + c_i t_j^2$? The a_i's should sum to 1200 as before. The other requirement would be that the sum of the 12 expressions $(b_i t_j + c_i t_j^2)$ must sum to zero for each value of j. The problem would become even more complicated if the ratios for different months appeared to follow different *types* of trends.

Freehand Graphic Approximations to Seasonal Patterns Changing in Nonlinear Ways

In most scientific problems, there are clear advantages in using reproducible methods. If they do not already exist, it should be fairly easy for computer scientists and economic statisticians jointly to develop a number of routine machine programs which would determine nonlinearly changing seasonal patterns in completely reproducible ways.

From a statistical standpoint, however, reproducible methods might have no advantage over a freehand graphic smoothing of the observations. For example, the standard deviation of the ratios for January is approximately six index points. The standard error of the mean based on 15 observations would be approximately 6/3.7 or more than one and one-half index points. From the standpoint of neatness, it may be desirable to pass the horizontal "trend" for the January ratios through the arithmetic means, but a freehand horizontal line which passed within one index point of the mean would be almost equally defensible.

We will see in Chapter 6 that both the constant term and the slope coefficients of linear regression lines are subject to statistical error of the same type that is reflected in the standard error of a mean. The standard error of estimate around a linear regression trend would be analogous to a standard deviation, and the standard error of any particular point on the regression line would be analogous to the standard error of an arithmetic mean. (More accurately, we might speak of a standard error of the *expected value* of the dependent variable for any specified value of the independent variable.) Analogous sampling considerations also apply to nonlinear regressions and trends.

Thus a rough and ready procedure of drawing freehand straight lines or curves through the 12 sets of observations in Figure 5.1 might do full justice to the material. For each year, the 12 seasonal index values could be read from the respective trends. If they did not sum precisely to 1200, they could be adjusted to do so. The 12 adjusted indices would constitute the appropriate divisors to be used for adjusting the actual observations in that year for "normal" seasonal variation.

Ingenious though they may be, all of these procedures are essentially recipes. Of course, the amount of irregular variation relative to the amplitude of the seasonal pattern will vary greatly from one series to another. Figure 5.1 seems to provide clear visual evidence of a change in the normal or expected seasonal pattern of hog prices over the period shown. The real challenge to the economist is to determine *why* the seasonal pattern has been changing in this particular way. For one or two years ahead, it will indeed be helpful simply to extend the trends indicated in the figure. But if we know why the seasonal pattern has been changing we are better prepared to anticipate the probable effects of specific economic or technological changes upon the future development of the pattern.

EXERCISES

Index Numbers

1. Much of the agricultural policy of the United States is based upon the "parity ratio," with base period of 1910–1914. From the discussion in this chapter, develop arguments for and against the use of this concept as a criterion by which major policy decisions are made.

2. Using the following data, carry out these operations:
(a) Compute a Laspeyres index.
(b) Compute a Paasche index.
(c) Compute a "value" index (combination of the two).
(d) Compute Fisher's "ideal index number."
(e) Indicate the economic implications of using the different indices (if any).

Annual Commercial Production of Beef and Pork and Annual Average Price
per 100 Pounds of Cattle and Hogs

	Beef Production[a]	Pork Production[a]	Choice Steers, Chicago	Barrows and Gilts, Eight Markets[b]
	Million lb		Dollars	
1951	8,549	10,190	35.96	20.56
1952	9,337	10,321	33.18	18.13
1953	12,055	8,971	24.14	21.99
1954	12,601	8,932	24.66	22.25
1955	13,213	10,027	23.16	15.19
1956	14,090	10,284	22.30	14.82
1957	13.852	9,579	23.83	18.29
1958	12,983	9,618	27.42	20.25
1959	13,233	11,131	27.83	14.64
1960	14,374	10,863	26.24	15.96

[a] Carcass weight of all commercial slaughter.
[b] Chicago, Omaha, Sioux City, St. Paul, St. Louis, Indianapolis, Kansas City, and St. Joseph.
Source: "Livestock and Meat Statistics," Statistical Bulletin No. 333, AMS, USDA.

Time Series

3. The discussion in the chapter uses the months of January and July for illustrative purposes. Take the months of April and October in the foregoing table and, using the same techniques, determine whether the conclusions about trend, seasonality, and cyclical influence are consistent with those for January and July.

4. Using a random number table, select a series of 36 numbers (corresponding to, say, quarterly data over a period of nine years). Partition this series into seasonal, trend, cyclical, random, and actual components. Presumably, random numbers should show none of these components to be of importance other than the random and the actual. Evaluate the effectiveness of your partitioning procedure on the basis of your random number table experiment.

5. Using the same random data as in Question 4, estimate the seasonal and trend components by regression techniques. Compare your results with those in Question 4.

REFERENCES

1. Allen, R. G. D., *Mathematical Economics*, Second edition, New York: The Macmillan Co., 1959.
2. Crowe, Walter R., *Index Numbers, Theory and Applications*, London: Macdonald and Evans, 1965.

3. *Economic Report of the President—Together with the Annual Report of the Council of Economic Advisers*, Washington: U.S. Government Printing Office, January 1967.
4. Fisher, Irving, *The Making of Index Numbers*, Third edition, Boston: Houghton Mifflin Co., 1927.
5. Haberler, Gottfried, *Der Sinn Der Indexzahlen*, Tubingen: Verlag von J. C. D. Mohr (Paul Siebeck), 1927.
6. Hannan, E. J., *Time Series Analysis*, New York: John Wiley and Sons, 1960.
7. Joint Economic Committee, United States Congress, *1964 Supplement to Economic Indicators: Historical and Descriptive Background*, Washington: U.S. Government Printing Office, 1964.
8. Kendall, M. G., *The Advanced Theory of Statistics*, Vol. II, London: Charles Griffin and Co., 1946.
9. Mudgett, B. D., *Index Numbers*, New York: John Wiley and Sons, 1951.
10. Theil, H., *Linear Aggregation of Economic Relations*, Amsterdam: North-Holland Publishing Co., 1954.
11. U.S. Department of Commerce, Office of Business Economics, *Survey of Current Business*, July 1966.

References 1, 3, 4, 5, 7, and 11 have also been quoted in Appendix A, with some comments on their special features.

CHAPTER 6

Simple Regression Analysis: Alternative Models

The economic meaning and the mechanics of simple regression analysis were presented in Chapter 4, but sampling concepts were not introduced except for passing references to degrees of freedom. In this chapter, we shall consider simple regression from the standpoint of sampling and statistical inference.

Historically, regression analysis was first applied to random samples from approximately normal distributions. The populations sampled were biological characteristics of plants, animals, and human beings which were influenced by a large number of factors not separately identifiable and measurable. These factors were, in general, not subject to control by the investigator, and the populations being sampled might reasonably be assumed to remain constant over time.

Paired values of two variables, each of which is normally distributed, form what is known as a *bivariate normal* (frequency) *distribution*. If we call the two variables Y and X, the regression coefficients β_{yx} and β_{xy} connecting these two variables in a normal bivariate population are regarded as fixed characteristics (parameters) of the population. Since the simple correlation coefficient ρ in the population is equal to the square root of the product of β_{yx} and β_{xy}, it also is a fixed characteristic or parameter of the population. The values of b_{yx}, b_{xy}, and r obtained from any given random sample are regarded as estimates of the fixed population values.

When the populations sampled were all bivariate normal, the sample correlation coefficients r were extremely useful in comparing the closeness of association between different pairs of variables in the same general fields of biological science. Thus textbooks on statistical methods written between 1900 and 1930, some of them by truly outstanding scholars, placed great

167

emphasis on correlation coefficients—simple, multiple, and partial. Significantly enough, some of the earliest and most basic contributions to correlation analysis appeared in the journal *Biometrika*, the name of which implies measurement in the biological sciences. The leaders in the field from 1890 to 1930 were concentrated in the United Kingdom.

As statistical methods were adopted by workers in other disciplines, the emphasis on correlation coefficients was taken over quite uncritically in many instances. In the 1920s, most economists who were measuring relationships between variables would have said they were doing *correlation* problems or *correlation* analyses. The success of such an analysis was appraised in terms of the nearness with which the correlation coefficient approach 1, or perfect correlation. Only a few of the more erudite economists paid much attention to related measures that emerged from the same calculations—the standard error of estimate, the regression coefficients, and the standard errors of the regression coefficients. (Some attention, although not enough, was given to the standard error of the correlation coefficient.) In the United States, "correlation analysis" spread like wildfire among the younger members of the economics profession until no doctoral dissertation was complete without some correlation coefficients. Older economists who had not been infected by the correlation virus felt that something was wrong, but often they did not have the mathematical or statistical resources to say precisely what. One economics professor, disturbed by the fanaticism of an otherwise promising graduate student, is said to have asked an influential colleage to "please talk to Smith and get him to stop *correlating*."

By the late 1920s, the emphasis of leaders in biometrics or biological statistics had shifted to controlled experiments in which values of one or more variables subject to human control were fixed and only the dependent variable was subject to random variations of the sort that give rise to a normal curve. If the values of X, (say) quantities of nitrogen fertilizer on a test plot, were evenly spaced by the investigator at ten-pound intervals from 0 to 100 pounds, X clearly did not have a normal distribution. It became quite clear to the experimenters that the dependent variable Y and the deliberately spaced independent variable X could not possibly be regarded as forming a bivariate normal distribution. Certain measures which had been more or less regarded as by-products of correlation analysis retained their original meanings and usefulness in these experimental situations, but the correlation coefficient proved to be extremely sensitive to changes in the ranges of values chosen for the controlled variables.

As of 1928 the distinction between "correlation models" and "regression models" was clearly understood by a very limited number of statisticians, among whom R. A. Fisher was the most prominent. These statisticians were engaged primarily in the design of controlled experiments. Since many problems of interest to economists did not lend themselves to controlled experimentation, it is not surprising that economists were slow in recognizing these distinctions and adapting them to yet a third situation, characteristic of economic time series, in which the values of the variables were neither normally distributed nor derived from controlled experiments. Only in the very late 1930s and early 1940s were formal models advanced which appeared to cover the special problems of regression analysis when applied to economic time series.

We shall start here with the simplest and least controversial case, that of the "regression model," using data from carefully designed and controlled experiments. With this as a foundation, the other two situations can be made clear.

6.1 THE REGRESSION MODEL: EXPERIMENTAL OBSERVATIONS

Since the regression model first emerged in connection with controlled biological experiments, it seems appropriate to draw our illustration from that field. Field crop experiments are perfectly concrete and tangible, and can be appreciated by anyone who has watered—or forgotten to water—a potted plant.

A "Controlled" Biological Experiment: An Agricultural Production Function. The mere fact that crops have to be irrigated in a certain area implies that water there is basically scarce. In many such areas, growing urban populations and expanding industries compete with agriculture for a limited water supply. From the standpoint of the individual farm operator, irrigation water costs money, and he has the usual profit incentive for using it efficiently.

Let us suppose we are conducting an experiment to estimate the effects of different quantities of irrigation water on the yield of alfalfa per unit of area. Assume further that we select at random some 30 plots of equal area on a large experimental farm. On 5 of these plots we apply a total of 1 foot of irrigation water during the growing season; on another 5, 2 feet of irrigation water; and so on at 1-foot intervals up to (say) 6 feet. At the proper times (there are several cuttings of alfalfa during a season) we have each plot of alfalfa carefully cut and weighed so that at the end of the season we have 30 observations, each representing the yield of alfalfa (in tons per acre) associated with the amount of irrigation water applied.

6.1.1 *The Results Interpreted as Six Separate Frequency Distributions*

The form of our experiment implies that we expect different amounts of irrigation water to have different consequences for alfalfa yields. If we try to anticipate the description of our experiment and its findings that we might reasonably expect to write at the end of the season, we may envision the following:

1. When 1 foot of water was applied, the following yields were obtained: 1.87, 1.63, 0.70, 2.87, and 2.87 tons. The mean of the five observations was 1.99 tons. The standard deviation was 0.92 ton, and the standard error of the mean yield was 0.41 ton.

2. When 2 feet of water were applied, the individual yields were 7.30, 6.62, 6.87, 6.37, and 6.37 tons. The mean yield was 6.71 tons, the standard deviation 0.39 ton, and the standard error of the mean yields 0.18 ton.

Thus we could look at the 30 observations as six separate frequency distributions. Within each frequency distribution of five yields, the yield variations among plots are logically independent of the amount of irrigation water applied because that amount is *fixed and identical* for all five observations.

For a concrete example, we may refer to the 30 hypothetical observations listed in Table 6.1. The mean yields $\overline{Y}_i$ obtained for each of the six levels W of water applied are:

Water Applied, feet	Average Yield of Alfalfa, tons	Number of Observations
W	$\overline{Y}_i$	n_i
1	1.99	5
2	6.71	5
3	8.88	5
4	11.03	5
5	11.53	5
6	12.71	5
Average of 30 observations: 3.50	8.806	30

Our general experience with plant life suggests that the relationship between W and Y is basically a continuous one. However, a purist might tell us that we really cannot estimate what yields would be if we applied 1.5 feet of water because we have not actually tried applying that particular amount.

Regression Analysis Involving Only Two Values of the Controlled Variable. Assume for the moment that we had only the five observations for $W = 1$ and the five observations for $W = 2$ and wished to estimate the effect of

Table 6.1   Alfalfa Yields and Irrigation Water Applied:
Original Observations[a]

Values of W	Values of Y	Values of W	Values of Y
1	1.87	4	11.37
1	1.63	4	10.63
1	0.70	4	11.87
1	2.87	4	11.13
1	2.87	4	10.13
2	7.30	5	11.38
2	6.62	5	12.37
2	6.87	5	11.63
2	6.37	5	12.37
2	6.37	5	9.91
3	9.13	6	12.87
3	8.87	6	13.30
3	8.13	6	11.38
3	9.87	6	14.37
3	8.38	6	11.63

[a] Hypothetical data.

irrigation water upon alfalfa yield over this range. The individual sample yields for $W = 2$ are 7.30, 6.62, 6.87, 6.37, and 6.37 tons. The five sample yields for $W = 1$ are 1.87, 1.63, 0.70, 2.87, and 2.87 tons. What would be the best way to use this information?

One approach is to take the means of the two sets (of five yields each) as our best estimates of the expected values of Y *given* $W = 2$ and $W = 1$, respectively. The mean values are, respectively, 6.706 and 1.988, and the difference between them is 4.718 tons.

As an alternative, we might simply fit a straight line to the ten observations by least squares. The resulting equation is

$$(6.1) \qquad \hat{Y} = -2.7300 + 4.7180W$$

If we insert the value $W = 1$ in this equation, we obtain $\hat{Y} = 1.988$. Similarly, if we let $W = 2$, we obtain $\hat{Y} = 6.706$. Evidently, the least squares regression line pass precisely through the mean of the two frequency distributions of Y values.

The standard error of estimate $\bar{S}_{Y.W}$, calculated with $10 - 2 = 8$ degrees of freedom, is 0.704 ton. Within each subgroup of five observations, there are evidently four degrees of freedom. We may calculate the standard deviation of Y for $W = 1$ with four degrees of freedom; this value is 0.9159. The corresponding standard deviation for $W = 2$ is 0.3912. If we square each of these values, divide the sum by 2, and take the square root, we obtain 0.7044, which is the standard error of estimate from the regression equation. The following summarizes our results to date.

1. If there are only two values of the controlled variable, the regression line passes precisely through the mean values of each of the two clusters of observations on the dependent variable. If the factors responsible for variation in Y_i for a given value of W are random and normally distributed, the mean of the five sample observations is our best estimate of the expected value of Y in the population, *given* the specified value of W. If we could take more and more observations of Y_i for the given value of W, we would expect the mean value, $\overline{Y}$, to approach more and more closely the population value.

2. The standard error of estimate is evidently equivalent to an estimate of the standard deviation of $\hat{Y}$, *given* any specified value of W. The standard deviation of Y about the mean of the ten observations is 2.5750. The standard deviations of Y *given* W are, as we have seen, 0.9159 for $W = 1$ and 0.3912 for $W = 2$. The standard error of estimate, 0.7044, is roughly intermediate between the two standard deviations.

We should not be surprised to find that the least squares regression line passes through the means of the two frequency distributions. The very name "least squares" implies that the sum of squared deviations around the regression line is smaller than about any other possible straight line. (See also the derivation in Chapter 4, Appendix A.) In Chapter 3 we noted that the sum of squared deviations about the arithmetic mean of a frequency distribution was smaller than that about any other possible point. Since the least squares regression line must "select" some value of Y for $W = 1$, it selects the arithmetic mean in order to minimize the sum of the squared deviations for that particular cluster of five observations. Similarly, since any straight line is uniquely determined by two points, the regression line "selects" the mean value of the five observations for $W = 2$ as this second point, for this minimizes the sum of the squared deviations for the remaining cluster of observations.

Therefore, we might have worked intuitively from the definition of least squares and the fact that any two points determine the exact position of a straight line and leaped at once to the conclusion that the "*least squares*" regression line must pass through the means of the Y values associated with each of the two values of W.

The complete set of straight line regression equations, each based on ten observations, for successive pairs of values of W (1 and 2, 2 and 3, 3 and 4, 4 and 5, and 5 and 6 feet of irrigation water, respectively) is as follows:

Range of Values
of W	Regression Equation
1 and 2	$\hat{Y} = -2.7300 + 4.7180\,W$
2 and 3	$\hat{Y} = 2.3660 + 2.1700\,W$
3 and 4	$\hat{Y} = 2.4260 + 2.1500\,W$
4 and 5	$\hat{Y} = 9.0021 + 0.5060\,W$
5 and 6	$\hat{Y} = 5.6420 + 1.1780\,W$

In each instance the regression coefficient of Y upon W is equal to the difference between the means of the two clusters of yield observations.

Regression Analysis with Three or More Values of the Controlled Variable. Suppose now that we fit a least squares straight line to the 15 observations for $W = 1$, $W = 2$, and $W = 3$. The equation of this line is

$$(6.2) \qquad\qquad \hat{Y} = -1.0313 + 3.4440\,W$$

It is clear that the three mean values of clusters of five do not lie in a straight line. The straight line must pass through the point of means of the 15 values as a group; in this case, $\overline{Y} = 5.8567$ and $\overline{W} = 2$. The means $\overline{Y}_i$ ($i = 1, 2, 3$) in the three clusters are, respectively, 1.988, 6.706, and 8.876 tons; the values of the corresponding points on the regression line are 2.413, 5.857, and 9.301. The mean of the three $\overline{Y}_i$'s is also, of course, 5.857 tons.

This time the sum of squared deviations about the regression line must be somewhat larger than the sum of squared deviations about the three group means. The sum of squares about each of the three means would have four degrees of freedom so the three sets of observations combined would have 12 degrees of freedom about the group means. The regression equation, however, takes up two degrees of freedom, one of which can be assigned to its level (in passing through the mean of the 15 observations) and the other to its regression slope. One degree of freedom is unaccounted for; this one must be associated with the fact that the three means do not lie upon a straight line. This degree of freedom, then, is assignable to squared deviations of the group means from the regression line, each multiplied by the number of observations, five, associated with the particular value of W.

It may be noted that the slope of the present regression line, 3.4440, is the arithmetic average of the slope of 4.718 obtained for $W = 1$ and 2 and the slope of 2.17 obtained for $W = 2$ and 3. However, the standard error of estimate for the equation based on 15 observations is 0.9296, larger than either of those associated with the two equations based on ten observations each, namely, 0.7044 and 0.5554.

If we fit a least squares straight line to all 30 observations, the line itself uses up two degrees of freedom. There remain 28 degrees of freedom for variations about the regression line, but only 24 degrees of freedom are taken up by variations of individual Y values about the six group means. The other four degrees of freedom are associated with deviations of the six group means from the regression line. The standard error of estimate about this straight line is 1.4377, considerably larger than any other standard error of estimate in Table 6.9. The reason for this is discussed in Section 6.1.3.

The equation of the straight line fitted to all 30 observations is

$$(6.3) \qquad \hat{Y} = 1.7825 + 2.0068\,W$$

6.1.2 Standard Errors of Regression Constants and the Regression Line

Let us return briefly to a straight line fitted to the ten observations for $W = 1$ and $W = 2$. The mean value of Y for the ten observations is 4.347 tons. The sum of the squared deviations of Y_i about this general mean $\overline{Y}$ proves to be 59.62. The sum of squared deviations about the regression line (and hence about the two group means $\overline{Y}_1$ and $\overline{Y}_2$) is 3.97, leaving a remainder of 55.65.

Each of the two subgroup means departs from the over-all mean by 2.36 tons. If we square 2.36 (equals 5.565) and multiply by 10, for the weight of ten observations is concentrated at these two points, the result is equal to the remaining variance of 55.65 just mentioned. We note in passing that the total variance of Y has been broken down into two components, one representing variance about the group means $\overline{Y}_1$ and $\overline{Y}_2$ and the other the variance of the group means (weighted by the number of observations in each group) about the general mean, $\overline{Y}$.

The total variance of Y is equal to $59.62/9 = 6.613$; the square root of this, 2.56 tons, is the standard deviation of Y. The standard error of the mean, then, is given by

$$(6.4) \qquad S_{\overline{Y}} = \frac{2.56}{\sqrt{10}} = \frac{2.56}{3.162} = 0.81$$

In calculating $S_{\overline{Y}}$ we do not use any information about the regression relationship between Y and W.

The regression line evidently "accounts for" 55.65 of the total variance of 59.62, or more than 93%. At each point at which we have an experimental value of W, the estimate $\hat{Y}$ *given* W is equal to the subgroup mean $\overline{Y}_i$. In this instance the regression line accounts precisely for the difference of 4.718 between the two subgroup means. The expected value of Y given that $W = 2$ is 4.718 tons larger than the expected value of Y given that $W = 1$.

Standard Error of the General Mean $\overline{Y}$, *Given* $\overline{W}$. If we look at one of the subgroups of five observations by itself, we can calculate the standard error of the mean as

$$(6.5) \qquad s_{\overline{Y}_1} = \frac{s_{y_1}}{\sqrt{5}}, \qquad \text{where} \quad s_{y_1} = \left(\frac{\sum\limits_{i=1}^{5} (Y_{i1} - \overline{Y}_1)^2}{5 - 1} \right)^{\frac{1}{2}}$$

We find that $s_{\overline{Y}_1} = 0.4097$ and $s_{\overline{Y}_2} = 0.1751$. The ratio of the variances

$$s_{y_1}^2 / s_{y_2}^2 = 3.3569/0.6130 = 5.41$$

is not significant at the 5% level, so we pool the variances for the two groups of observations and obtain for the standard error of the general mean $\overline{Y}$

$$s_{\overline{Y}} = \frac{0.7044}{\sqrt{10}} = \frac{0.7044}{3.162} = 0.2228$$

The general mean of Y, $\overline{Y}$, in this instance is intermediate between the two subgroup means. The standard error of each group mean taken separately is an estimate of our degree of uncertainty concerning the population value of $\hat{Y}$ for a particular value of W. An assumption of ordinary least squares regression is that the variance of residuals from regression in the population is constant for all values of the independent variable. The standard errors of the two subgroup means are somewhat different in the sample, but the difference is not statistically significant at the 5% level so there is no reason not to accept the usual automatic pooling of variances implied in regression analysis.

Thus, when W is at its mean value of 1.5 feet of irrigation water, we may write

$$(6.6) \qquad \overline{Y} \text{ (given } \overline{W} = 1.5) = 4.367 \pm 0.2228$$

as a confidence interval in making inferences concerning the expected value of Y in the population *given* $W = 1.5$. (The "population" in this instance may be thought of as a population of all possible values of Y associated with values of W between 1 and 2.) The standard error of $\overline{Y}$ given $\overline{W}$ is measured in the vertical direction and in units of Y. If we drew successive samples of 10, with five observations for each of the two values of W ($W = 1$ and $W = 2$), $\overline{W}$ would always equal 1.5, but $\overline{Y}$ *given* $\overline{W}$ could vary randomly about its population value.

Standard Error of the Regression Coefficient (Slope) b. The standard error of the slope of the regression line involves some different considerations.

In this particular case, the regression line also passes through each of the group means $\bar{Y}_1$ and $\bar{Y}_2$. Hence $\hat{Y}_1$ (given $W = 1$) $= \bar{Y}_1$ and $\hat{Y}_2$ (given $W = 2$) $= \bar{Y}_2$. The standard error of estimate is essentially an average of the standard deviations s_{y_1} and s_{y_2}:

$$\bar{S}_{Y.W} = \sqrt{\frac{4s_{y_1}{}^2 + 4s_{y_2}{}^2}{8}} = 0.7044$$

The standard error of each of the group means may be approximated as

$$s_{\bar{Y}_1} = s_{\bar{Y}_2} = \frac{0.7044}{\sqrt{5}} = \frac{0.7044}{2.236} = 0.317$$

One end of the regression line rests on the point ($\bar{Y}_1$, $W = 1$) and the other end on the point ($\bar{Y}_2$, $W = 2$). In successive samples of 10, the Y coordinate of each endpoint of the regression line would have a sampling distribution with 0.317 as its standard error. By assumption, the variations of individual observations around the population values of $\hat{Y}_1$ and $\hat{Y}_2$ are random and uncorrelated between the two subgroups. Hence the standard error of the *difference* between the two endpoints of the regression line is approximately equal to the standard error of the difference between the two means $\bar{Y}_1$ and $\bar{Y}_2$:

$$s_{(\bar{Y}_2 - \bar{Y}_1)} = \sqrt{s_{\bar{Y}_1}{}^2 + s_{\bar{Y}_2}{}^2} = \sqrt{2s_{\bar{Y}_1}{}^2}$$

Therefore

$$s_{(\bar{Y}_2 - \bar{Y}_1)} = \sqrt{2(0.317)^2} = \sqrt{2(0.100)} = \sqrt{0.20} = 0.45$$

The regression slope is measured as the number of units increase in Y per one unit increase in W. Hence our uncertainty as to the slope of the population regression as estimated from a particular sample must be expressed in the same dimensions, that is, a change in Y per unit change in W. In this instance, W differs by 1.0 between the endpoints in question, so our measure of uncertainty concerning the regression slope is simply $0.45/1.0 = 0.45$. From Table 6.9 we see that this is indeed the value of the standard error of the regression slope as calculated from the usual formula.

Because the sampling error of the regression slope has the dimensions or units Y/W, our uncertainty as to the actual level of $\hat{Y}$ given W increases in direct proportion as W departs from its general mean of 1.5, assuming the point of means to be a fixed value. When $w = (W - \bar{W}) = 0$, this component of our uncertainty concerning $\hat{Y}$ is reduced to zero.

Standard Error of $\hat{Y}$, the Expected Value of Y Given Any Specified Value of W. We have seen that our estimate of the general population mean based on a sample of 10 has a sampling error of about 0.22. If the slope of the regression line in successive samples is regarded as fixed, the standard error of $\overline{Y}$ given $\overline{W}$ reflects shifts in this line up and down parallel to the Y axis. Under our assumptions of random sampling and constant variance of residuals in the population, the variances of these two components of uncertainty concerning $\hat{Y}$ *given* W combine additively. The square root of the sum of these variances, which varies with $w = W - \overline{W}$, is given by (6.7):

(6.7) $$s_{\hat{Y}} = \sqrt{s_{\overline{Y}}^2 + (s_b w)^2}$$

This measure $s_{\hat{Y}}$ is sometimes called the *standard error of the function or of the regression line.*

If we draw two curves, one on either side of the regression line, at a distance $2s_{\hat{Y}}$ from it, we obtain results of the type shown in Figure 6.1.

Note again how the two components of the standard error of $\hat{Y}$ operate:

1. If $\overline{Y}$ given $\overline{W}$ were fixed, the error zones in Figure 6.1b would be straight lines passing through the point of means, with slopes equal to $b \pm 2s_b$.[1]

2. Conversely, if the slope were measured without error, the error zone reflecting the standard error of $\overline{Y}$ given $\overline{W}$ would be two lines parallel to the sample regression line itself, at vertical distances of $2s_{Y.W}$ above and below it.

3. When the two components are combined additively and the square root of the sum is extracted, we obtain the curved error boundaries or confidence intervals shown in the figure. Obviously, $s_{\hat{Y}}$ is smallest at the point of means and increases progressively as the independent variable departs farther and farther from its own mean. It is also clear that the error formula for a straight line is symmetrical for deviations of the independent variable from its mean in either direction.

On logical grounds, unless we are quite sure from other evidence that the particular equation we choose for a sample regression applies to the relationship between the variables over an unlimited range of values of the independent variable, we are not justified in extrapolating the regression line or its confidence interval beyond the range of our actual experiment. In Figure 6.1, this advice is ignored for expository purposes, so that the regression lines and confidence intervals are shown in each instance extending from $W = 1$ to $W = 6$. In Figure 6.1b and d, $\overline{W} = 3.5$ and is equidistant from $W = 1$ and $W = 6$. Hence the confidence intervals are symmetrical about $\overline{W}$.

In part *a*, in which $\overline{W} = 1.5$, the confidence interval widens considerably

---

[1] In Figure 6.1 our zones all reflect two standard errors on either side of the regression line.

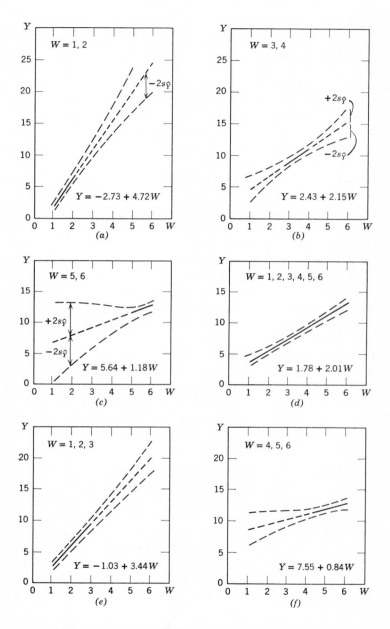

Figure 6.1 Alfalfa yields and irrigation water applied: effects of selecting different levels and ranges of values of the independent variable and fitting linear as well as parabolic regressions.

as we reach the higher values of W. In part e, in which $\overline{W} = 2.0$, the general pattern of the confidence interval is similar, but the larger values of W are associated with smaller deviations w ($= W - 2$) and have less "leverage" than when $w = W - 1.5$.

In principle and arithmetic, parts c and f are counterparts of a and e. However, the slopes of the sample regressions for $W = 4$ through $W = 6$ are much more nearly horizontal than those for smaller values of W. Hence in parts c and f, when we use a confidence interval of plus or minus $2s_{\hat{Y}}$ the upper or positive bound is nearly horizontal in part f and actually slopes downward slightly from left to right in part c.

Standard Error of Forecast of an Individual Value of Y. If we assume that an arithmetic straight line designates the form of the relationship of Y to W in the parent population, (6.6) still expresses our uncertainty only about the *expected value* of Y for given values of W, namely, $\hat{Y} = a + bW$.

Before we touched on the subject of sampling error, we pointed out that a least squares regression line divides the original sum of squares of deviations of the dependent variable about its general mean into two components, one consisting of the sum of squared deviations of $\hat{Y}$ from $\overline{Y}$ and the other composed of the sum of squared deviations of Y from $\hat{Y}$ i.e. from the regression line. The "root mean square" of the latter deviations is the standard error of estimate. If deviations from regression in the parent population are randomly and approximately normally distributed, about two-thirds of the sample residuals will fall within a zone of plus or minus one standard error of estimate around the sample regression line. The squared standard error of estimate in a sample is taken as an estimate of the corresponding variance of deviations from regression in the population.

Since a basic assumption of the regression model is that the values of the dependent variable are subject to random variation in addition to the systematic effect of the independent variable, the kind of uncertainty about future individual values of Y expressed in $\overline{S}_{y.w}$ would exist even if we knew (1) the exact regression relationship in the population and (2) the exact standard deviation of residuals of Y about this regression. The standard error of estimate is not affected systematically by increases in sample size.

This contrasts with the two components of the standard error of the regression line. In squared form, each of these components has n, the number of observations in the sample, in its denominator. Hence, as n approaches infinity, each of the two components of $s_{\hat{Y}}$, namely $s_{\overline{Y}}$ and s_b, approaches zero. If we imagine ourselves to be drawing observations from the population and not replacing them, and further assume that the population is finite (for example, the number of individual human beings living in the United States on January 1, 1966), we could eventually exhaust the entire population and compute a "sample" regression identical with that in the entire population. Our standard error of estimate would then be identical with the random component of the individual values of Y given W in the population, but our "sampling errors" of the mean and the regression slope would have disappeared.

In any finite sample, however, we must deal with all three error components in establishing confidence intervals for our forecasts of the values of new individual observations drawn randomly from the original parent population. In squared form this measure, the standard error of forecast, is

$$(6.8) \qquad s_{Y'}{}^2 = \bar{S}_{Y.W}{}^2 + s_{Y.\overline{W}}{}^2 + (s_b w)^2$$

The square root of this expression, $s_{Y'}$, gives us the desired estimate of the combined uncertainty (or confidence interval) applicable to new individual observations not included in the original sample but drawn from the same population. In our alfalfa yield example, $\hat{Y} \pm s_{Y'}$ would be our estimate of the range within which about two-thirds of the values of Y would fall, *for specified values of W*, in additional experiments.

In assuming that factors other than W operating on Y are of a random character, we assume away the possibility of a multiple regression rather than a simple regression relationship. In Chapter 4 and its appendices we saw that the arithmetic involved in fitting a second-degree parabola by least squares was identical with the arithmetic employed in fitting a three-variable linear regression equation or "regression plane" in three dimensions. Similarly, standard error formulas can be extended to each coefficient of a second-degree parabola or a linear multiple regression equation. The same sampling considerations lead to estimates of the standard error of the regression equation and the standard error of forecast for parabolas and linear equations with two or more independent variables. These formulas will not be elaborated at this point but will be touched upon in the Appendix A to this chapter and in Chapter 7 when we deal with multiple regression.

6.1.3 *The Regression Model for a Parabolic Relationship*

The error zones or confidence intervals shown in Figure 6.1 demonstrate one of the considerations underlying the dangers of extrapolating a regression line beyond one's data. However, every part of Figure 6.1 implicitly makes the charitable assumption that the true relationship between Y and W in the parent population is an arithmetic straight line. Actually, parts *a* and *c* represent the first and last segments of Figure 6.2*b*. Each regression line, then, is a linear approximation, based on ten observations, to a short segment of a true relationship that is parabolic. In Figure 6.1*a*, the *lower* bound of the

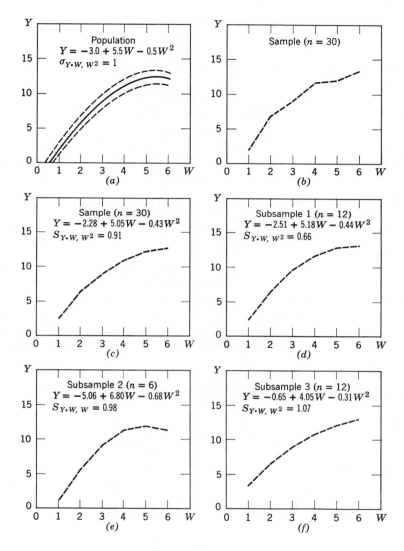

Figure 6.2 Alfalfa yields and irrigation water applied: parabolic regressions in population, in sample of 30 observations, and in proportional subsamples of six and 12 observations covering the complete range of values of the independent variable.

▬▬▬ Range of observations to which regression was fitted.
▬ ▬ ▬ Extrapolation of regression beyond range of subsample to which fitted.
– – – Regression line $\pm 2s_F$, where s_F is the standard error of the function at the specified value of W.

confidence interval for $W = 6$ is 21.56 tons. Yet in Table 6.1, the *highest* single value among our 30 original observations is only 14.37 tons. Clearly, any statement we might make as to probable values of $\hat{Y}$ given $W = 6$ on the basis of part *a* would be completely inapplicable to the true parabolic relationship in the population. Similarly, in Figure 6.2*f*, the lower bound of the confidence interval for $W = 1$ is 5.88, whereas the highest value of Y among the five sample observations for $W = 1$ is 2.87.

Hence, if we have no rigorous theory to guide us but simply assume a particular form of regression equation arbitrarily, we should not make extrapolations and probability statements any considerable distance beyond the range of our original observations. Within that range, certain tests can be made as to whether the probable relationship in the parent population is nonlinear. In our particular example, we could not possibly test an assumption of nonlinearity if our observations come from only two values of W. The conclusiveness of such a test would depend on the degree of curvature of the true relationship and the range from which our sample observations are drawn.

The 30 observations in Table 6.1 were generated by means of the model summarized in Figure 6.2*a*. For each value of W, the expected value of Y, $\hat{Y}$, was calculated from the "population regression," $\hat{Y} = -3.0 + 5.5W - 0.5W^2$. For example, when $W = 1$, $\hat{Y} = 2.0$. Then, 30 drawings from a table of random numbers were identified with class intervals of a normal distribution with a standard deviation of 1.0. These "random deviations" were added algebraically to the values of $\hat{Y}$, which were 2, 6, 9, 11, 12, and 12 for $W = 1, 2, 3, 4, 5$, and 6, respectively.

The random variation in the 30 observations consists entirely of random deviations from the fixed population regression curve, $\hat{Y} = -3.0 + 5.5W - 0.5W^2$. The deviations of the group means from the population values of $\hat{Y}$ (2, 6, 9, 11, 12, 12) must also be attributed to these random elements in the individual observations. The random component of the observations is also responsible for the standard error of estimate, the standard error of the mean of the 30 observations, and the standard errors or degrees of uncertainty attached to the three constants of the sample regression equation.

The least squares parabola fitted to the sample of 30 observations is

$$(6.9) \qquad \hat{Y} = -2.28 + 5.05W - 0.43W^2$$
$$(0.73) \quad (0.48) \qquad (0.07)$$

The numbers in parentheses below the three regression constants are the corresponding standard errors. Each of the three coefficients is within about one standard error of the "true" relationship in the parent population. If we considered the distribution of each coefficient separately in a large number of samples of 30 observations, we would expect about two-thirds of the sample coefficients to lie within plus or minus one standard error of the population value. It appears that the differences between the sample regression and the true population value are consistent with the random procedure by which deviations from the population regression were derived.

Some additional comments on the results of this exercise are contained in Appendix B of this chapter.

6.2   THE REGRESSION MODEL: AN INTERMEDIATE CASE— EXPERIMENTAL OR NONEXPERIMENTAL?

Table 6.2 is based on an auto trip by the author. A total of 1367 miles was traveled. The gas tank was filled at the beginning of the trip and was refilled six times along the way. At each refueling stop, we recorded the number of miles traveled, the number of gallons of gasoline needed to refill the tank, the total charge for that amount of gasoline, and the price per gallon of this replacement fuel.

The circumstances of this example seem quite different from those of a controlled biological experiment such as we have previously discussed. In what sense does the present example represent an experiment?

The controlled or independent variable was mileage traveled. Since service stations on some of the turnpikes were several miles apart, it was not possible to specify the exact values of this variable X_2 in advance, but this is immaterial, as will be shown later. The dependent variable was clearly "quantity of gasoline used" in traveling the observed mileage.

Table 6.2   Miles Traveled and Gallons of Gasoline Used
(Actual Data)

Observation Number	X_1, Gallons of Gasoline Used	X_2, Miles Traveled
1	11.3	184
2	12.9	204
3	15.7	252
4	17.5	275
5	11.6	184
6	15.6	268

Even if the original selection of service stations, and hence of the successive values of X_2, were quite arbitrary, once they had been selected, we could, in principle, have the same driver repeat the drive several times, each time stopping at the same six service stations. Hence the six values of X_2 would be the same in all cases; the roads traveled and the automobile and driver would be the same; and we would generate as many values of the quantity of gasoline used, X_1, as there were repetitions of the same experiment. We conclude therefore that the values of X_2 may be treated in the same fashion as the values of W in our previous example.

What are the random or stochastic elements in the amounts of gasoline used, X_1? A number of possible sources come to mind including (1) errors of measurement (different attendants had somewhat different notions as to just when the tank was "full"); (2) differences in driving conditions; and (3) differences in quality of gasoline.

Our basic hypothesis in the subsequent analysis is that there is a straight line relationship between miles traveled and gasoline consumed. It also seems reasonable to expect that the constant term in the least squares straight line will not differ significantly from zero.

With the price of gasoline averaging around 30 cents a gallon, attendants' behavior, such as stopping the meter on the gasoline tank at a figure ending in five cents or even ten cents, should not have occasioned a standard error of "measurement" of more than 0.2 to 0.3 gallons. An experienced automotive engineer or mechanic could perhaps estimate the orders of magnitude of variation in X_1 that might be expected from the other possible sources of variation.

A least squares regression line fitted to the six observations gives us

$$(6.10) \qquad X_1 = 0.681997 + 0.058894 X_2$$
$$ (1.381615) \quad (0.005980)$$

The standard error of estimate is 0.5620 gallons, and $r^2 = 0.9604$.

The relationship seems very close, as we expected, and the standard error of estimate of a little more than half a gallon seems moderate in relation to the average amount of gasoline used between stops, 14.1 gallons. The constant term of the regression equation is considerably smaller than its standard error, so our hypothesis that the relationship between X_1 and X_2 is a proportional one is certainly not overturned. The regression slope, 0.059 gallons per mile, is not very different from that of a line drawn from the origin through the point of means, $X_1 = 14.1$ gallons and $X_2 = 227.833$ miles traveled. The slope of the latter line would be approximately 0.062 gallons per mile and its reciprocal would be slightly over 16 miles per gallon.

6.2.1 *Effects of the Standard Deviation of the Independent Variable upon Sampling Errors*

We have already given a formula for the standard error of the regression slope. However, the hypothetical cases A and B in Table 6.3 may serve to make the implications perfectly clear.

In case A, we specified two values of X_2, 210 miles and 240 miles, respectively; we also specified corresponding population values of X_1, gasoline consumption, at 14.0 and 16.0 gallons. We then drew random numbers from a population with a variance of 1, and added these to the originally specified values (population values) of X_1. In case B, we specified the two values of X_2 as 150 and 270 miles, respectively, and corresponding population values of gasoline consumption at 10.0 and 18.0 gallons, respectively. The random deviations added (algebraically) to the lower value of X_1 in case A were also added to the lower value in B. Similarly, the deviations added to the higher value of X_1 in case A were also added to the higher value of X_1 in B. The results of fitting an arithmetic straight regression line to each of these cases follows.

Case A

(6.11)
$$\hat{X}_1 = -0.43655 + 0.06933 X_2$$
$$(3.93784) \quad (0.01746)$$

The standard error of estimate is 0.6416 and $r^2 = 0.7976$.

Case B

(6.12)
$$\hat{X}_1 = 0.002334 + 0.067333 X_2$$
$$(0.953491) \quad (0.004366)$$

The standard error of estimate is 0.6416, precisely as in case A, but the value of r^2 is much higher, 0.9835.

In case A, the sum of squared deviations of X_2 about $\bar{X}_2$ is 1350, compared with 21,600 in B. If we divide by six and take the square root of the result, we have standard deviations (*not* adjusted for degrees of freedom) of 15 in case A and 60 in B. These are in the ratio of one to four; if each standard deviation were adjusted for degrees of freedom in the ratio $\sqrt{\frac{6}{5}}$) the ratio of the two standard deviations would be unchanged.

A little arithmetic will show that the standard error of the regression coefficient in case A is four times as large as the standard error of the regression slope in B. This is the reciprocal of the ratio of the two standard deviations of X_2, which is expected since the standard deviation of X_2 appears in the *denominator* of the formula for s_b.

The standard error of the constant term in case A is *roughly* four times as large as the corresponding error in case B. The standard error of $\bar{X}_1$ given

Table 6.3   Miles Traveled and Gasoline Used
(Hypothetical Data)

Observation Number	X_1, Gallons Used	X_2, Miles Traveled
	Case A	
1	14.62	210
2	14.62	210
3	13.13	210
4	15.87	240
5	16.37	240
6	16.37	240
	Case B	
7	10.62	150
8	10.62	150
9	9.13	150
10	17.87	270
11	18.37	270
12	18.37	270

$\bar{X}_2$ would be precisely four times as large in case A as in case B. However, the mean value of X_2 in case A is 225 miles compared with 210 miles in case B, and this factor causes the standard error of the constant term to be slightly different than in the ratio of four to one.

6.2.2 Further Aspects of the Regression Model with Experimental Observations: The Meaning of Best Linear Unbiased Estimates

The sample mean is the best linear unbiased estimate of the population mean under conditions of random sampling. It is best in the sense that it has *minimum* variance; this is related to the fact that the sum of squared deviations about the arithmetic mean of a frequency distribution is smaller than that about any other possible point. As one degree of freedom would be used up in the arbitrary selection of any other point, the degrees of freedom associated with the sum of squares would be the same, $n - 1$, regardless of what point of origin was selected. Hence the variance and standard error of the arithmetic mean would also be smaller than the variance and standard error of any other point or value which might be used as an estimator of the population mean.

The arithmetic mean is a *linear* estimate in the sense that the relationship connecting the individual values with the arithmetic mean makes the latter a linear function of the individual observations. In calculating the arithmetic mean, each observation gets a weight of 1; thus if there are five observations, we might show the linear relationship between the arithmetic mean and the individual observations as follows:

(6.13)

$$\hat{X} = 0 + 1X_1$$
$$\hat{X} = 0 + 1X_2$$
$$\hat{X} = 0 + 1X_3$$
$$\hat{X} = 0 + 1X_4$$
$$\hat{X} = 0 + 1X_5$$

Total $$5\hat{X} = 0 + 1 \cdot \sum_{i=1}^{5} X_i$$

Means $$\bar{X} = 0 + 1 \cdot \frac{\sum_{i=1}^{5} X_i}{5}$$

The form of the right-hand members of the foregoing equations is designed to show that $\hat{X}_1$ as estimated from a straight line regression equation is a linear function of the individual values of the independent variable X_2. And this concept can be extended to regression equations in any number of variables provided that the coefficients which are to be determined by least squares enter linearly, that is, only in the original or "first power" form. In a second-degree parabola, even though X_2 enters in squared form, the *coefficient* of this term is constant for all values of $X_2{}^2$; furthermore we do not have two regression coefficients, or a slope coefficient and a constant term, appearing multiplicatively in any term of the least squares regression formula of a parabola.

The arithmetic mean is an *unbiased* estimate of the population mean in the sense that, under conditions of random sampling, we can reduce the standard error of the mean as far as we like simply by increasing the size of the sample. We may say that the arithmetic mean converges in probability to the population mean as n, the sample size, approaches infinity. The same property is shared by the regression estimate $\hat{X}_1$ from any specified value of X_2 provided that the values of X_1 *given* X_2 result from a random sampling procedure. Here the regression equation itself is the best linear unbiased estimator of the expected value of the dependent variable *given* specified values of the independent variable or variables.

We have seen how the sample size n enters the denominator of the standard error formulas for the regression slope or slopes and the constant term.

Clearly, as n increases indefinitely, each of these standard errors decreases in the ratio $\sqrt{1/n}$ and can be made as small as we like if we are at liberty to make n indefinitely large.

6.3 THE REGRESSION MODEL: NONEXPERIMENTAL OBSERVATIONS

Most of the data with which economists work are nonexperimental in nature. Economic statisticians are beginning to display ingenuity in designing controlled experiments where these are feasible. But macroeconomic time series belong to history—we cannot go back and rerun the 1930s with different sets of values of controlled variables. The owner of a chain of stores might conceivably agree to run some of them in a tight experimental design, but we cannot expect to find deliberate experimental behavior in aggregative time series at national or industrial levels.

The mechanics and calculations of regression analysis for nonexperimental data are all precisely the same as for experimental data; only the interpretations are different. We will not bother with a new example at this point. We might simply mention that the beef demand equation of Chapter 4 fits the description of the nonexperimental case and there will be at least one other example of it in Chapter 7, as well as in subsequent chapters.

Astronomers and meteorologists as well as economists must form judgments on the basis of nonexperimental data. And the nature and degree of control in a "controlled" experiment is by no means absolute in most instances. The designers of an elaborate and classically successful experiment on the response of crop yields to fertilizer made the following comment:

"The predictions apply to particular soils in a particular year; production surfaces obtained under other rainfall and soil conditions can be expected to differ from those obtained in the experiments recorded. . . . Traditional experimental procedures (wherein a few rates of one or more nutrients are applied) also refer to the rainfall, climatic, insect and crop conditions of the particular year."[2]

Nonexperimental data in the form of economic time series are a special case. There is only one actual observation available for a given period and no way of generating others. Consider our beef consumption example from Chapter 4.

[2] Earl O. Heady, John T. Pesek, and William G. Brown, "Crop Response Surfaces and Economic Optima in Fertilizer Use," *Iowa Ag. Exp. Sta. Res. Bul. 424*, p. 325 (March 1955).

The quantity of beef sold nationally in a given year is largely predetermined in the previous year or two. Therefore, we may regard the consumption of beef as essentially a predetermined variable, much like the arbitrarily assigned values of W in the alfalfa yield experiment. But in the same year other variables which influenced the price of beef *might have taken* any of a number of combinations of values, resulting in random deviations of price, P, about its average regression on the consumption of beef, Q_b. We could think of these excluded variables as "demand curve shifters" or simply "disturbances."

If other variables such as the supply of pork, Q_p, and disposable personal income, Y, are correlated with residuals from the regression equation $P = f(Q_{beef})$, we have a multiple regression problem. We estimate the systematic effects of pork supplies and disposable income by including them in the regression equation and assume that the remaining residuals from the equation $P = f(Q_b, Q_p, Y)$ result from a number of minor and essentially random causes.

These would include errors of measurement in P as well as effects of weather, temperature, changes in income distribution, and any other relevant factors. The effects of these other variables and factors, presumed to be individually small, provide the stochastic element in the dependent variable P. The residuals from the regression equation in the period for which that equation was fitted are regarded as random drawings from the population of residuals which could have been generated by all these minor sources of variability.

In this fashion, we can give our beef example a probability interpretation for the 1949–1960 period. For subsequent years, we must bring judgment and new information to bear on the question of how rapidly the regression coefficients (parameters) of the population may be changing and whether 1961–1970 residuals from the 1949–1960 regression line may still be regarded as "random drawings" from the same probability distribution that existed in 1949–1960.

One of the points most frequently overlooked by economists until recent years was the fact that the correlation coefficient and the standard errors of the regression constants were quite sensitive to changes in the standard deviations of the independent variables. This was demonstrated clearly in cases A and B of our hypothetical example on gasoline mileage when an increase in the standard deviation of X_2 in the ratio of four to one reduced s_b to one-fourth of its previous level and raised r^2 from 0.7976 to 0.9835.

Close analogies exist in economic time series. In the United States during 1922–1941, disposable personal income varied over a wide range. And two of the worst droughts in recorded history forced liquidation of cattle and hog numbers during the mid-1930s and resulted in much greater variations in the consumption of livestock products from year to year than has been typical in most other periods. The statistical consequences of these unusually wide ranges of consumption and income were similar to those of the conscious selection of a wide range of values of the controlled variables in an experiment.

Standard errors of quantity-income and price-income regression coefficients in consumer demand functions for livestock products using *first differences* (year-to-year changes) in disposable personal income were quite small in the 1922–1941 period. The standard errors of similar coefficients in 1949–1960 are larger primarily because of the much smaller year-to-year changes in disposable income in the later period.

6.4   THE CORRELATION MODEL

The calculations involved in the correlation model are the same as in the regression model, but the interpretation and bases for inference are somewhat different. Appendix C explains the correlation model and its integral relationship with the bivariate normal distribution.

6.5   AUTOCORRELATION: A SPECIAL PROBLEM IN REGRESSION ANALYSIS OF TIME SERIES

One assumption in least squares regression analysis is that, in the parent population, the random elements in successive observations are independent of one another (that is, uncorrelated). The designs of sample surveys and controlled experiments are intended to achieve this result and others.

But time series observations appear in a unique sequence which the investigator cannot control. In economic time series, the original observations frequently show strong trends and cycles, so that successive observations show high positive correlation—if X_t is above the mean of the series, X_{t+1} is also above the mean. This situation can also be illustrated in meteorological data.

Consider the following series of average monthly temperatures (in degrees Fahrenheit):

January	30	May	65	September	65
February	35	June	70	October	55
March	45	July	75	November	45
April	55	August	70	December	35

It is clear that the successive monthly temperatures tend to be positively correlated. We may think in terms of a correlation coefficient between successive deviations of monthly temperatures from their annual average. Under such circumstances of *positive autocorrelation*, the differences between the temperatures in successive months may be considerably smaller than the deviations of the monthly temperatures from the annual average. A very rough calculation indicates that the standard deviation of the first differences in the foregoing series is less than half as large as the standard deviation of the original values. The *variance* of the first differences is only about one-fourth as large as the variance of the original observations.

If the original observations were randomly ordered over time, the ratio of variances would be very different from what it is in the temperature series. If the time series formed by the original values of a variable is random, in the sense that successive deviations from the mean have an expected correlation of zero in the parent population, the expected value of $(x_{t+1} - x_t)^2$ is equal to $x_{t+1}^2 + x_t^2$, or $2x_t^2$. Hence, reasoning in the reverse direction, we may say that if the variance of the first differences of a series is approximately twice as large as the variance of the original series itself, the original series is not significantly *autocorrelated*.

In the regression model, we are not disturbed by trends or cycles in the independent variables.[3] We do not require that they be random drawings. If the independent variable X in simple straight line regression contains a major cycle, $\hat{Y} (= a + bX)$ will contain precisely the same cycle multiplied by the regression coefficient b. This is an automatic consequence of the nonrandom pattern in X, so we do not require that the successive values of $\hat{Y}$ be random.

But the *deviations* $z = Y - \hat{Y}$ *around the regression line* should be random because all of the standard error formulas in regression analysis are predicated on the assumption that the squared standard error of estimate, $\bar{S}_{Y.X}^2$, is an unbiased estimate of the variance s_u^2 of the individual Y values about the population regression $Y = \alpha + \beta X + u$. If this is so, the sample regression coefficients a and b can be interpreted as unbiased estimates of the population parameters α and β and we can make the usual probability statements based on the standard errors of a and b.

Perhaps we can make this clear in terms of the standard error of estimate, $\bar{S}_{Y.X}$, for it enters into the formulas for s_a and s_b and is the only element in those formulas that should be random or stochastic in regression theory. Assume that the monthly temperature series just cited, is in fact a time sequence of residuals from a regression equation. The standard error of estimate calculated from these 12 residuals is

$$\bar{S}_{Y.X}^2 = \frac{12}{10} \left[\frac{37,325}{12} - (53.75)^2 \right] = (3114.2 - 2889.1) \frac{12}{10}$$

$$= 22.51(12) = 270.12 \quad \text{and} \quad \bar{S}_{Y.X} = 16.4$$

[3] Except as these attributes *may* be associated with multicollinearity—a problem logically separate from autocorrelation.

Our conventional probability statement would be that, regardless of the value of z_t, we would expect the value of z_{t+1} to fall within the range -16 to 16 about two-thirds of the time in repeated random drawings. The values of z_t and of $\pm \bar{S}_{Y.X}$ compare as follows (rounded to the nearest integer):

	z_t	$\pm \bar{S}_{Y.X}$
January	-24	-16–16
February	-19	-16–16
March	-9	-16–16
April	1	-16–16
May	11	-16–16
June	16	-16–16
July	21	-16–16
August	16	-16–16
September	11	-16–16
October	1	-16–16
November	-9	-16–16
December	-19	-16–16

If the z_t were really generated by a 12-month seasonal process that repeated the 12 values of z_t exactly in every year, our conventional probability statement about z_{t+1} would be *wrong* when z_{t+1} refers to January, February, July, or December because no value of z_{t+1} for these months would ever fall within $\pm \bar{S}_{Y.X}$. The conventional statement would be *wrong* when z_{t+1} refers to March, April, May, September, October, or November because no value of z_{t+1} would ever fall outside the range $\pm \bar{S}_{Y.X}$. Our forecasting record for January, February, July, and December would be much worse and for six other months much better than the value of $\bar{S}_{Y.X}$ would lead us to expect.

Experience has, of course, put us on guard in dealing with seasonal patterns. But consider the pattern of residuals about the straight line demand equation for beef in Table 4.4, based on annual data. The residuals, rounded, form the time sequence shown in Table 6.4.

The runs of positive and negative values of z_t are not *highly* improbable in a basically random series if we consider only their signs. But also consider that z_t shows a run of seven consecutive positive year-to-year changes (1953 to 1960), that is, a series of eight observations each one of which is larger in the algebraic sense than its immediate predecessor. Intuitively it would seem that such a sequence would not appear oftener than one out of 256 times in random samples of eight observations, so we cannot regard z_t as random.[4] Similarly, the residuals for 1958, 1959, and 1960 all lie between

---

[4] The 1/256 figure is not intended as a rigorous probability statement but simply as an intuitive order of magnitude.

Table 6.4

Year	(1) z_t	(2) z_t^2	(3) $\pm \bar{S}_{Y.x}$	(4) $\Delta z = (z_{t+1} - z_t)$	(5) $(\Delta z)^2$
1949	−9	81	−5–5	−	−
1950	−2	4	−5–5	7	49
1951	−1	1	−5–5	1	1
1952	1	1	−5–5	2	4
1953	−4	16	−5–5	−5	25
1954	−3	9	−5–5	1	1
1955	−2	4	−5–5	1	1
1956	−1	1	−5–5	1	1
1957	1	1	−5–5	2	4
1958	5	25	−5–5	4	16
1959	7	49	−5–5	2	4
1960	8	64	−5–5	1	1
$\sum\limits_{t=1}^{12} z_t$	0	256		17	107

$\bar{S}_{Y.x}$ and $2\bar{S}_{Y.x}$ *above* the regression line. In random sampling from a normal distribution with $\sigma = 5$, the probability of each of these observations would be about 1/6 and the probability of the 3-value sequence would be about $1/6^3 = 1/216$. The 1949 value of z_t is nearly $2\bar{S}_{Y.x}$ below the regression line and the 1958, 1959, and 1960 values average about $1.3\bar{S}_{Y.x}$ above the regression line. If we were using the 1949–1960 equation $\hat{Y} = a + bX$ to forecast Y in 1961, 1962, and 1963 we would be predicting the expected value of z_t as zero in each year, even though the 1958–1960 values were all at least five cents above the regression line and apparently on a rising trend.

Perhaps this illustration is enough to show that autocorrelation can be a serious problem even in annual data and can turn our usual probability statements about the regression equation into sheer nonsense. Hence a test for autocorrelation in the residuals should always be run in connection with regression analyses based on time series.

Measures of autocorrelation which take into account all the residuals in the sample simultaneously are available and are customarily used. We shall mention here only the von Neumann ratio δ (see Table 6.5).

The von Neumann ratio is based on the proposition previously mentioned that the expected value of the variance of the first differences of a random time series is twice as large as the variance of the original series. In practice

Table 6.5 5 and 1 Percent Significance Points for the Ratio of the Mean Square Successive Difference to the Variance[a]

N	Values of K		Values of K'		N	Values of K		Values of K'	
	$P = 0.01$	$P = 0.05$	$P = 0.05$	$P = 0.01$		$P = 0.01$	$P = 0.05$	$P = 0.05$	$P = 0.01$
4	0.8341	1.0406	4.2927	4.4992	33	1.2667	1.4885	2.6365	2.8583
5	0.6724	1.0255	3.9745	4.3276	34	1.2761	1.4951	2.6262	2.8451
6	0.6738	1.0682	3.7318	4.1262	35	1.2852	1.5014	2.6163	2.8324
7	0.7163	1.0919	3.5748	3.9504	36	1.2940	1.5075	2.6068	2.8202
8	0.7575	1.1228	3.4486	3.8139	37	1.3025	1.5135	2.5977	2.8085
9	0.7974	1.1524	3.3476	3.7025	38	1.3108	1.5193	2.5889	2.7973
10	0.8353	1.1803	3.2642	3.6091	39	1.3188	1.5249	2.5804	2.7865
11	0.8706	1.2062	3.1938	3.5294	40	1.3266	1.5304	2.5722	2.7760
12	0.9033	1.2301	3.1335	3.4603	41	1.3342	1.5357	2.5643	2.7658
13	0.9336	1.2521	3.0812	3.3996	42	1.3415	1.5408	2.5567	2.7560
14	0.9618	1.2725	3.0352	3.3458	43	1.3486	1.5458	2.5494	2.7466
15	0.9880	1.2914	2.9943	3.2977	44	1.3554	1.5506	2.5424	2.7376
16	1.0124	1.3090	2.9577	3.2543	45	1.3620	1.5552	2.5357	2.7289
17	1.0352	1.3253	2.9247	3.2148	46	1.3684	1.5596	2.5293	2.7205
18	1.0566	1.3405	2.8948	3.1787	47	1.3745	1.5638	2.5232	2.7125

Table 6.5 (continued)

N					N				
19	1.0766	1.3547	2.8675	3.1456	48	1.3802	1.5678	2.5173	2.7049
20	1.0954	1.3680	2.8425	3.1151	49	1.3856	1.5716	2.5117	2.6977
21	1.1131	1.3805	2.8195	3.0869	50	1.3907	1.5752	2.5064	2.6908
22	1.1298	1.3923	2.7982	3.0607	51	1.3957	1.5787	2.5013	2.6842
23	1.1456	1.4035	2.7784	3.0362	52	1.4007	1.5822	2.4963	2.6777
24	1.1606	1.4141	2.7599	3.0133	53	1.4057	1.5856	2.4914	2.6712
25	1.1748	1.4241	2.7426	2.9919	54	1.4107	1.5890	2.4866	2.6648
26	1.1883	1.4336	2.7264	2.9718	55	1.4156	1.5923	2.4819	2.6585
27	1.2012	1.4426	2.7112	2.9528	56	1.4203	1.5955	2.4773	2.6524
28	1.2135	1.4512	2.6969	2.9348	57	1.4249	1.5987	2.4728	2.6465
29	1.2252	1.4594	2.6834	2.9177	58	1.4294	1.6019	2.4684	2.6407
30	1.2363	1.4672	2.6707	2.9016	59	1.4339	1.6051	2.4640	2.6350
31	1.2469	1.4746	2.6587	2.8864	60	1.4384	1.6082	2.4596	2.6294
32	1.2570	1.4817	2.6473	2.8720					

[a] Adapted, with the kind permission of the editor, from B. I. Hart and J. von Neumann: "Tabulation of the Probabilities for the Ratio of the Mean Square Successive Difference to the Variance," *Annals of Mathematical Statistics*, **13**, No. 4, p. 446 (1942).

At the given level of significance and the appropriate sample size, N, a computed δ is indicative of positive autocorrelation if it falls below the critical value of K, and is indicative of negative autocorrelation if it exceeds the corresponding critical value of K'; if it falls between the two critical values, no evidence of autocorrelation is present.

195

these variances are estimated from the sample and must be appropriately adjusted for degrees of freedom.

Thus in Table 6.6 for pork (1949–1960) the calculation is

$$\delta = \frac{\dfrac{107}{(12-3)}}{\dfrac{256}{(12-2)}} = \frac{10}{9}\left(\frac{107}{256}\right) = 1.11(0.418) = 0.464$$

Since a value of δ smaller than 1.1803 would be expected less than five times in 100 in random samples with ten degrees of freedom, the test confirms our visual impression that the series z_t is not random.

We proceed now to a complete empirical example. Our basic data are time series of annual observations during 1922–1941 on the retail price of pork, X_1, pork consumption per capita, X_2, and disposable income per capita in current dollars, X_3.

We first calculate the simple straight line regression of X_1 on X_2 as follows:

(6.14)
$$X_1 = 36.1580 - 0.16457X_2 + z_{1.2}$$
$$(12.0286) \quad (0.17677)$$

The standard error of estimate is 5.2497 cents per pound, slightly larger than the original standard deviation of X_1 ($s_1 = 5.2313$). The residuals, $z_{1.2}$, are tabulated in Column (1) of Table 6.6.

The 20 residuals from the regression equation contain 18 degrees of freedom. In passing to first differences, we lose one observation. Hence when comparing the mean square of the first differences with the mean square or variance of the original deviations, we divide the former sum of squares by 17 and the latter by $20 - 2$, or 18. The formula for von Neuman's ratio may be written

(6.15)
$$\delta = \frac{(18)}{(17)}\frac{[\sum (\Delta z_{1.2})^2]}{\sum z_{1.2}^2} = 1.058824\left(\frac{207.288607}{496.07384}\right)$$

$$= 1.058824(0.417853) = 0.442433$$

This ratio, and the original $z_{1.2}$ values in Column (1), suggest a very high degree of positive autocorrelation. The sampling distribution of von Neumann's ratio has been tabulated, and it enables us to say that a value of the ratio smaller than 1.3405, given 18 degrees of freedom in the original series, would occur less than 5% of the time if the population from which the original residuals were drawn had no autocorrelation. We must therefore reject the hypothesis that the residuals z_1 are random.

Our first equation expressed actual price as a function of the actual level of consumption. It makes equally good economic sense to express the *change*

Table 6.6 Residuals from Four Regression Equations Involving the Consumption and Retail Price of Pork, United States, 1922–1941 [a]

Year	(1) $z_{1.2}$	(2) $z_{4.5}$	(3) X_7	(4) $z_{4.57}$	(5) $z_{1.23}$
1922	1.5	–	–	–	2.3
1923	1.4	3.0	75	– 0.1	0.3
1924	1.3	– 0.1	– 6	0.5	0.5
1925	5.9	2.0	26	1.6	2.3
1926	7.7	0.8	15	0.6	2.7
1927	6.2	– 0.2	– 6	0.3	2.3
1928	5.0	0.0	8	– 0.1	1.4
1929	5.6	0.1	29	– 0.7	0.3
1930	4.0	– 2.5	– 78	1.2	2.0
1931	– 1.2	– 4.6	– 89	– 0.6	1.5
1932	– 8.9	– 6.8	– 125	– 1.4	0.5
1933	– 10.8	– 2.2	– 26	– 0.8	– 0.4
1934	– 7.0	1.5	47	0.1	– 0.3
1935	– 0.8	0.8	48	– 0.2	0.3
1936	– 0.2	3.1	58	0.7	– 0.5
1937	0.7	1.2	34	0.1	– 1.1
1938	– 2.1	– 1.9	– 45	0.2	– 1.2
1939	– 3.3	1.2	32	– 0.1	– 2.6
1940	– 4.8	1.8	38	0.2	– 4.0
1941	– 0.2	2.7	121	– 1.8	– 6.5

[a] Subscripts of the z's identify them with specific equations listed in the text.

in price from one year to the next as a function of the corresponding *change* in consumption. In some situations a first difference transformation,

$$\Delta X_1 = [X_{1(t+1)} - X_{1(t)}] \quad \text{and} \quad \Delta X_2 = [X_{2(t+1)} - X_{2(t)}]$$

may eliminate most of the systematic elements other than X_2 which were responsible for autocorrelation in the residuals $z_{1(t)} = X_{1(t)} - \hat{X}_{1(t)}$. Table 6.6 shows similar calculations for the residuals from $\Delta X_1 = f(\Delta X_2)$. Letting $X_4 = \Delta X_1$ and $X_5 = \Delta X_2$, we may write

$$(6.16) \qquad X_4 = -0.03527 - 0.5303 X_5 + z_{4.5}$$
$$ (0.6372) \quad (0.1076)$$

The standard error of estimate is 2.6938 cents a pound, compared with 5.2497 cents in the preceding instance.

Since one observation was lost in passing from original values to first differences of X_1, the residuals from the regression, based on 19 observations, have 17 degrees of freedom; the first differences of these residuals have 16 degrees of freedom. The resulting value of von Neumann's ratio is $\delta = 0.838863$. Although the degree of positive autocorrelation in $z_{4.5}$ is less than that in the preceding case, values of δ smaller than 1.3253 would be expected only five times in 100 if the population from which the $z_{4.5}$'s were randomly drawn contained no autocorrelation. On visual inspection, $z_{4.5}$ shows runs of several consecutive negative and several consecutive positive values.

A comparison of Columns (2) and (3) of Table 6.6 shows that these runs of residuals in the price of pork, which are not explained by or associated with changes in pork supplies, are rather closely associated with changes in the disposable income of consumers, X_7. On economic grounds, of course, disposable personal income belongs with pork supplies in explaining changes in pork prices.

In Table 6.6, the fourth column contains residuals from the equation

$$(6.17) \qquad X_4 = -0.3835 - 0.4899X_5 + 0.04172X_7 + z_{4.57}$$
$$(0.2054) \quad (0.0344) \qquad (0.00339)$$

where X_4 and X_5 are the same as before and X_7 is equal to ΔX_3, X_3 being per capita disposable income. The standard error of estimate from this equation is 0.8577 cent a pound. The regression coefficients on X_5 and X_7 are, respectively, 14 and 12 times their standard errors. There is a suggestion that the constant term *may* be negative, which, in a first difference equation, suggests a linear downward trend in the original values of pork price for any given combination of values of pork supplies and disposable income.

The residuals in Column (4) now contain 16 degrees of freedom $(19 - 3)$, and the first differences of these residuals contain 15 degrees of freedom. The corresponding value of von Neumann's ratio is $\delta = 1.517395$. Some 5% of all random samples with these numbers of degrees of freedom from a population in which no autocorrelation exists would yield a von Neumann ratio smaller than 1.3090. The norm for the von Neumann ratio in very large samples is approximately 2.0 when autocorrelation in the population is zero. Hence, because the value of δ in Table 6.6 lies between 1.3090 and 2, we cannot reject the hypothesis that the autocorrelation of deviations from the regression $\hat{X}_4 = \alpha + \beta_5 X_5 + \beta_7 X_7$ in the parent population is zero.

An equation in terms of the original values of the same three series, pork price, pork consumption per capita, and per capita disposable income,

$$(6.18) \qquad X_1 = 22.8730 - 0.38265X_2 + 0.049514X_3 + z_{1.23}$$
$$(5.8037) \quad (0.08577) \qquad (0.006024)$$

with a standard error of estimate of 2.4221 cents a pound fails to pass the autocorrelation test. Since there were 20 observations originally, there are 17 degrees of freedom in the residuals and 16 in the first differences of residuals.

The von Neumann ratio proves to be $\delta = 0.276464$, a value which would be extremely unlikely if autocorrelation in the population were zero.

Positive autocorrelation in the original values of economic time series is widely prevalent. Economic growth and business cycles are the principal reasons for this.

In such instances, transforming the original variables into first differences usually reduces the degree of autocorrelation. In many time series analyses performed by one of the authors over a period of years, the first difference transformation with a logically selected set of variables has in almost all cases rendered autocorrelation in the residuals nonsignificant at the 5% probability level.

But this result cannot be depended upon universally. As economists, we should try to bring economic reasoning to bear as far as possible in finding out why the autocorrelation exists. Sometimes the culprit may simply be a smoothing process by means of which government statisticians interpolate quarterly values from basic annual information or chain together successive samples. Or, a variable may have been omitted from the equation which, on economic grounds, might be expected to have a significant effect upon the dependent variable. If a data transformation is chosen, it should make sense in terms of both the economic and the statistical aspects of the problem under investigation.

APPENDIX A

CALCULATION OF SAMPLING ERRORS IN SIMPLE REGRESSION ANALYSIS

Straight Line

In the text of Chapter 6 we have given intuitive derivations of formulas for the standard errors of (1) the mean of X_1 (or $\bar{X}_1$) *given* $\bar{X}_2$; (2) the regression slope b; (3) the estimated value of X_1 (or $\hat{X}_1$) given any specified value of X_2; and (4) an individual (new) value of X_1 not included in the original sample. The formulas may be recapitulated as follows:

1. Standard error of $\bar{X}_1$ with no knowledge of regression relationship with X_2:

(A.1)
$$s_{\bar{X}_1} = \frac{s_1}{\sqrt{n}}$$

where s_1 is the sample standard deviation of X_1 calculated with $n - 1$ degrees of freedom.

2. Standard error of $\bar{X}_1$ *given* $\bar{X}_2$ and knowledge of the straight line regression relationship, $\hat{X}_1 = b_0 + b_{12}X_2$:

(A.2)
$$s_{(\bar{X}_1|\bar{X}_2)} = \frac{\bar{S}_{1.2}}{\sqrt{n}}$$

where $\bar{S}_{1.2}$ is the sample standard error of estimate calculated with $n - 2$ degrees of freedom.

The corresponding formula for the second-degree parabola $\hat{X}_1 = b_0 + b_{12}X_2 + b_{13}X_2{}^2$ is

(A.2a)
$$s_{[\bar{X}_1|\bar{X}_2,(\bar{X}_2{}^2)]} = \frac{\bar{S}_{1.(2,2^2)}}{\sqrt{n}}$$

where $\bar{S}_{1.(2,2^2)}$ is the sample standard error of estimate calculated with $n - 3$ degrees of freedom. Any variable such as $X_2{}^2$ is treated arithmetically as though it were a new variable not connected with X_2 (say, $u_3 = X_2{}^2$ and $\bar{u}_3 = \bar{X}_2{}^2$). More generally, for a higher degree parabola involving a total of $k - 1$ terms ($X_2, X_2{}^2, X_2{}^3, \ldots, X_2^{k-1}$), the standard error of $\bar{X}_1$ when all $k - 1$ terms are at their respective mean values is

(A.2b)
$$s_{[\bar{X}_1|\bar{X}_2,(\bar{X}_2{}^2),\ldots,(\bar{X}_2^{k-1})]} = \frac{\bar{S}_{1.2,2^2,\ldots,2^{k-1}}}{\sqrt{n}}$$

where $\bar{S}_{1.2,2^2,\ldots,2^{k-1}}$ is calculated with $n - k$ degrees of freedom. The same formula applies to *multiple* regression equations with $k - 1$ independent variables.

3. Standard error of the regression (slope) coefficient b_{12}:

(A.3)
$$s_{b_{12}} = \frac{\bar{S}_{1.2}}{s_2\sqrt{n}}$$

where s_2 is the standard deviation of X_2 calculated with $n - 1$ degrees of freedom.

4. Standard error of $\hat{X}_1 = b_0 + b_{12}X_2$:

(A.4)
$$s_{(\hat{X}_1|X_2)}^2 = \bar{S}_{1.2}^2\left(\frac{1}{n} + \frac{x_2{}^2}{s_2{}^2 \cdot n}\right) = \frac{\bar{S}_{1.2}^2}{n} + \left(\frac{\bar{S}_{1.2}^2}{ns_2{}^2}\right)x_2{}^2$$

which, from (A.2) and (A.3), gives us

(A.4a) $s^2_{(\hat{X}_1|X_2)} = s^2_{(\hat{X}_1|\bar{X}_2)} + (s_{b_{12}}x_2)^2$ where $x_2 = X_2 - \bar{X}_2$

Of course,

(A.4b) $s_{(\hat{X}_1|X_2)} = \sqrt{s^2_{(\hat{X}_1|\bar{X}_2)} + (s_{b_{12}}x_2)^2}$

In particular, the standard error of the constant term b_0 is

(A.4c) $s_{b_0} = \sqrt{s^2_{(\hat{X}_1|\bar{X}_2)} + (s_{b_{12}}\bar{X}_2)^2}$

5. The squared standard error, or variance, of forecast of a new individual observation X_1 is

(A.5) $s^2_{(\hat{X}_1|X_2)} = \bar{S}^2_{1.2}\left[1 + \frac{1}{n} + (s_{b_{12}}x_2)^2\right]$

Second-degree parabola

In the equation $\hat{X}_1 = b_0 + b_{12}X_2 + b_{13}(X_2^2)$, it will be notationally convenient to let $X_2^2 = X_3$; therefore,

(A.6) $\hat{X}_1 = b_0 + b_{12}X_2 + b_{13}X_3$

in particular,

(A.6a) $\bar{X}_1 = b_0 + b_{12}\bar{X}_2 + b_{13}\bar{X}_3$

The standard error of estimate $\bar{S}_{1.23}$ is calculated with $n - 3$ degrees of freedom. Equation (A.1) applies without modification, and (A.2) with a minor change in notation:

(A.2a) $s_{(X_1|X_2,X_3)} = \dfrac{\bar{S}_{1.23}}{\sqrt{n}}$

However, the standard errors of b_0, b_{12}, and b_{13} present new problems, which can best be handled in matrix notation. We will carry through a complete numerical example, using the matrix notation and operations introduced in Appendix A of Chapter 4.

The original observations, means, and sums of squares and products are shown in Table 6.7. The arithmetic is straightforward, but as an exercise we will carry through even the preliminary observations in matrix notation. We include a "dummy variable" $X_0 = 1$ in every observation for purposes which will become clear.

The basic data of our problem may be written as

$$X_{1(i)} = \begin{bmatrix} 0.70 \\ 6.87 \\ 8.13 \\ 11.87 \\ 11.63 \\ 11.38 \end{bmatrix}; \quad X_{023} = \begin{bmatrix} 1 & 1 & 1 \\ 1 & 2 & 4 \\ 1 & 3 & 9 \\ 1 & 4 & 16 \\ 1 & 5 & 25 \\ 1 & 6 & 36 \end{bmatrix};$$

$$6 \times 1 \qquad\qquad 6 \times 3$$

(A.7)

$$z_{(i)} = \begin{bmatrix} z_{(1)} \\ z_{(2)} \\ z_{(3)} \\ z_{(4)} \\ z_{(5)} \\ z_{(6)} \end{bmatrix}; \quad b = \begin{bmatrix} b_0 \\ b_{12} \\ b_{13} \end{bmatrix}$$

$$6 \times 1 \qquad\qquad 3 \times 1$$

In matrix equation form we have

(A.8)
$$\begin{bmatrix} 0.70 \\ 6.87 \\ \vdots \\ 11.38 \end{bmatrix} = \begin{bmatrix} 1 & 1 & 1 \\ 1 & 2 & 4 \\ \vdots & \vdots & \vdots \\ 1 & 6 & 36 \end{bmatrix} \begin{bmatrix} b_0 \\ b_{12} \\ b_{13} \end{bmatrix} + \begin{bmatrix} z_{(1)} \\ z_{(2)} \\ \vdots \\ z_{(6)} \end{bmatrix}$$

therefore

(A.9)
$$\begin{bmatrix} z_{(1)} \\ z_{(2)} \\ \vdots \\ z_{(6)} \end{bmatrix} = \begin{bmatrix} 0.70 \\ 6.87 \\ \vdots \\ 11.38 \end{bmatrix} - \begin{bmatrix} 1 & 1 & 1 \\ 1 & 2 & 4 \\ \vdots & \vdots & \vdots \\ 1 & 6 & 36 \end{bmatrix} \begin{bmatrix} b_0 \\ b_{12} \\ b_{13} \end{bmatrix}$$

To obtain the least squares value of the estimators $b = \begin{bmatrix} b_0 \\ b_{12} \\ b_{13} \end{bmatrix}$ of the

population parameters $\beta = \begin{bmatrix} \beta_0 \\ \beta_{12} \\ \beta_{13} \end{bmatrix}$ we must minimize the sum of squared

Table 6.7 Original Observations, Sums, Means, and Sums of Squares and Cross Products for Linear and Parabolic Regression Example (based on data from Table 6.1, p. 171 of alfalfa example)

Obs.	X₁	X₂	X₃	X₀	X_1^2	X_1X_2	X_1X_3	X_1X_0	X_2^2	X_2X_3	X_2X_0	X_3^2	X_3X_0	X_0^2
3 1	0.70	1	1	1	0.4900	0.70	0.70	0.70	1	1	1	1	1	1
8 2	6.87	2	4	1	47.1969	13.74	27.48	6.87	4	8	2	16	4	1
13 3	8.13	3	9	1	66.0969	24.39	73.17	8.13	9	27	3	81	9	1
18 4	11.87	4	16	1	140.8969	47.48	189.92	11.87	16	64	4	256	16	1
23 5	11.63	5	25	1	135.2569	58.15	290.75	11.63	25	125	5	625	25	1
28 6	11.38	6	36	1	129.5044	68.28	409.68	11.38	36	216	6	1296	36	1
Sums	50.58	21	91	6	519.442	212.74	991.70	50.58	91	441	21	2275	91	6
Observations														
(n)	6	6	6	6										
Means	8.430	3.500	15.167	1										
Adjustment factors ($n\bar{X}_i\bar{X}_j$)					426.3894	177.03	767.15	50.58	73.50	318.50	21	1380.1667	91	6
Adjusted sums					93.0526	35.71	224.55	0	17.50	122.50	0	894.8333	0	0

203

residuals, $z_{(1)}^2 + z_{(2)}^2 + \cdots + z_{(6)}^2$, with respect to the vector b (or, which is the same, with respect to b_0, b_{12}, and b_{13} separately).

By convention, in matrix multiplication we multiply each *row* of the matrix to the left by each *column* of the matrix to the right. The product matrix will have the same number of *rows* as the matrix to the left and the same number of *columns* as the matrix to the right. Thus, if we wish to obtain the 1 by 1 matrix, $\sum_{i=1}^{6} z_{(i)}^2$, we perform the matrix operation,

$$(A.10) \qquad z'z = [z_{(1)} \quad z_{(2)} \quad \cdots \quad z_{(6)}] \begin{bmatrix} z_{(1)} \\ z_{(2)} \\ \vdots \\ z_{(6)} \end{bmatrix} = \sum_{i=1}^{6} z_{(i)}^2$$

$$1 \times 1 \qquad\qquad 1 \times 6 \qquad\qquad 6 \times 1$$

where z' is the transpose of z. (Each *row* of the transpose is equal to the corresponding *column* of the original matrix.)

As an intermediate step we may write

$$(A.11) \quad z' = [0.70 \quad 6.87 \quad \cdots \quad 11.38] - [b_0 \quad b_{12} \quad b_{13}] \begin{bmatrix} 1 & 1 & \cdots & 1 \\ 1 & 2 & \cdots & 6 \\ 1 & 4 & \cdots & 36 \end{bmatrix}$$

$$1 \times 6 \qquad\qquad 1 \times 3 \qquad\qquad 3 \times 6$$

or

$$(A.11a) \qquad\qquad z' = X'_1 - b'X'_{023}$$

Then

$$(A.12) \qquad z'z = (X'_1 - b'X'_{023})(X_1 - X_{023}b)$$
$$= X'_1X_1 - 2X'_1X_{023}b + b'X'_{023}X_{023}b$$

It can be shown that

$$(A.13) \qquad\qquad b'X'_{023}X_1 \equiv X'_1X_{023}b$$

for the left-hand side becomes

$$(A.13a) \qquad [b_0\, b_{12}\, b_{13}] \begin{bmatrix} 1 & 1 & 1 & 1 & 1 & 1 \\ 1 & 2 & 3 & 4 & 5 & 6 \\ 1 & 4 & 9 & 16 & 25 & 36 \end{bmatrix} \begin{bmatrix} 0.70 \\ 6.87 \\ 8.13 \\ 11.87 \\ 11.63 \\ 11.38 \end{bmatrix}$$

$$1 \times 3 \qquad\qquad 3 \times 6 \qquad\qquad 6 \times 1$$

If we postmultiply the second matrix by the third, we obtain a matrix of the dimension 3 rows by 1 column; this product matrix times b' yields

(A.13a.1) $\qquad b_0 \sum X_1 X_0 + b_{12} \sum X_1 X_2 + b_{13} \sum X_1 X_3$

The right-hand side of (A.13) becomes

(A.13b) $\quad [0.70 \quad 6.87 \quad \cdots \quad 11.38] \begin{bmatrix} 1 & 1 & 1 \\ 1 & 2 & 4 \\ 1 & 3 & 9 \\ 1 & 4 & 16 \\ 1 & 5 & 25 \\ 1 & 6 & 36 \end{bmatrix} \begin{bmatrix} b_0 \\ b_{12} \\ b_{13} \end{bmatrix}$

$\qquad\qquad 1 \times 6 \qquad\qquad 6 \times 3 \qquad 3 \times 1$

If we multiply the first matrix by the second, we obtain a matrix of 1 row and 3 columns; this product matrix times b yields

(A.13b.1) $\qquad b_0 \sum X_1 X_0 + b_{12} \sum X_1 X_2 + b_{13} \sum X_1 X_3$

as before.

We may also write out $b' X'_{023} X_{023}$ as follows:

(A.14) $\quad [b_0\, b_{12}\, b_{13}] \begin{bmatrix} 1 & 1 & 1 & 1 & 1 & 1 \\ 1 & 2 & 3 & 4 & 5 & 6 \\ 1 & 4 & 9 & 16 & 25 & 36 \end{bmatrix} \begin{bmatrix} 1 & 1 & 1 \\ 1 & 2 & 4 \\ 1 & 3 & 9 \\ 1 & 4 & 16 \\ 1 & 5 & 25 \\ 1 & 6 & 36 \end{bmatrix}$

$\qquad\qquad 1 \times 3 \qquad\qquad 3 \times 6 \qquad\qquad 6 \times 3$

If we multiply the second matrix by the third, we obtain a matrix of 3 rows and 3 columns,

(A.14a) $\qquad X'_{023} X_{023} = \begin{bmatrix} \sum X_0{}^2 & \sum X_0 X_2 & \sum X_0 X_3 \\ \sum X_0 X_2 & \sum X_2 & \sum X_2 X_3 \\ \sum X_0 X_3 & \sum X_2 X_3 & \sum X_3{}^2 \end{bmatrix}$

If we premultiply this matrix by b' we obtain a matrix of 1 row and 3 columns,

(A.14b) $\quad [(b_0 \sum X_0{}^2 + b_{12} \sum X_0 X_2 + b_{13} \sum X_0 X_2);$
$\qquad (b_0 \sum X_0 X_2 + b_{12} \sum X_2{}^2 + b_{13} \sum X_2 X_3);$
$\qquad \text{and} \quad (b_0 \sum X_0 X_3 + b_{12} \sum X_2 X_3 + b_{13} \sum X_3{}^2)]$

Multiplying this in turn by b we obtain a 1 by 1 matrix which consists of nine additive terms in $b_0{}^2$, $b_{12}{}^2$, $b_{13}{}^2$, $b_0 b_{12}$, $b_0 b_{13}$, and $b_{12} b_{13}$. Because of symmetry, there are two each of the last three terms.

If we differentiate the left-hand side of (A.12) with respect to b and set the result equal to zero to minimize the sum of the squared residuals, we obtain

(A.15)
$$\frac{\partial(z'z)}{\partial b} = -2X'_1 X_{023} + 2X'_{023} X_{023} b = 0$$

or, dividing each term by 2 and transposing,

(A.16)
$$X'_{023} X_{023} b = X'_1 X_{023}$$

The term $(X'_{023} X_{023})$ is defined in (A.14a), and the term $(X'_1 X_{023})$ is simply

(A.16a)
$$X'_1 X_{023} = [\sum X_1 X_0 \quad \sum X_1 X_2 \quad \sum X_1 X_3]$$

If we premultiply both sides of (A.16) by the inverse of $X'_{023} X_{023}$ (see Chapter 4, Appendix A) we obtain

(A.17)
$$\begin{bmatrix} 1 & 0 & 0 \\ 0 & 1 & 0 \\ 0 & 0 & 1 \end{bmatrix} \begin{bmatrix} b_0 \\ b_{12} \\ b_{13} \end{bmatrix} = (X'_{023} X_{023})^{-1} X'_1 X_{023}$$

or simply,

(A.17a)
$$b = (X'_{023} X_{023})^{-1} X'_1 X_{023}$$

We may note the *analogy* of (A.17a) to the formula for the simple regression coefficient (say, of X_1 on X_2),

(A.17b)
$$b_{12} = \frac{\sum x_1 x_2}{\sum x_2{}^2} = \frac{1}{\sum x_2{}^2} (\sum x_1 x_2)$$

We skip some intervening steps (see Chapter 7) and simply write down the formula for the *variance* of the least squares estimator b of the population vector β:

(A.18)
$$E (b - \beta)(b - \beta)' = \bar{S}^2_{1.023}(X'_{023} X_{023})^{-1}$$

or

(A.18a)
$$V(b) = \bar{S}^2_{1.023}(X'_{023} X_{023})^{-1}$$

We may note again the analogy of (A.18a) with

(A.18b)
$$s^2_{b_{12}} = \frac{\bar{S}^2_{1.2}}{n s_{X_2}{}^2} = \bar{S}^2_{1.2}\left(\frac{1}{\sum x_2{}^2}\right)$$

First, let us discard X_3 for a moment and see what $V(b)$ means for the straight line

(A.19) $$\hat{X}_1 = b_0(X_0 = 1) + b_{12}X_2$$

We need the inverse of the matrix

(A.20) $$(X'_{02}X_{02}) = \begin{bmatrix} \sum X_0^2 & \sum X_0 X_2 \\ \sum X_0 X_2 & \sum X_2^2 \end{bmatrix} = \begin{bmatrix} 6 & 21 \\ 21 & 91 \end{bmatrix}$$

The determinant of the matrix is

(A.21) $$\Delta = \sum X_0^2 \cdot \sum X_2^2 - (\sum X_0 X_2)^2 = 6(91) - (21)^2 = 546 - 441$$
$$= 105$$

Since the matrix is symmetrical, the adjugate and adjoint are identical,

(A.22) $$\text{adj } (X'_{02}X_{02}) = \begin{bmatrix} 91 & -21 \\ -21 & 6 \end{bmatrix}$$

and the inverse is

(A.23) $$(X'_{02}X_{02})^{-1} = \frac{1}{105}\begin{bmatrix} 91 & -21 \\ -21 & 6 \end{bmatrix} = \begin{bmatrix} 0.8667 & -0.2000 \\ -0.2000 & 0.0571 \end{bmatrix}$$

From (A.18a),

(A.24) $$\begin{bmatrix} s_{b_0}^2 & s_{b_0 b_{12}} \\ s_{b_0 b_{12}} & s_{b_{12}}^2 \end{bmatrix} = 5.0460\begin{bmatrix} 0.8667 & -0.2000 \\ -0.2000 & 0.0571 \end{bmatrix}$$
$$= \begin{bmatrix} 4.3734 & -1.0092 \\ -1.0092 & 0.2881 \end{bmatrix}$$

and

(A.24a) $$s_{b_0} = \sqrt{4.3734} = 2.0912$$

(A.24b) $$s_{b_{12}} = \sqrt{0.2881} = 0.5370$$

We recall that the variance of $\hat{X}_1$ given the regression equation is

(A.25) $$s_{\hat{X}_1}^2 = s_{X_1}^2 + [s_{b_{12}}(X_2 - \bar{X}_2)]^2 = 0.84074 + (0.2883)(X_2 - \bar{X}_2)^2$$

Equation (A.25) may also be written

(A.25a) $$s_{\hat{X}_1}^2 = \bar{S}_{1.02}^2\left[\frac{1}{n} + \frac{1}{ns_{X_2}^2}(X_2 - \bar{X}_2)^2\right]$$

In this particular example, the reader may verify that the values of $s_{\hat{x}_1}$ are as follows:

X_2	$s_{\hat{x}_1}$	X_2	$s_{\hat{x}_1}$
1	1.6258	4	0.9556
2	1.2206	5	1.2206
3	0.9556	6	1.6258

The values of X_2 are symmetrical about $\overline{X}_2 = 3.5$, so the corresponding values of $s_{\hat{x}_1}$ are also symmetrical. The minimum value of $s_{\hat{x}_1}$, 0.8407, occurs when $X_2 = \overline{X}_1 = 3.5$.

To make analogous calculations for the second-degree parabola, we need the inverse of

$$(A.26) \quad (X'_{023}X_{023}) = \begin{bmatrix} \sum X_2^2 & \sum X_2 X_3 & \sum X_2 X_0 \\ \sum X_2 X_3 & \sum X_3^2 & \sum X_3 X_0 \\ \sum X_2 X_0 & \sum X_3 X_0 & \sum X_0^2 \end{bmatrix} = \begin{bmatrix} 91 & 441 & 21 \\ 441 & 2275 & 91 \\ 21 & 91 & 6 \end{bmatrix}$$

The determinant of the matrix is

$$[91(2275)6 + 2(441)(91)(21) - 2275(21)^2 - 6(441)^2 - (91)^3 = \underline{3920}]$$

The adjoint (and adjugate) of the matrix (A.26) is

$$(A.27) \quad \text{adj } (X'_{230}X_{230})$$
$$= \begin{bmatrix} 6(2275) - (91)^2 & -6(441) + 91(21) & 441(91) - 2275(21) \\ -6(441) + (91)21 & 91(6) - (21)^2 & -(91)^2 + 21(441) \\ 441(91) - 2275(21) & -(91)^2 + 21(441) & 91(2275) - (441)^2 \end{bmatrix}$$

Dividing each element of (A.27) by the value of the determinant, $\Delta = 3920$, we obtain the inverse

$$(A.28) \quad (X'_{230}X_{230})^{-1} = \begin{bmatrix} 1.36964 & -0.18750 & -1.95000 \\ -0.18750 & 0.02679 & 0.25000 \\ -1.95000 & 0.25000 & 3.20000 \end{bmatrix}$$

The variance of residuals from the regression equation, with $6 - 3 = 3$ degrees of freedom is

$$(A.29) \qquad \overline{S}_{1.230}^2 = 0.967569$$

and the variances and covariances of the standard errors of b_0, b_{12}, and b_{13}

may be written as follows, rearranging the order of rows and columns in the inverse to agree with $(X'_{023}X_{023})^{-1}$:

(A.30)

$$\begin{bmatrix} s_{b_0}{}^2 & s_{b_0 b_{12}} & s_{b_0 b_{13}} \\ s_{b_0 b_{12}} & s_{b_{12}}^2 & s_{b_{12} b_{13}} \\ s_{b_0 b_{13}} & s_{b_{12} b_{13}} & s_{b_{13}}^2 \end{bmatrix}$$

$$= 0.967569 \begin{bmatrix} 3.20000 & -1.95000 & 0.25000 \\ -1.95000 & 1.36964 & -0.18750 \\ 0.25000 & -0.18750 & 0.02679 \end{bmatrix}$$

Then

(A.30a) $s_{b_0} = \sqrt{0.967569(3.20000)} = 1.75961$

(A.30b) $s_{b_{12}} = \sqrt{0.967569(1.36964)} = 1.15118$

(A.30c) $s_{b_{13}} = \sqrt{0.967569(0.02679)} = 0.16099$

The variance of $\hat{X}_1$ for any combination of values of X_2 and X_3 may be written

(A.31) $s_{\hat{X}_1}{}^2 = s_{\bar{X}_1}{}^2 + (s_{b_{12}} x_2)^2 + (s_{b_{13}} x_3)^2 + 2 s_{b_{12}} s_{b_{13}} x_2 x_3$

where $x_2 = X_2 - \bar{X}_2$ and $x_3 = X_3 - \bar{X}_3$.

When all variables are expressed as deviations from their respective means, $x_0 = 1 - 1 = 0$ for all observations, $\sum x_0{}^2 = 0$, $\sum x_0 x_2 = 0$, and $\sum x_0 x_3 = 0$. The first term on the right-hand side of (A.31) is the squared standard error of $\hat{X}_1$ under these circumstances. The matrix (A.26) would shrink from 3 by 3 to 2 by 2 and the sums of squares and products of original values would be replaced by sums of squares and products of x_2 and x_3. Instead of (A.26) we obtain

(A.32) $(x'_{23} x_{23}) = \begin{bmatrix} \sum x_2{}^2 & \sum x_2 x_3 \\ \sum x_2 x_3 & \sum x_3{}^2 \end{bmatrix} = \begin{bmatrix} \sum X_2{}^2 & \sum X_2 X_3 & \sum X_2 X_0 \\ \sum X_2 X_3 & \sum X_3{}^2 & \sum X_3 X_0 \\ \sum X_2 X_0 & \sum X_3 X_0 & \sum X_0{}^2 \end{bmatrix}$

$$-n \begin{bmatrix} \bar{X}_2{}^2 & \bar{X}_2 \bar{X}_3 & \bar{X}_2 \bar{X}_0 \\ \bar{X}_2 \bar{X}_3 & \bar{X}_3{}^2 & \bar{X}_3 \bar{X}_0 \\ \bar{X}_2 \bar{X}_0 & \bar{X}_3 \bar{X}_0 & \bar{X}_0{}^2 \end{bmatrix}$$

As $X_0 = 1$ in all instances, we have

(A.32a) $\begin{bmatrix} \sum X_2{}^2 & \sum X_2 X_3 & n \bar{X}_2 \\ \sum X_2 X_3 & \sum X_3{}^2 & n \bar{X}_3 \\ n \bar{X}_2 & n \bar{X}_3 & n \end{bmatrix} - \begin{bmatrix} n \bar{X}_2{}^2 & n \bar{X}_2 \bar{X}_3 & n \bar{X}_2 \\ n \bar{X}_2 \bar{X}_3 & n \bar{X}_3{}^2 & n \bar{X}_3 \\ n \bar{X}_2 & n \bar{X}_3 & n \end{bmatrix}$

so the elements in row 3 and column 3 of the remainder matrix all become zeros, leaving us with the 2 by 2 matrix (A.32).

Numerically (A.32) is

(A.32b)
$$\begin{bmatrix} 17.50 & 122.50 \\ 122.50 & 894.83 \end{bmatrix}$$

The value of the determinant is $[17.50(894.83) - (122.50)^2] = 653.2750$. The adjoint is $\begin{bmatrix} 894.83 & -122.50 \\ -122.50 & 17.50 \end{bmatrix}$, and the inverse is

(A.32c)
$$(x'_{23}x_{23})^{-1} = \begin{bmatrix} 1.36964 & -0.18750 \\ -0.18750 & 0.02679 \end{bmatrix}$$

This is identical with the corresponding submatrix of (A.30).

We may think of the terms in (A.31) other than $s_{\bar{X}_1}{}^2$ as being computed in the following way:

(A.33)
$$s_{\hat{X}_1}{}^2 - s_{\bar{X}_1}{}^2 = \begin{bmatrix} s_{b_{12}}^2 & s_{b_{12}b_{13}} \\ s_{b_{12}b_{13}} & s_{b_{13}}^2 \end{bmatrix} \begin{bmatrix} x_2{}^2 & x_2x_3 \\ x_2x_3 & x_3{}^2 \end{bmatrix}$$
$$= s_{b_{12}}^2 x_2{}^2 + 2s_{b_{12}b_{13}}x_2x_3 + s_{b_{13}}^2 x_3{}^2$$

In this example, noting that $s_{b_{12}}^2 = 0.967569(1.36964) = 1.325222$, and so on, we have

(A.33a) $s_{\hat{X}_1}{}^2 = [1.325222x_2{}^2 - 2(0.1815)x_2x_3 + 0.025917x_3{}^2] + 0.161262$

The values of $s_{\hat{X}_1}$ for all six values of X_2 are as follows:

X_2	$X_3(= X_2{}^2)$	$s_{\hat{X}_1}$	X_2	$X_3(= X_2{}^2)$	$s_{\hat{X}_1}$
1	1	0.891465	4	16	0.599525
2	4	0.545146	5	25	0.545148
3	9	0.599522	6	36	0.891460

It is interesting to note how the different terms in (A.33a) tend to offset one another and to produce a nearly symmetrical pattern even though two of its components are definitely asymmetrical:

X_2	$(s_{b_{12}}^2)x_2{}^2$	$(s_{b_{13}}^2)x_3{}^2$	$2s_{b_{12}b_{13}}x_2x_3$	$s_{\bar{X}_1}{}^2$
1	8.28	5.20	-12.85	0.16
2	2.98	3.23	-6.08	0.16
3	0.33	0.99	-1.12	0.16
4	0.33	0.02	-0.15	0.16
5	2.98	2.51	-5.35	0.16
6	8.28	11.25	-18.90	0.16

The term in x_2^2 is symmetrical around $\bar{X}_2 = 3.5$ and reaches its minimum value (zero) at $\bar{X}_2$. The term in x_3^2 goes to zero when $X_3 = \bar{X}_3 = 15.167$, and is still very small when $X_3 = 16$ and $X_2 = 4$. The term in $x_2 x_3$ must go to zero (a) when $X_2 = \bar{X}_2 = 3.5$ and (b) when $X_3 = \bar{X}_3 = 15.167$, so that $X_2 = \sqrt{15.167} = 3.895$.

APPENDIX B

REGRESSION ANALYSIS BASED ON CONTROLLED EXPERIMENTS: ADDITIONAL REGRESSION RESULTS USING THE HYPOTHETICAL DATA ON ALFALFA YIELDS AND IRRIGATION WATER

Standard errors of regression coefficients, their t-ratios, standard errors of the function $\hat{Y}$ for different values of W, and some other results are presented for a large number of straight line and parabolic regression equations including and in addition to those discussed in the text.

APPENDIX C

GENERATING BIVARIATE NORMAL DISTRIBUTIONS

In the introductory section of this chapter, we mentioned the origin of the correlation model and its integral relationship with the bivariate normal distribution. To clarify this relationship we shall again use a constructed example.

Each of the two variables in a bivariate normal distribution must itself follow a normal distribution *in the parent population* from which a sample is to be drawn. The variables in Table 6.11 were derived in the following fashion:

First, 20 random numbers, which we shall call z_1, were drawn from a table of such numbers and identified with the midpoints of particular class intervals in a normal distribution with unit variance and standard deviation. We then constructed the variable $X_1 = z_1 + 4$, and another variable, $X_2 = 0.8X_1 + 0.2$.

Then another set of 20 random numbers, which we shall call z_2, was drawn and multiplied, respectively, by 0.4 and 0.8. Again, the population or expected value of the variance of z_2 was 1. We then constructed the

Table 6.8 Alfalfa Yields and Irrigation Water Applied: Proportional Subsamples of Original Thirty Observations Covering Complete Range of Values of the Independent Variables[a]

	(1)	(2)	(3)	(4)	(5)	(6)	(7)	(8)	(9)
				Residuals from Linear Regressions			Residuals from Parabolic Regressions		
Observation Number	Y, Yield (tons per acre)	W, Water Applied (feet)	W^2	3 Separate Subsamples	Subsamples 1 and 2 Combined	Complete Sample of 30 Observations	3 Separate Subsamples	Subsamples 1 and 2 Combined	Complete Samples of 30 Observations
Subsample 1 (12 observations)									
1	1.87	1	1	−1.83	−1.71	−1.92	−0.36	0.03	−0.47
2	1.63	1	1	−2.07	−1.95	−2.16	−0.60	−0.21	−0.71
3	7.30	2	4	1.50	1.64	1.50	1.21	1.30	1.21
4	6.62	2	4	0.82	0.96	0.82	0.53	0.62	0.53
5	9.13	3	9	1.23	1.40	1.33	0.06	0.01	0.17
6	8.87	3	9	0.97	1.14	1.07	−0.20	−0.25	−0.09
7	11.37	4	16	1.38	1.56	1.56	0.20	0.17	0.40
8	10.63	4	16	0.64	0.82	0.82	−0.54	−0.57	−0.34
9	11.38	5	25	−0.71	−0.51	−0.44	−1.00	−0.86	−0.73
10	12.37	5	25	0.28	0.48	0.55	−0.02	0.13	0.26
11	12.87	6	36	−1.32	−1.10	−0.95	0.15	0.64	0.50
12	13.30	6	36	−0.89	−0.67	−0.52	0.58	1.06	0.93

212

Subsample 2 (6 observations)

13	0.70	1	1	−2.63	−2.88	−3.09	−0.36	−1.14	−1.64
14	6.87	2	4	1.50	1.22	−2.16	1.05	0.87	0.78
15	8.13	3	9	0.72	0.40	−1.92	−1.09	−0.99	−0.83
16	11.87	4	16	2.42	2.06	−0.92	0.60	0.67	0.90
17	11.63	5	25	0.14	−0.26	−0.92	−0.31	−0.61	−0.34
18	11.38	6	36	−2.15	−2.59	0.57	0.12	−0.86	−0.73

Subsample 3 (12 observations)

19	2.87	1	1	−1.24	—	−0.92	−0.22	—	0.53
20	2.87	1	1	−1.24	—	−0.92	−0.22	—	0.53
21	6.37	2	4	0.36	—	0.16	0.16	—	0.28
22	6.37	2	4	0.36	—	0.16	0.16	—	0.28
23	9.87	3	9	1.96	—	1.15	1.15	—	0.91
24	8.38	3	9	0.47	—	−0.34	−0.34	—	−0.58
25	11.13	4	16	1.32	—	0.51	0.51	—	0.16
26	10.13	4	16	0.32	—	−0.49	−0.49	—	−0.84
27	12.37	5	25	0.67	—	0.46	0.46	—	0.26
28	9.91	5	25	−1.79	—	−2.00	−2.00	—	−2.20
29	14.37	6	36	0.77	—	1.79	1.79	—	2.00
30	11.63	6	36	−1.97	—	−0.95	−0.95	—	−0.48

[a] Hypothetical data.

Table 6.9 Alfalfa Yields and Irrigation Water Applied: Effects of Selecting Different Levels and Ranges of Values of the Independent Variable upon Regression Constants and Standard Errors[a]

Range of Values of W	Dependent Variable, Y	Constant Term, b_0	Regression Coefficients of Y upon W	W^2	Standard Deviation of Y	Standard Error of Estimate $\bar{S}_{Y.W}$ or $\bar{S}_{Y.W,W^2}$	Coefficient of Determination r^2 or R^2	Standard Error of the Function $\hat{Y}$ when W equals 3	1	6
Linear Regression Equations (10 observations)										
1 and 2	Y =	−2.7300 (0.7044)	+4.7180 (0.4455)	—	2.5738	0.7044	0.9334	0.7044	0.3150	2.0172
	t:	3.8755	10.5898			Means:	Y 4.347	W 1.500	W^2 2.500	
2 and 3	Y =	2.3660 (0.8956)	+2.1700 (0.3513)	—	1.2579	0.5554	0.8267	0.2484	0.5554	1.2420
	t:	2.6418	6.1773			Means:	7.791	2.500	6.500	
3 and 4	Y =	2.4260 (1.5117)	+2.1500 (0.4276)	—	1.3001	0.6760	0.7597	0.3023	1.0901	1.0901
	t:	1.60	5.03			Means:	9.951	3.500	12.500	
4 and 5	Y =	9.0021 (2.4527)	+0.5060 (0.5417)	—	0.8504	0.8565	0.0983	0.8565	1.9153	0.8565
	t:	3.67	0.93			Means:	11.279	4.500	20.500	
5 and 6	Y =	5.6420 (3.9309)	+1.1780 (0.7118)	—	1.2293	1.1254	0.2551	1.8147	3.2227	0.5033
	t:	1.44	1.66			Means:	12.121	5.500	30.500	

214

Linear Regression Equations (15 observations)

1 to 3	Y =	−1.0313	+3.4440	—	3.0454	0.9296	0.9135	0.3795	0.3795	1.2002
		(0.6351)	(0.2940)							
	t:	1.62	11.72							
						Means:	5.857	2.000	4.667	
4 to 6	Y =	7.5460	+0.8420	—	1.1772	0.9731	0.3654	0.6648	1.2563	0.3973
		(1.5590)	(0.3077)							
	t:	4.84	2.74							
						Means:	11.756	5.000	24.667	

Linear Regression Equations (30 observations)

1 to 6	Y =	1.7825	+2.0068	—	3.7612	1.4377	0.8589	0.2735	0.4654	0.4654
		(0.5986)	(0.1537)							
	t:	2.98	13.06							
						Means:	8.805	3.500	15.167	

Parabolic Regression Equations (15 observations)

1 to 3	Y =	−5.2780	+8.5400	−1.2740	3.0454	0.6967	0.9551	0.3115	0.3115	5.9199
		(1.3581)	(1.5422)	(0.3816)						
	t:	3.89	5.54	3.33						
2 to 4	Y =	2.3062	+2.2199	−0.0100	1.9072	0.5965	0.9162	0.2668	1.1626	2.7848
		(2.7849)	(1.9692)	(0.3267)						
	t:	0.83	1.13	0.03						
3 to 5	Y =	−7.4371	+7.9035	−0.8219	1.4044	0.8023	0.7203	0.3587	3.7459	1.5632
		(6.8173)	(3.5247)	(0.4394)						
	t:	1.09	2.24	1.87						
4 to 6	Y =	15.7180	−2.5164	+0.3358	1.1772	0.9972	0.3848	1.9436	8.4724	0.4459
		(13.3852)	(5.4706)	(0.5461)						
	t:	1.74	0.46	0.61						

215

Continued

Table 6.9 (*continued*)

Range of Values of W	Dependent Variable, Y	Constant Term, b_0	Regression Coefficients of Y upon		Standard Deviation of Y	Standard Error of Estimate $\bar{S}_{Y.w}$ or $\bar{S}_{Y.w.w^2}$	Coefficient of Determination r^2 or R^2	Standard Error of the Function $\hat{Y}$ when W equals		
			W	W^2				3	1	6
Parabolic Regression Equations (20 observations)										
1 to 4	Y =	−3.3820	+6.1384	−0.6420	3.4933	0.7366	0.9602	0.2443	0.3211	1.8909
		(0.9171)	(0.8366)	(0.1647)						
	t:	3.69	7.34	3.90						
2 to 5	Y =	−0.8608	+4.5748	−0.4160	2.0721	0.7275	0.8897	0.2413	0.9057	0.9057
		(1.8675)	(1.1479)	(0.1627)						
	t:	0.46	3.99	2.56						
3 to 6	Y =	1.0150	+3.3880	−0.2430	1.6600	0.9434	0.7110	0.4112	2.4217	0.4111
		(4.1023)	(1.9079)	(0.2109)						
	t:	0.25	1.78	1.15						
Parabolic Regression Equations (30 observations)										
1 to 6	Y =	−2.2767	+5.0513	−0.4349	3.7612	0.9143	0.9450	0.2492	0.3706	0.3706
		(0.7314)	(0.4785)	(0.0669)						
	t:	3.11	10.56	6.50						

[a] Hypothetical data.

Table 6.10 Alfalfa Yields and Irrigation Water Applied: Linear and Parabolic Regressions Fitted to Proportional Subsamples of Original 30 Observations[a]

Sub-sample Number	Number of Observations n	Dependent Variable Y	Constant Term b_0	Regression Coefficients of Y upon W	W^2	Standard Deviation of Y	Standard Error of Estimate $\bar{S}_{Y.w}$ or $\bar{S}_{Y.w,w}{}^2$	Coefficient of Determination r^2 or R^2	Standard Error of the Function $\hat{Y}$ when W Equals 3	1	6
Linear Regression Equations											
1	12	$Y =$	1.6030 (0.8942)	+2.0977 (0.2296)	—	3.9597	1.3584	0.8930	0.4086	0.6952	0.6952
		t:	1.79	9.14							
2	6	$Y =$	1.2880 (2.0912)	+2.0406 (0.5370)	—	4.3140	2.2463	0.7831	0.9556	1.6258	1.6258
		t:	0.6159	3.8001							
3	12	$Y =$	2.2093 (0.8687)	+1.8990 (0.2231)	—	3.6135	1.3197	0.8788	0.3969	0.6754	0.6754
		t:	2.5432	8.5133							
1 and 2	18	$Y =$	1.4980 (0.8470)	+2.0787 (0.2175)	—	3.9600	1.5759	0.8509	0.3870	0.6585	0.6585
		t:	1.79	3.56							
1, 2, and 3	30	$Y =$	1.7825 (0.5986)	+2.0068 (0.1537)	—	3.7612	1.4377	0.8589	0.2735	0.4654	0.4654
		t:	2.9780	13.0565							

Continued

217

Table 6.10 (continued)

Sub-sample Number	Number of Observations n	Dependent Variable Y	Constant Term b_0	Regression Coefficients of Y upon		Standard Deviation of Y	Standard Error of Estimate $\bar{S}_{Y.w}$ or $\bar{S}_{Y.w,w^2}$	Coefficient of Determination r^2 or R^2	Standard Error of the Function $\hat{Y}$ when W Equals		
				W	W^2				3	1	6
Parabolic Regression Equations											
1	12	Y =	−2.5070	+5.1802	−0.44036	3.9597	0.6645	0.9770	0.2864	0.4259	0.4260
			(0.8406)	(0.5499)	(0.07691)						
		t:	2.9824	9.4196	5.7259						
2	6	Y =	−5.0620	+6.8031	−0.6804	4.3140	0.9836	0.9688	0.5995	0.8915	0.8915
			(1.7596)	(1.1512)	(0.1610)						
		t:	2.8768	5.9096	4.2262						
3	12	Y =	−0.6540	+4.0465	−0.3068	3.6135	1.0743	0.9277	0.4630	0.6885	0.6886
			(1.3589)	(0.8891)	(0.1243)						
		t:	0.4813	4.5515	2.4675						
1 and 2	18	Y =	−3.3586	+5.7212	−0.5204	3.9600	0.7920	0.9647	0.2787	0.4144	0.4143
			(0.8180)	(0.5352)	(0.0748)						
		t:	4.105803	10.6903	6.9528						
1, 2, and 3	30	Y =	−2.2767	+5.0513	−0.4349	3.7612	0.9143	0.9450	0.2492	0.3706	0.3706
			(0.7314)	(0.4785)	(0.0669)						
		t:	3.11	10.56	6.50						

[a] Hypothetical data.

variables $X_3 = X_2 + 0.4z_2$ and $X_4 = X_2 + 0.8z_2$. Finally, we constructed the variable $X_5 = z_2 + 4$.

Table 6.12 shows the simple correlation coefficients r for each pair of variables. We see that X_2 is perfectly correlated with X_1, or, X_2 is an exact linear transformation of X_1.

Interpretation of the Correlation Coefficients

The random components of X_i may be summarized as follows:

Table 6.11 Bivariate Normal Distributions: Constructed Series in Which the Random Components Consist of Two Independent Random Drawings from a Normal Distribution with Unit Variance[a]

Observation Number	X_1 $(z_1 + 4)$	X_2 $(0.8X_1 + 0.2)$	X_3 $(X_2 + 0.4z_2)$	X_4 $(X_2 + 0.8z_2)$	X_5 $(z_2 + 4)$
1	4.13	3.504	3.556	3.608	4.13
2	4.62	3.896	3.844	3.792	3.87
3	3.87	3.296	2.948	2.600	3.13
4	4.37	3.696	4.044	4.392	4.87
5	3.87	3.296	3.048	2.800	3.38
6	3.87	3.296	3.444	3.592	4.37
7	3.63	3.104	2.956	2.808	3.63
8	2.89	2.512	2.860	3.208	4.87
9	5.11	4.288	4.340	4.392	4.13
10	5.59	4.672	4.324	3.976	3.13
11	4.37	3.696	3.448	3.200	3.38
12	3.87	3.296	3.444	3.592	4.37
13	2.41	2.128	1.980	1.832	3.63
14	5.30	4.440	4.588	4.736	4.37
15	3.87	3.296	2.460	1.624	1.91
16	5.59	4.672	5.020	5.368	4.87
17	2.14	1.912	2.432	2.952	5.30
18	3.38	2.904	2.656	2.408	3.38
19	4.37	3.696	4.644	5.592	6.37
20	2.70	2.360	2.212	2.064	3.63

[a] Values of z_1 and z_2 are the sources of the random components in all five series X_1, X_2, X_3, X_4, and X_5. $X_1 = f(z_1)$; $X_2 = f(z_1)$; $X_3 = f(z_1, z_2)$; $X_4 = f(z_1, z_2)$; $X_5 = f(z_2)$.

Table 6.12   Correlation Coefficients between All Pairs of "Constructed" Variables

	X_1	X_2	X_3	X_4	X_5
X_1	1.0000	1.0000	0.8991	0.7175	0.0061
X_2	1.0000	1.0000	0.8991	0.7175	0.0061
X_3	0.8991	0.8991	1.0000	0.9500	0.4432
X_4	0.7175	0.7175	0.9500	1.0000	0.7009
X_5	0.0061	0.0061	0.4432	0.7009	1.0000

(C.1) $s_{X_1}{}^2 = s_{z_1}{}^2$

(C.2) $s_{X_2}{}^2 = s^2(0.8X_1) = s^2(0.8z_1) = 0.64s_{z_1}{}^2$

(C.3) $s_{X_3}{}^2 = s^2(0.8z_1 + 0.4z_2)^2 = 0.64s_{z_1}{}^2 + 0.16s_{z_2}{}^2 + 2(0.8)(0.4)r_{z_1 z_2}$

(C.4) $s_{X_4}{}^2 = s^2(0.8z_1 + 0.8z_2) = 0.64s_{z_1}{}^2 + 0.64s_{z_2}{}^2 + 2(0.8)(0.8)r_{z_1 z_2}$

(C.5) $s_{X_5}{}^2 = s_{z_2}{}^2$

The correlation coefficient between X_1 and X_5 is $r_{15} = 0.0061$. Since X_1 and X_5 are equal, respectively, to $(z_1 + 4)$ and $(z_2 + 4)$, this is precisely the sample correlation coefficient between z_1 and z_2, so $r_{z_1 z_2} = 0.0061$ also. Although the expected correlation of X_1 and X_5 in the population is 0, the nearness with which the *sample* coefficient r_{15} approaches 0 in this instance is somewhat coincidental, as the standard error of $r_{z_1 z_2}$ for samples of 20 observations from an uncorrelated population is about 0.2.

The expected value of r^2 between two variables in random samples from a bivariate normal population may be thought of as the proportion of the total variance of each which is common to both. The variables X_1 and X_5 have (in the population) no common variance. All the variance in X_2 is common to both X_2 and X_1, so $r_{12}{}^2 = 1$. If $r_{z_1 z_2}$ were identically equal to zero, X_3 would have $0.64s_{z_1}{}^2/(0.64s_{z_1}{}^2 + 0.16s_{z_2}{}^2) = 80\%$ of its variance in common with X_2 and also with X_1. Again, if $r_{z_1 z_2} = 0$, X_4 would have 50% of its variance in common with X_1, 50% with X_2, and 50% with X_5.

For $r_{34}{}^2$ we resort to the basic formula,

$$r_{34} = \frac{1/n \sum_{1}^{20} (0.8z_1 + 0.4z_2)(0.8z_1 + 0.8z_2)}{[(0.64s_{z_1}{}^2 + 0.16s_{z_2}{}^2)(0.64s_{z_1}{}^2 + 0.64s_{z_1}{}^2)]^{\frac{1}{2}}}$$

In the population $s_{z_1}{}^2 = s_{z_2}{}^2 = 1$ and $r_{z_1 z_2} = 0$. Hence the expected value of

$$r_{34} = \frac{(0.64 + 0.32)}{[(0.80)(1.28)]^{\frac{1}{2}}} \quad \text{or} \quad r_{34} = \frac{0.96}{1.024} = 0.94$$

Finally, X_3 has only $0.16/(0.64 + 0.16) = 20\%$ of its variance in common with X_5. The proportions of variance are, of course, estimates of r^2 rather than r.

Hence the expected values of the correlation coefficients would be

	X_1	X_2	X_3	X_4	X_5
X_1	1				
X_2	1	1			
$\rho_{ij} = X_3$	0.894	0.894	1		
X_4	0.707	0.707	0.938	1	
X_5	0	0	0.447	0.707	1

The extremely close correspondence of the sample correlation coefficients to the expected values must be regarded as a coincidence, since $r_{z_1 z_2}$ was very close to zero in this sample, even though its standard error was about 0.2. Standard errors of the other coefficients would range from about 0.13 for r_{35} through 0.07 for r_{14}, r_{24}, and r_{45} to less than 0.05 for r_{13}, r_{23}, and r_{34}.

It may appear that, although X_1, X_2, and X_5 are indeed random variables, X_3 and X_4 are not. However, it can be shown that the sum of two random variables, each having a normal distribution, is also a random variable with a normal distribution. In fact, any linear combination of two or more random variables is a random variable. So any pair of the X's in Table 6.11 forms a bivariate normal distribution; the random component of every one of the X's is either a random variable (a function of z_1 or z_2) or a linear combination of random variables (a function of z_1 and z_2).

The regression equations, standard errors of estimate, and r^2 for most of the pairs of X's are shown in Table 6.13. If we were to plot scatter diagrams of the 20 residuals about each of these equations, we should see that the "scatter" of X_1 and X_2 would be a straight line with no residuals around it. Except for a change in slope and slight change in level, the scatter diagrams of X_2 with X_3, X_4, and X_5 would look the same as the scatter diagrams between X_1 and X_3, X_4, and X_5; in fact, as we see from the tables, the correlation coefficients between X_2 and each of the other variables are identical with the corresponding correlation coefficients involving X_1. The scatter diagram between X_3 and X_5 would show a relatively large scatter of deviations around the regression line; scatters between X_4 and X_5, and X_4 and X_3 would be progressively smaller.

The scatter diagrams in the parent population or in very large samples would range from a virtually perfect circle for X_1 and X_5 through a broad oval or ellipse for X_3 and X_5 and progressively narrower ellipses for X_4 and X_5, X_4 and X_2, X_2 and X_3, and X_4 and X_3 to a straight line connecting X_1

Table 6.13 Regression Equations, Standard Errors of Estimate, and Values of r^2 for Different Pairs of X's

Equation Number		$\bar{S}$	r^2
1	$X_2 = 0.2000 + 0.8000X_1$	0.0000	1.0000
	$(0.0000) \quad (0.0000)$		
2	$X_3 = 0.2049 + 0.8024X_1$	0.3939	0.8084
	$(0.3785) \quad (0.0921)$		
3	$X_3 = 0.0043 + 1.0030X_2$	0.3939	0.8084
	$(0.4009) \quad (0.1151)$		
4	$X_4 = 0.2098 + 0.8048X_1$	0.7879	0.5148
	$(0.7569) \quad (0.1841)$		
5	$X_4 = 0.0086 + 1.0060X_2$	0.7879	0.5148
	$(0.8018) \quad (0.2302)$		
6	$X_4 = -0.6476 + 1.1940X_3$	0.3531	0.9025
	$(0.3253) \quad (0.0925)$		

and X_2, with no residuals. The straight line, then, is the limiting shape of an ellipse when $r = 1$ and the circular scatter of X_1 and X_5 is the limiting form of an ellipse when $r = 0$.

Having gone so far with "descriptive geometry" we recall the joint frequency table and joint frequency distribution of family income and clothing expenditures in Chapter 4. If we were to construct a three-dimensional model and erect on each small unit of area in the joint frequency distribution "ellipse" a vertical rod with height proportional to the number of observations falling on that area, we would find a strong central tendency in the resulting solid figure. If we had several thousand observations, the surface of this three-dimensional figure would become fairly smooth.

Let us assume that the two variables have equal population variances. Then the bivariate joint frequency surface for $r = 0$ could be generated by taking a normal curve with the appropriate variance, erecting it in a plane perpendicular to the surface of the scatter diagram with its mean directly over the point of means of the scatter, and then rotating the normal curve through 180 degrees.

As the degree of correlation between the two variables increased, the shape of the three-dimensional frequency surface would be better described by saying that any vertical slice through the surface parallel with one of the axes would have as its cross section a normal curve. This is related to the assumption in least squares regression that the residuals are normally distributed (in the parent population) with constant variance. Although it might be tempting to take such slices perpendicular to the long axis of the ellipse, actually the regression of (say) X_1 on X_3, except in the case of perfect correlation, will lie at an angle with this major axis. Conversely, the regression line of X_3 on X_1 under the assumptions of our illustration would lie at an angle with the major axis and on the opposite side of it from the regression line of X_1 on X_3.

The relationship in (6) of Table 6.13 is interesting because each of the two variables, X_4 and X_3, is a linear combination of the same two random variables, z_1 and z_2. The random variables z_1 and z_2 have almost zero correlation in the sample, and the closeness of correlation between X_4 and X_3 is a function of the relative weights used in combining z_1 and z_2 in the two instances. If the relative weights were the same in each case, there would be perfect correlation between X_4 and X_3. At the other extreme, if the weights were 1 and 0 for (say) X_4 and 0 and 1 for X_3, the correlation between X_4 and X_3 would be virtually 0, as is the sample correlation between z_1 and z_2.[1]

There is no need to reiterate the limited applicability of the correlation model in economic time series. The correlation coefficient and standard error formulas are quite sensitive to changes in the standard deviations of the independent variable from period to period. If we are interested in obtaining quite accurate estimates of regression coefficients, and if it is possible to subject the independent variable to experimental control, one can obtain small standard errors with a modest number of observations provided that the observations are spread out thinly over a wide range. Under such conditions, and supposing that there also exists a "natural" population of values of the independent variable from which we *could* sample at random, the random sample will inevitably provide us with a large number of values relatively close to the mean and contributing relatively little to the standard deviation of the independent variable. Random sampling when controlled experimentation is possible is quite inefficient in terms of information gleaned per observation. If the observations can be obtained by both random and controlled experimental methods, the designed experiment should be used.

EXERCISES

1. Distinguish carefully between the *standard error of estimate* and the *standard error of the estimator*.

2. It was stated in the text in that when we fit a straight least squares regression line through the six groups, only four degrees of freedom are absorbed by

[1] In matrix form we would have $\begin{bmatrix} X_4 \\ X_3 \end{bmatrix} = \begin{bmatrix} 1 & 0 \\ 0 & 1 \end{bmatrix} \begin{bmatrix} z_1 \\ z_2 \end{bmatrix}$ in the instance that yields zero correlation between X_4 and X_3. The situation that yields perfect correlation between X_4 and X_3 is $\begin{bmatrix} X_4 \\ X_3 \end{bmatrix} = \begin{bmatrix} \lambda_1 & 1 - \lambda_1 \\ \lambda_1 & 1 - \lambda_1 \end{bmatrix} \begin{bmatrix} z_1 \\ z_2 \end{bmatrix}$.

deviations of the six group means from the regression line. Explain why this is so.

3. To say that there is a standard error of the slope regression coefficient b of course implies that b is a random variable. Explain carefully the meaning of b as a random variable in simple regression analysis.

4. What are the main problems involved in using simple least squares regression analysis for forecasting purposes, with particular reference to the assumptions necessary for least squares estimation?

5. If we have a simple regression model of the form:

$$y_i = \alpha + \beta x_i + z_i \qquad (i = 1, 2, \ldots, N)$$

where we assume that:

(i) $E(z_i) = 0$ (iii) $V(z_i) = \sigma^2$

(ii) $E(z_i, z_j) = 0$ for $i \neq j$ (iv) the x_i are fixed (that is, measured without error)

prove that $\hat{\alpha}$ and $\hat{\beta}$, the least squares estimators for α and β are best, linear, unbiased (BLUE) estimators. (This is a proof of the Gauss-Markov theorem.)

6. Suppose we have a model of the form:

$$y_t = \alpha + \beta x_t + z_t \qquad (\text{where } t = 1, 2, \ldots, n)$$

where there is autocorrelation caused by a linear trend in the y_t and the x_t, for example, for the variable x,

$$x_t = \gamma + \delta t$$

and similarly for the variable y. Suggest a possible transformation of the data to eliminate the autocorrelation, specify the new transformed regression equation, and derive the least squares estimators of the transformed regression.

REFERENCES

1. Dwyer, P. S., *Linear Computations*, New York: John Wiley and Sons, 1951.
2. Ezekiel, Mordecai and Karl A. Fox, *Methods of Correlation and Regression Analysis*, Third edition, New York: John Wiley and Sons, 1959.
3. Ferber, R. and P. J. Verdoorn, *Research Methods in Economics and Business*, New York: The Macmillan Co., 1962.
4. Foote, R. J., "Analytical Tools for Studying Demand and Price Structures," Washington: United States Department of Agriculture, *Agriculture Handbook* No. 146, 1958.
5. Hart, B. I. and J. von Neumann, "Tabulation of the Probabilities for the Ratio of the Mean Square Successive Difference to the Variance," *The Annals of Mathematical Statistics* 13, No. 2, pp. 207–214, June 1942.
6. Theil, H., *Applied Economic Forecasting*, Amsterdam: North-Holland Publishing Co., and Chicago: Rand McNally and Co., 1966.
7. von Neumann, J., R. H. Kent, H. R. Bellinson, and B. I. Hart, "The Mean Square Successive Difference," *The Annals of Mathematical Statistics* 12, No. 2, pp. 153–162, June 1941.
8. Williams, E. J., *Regression Analysis*, New York: John Wiley and Sons, 1959.

CHAPTER 7

Multiple Regression Analysis

All of the basic logical concepts of regression analysis have been introduced in Chapter 6. Since the computations for three-variable linear regression analysis are identical with those for the second-degree parabola, little novelty will be involved.

In this chapter, we shall

1. Illustrate with some examples the range of economic models or problems that require multiple regression methods.

2. Illustrate the multiple regression model with experimental data for the three-variable case, and touch briefly once again on the regression model with nonexperimental observations.

3. Extend the correlation model into the three-variable case with particular attention to sampling fluctuations when the number of observations is small.

4. Analyze some new problems which become important in multiple, as distinct from simple, regression, including the effects of intercorrelation among the independent variables (in extreme form, multicollinearity), "hidden extrapolation," and the effects of random errors in the variables.[1]

5. Point out some instances of the cumulative increase in our knowledge which can sometimes be attained by applying multiple regression methods appropriately to large numbers of related problems in a specialized field.

The chapter appendices are quite extensive. Appendix A includes some notes on the intercorrelation problem with three variables. Appendix B summarizes multiple regression theory in matrix notation. And Appendix C

---

[1] The effects of random errors in variables are also important in the two-variable case, but the discussion is consolidated with that of the three-variable instance in this chapter.

outlines the principle and technique of multiple regression analysis by the short-cut graphic method.

7.1   ECONOMIC MODELS INVOLVING MULTIPLE REGRESSION ANALYSIS

Several examples of economic problems involving simple regression analysis were given in Chapter 4. Multiple regression analysis is very frequently involved in the empirical derivation of demand functions, production functions, Engel curves, and various macroeconomic relationships. A few illustrations follow.

7.1.1 *Consumer Demand Functions*

The theory of consumer demand states that an individual's purchases of a particular commodity will be influenced by the price of the given commodity, the prices of closely related (usually competitive) commodities, and the individual's income. The least complex representation of these elements in an empirical demand function would be

(7.1) $$q_1 = a_1 + b_{11}p_1 + b_{12}p_2 + c_1 y + z_1$$

calling for a multiple regression equation in four variables, one dependent and three independent. The most general statement of demand theory would make q_1 depend on the prices of *all* consumer goods and services; if p_2 is an index of prices of all consumer goods and services other than commodity 1, (7.1) takes at least formal cognizance of this principle.

The precision of demand analysis based on time series is usually limited by relatively small numbers of observations. In addition, research and development in the consumer goods and services industries tend to modify products and the competitive relationships between them, so that regression relationships calculated for one decade may suffer at least a gradual erosion of their inferential value during the succeeding one. For these reasons it is seldom possible to demonstrate statistically significant relationships between the consumption of a given commodity and the prices of more than two or three distinct competing commodities or commodity groups.

Table 7.1 shows several demand functions for food livestock products, all meat and individual meats in the United States. All variables were expressed in terms of first differences of logarithms; the constant terms are omitted from the table. The net effects in the first column under retail price are estimates of the elasticity of demand for the commodity with respect to its own price.

It will be noted that the own-price elasticities are larger (in absolute value) for individual meats than for all meats as a group, and larger for all meat than for all food livestock products (including meats, poultry and eggs, and dairy products). This progression from greater to smaller elasticities is to be expected when groups of competing commodities are aggregated. An increase in the prices of all other consumer goods and services evidently made livestock products and meat more attractive to consumers at any given level of food livestock and meat prices. The equations for beef and lamb indicate that an increase in the supply of competing meats tended to reduce the consumption of the given meat. The most important mechanism was probably the following: (1) An increase in the supply of pork would reduce the price of pork; (2) this would make beef and lamb relatively less attractive to consumers at the prices of beef and lamb previously existing, so that purchases of beef and lamb would fall *if* their prices were held constant.

Actually, the three meats listed, along with broilers and turkeys, form an interrelated system which can be treated in more consistent and elegant ways than those shown in Table 7.1. However, the individual coefficients and equations in Table 7.1 have been quite useful for economic forecasting and for analyzing some of the impact of proposed farm policies.

7.1.2 *Engel Curves or Family Expenditure Functions*

The first section in Chapter 4 involved family income and expenditure data and little more need be said here.

Houthakker (1957) fitted logarithmic multiple regression equations to data from family budget studies for a number of different countries. The equations were of the form

$$(7.2) \qquad \log Y_i = a_i + b_i \log X_1 + c_i \log X_2 + z_i$$

where Y_i is expenditure on the ith group of items, X_1 is total expenditure, X_2 is family size, z_i is a disturbance term, and a_i, b_i, and c_i are constants to be estimated. The parameters were estimated by means of least squares regression; however, the observations, which were averages of incomes and expenditures for groups of families within specified intervals of family income, were weighted according to the number of households represented in each group average. The multiple regression coefficients, b_i and c_i, are the partial elasticities of the ith group of items with respect to total expenditure and family size, respectively.[2]

[2] Hendrik S. Houthakker, "An International Comparison of Household Expenditure Patterns, Commemorating the Centenary of Engel's Law," *Econometrica*, p. 539 (October 1957).

Table 7.1 Food Livestock Products: Factors Affecting Year-to-Year Changes in per Capita Consumption, United States, 1922–1941

Commodity or Group	Coefficient of Determination (Multiple)	Effects of 1% Changes in							
		Retail Price		Price of All Other Commodities		Disposable Income[a]		Supply of Competing Commodities[a]	
		Net Effect	Standard Error	Net Effect	Standard Error	Net Effect	Standard Error	Net Effect	Standard Error
		Percent[b]		Percent[b]		Percent[b]		Percent[b]	
All food livestock products									
Actual income	0.91	−0.56	(0.04)			0.47	(0.04)		
Deflated income	0.95	−0.52	(0.03)	0.70[c]	(0.10)	0.40[d]	(0.03)		
All meat									
Actual income	0.96	−0.64	(0.03)			0.56	(0.04)		
Deflated income	0.96	−0.62	(0.04)	0.69[e]	(0.15)	0.51[d]	(0.05)		
Individual meats									
Pork	0.94	−0.81	(0.05)			0.72	(0.07)		
Beef	0.86	−0.79	(0.09)			0.73	(0.08)	−0.41[f]	(0.09)
Lamb	0.59	−0.91[g]	(0.26)			0.65	(0.23)	−0.83[f]	(0.20)

[a] Per capita basis.
[b] Coefficients based on first differences of logarithms.
[c] Special index, retail prices other than food livestock products.
[d] Disposable income deflated by retail price index.
[e] Special index, retail prices other than meat.
[f] Consumption per capita, other meats.
[g] Probably understates true effect of price upon consumption.

Source: Karl A. Fox, *Econometric Analysis for Public Policy* (Ames: Iowa State University Press), 1958, p. 116.

A specific example of Houthakker's results for large cities in the northern United States in 1950 follows (omitting the constant term):

	b	c
Food	$\log Y_1 = a_1 + 0.693 \log X_1$	$+ 0.224 \log X_2 + z_1$
	(0.017)	(0.016)
Clothing	$\log Y_2 = a_2 + 1.399 \log X_1$	$+ 0.016 \log X_2 + z_2$
	(0.059)	(0.054)
Housing	$\log Y_3 = a_3 + 0.764 \log X_1$	$- 0.155 \log X_2 + z_3$
	(0.011)	(0.010)
Miscellaneous	$\log Y_4 = a_4 + 1.367 \log X_1$	$- 0.111 \log X_2 + z_4$
	(0.011)	(0.010)

An interesting feature of these four equations is that, although they are fitted independently by least squares, the four b coefficients, each weighted by the proportion of total expenditure spent on the commodity concerned, must sum to unity since the four expenditure categories add up precisely to X_1, total consumption expenditure. Similarly, the weighted average of the c coefficients is zero, the weights again being the proportions of total expenditure for each of the four categories. It is clear from these constraints that if some income elasticities are less than one, others must be greater than one; also, that if (at some constant level of total expenditure) the expenditure for food increases with family size, the expenditures for one or more other categories must decrease as family size increases.

7.1.3 Macroeconomic Models

Since the end of World War II, economists have shown much interest in "models" or sets of equations to express the main features of the operation of a national economy. As noted in Chapter 5, "macroeconomic" thinking received great impetus from Keynes' *General Theory of Employment, Interest and Money* (1936) and from the work of several outstanding economists in Sweden. A Dutch economist, Tinbergen, developed an empirical model of the United States economy from 1919–1932 data with the object of testing Keynes' and other theories of the business cycle. The variables in Tinbergen's model were, of course, economic time series; they were highly aggregative; and each of the individual equations was estimated by means of multiple regression.

During the 1950s and 1960s, a number of models was designed to throw light upon particular mechanisms or sectors of the economy within the framework of total economic activity. Two equations developed by Duesenberry, Eckstein, and Fromm will illustrate this kind of model.[3]

The first equation expresses the net change in inventories (ΔI_t) for the national economy as a function of the current level of sales (S_t), the change in sales since the preceding quarter (ΔS_t), the change in new orders since the preceding quarter (ΔO_t), the rate of net inventory accumulation in the preceding quarter (ΔI_{t-1}), and the actual levels of inventories (I_{t-1}) and new orders (O_{t-1}) during the preceding quarter:

$$(7.3) \quad \Delta I_t = \underset{(0.078)}{0.295}S_t - \underset{(0.267)}{0.947}I_{t-1} - \underset{(0.107)}{0.333}\,\Delta S_t + \underset{(0.139)}{0.771}\,\Delta O_{t-1}$$
$$+ \underset{(0.054)}{0.115}O_{t-1} + \underset{(0.115)}{0.341}\,\Delta I_{t-1} + 8.508$$

The standard error of estimate was \$1.74 billion and $R^2 = 0.81$.

A second equation from the same model expresses changes in personal consumption expenditures (seasonally adjusted in 1947–1949 dollars per capita) as a function of consumption and income variables for earlier periods:

$$(7.4) \quad \frac{c_t}{y_{t-1}} = 0.5353 - \underset{(0.0217)}{0.1366}\frac{y_{t-1}}{y_{0t-1}} + \underset{(0.0457)}{0.5704}\frac{c_{t-1}}{y_{t-2}}$$

The standard error of estimate was 0.0168 (or 1.68 percentage points) and $R^2 = 0.83$. The von Neumann ratio was 2.18, so there was no evidence of autocorrelation in residuals from the equation.

A number of interesting aspects of these equations follow:

1. Personal consumption expenditures in the current quarter (c_t) are expressed as a ratio to disposable personal income during the preceding quarter (y_{t-1}) implying a three-month average lag on the part of consumers in adjusting their expenditure behavior to changes in their incomes.

2. The variable y_0 stands for the highest level of disposable income per capita actually realized before the current period, the theory being that consumers will tend to maintain their expenditures (hence their standards of living) at the highest level previously attained in the event that current income drops below the previous peak.

3. The inertia in consumer spending was further expressed by including as the second independent variable the ratio of consumption expenditures in the previous quarter (c_{t-1}) to disposable personal income in the quarter preceding that (y_{t-2}). All variables are on a per capita basis.

---

[3] The equations are taken from pp. 798 and 804 of J. S. Duesenberry, Otto Eckstein, and Gary Fromm, "A Simulation of the United States Economy in Recession," *Econometrica*, **28**, No. 4, pp. 749–809 (October 1960).

7.2 THE MULTIPLE REGRESSION MODEL

The multiple regression model, like the simple regression model of Chapter 6, may be applied either to controlled experiments or to nonexperimental observations. We shall deal first with the experimental case.

7.2.1 Multiple Regression Analysis and the Design of Experiments: A Production Function Example

Table 7.2 shows the values of corn yields obtained on 32 experimental plots to which the specified combinations of nitrogen and phosphate fertilizers were applied. Geometrically, these observations would cluster about a production surface in three dimensions, with the axis for corn yields perpendicular to the page. Note that there are two observations on corn yields for each "treatment," a treatment consisting of a particular *combination* of values of P and N. The form of the relationship between Y and N on the one hand and Y and P on the other is unclear when either P or N, respectively, equals zero; for each of the other levels of P or N, there appears to be a diminishing returns curve (see Chapter 2, Figure 2.5) connecting Y and the other kind of fertilizer. There is some suggestion that the maximum yield is reached for combinations involving somewhat less than 240 pounds of each fertilizer.

We could calculate the arithmetic mean of each of the 16 pairs of values in Table 7.2. For $P = 0$, the four means of the pairs of Y values could be

Table 7.2 Corn Yields Related to Amounts of Phosphorus and Nitrogen Applied, Iowa, 1952

Phosphate (Pounds per Acre)	Nitrogen (Pounds per Acre)			
	0	80	160	240
	Corn Yields (Bushels per Acre)			
0	24.5	28.7	17.3	16.2
	6.2	6.4	4.2	6.8
80	22.1	99.5	115.9	112.4
	30.6	115.4	72.6	125.6
160	12.0	102.2	129.7	130.5
	34.0	108.5	116.3	124.3
240	38.0	97.2	127.6	121.1
	35.0	107.8	125.8	114.2

Source: Heady, Pesek, and Brown, *op. cit.*

connected by broken lines, with N on the horizontal scale and Y on the vertical. The three similar lines for the other values of P would give a visual impression of the contours of the production surface (see Figure 2.6) when viewed perpendicularly to the YN plane. Conversely, we could connect the 16 "means of pairs" into four sets of four each with Y on the vertical axis and P on the horizontal scale to obtain a visual impression of the contours of the production surface as they might be projected by rays or beams of light perpendicular to the YP plane.

The variance of each pair of observations about the mean for that pair cannot be attributed to differences in the quantities of the two fertilizers applied. Hence this variance, with one degree of freedom for each pair or 16 degrees of freedom for the 16 pairs, might be taken as an estimate of the experimental error in corn yields—that is, the level of variation in Y not associated with variations in P and N. Of course, means based on samples of two observations are quite unstable, and it is quite unlikely that the "true" population regression of Y on some function of P and N would pass precisely through these 16 sample means.

In the following, we shall ignore the particular opportunity involved by the duplication of treatments or combinations of values of P and N. The point will be discussed further in Chapter 8 on analysis of variance.

Table 7.3 presents the same 32 observations in three parallel columns as a starting point for data transformations and multiple regression computations. These observations come from an actual experiment involving 114 experimental plots, but only 32 of these observations are shown here in order to conserve space and achieve simplicity in other respects.

Column 2 indicates that four different levels of application of *phosphate* were used: 0, 80, 160, and 240 pounds per acre, respectively. Eight experimental plots received each of these application levels.

Column 3 indicates that, among any eight experimental plots receiving the same amount of phosphate, two received no *nitrogen*, two received 80 pounds, two received 160 pounds, and two received 240 pounds of nitrogen. Thus from observations one through eight we could fit a simple regression of Y on N. We could fit a similar simple regression, $Y = a + bN$, to observations 9 through 16; another to observations 17 through 24; and a fourth to observations 25 through 32.

Conversely, we could select the eight observations which received no nitrogen (observations 1, 2, 9, 10, 17, 18, 25, and 26) and fit a simple regression, $Y = a + bP$, to them. A similar simple regression could be fitted for each of the three other levels of nitrogen application. If the simple regressions of Y on P and on N separately were linear, our multiple regression equation would be simply $Y = a + bP + cN$; the net contributions of P and N would be strictly additive. The other columns of Table 7.3 carry square, cross product, and square root transformations of the original variables to be used in nonlinear multiple regressions.

Consider the economic meaning of the linear production function $\hat{Y} = a + bP + cN$. The coefficient b implies that, regardless of the quantity of phosphate already applied to a field, another unit of phosphate will increase the expected yield by b units. For large values of P this violates common sense and the principle of diminishing physical returns. If the equation held good in real life, we could grow an unlimited amount of corn on a single acre of land. The coefficient c has the same implication for the response of corn yields to nitrogen.

The law of diminishing returns calls for a production function or surface which is convex from above, like that of Figures 2.5 and 2.6, and which reaches an absolute maximum yield at some combination of values of P and N. One of the simplest functions with these properties is the second-degree parabola in both variables, $\hat{Y} = a + b_1P + b_2P^2 + c_1N + c_2N^2$, which still implies that the effects of phosphate and nitrogen are strictly additive. If we wanted to test the hypothesis that a unit of nitrogen would be more effective in raising the yield if some phosphate were also used than if no phosphate were used, we would have to include an additional term which contained both N and P in a joint or multiplicative form, such as NP or $\sqrt{NP}$.

The following regression equations were obtained by fitting different functional forms to the 32 observations in Table 7.3.

Linear

(7.5) $Y = 2.9738 + 0.3176P + 0.2640N$ $\bar{S} = 32.5174$
$(0.0643)\quad(0.0643)$ $R^2 = 0.5875$

Cross Product

(7.6) $Y = 23.7660 + 0.1443P + 0.0908N$
$(0.1015)\quad(0.1015)$
$+ 0.001444NP$ $\bar{S} = 30.7026$
(0.000678) $R^2 = 0.6449$

(7.7) $Y = 7.3652 + 0.8177P + 0.5848N - 0.002806P^2$
$(0.1490)\quad(0.1490)\quad(0.000556)$
$- 0.002059N^2 + 0.001444NP$ $\bar{S} = 20.1169$
$(0.000556)\quad(0.000444)$ $R^2 = 0.8584$

Square Root

(7.8) $Y = 4.9011 - 0.4301P - 0.2971N + 7.7879\sqrt{P}$
$(0.1006)\quad(0.1006)\quad(1.6827)$
$+ 4.8142\sqrt{N} + 0.4456\sqrt{NP}$ $\bar{S} = 13.9679$
$(1.6827)\quad(0.0725)$ $R^2 = 0.9318$

Table 7.3 Corn Yields as a Function of Quantities of Nitrogen and Phosphate Fertilizers Applied[a]

Observation Number	X_1 Y Corn Yield (Bushels per Acre)	X_2 P Phosphate (Pounds per Acre)	X_3 N Nitrogen (Pounds per Acre)	X_4 P^2	X_5 N^2	X_6 NP	X_7 $\sqrt{P}$	X_8 $\sqrt{N}$	X_9 $\sqrt{NP}$
1	24.5	0	0	0	0	0	0	0	0
2	6.2	0	0	0	0	0	0	0	0
3	28.7	0	80	0	6,400	0	0	8.94	0
4	6.4	0	80	0	6,400	0	0	8.94	0
5	17.3	0	160	0	25,600	0	0	12.65	0
6	4.2	0	160	0	25,600	0	0	12.65	0
7	16.2	0	240	0	57,600	0	0	15.49	0
8	6.8	0	240	0	57,600	0	0	15.49	0
9	22.1	80	0	6,400	0	0	8.94	0	0
10	30.6	80	0	6,400	0	0	8.94	0	0
11	99.5	80	80	6,400	6,400	6,400	8.94	8.94	80
12	115.4	80	80	6,400	6,400	6,400	8.94	8.94	80
13	115.9	80	160	6,400	25,600	12,800	8.94	12.65	113.14
14	72.6	80	160	6,400	25,600	12,800	8.94	12.65	113.14
15	112.4	80	240	6,400	57,600	19,200	8.94	15.49	138.56

16	125.6	80	240	6,400	57,600	19,200	8.94	15.49	138.56
17	12.0	160	0	25,600	0	0	12.65	0	0
18	34.0	160	0	25,600	0	0	12.65	0	0
19	102.2	160	80	25,600	6,400	12,800	12.65	8.94	113.14
20	108.5	160	80	25,600	6,400	12,800	12.65	8.94	113.14
21	129.7	160	160	25,600	25,600	25,600	12.65	12.65	160.00
22	116.3	160	160	25,600	25,600	25,600	12.65	12.65	160.00
23	130.5	160	240	25,600	57,600	38,400	12.65	15.49	195.96
24	124.3	160	240	25,600	57,600	38,400	12.65	15.49	195.96
25	38.0	240	0	57,600	0	0	15.49	0	0
26	35.0	240	0	57,600	0	0	15.49	0	0
27	97.2	240	80	57,600	6,400	19,200	15.49	8.94	138.56
28	107.8	240	80	57,600	6,400	19,200	15.49	8.94	138.56
29	127.6	240	160	57,600	25,600	38,400	15.49	12.65	195.96
30	125.8	240	160	57,600	25,600	38,400	15.49	12.65	195.96
31	121.1	240	240	57,600	57,600	57,600	15.49	15.49	240.00
32	114.2	240	240	57,600	57,600	57,600	15.49	15.49	240.00

[a] Based on data from Earl O. Heady, John T. Pesek, and William G. Brown, "Crop Response Surfaces and Economic Optima in Fertilizer Use, *Ag. Exp. Sta. Res. Bul. 424*, Iowa State University, Ames, Iowa, March 1955.

Each successive equation appears to give a closer fit to the data. The original standard deviation of Y is 48.967 bushels per acre and the sum of squares $(Y - \bar{Y})^2$ is 74,332 for all four equations.

An interesting feature of the experimental design is shown in Table 7.4. The distributions of values of P and N have been chosen in such a way that the correlation between them is zero. Moreover, the correlations between P and the square root of N and between N and the square root of P are also zero. We shall see later in this chapter that intercorrelation among the independent variables in multiple regression analysis is a major problem with nonexperimental observations and particularly with time series. When controlled experiments are possible and appropriate, as in the present example, the problem of intercorrelation can be "designed out" and intercorrelations reduced to zero.

The correlation matrix (Table 7.4) indicates high correlations between P and the square root of P and between N and the square root of N. Intercorrelations between the square root of NP and the other variables (except for Y) are fairly moderate. As the matrix of correlation coefficients is symmetrical about the diagonal, Table 7.4 displays only the lower triangle.

This example will also serve to illustrate in passing the relationship between multiple regression analysis and the analysis of variance, which will be treated more extensively in a later chapter. We shall illustrate this in connection with a comparison between (7.5) and (7.8).

Equation (7.5) uses three degrees of freedom and apparently accounts for 58.75% of the total variance of Y about its mean. Equation (7.8) apparently accounts for 93.18% of the original variance in Y and, arithmetically speaking, the increase over 58.75% must be accounted for by the terms in square root of P, square root of N, and square root of NP. The R^2's for the two equations may reasonably be compared since they refer to the same basic population of Y, P, and N values.

Table 7.4 Corn Yields: Matrix of Simple Correlation Coefficients Associated with the Square Root Function (Eq. 7.8)

Variable \ Variable	Y	P	N	$\sqrt{P}$	$\sqrt{N}$	$\sqrt{NP}$
Y	1.0000					
P	0.5894	1.0000				
N	0.4900	0	1.0000			
$\sqrt{P}$	0.6754	0.9616	0	1.0000		
$\sqrt{N}$	0.5528	0	0.9616	0	1.0000	
$\sqrt{NP}$	0.9215	0.6212	0.6212	0.6460	0.6460	1.0000

The increase in R^2 between (7.5) and (7.8) certainly looks important. Is there a way of assessing its significance in a rigorous statistical sense? The following indicates the sort of test that can be made:

Source of Variation	Degrees of Freedom	Sum of Squares	Mean Square
Total	31	74,332	–
Linear regression	2	43,668	21,834
Additional variation accounted for by terms in square root of P, square root of N, and square root of NP	3	25,591	8,530
Residuals from cross-product regression	26	5,073	195

The significance of the increase in variation accounted for by adding the three square root terms can be tested by calculating

$$F = \frac{8530}{195} = 43.7$$

By referring to an F-table for ratios of mean squares based on three degrees of freedom in the numerator and 26 in the denominator, we find that values of F larger than about 4.7 could be expected to occur by chance only once in 100 samples if there were no significant difference between the two mean squares in the population. The increase in explained variance occasioned by adding the three square root terms cannot be attributed to chance.

7.2.2 Extension of the Assumptions of the Regression Model to Three or More Variables

The assumption of the simple regression model will be recalled from Chapter 6. A more rigorous statement is contained in Appendix B of this chapter. The main points are the following.

1. The values of the independent variables are regarded as fixed numbers, not subject to random or stochastic variation. If inferences are to be made from a sample to a population, strictly speaking the population is composed of all possible values of the dependent variable that might appear in indefinitely repeated samples, each of which contains precisely the same set of combinations of values of the independent variables. As we have seen in Chapter 6, the standard errors of regression constants and functions are quite sensitive to variations in the standard deviations of the independent variables. We shall see later in this chapter that the error formulas are also highly sensitive

to changes in the degree of intercorrelation among the independent variables from one sample or experimental design to another.

2. In the population, the residuals from regression are assumed to be uncorrelated with the independent variables.

3. In the population, the expected value of the residuals is zero; the variance of the residuals is assumed constant for all possible combinations of values of the independent variables; and the successive residuals (when some logical basis for ordering exists, as in time series) are uncorrelated.

7.2.3 *Multiple Regression Model with Nonexperimental Observations*

As noted in Chapter 6, the calculations are the same in experimental and nonexperimental instances, but the interpretations are somewhat different. The following equation by Fox and Boles (1961) is based on observations for 99 Iowa counties in the year 1955:

$$(7.9) \qquad \hat{X}_1 = 22.98 + 1.4986 X_2 - 0.3912 X_3 \qquad \bar{S} = \$2.59$$
$$\qquad\qquad\qquad (0.1459) \qquad (0.0200) \qquad R^2 = 0.814$$

where X_1 equals expenditures on Old Age and Survivors Insurance annuities per capita of the total county population, X_2 equals percentage of population 65 years of age and older in 1955, and X_3 equals percentage of the total population of the county in 1950 living on farms.

An eligible individual can collect OASI benefit payments calculated on the basis of definite formulas which include his average earnings in employment covered by the program. Before 1955, farm operators and other self-employed persons were not required to participate in the program and many stayed out of it. In the earlier years of the program, employees of very small firms, like those found more frequently in rural than in urban areas, were not required to participate. Thus, through 1955, the OASI program primarily affected urban workers.

Hence, a larger than average percentage of rural farm population in a county implies that a smaller proportion of the people over age 65 were eligible for OASI and also that some of those who were eligible would have established lower annuity rights than average workers of their age group in more urban and industrialized counties. The larger the percentage of elderly workers in the population, the larger would be OASI payments per capita of the total population.

It could be argued that the standard errors of the regression coefficients in (7.9) are inappropriate because there are only 99 counties in Iowa, there was only one set of financial records per county in the year 1955, and hence our sample coincides with the population.

An alternative viewpoint is: The residual variance in X_1 is accounted for by a variety of factors not correlated with X_2 and X_3; these factors might have assumed any number of different combinations of values in 1955; hence although the 99 values each of X_2 and X_3 *might* be regarded as exhausting the population of those values, still the residuals $z_{1.23} = X_1 - \hat{X}_1$ may be regarded as coming from one of an infinite number of possible random samples of X_1 *given* the specified combination of values of X_2 and X_3.

One more equation from the same study by Fox and Boles may be included:

$$(7.10) \quad X_1 = -11.3758 + 0.1656X_2 + 0.0972X_3 \qquad \bar{S} = 14.46 \text{ miles}$$
$$(0.0124) \qquad (0.0311) \qquad R^2 = 0.6706$$

where X_1 is the mileage of primary roads in a given county, X_2 is the area of the county in square miles, and X_3 is the density of the total population of the county in persons per square mile. Road mileages are as of December 31, 1957, and population density as given by the 1950 Census of Population. An average county in Iowa includes about 576 square miles and contained (in 1957) about 87 miles of primary roads. Thus the coefficient of X_2 is consistent with an average increase of one-sixth of a mile of primary road mileage for each increase of one square mile in county area above the average for the 99 counties. Since the main function of primary roads is to connect towns and cities of 1000 population or larger, total population density within a state with a relatively homogeneous agricultural base will vary almost exclusively with variations in urban population. A larger than average urban population in a given county is likely to mean a larger than average number of towns of 1000 population or more.

Although the values of county area and total population density for each of 99 counties exhausted the population of such values in Iowa, we could still argue that many different values of X_1 might have emerged in any county even with a specified pair of values of area and total population density. One could, of course, regard the equation for Iowa as throwing some light on a larger population that includes similar variables for several or many other states.

The rationale for interpreting multiple regression equations based on time series observations is similar to the foregoing explanation and has already been discussed in Chapter 6. The problem of autocorrelation, and methods of reducing it in many practical situations, have also been discussed in Chapter 6. No new problems are presented by an increase in the number of independent variables; the problem of autocorrelation inheres only in the residuals in the equation. Since many economic time series show positive autocorrelation in their original values, first difference transformations typically, although not inevitably, reduce autocorrelation in the residuals.

7.3 FLUCTUATIONS OF CORRELATION AND REGRESSION COEFFICIENTS IN SMALL SAMPLES FROM NONCORRELATED POPULATIONS

The assumptions of multiple regression theory are stated mainly in terms of population parameters or *expected* values. A population value of zero for a correlation coefficient is consistent with a wide range of nonzero values for the corresponding coefficient in successive random samples, particularly if these samples are small.

We shall try to clarify some problems of sampling errors and the interpretation of significance tests in small samples for the multiple regression and correlation models, for the two are similar in these respects.

Table 7.5 contains six series, each of 14 random numbers, derived from a table of random numbers. The numbers drawn were identified with the midpoints of specified intervals of a normal curve distribution with unit variance. The result is that the *expected value* of z_i^2 for each of the six variables is equal to 1.0; the *expected value* of $(z_i z_j)$, for j not equal to i, is zero.

In brief, each of the six series is a random sample from a normal distribution. We could also think of each of the six z_i's as a sample from a *different* normally distributed population with unit variance. If z_1 and z_2 have a correlation of zero in the normal bivariate population to which they belong,

Table 7.5 Random Numbers Translated into Unit Normal Curve Deviations with Population Mean Zero and Population Variance Unity[a]

Observation Number	Sample 1, z_1	Sample 2, z_2	Sample 3, z_3	Sample 4, z_4	Sample 5, z_5	Sample 6, z_6
1	0.37	1.11	0.13	−2.37	0.37	−0.37
2	−1.86	1.30	0.62	0.37	0.13	−0.37
3	0.62	2.09	−1.30	0.62	−2.59	1.86
4	1.11	−0.13	0.87	−1.30	0.13	−0.62
5	−0.13	−1.11	−0.37	1.11	0.37	0.13
6	0.37	−0.62	0.13	−0.62	1.11	−0.62
7	−1.11	−1.86	0.13	0.37	1.86	−0.13
8	1.86	2.09	0.87	−0.87	1.30	−0.37
9	1.11	−0.13	−1.30	0.37	0.62	−0.62
10	−1.11	0.13	−0.13	0.37	−0.37	0.37
11	−0.87	0.62	0.37	−1.11	−2.37	−0.37
12	−0.13	1.11	−0.13	−0.62	−0.13	0.37
13	−1.30	0.13	1.86	1.59	−0.37	−2.37
14	−0.62	0.62	1.59	−0.62	−0.62	−0.13

[a] $E(z_i) = 0$, $E(z_i^2) = 1$, $E(z_i z_j) = 0$ for $i, j = 1, 2, \ldots, 6$, $i \neq j$.

the scatter diagram between them for a sufficiently large sample should appear roughly circular.

We could also conceive of a scatter diagram in three dimensions in which the (z_1, z_2, z_3) observations might be represented by black beads on the ends of vertical wires of lengths z_1, thrust into (say) a soft composition board representing the z_2, z_3 plane. Then if the correlations among all pairs of z's in the three-variable normal distribution are zero, a sufficiently large sample will give us an approximately spherical cluster of observation beads.

In our example the expected value of each z is zero. Hence, if our random sample became sufficiently large, the mean values of each of the three z's would converge toward the point $(0, 0, 0)$ as closely as we might wish.

As we get into distributions involving four or more variables we can no longer use geometrical representations, but algebraic representations can be generalized for any number of variables. Thus the six series in Table 7.5 could be regarded as a sample of 14 observations drawn from a multivariate distribution in six dimensions. If the size of our sample were increased to several hundred or several thousand observations, the mean values of all six z's would approach zero, and the "centroid" or point of means of the complete six-variable distribution would approach the point $(0, 0, 0, 0, 0, 0)$ as closely as we liked.

7.3.1 *Variations in Sample Means*

It is important to recognize that population values of parameters such as the mean, the variance, and the correlation coefficient may be approximated only roughly in any particular small sample. Table 7.6 illustrates this point very clearly. Although the population means are all zero, the six means for samples of 12 observations range from -0.307 to 0.383; the six means for samples of 14 observations range from -0.231 to $+0.382$. Since the standard error of the mean for samples with standard error of estimate equal to one and with 11 or 13 degrees of freedom is about 0.3, only three out of the 12 means depart from zero by more than one standard error of the mean. This is about what we should expect in a series of 12 random samples.

7.3.2 *Differences between Sample Variances and Population Variances*

In this particular example, since the mean and variance of the population from which we are drawing are both known, we could take the unadjusted sum of squares of z_1 and divide by the actual number of observations to check the correspondence of the sample variance with the known population variance. Or we could use the sum of squared deviations of z_1 from its sample mean and divide by one less than the number of observations.

Table 7.6 Variance-Covariance and Correlation Matrices of Normally Distributed Random Numbers from a Population in Which $E(z_i^2) = 1$, $E(z_i z_j) = 0$

A. 12 Observations

Item	Variable	z_1	z_2	z_3	z_4	z_5	z_6
(1) Unadjusted Sums of Squares and Products	z_1	13.30					
	z_2	4.04	18.40				
	z_3	-0.98	0.26	5.64			
	z_4	-3.98	-5.42	-4.08	12.23		
	z_5	2.33	-8.43	3.37	-0.52	19.55	
	z_6	-0.60	3.09	-3.13	3.59	-6.14	5.47
(2) Adjusted Sums of Squares and Products	z_1	13.29					
	z_2	3.95	16.64				
	z_3	-0.98	0.31	5.64			
	z_4	-3.91	-4.00	-4.11	11.10		
	z_5	2.32	-8.60	3.38	-0.39	19.54	
	z_6	-0.58	3.38	3.14	3.36	-6.11	5.42
(3) Correlation Coefficients	z_1	1.00					
	z_2	0.27	1.00				
	z_3	-0.11	0.03	1.00			
	z_4	-0.32	-0.29	-0.52	1.00		
	z_5	0.14	-0.48	0.32	-0.03	1.00	
	z_6	-0.07	0.36	-0.57	0.43	-0.59	1.00

B. 14 Observations

Item	Variable	z_1	z_2	z_3	z_4	z_5	z_6
(1) Unadjusted Sums of Squares and Products	z_1	15.37					
	z_2	3.49	18.80				
	z_3	-4.38	1.49	11.62			
	z_4	-5.66	-5.59	-2.10	15.14		
	z_5	3.19	-8.87	1.70	-0.72	20.07	
	z_6	2.56	2.71	-7.74	-0.10	-5.18	11.10
(2) Adjusted Sums of Squares and Products	z_1	15.17					
	z_2	4.13	16.76				
	z_3	-3.98	0.22	10.83			
	z_4	-5.99	-4.56	-1.46	14.62		
	z_5	3.13	-8.65	1.83	-0.83	20.05	
	z_6	2.17	3.94	-6.97	-0.72	-5.31	10.35
(3) Correlation Coefficients	z_1	1.00					
	z_2	0.26	1.00				
	z_3	-0.31	0.02	1.00			
	z_4	-0.40	-0.29	-0.12	1.00		
	z_5	0.18	-0.47	0.12	-0.05	1.00	
	z_6	0.17	0.30	-0.66	-0.06	-0.37	1.00

In Table 7.6, the expected values of the *diagonal* elements of matrix $A(1)$ would all be 12; those in $B(1)$, with 14 observations, would all be 14. Similarly, matrix $A(2)$, with 11 degrees of freedom, would have an expected value of 11 for each diagonal element, and matrix $B(2)$, with 13 degrees of freedom, would have an expected value of 13 for each of the diagonal elements. However, in matrix $A(2)$ the adjusted sums of squares range all the way from 5.42 to 19.54; the corresponding variances range from about 0.5 to nearly 1.8, using 11 degrees of freedom.

This sort of instability is a result of the small size of our samples. When we include two more observations, the two smallest sums of squares in matrix $A(2)$ are both sharply increased, so that the smallest sum of squares yields a sample variance of about 0.8 and the largest yields a sample variance of about 1.5.

If we make an individual F-test for each of the 30 possible ratios of variances in the two sample sizes, we find no ratio which would cause us to reject the hypothesis that the two samples being compared were derived from the same population (or, more precisely, from populations with identical variances). About four ratios can be formed (all within the samples of 12 observations) which would occur less than five times in 100 samples from populations with identical variances. The number of relatively large negative correlation coefficients in matrix $A(3)$ suggests that we may indeed have a relatively unusual sample. But remember that samples at best yield statements of probabilities and not certainties.

7.3.3 *Sampling Fluctuations in Correlation Coefficients*

The main trouble with small samples for purposes of inference is that they *are* small. If we compare matrices $A(3)$ and $B(3)$, containing all the simple correlation coefficients, we find that the addition of two observations to the original 12 has made the following changes: r_{16} changes from -0.07 to $+0.17$; r_{34} changes from -0.52 to -0.12; r_{35} changes from 0.32 to 0.12; and r_{46} changes from 0.43 to -0.06.

The *expected values* of the off-diagonal elements in matrices $A(3)$ and $B(3)$ would be zero in all instances. Similarly, the expected values of the off-diagonal elements in matrices $A(1)$, $A(2)$, $B(1)$, and $B(2)$ (that is, the population values) would also be zero in every case.

7.3.4 *Multiple Regression Equations among Variables Not Correlated in the Population*

Table 7.7 shows regression coefficients, including constant terms, and their t-ratios for a number of regression equations computed from the random variables z_1 through z_6 for 12 and 14 observations, respectively. Generally,

Table 7.7 Regression Coefficients and t-Ratios for Selected Regression Equations among Normally Distributed Random Variables with $E(z_i^2) = 1$, $E(z_i z_j) = 0$

Dependent Variable	Independent Variable				Independent Variable			
	z_2	z_3	z_4	$X_0 = 1$	z_2	z_3	z_4	$X_0 = 1$
	Regression Coefficients (b_{ij})			b_o	t-Ratios $(b_{ij}/s_{b_{ij}})$			b_o/s_{b_0}
A. 12 Observations								
z_1	0.237			−0.072	0.871			−0.213
z_1		−0.173		0.018		−0.359		0.053
z_1			−0.352	−0.089			−1.075	−0.269
z_1	0.241	−0.186		−0.075	0.845	−0.381		−0.212
z_1	0.124	−0.554	−0.512	−0.191	0.423	−0.981	−1.218	−0.534
z_2		0.054		0.384		0.100		1.031
z_2			−0.361	0.273			−0.975	0.730
z_2		−0.286	−0.467	0.238		−0.451	−1.034	0.599
z_3			−0.370	−0.123			−1.923	−0.631
z_3	−0.077		−0.398	−0.102	−0.451		−1.895	−0.488
z_4	−0.228	−0.717		−0.226	−1.034	−1.895		−0.830
B. 14 Observations								
z_1	0.247			−0.215	0.929			−0.699
z_1		−0.368		−0.033		−1.132		−0.112
z_1			−0.410	−0.200			−1.522	−0.714
z_1	0.251	−0.373		−0.128	0.959	−1.143		−0.409
z_1	0.141	−0.425	−0.408	−0.152	0.540	−1.360	−1.451	−0.509
z_2		0.020		0.377		0.055		1.153
z_2			−0.312	0.322			−1.054	1.046
z_2		−0.022	−0.314	0.327		−0.062	−1.010	0.988
z_3			−0.100	0.219			−0.404	0.854
z_3	−0.016		−0.105	0.224	−0.062		−0.388	0.801
z_4	−0.270	−0.129		−0.059	−1.010	−0.388		−0.186

with approximately ten degrees of freedom in the residuals in most instances, t-ratios greater in absolute value than two would be expected to occur seven or 8 times out of 100 (assuming that each of the coefficients estimated is distributed independently of the other coefficients). In the four-right-hand columns of Table 7.7, we find no t-ratios exceeding two in absolute value, although several range from −1.360 to −1.923. Of 56 t-ratios in the table about two-thirds are less than one and the remainder less than two (in absolute value).

An investigator straining for "significant" results might be tempted to report certain regression coefficients having t-ratios of (say) −1.895 or −1.923 as supporting the hypothesis that the particular samples are drawn from a population in which a nonzero regression relationship exists. But they were in fact generated from noncorrelated populations.

7.3.5 *Sample Correlations between Variables Not Correlated in the Population*

In general, r^2 is a better indicator of closeness of relationship than r itself. For example, $r_{12}^2 = 0.0729$ indicates that a regression equation using up two out of a total of 11 degrees of freedom accounts for only 7.29% of the total variance in z_1. The F-ratio used to test the significance of this relationship would be less than 1. In squared form, the correlation coefficients for z_1 and z_3, z_2 and z_3, z_4 and z_5 are negligible.

However, $r_{46}^2 = 0.1849$ and $r_{56}^2 = 0.3481$. One correlation coefficient is positive and the other is negative. There is at least a suggestion that the relationship between z_6 and z_5 may be "significantly" different from that between z_6 and z_4. On the basis of the model which gave rise to our samples, such an inference to the parent population is invalid.

7.4 REGRESSION ANALYSIS IN A MULTIVARIATE NORMAL DISTRIBUTION WITH KNOWN POPULATION VARIANCES AND REGRESSION COEFFICIENTS: THE PROBLEM OF RANDOM ERRORS IN THE VARIABLES

Examples of multivariate normal distributions in economics are difficult to find and would be most unusual in sets of economic time series. For this and other reasons we will construct a multivariate normal distribution of our

Table 7.8   Random Errors Added to X_1, X_2, and X_3 to Form X_{1e}, X_{2e}, and X_{3e}

Observation Number	Random Errors		
	z_1	z_2	z_3
1	0.37	1.11	0.13
2	−1.86	1.30	0.62
3	0.62	2.09	−1.30
4	1.11	−0.13	0.87
5	−0.13	−1.11	−0.37
6	0.37	−0.62	0.13
7	−1.11	−1.86	0.13
8	1.86	2.09	0.87
9	1.11	−0.13	−1.30
10	−1.11	0.13	−0.13
11	−0.87	0.62	0.37
12	−0.13	1.11	−0.13

own, starting with the first 12 values of each of the random variables z_1, z_2, and z_3 in Table 7.5. We shall limit ourselves to the first 12 observations. The 12 values of z_1, z_2, and z_3 are tabulated in Table 7.8.

In Table 7.9, $X_1 = X_2 + X_3$. The regression equation of X_1 on X_2 and X_3 is $\hat{X}_1 = 0 + 1X_2 + 1X_3$, with $\bar{S}_{1.23} = 0$ and $R^2_{1.23} = 1$.[4]

In the next three columns of Table 7.9, we add to each X_2 the corresponding observation on z_2, to each X_3 the corresponding z_3, and to each X_1 the corresponding z_1. The resulting variables are X_{1e} ($= X_1 + z_1$); X_{2e} ($= X_2 + z_2$); and X_{3e} ($= X_3 + z_3$). We note that in the parent population, the expected values of $z_1{}^2$, $z_2{}^2$, and $z_3{}^2$ are all 1 and the expected values of $(z_1 z_2)$, $(z_1 z_3)$, and $(z_2 z_3)$ are all 0.

7.4.1 *Effects of Random Errors in Values of the Variables*

The correlation matrix of the three error-free variables X_1, X_2, and X_3 is

$$\begin{array}{c c} & \begin{array}{ccc} X_1 & X_2 & X_3 \end{array} \\ \begin{array}{c} X_1 \\ X_2 \\ X_3 \end{array} & \left[\begin{array}{ccc} 1.00 & & \\ 0.43 & 1.00 & \\ 0.89 & 0.03 & 1.00 \end{array}\right] \end{array}$$

As correlation matrices are symmetrical about the major diagonal, it is customary to show them in *lower triangular* form, as done here.

The correlation matrix of the three variables with the random error components z_1, z_2, and z_3 added to the original values, respectively, of X_1, X_2, and X_3 is

$$\begin{array}{c c} & \begin{array}{ccc} X_{1e} & X_{2e} & X_{3e} \end{array} \\ \begin{array}{c} X_{1e} \\ X_{2e} \\ X_{3e} \end{array} & \left[\begin{array}{ccc} 1.00 & & \\ 0.04 & 1.00 & \\ 0.85 & -0.38 & 1.00 \end{array}\right] \end{array}$$

By definition, each diagonal element is the correlation coefficient between a variable and itself, so the diagonal elements in a correlation matrix are always 1. However, the differences between the corresponding nondiagonal elements in the two matrices clearly reflect the fact that the addition of random error components has changed the *apparent* correlations among the three variables.

[4] It may be noted that X_2 and X_3 are simply multiples of two of the random variables in Table 7.5 which were random samples from normally distributed populations with unit variance. Thus $X_2 = 2z_4$ and $X_3 = 3z_5$. Since $X_1 = X_2 + X_3$, it is also true that $X_1 = 2z_4 + 3z_5$ and is therefore a weighted sum of random variables from a normal bivariate population with correlation zero between z_4 and z_5 in the population.

Table 7.9 Effects of Random Errors and Linear Coding upon Regression Results: Samples from a Multivariate Normal Population

Observation Number	Original Variables			Plus Random Errors			Plus Errors and Linear Coding		
	$X_1 =$ $(X_2 + X_3)$	$X_2 =$ $2z_4$	$X_3 =$ $3z_5$	$X_{1e} =$ $X_1 + z_1$	$X_{2e} =$ $X_2 + z_2$	$X_{3e} =$ $X_3 + z_3$	$X_{1e}^a = 100$ $+ X_{1e}$	$X_{2e}^a = 40$ $+ X_{2e}$	$X_{3e}^a = 30$ $+ X_{3e}$
1	-3.63	-4.74	1.11	-3.26	-3.63	1.24	96.74	36.37	31.24
2	1.13	0.74	0.39	-0.73	2.04	1.01	99.27	42.04	31.01
3	-6.53	1.24	-7.77	-5.91	3.33	-9.07	94.09	43.33	20.93
4	-2.21	-2.60	0.39	-1.10	-2.73	1.26	98.90	37.27	31.26
5	3.33	2.22	1.11	3.20	1.11	0.74	103.20	41.11	30.74
6	2.09	-1.24	3.33	2.46	-1.86	3.46	102.46	38.14	33.46
7	6.32	0.74	5.58	5.21	-1.12	5.71	105.21	38.88	35.71
8	2.16	-1.74	3.90	4.02	0.35	4.77	104.02	40.35	34.77
9	2.60	0.74	1.86	3.71	0.61	0.56	103.71	40.61	30.56
10	-0.37	0.74	-1.11	-1.48	0.87	-1.24	98.52	40.87	28.76
11	-9.33	-2.22	-7.11	-10.20	-1.60	-6.74	89.80	38.40	23.26
12	-1.63	-1.24	-0.39	-1.76	-0.13	-0.52	98.24	39.87	29.48

For published economic time series, we usually have only one set of reported values for each variable over a given period. These values correspond to the variables-with-errors X_{1e}, X_{2e}, and X_{3e} in the example. As scientists concerned with economic structure, we would *like* to start out with the error-free variables X_1, X_2, and X_3 and measure the relationships among them. Failing this, we would at least like to use the series X_{1e}, X_{2e}, and X_{3e} in such a way as to obtain the best *estimates* we can of the true relationships among the error-free variables X_1, X_2, and X_3.

In Praise of Correlation Coefficients—for Some Purposes. Although we have deprecated the value of correlation coefficients as measures of the relative success of regression analyses for different time periods or for samples based on widely different sets of values of the independent variables, matrices of correlation coefficients are frequently used (1) as a stage in regression computations and (2) as a basis for quick visual diagnosis of problems such as high intercorrelation which may give trouble at later stages of the analysis.

From the computing standpoint, it is a fact that the simple regression coefficient between any two variables is equal to the correlation coefficient multiplied by the ratio of the standard deviation of the dependent variable to that of the independent variable:

(7.11)
$$b_{12} = r_{12}\left(\frac{s_1}{s_2}\right)$$

Both b_{12} and r_{12} can be calculated directly from the sums of squares and cross products of deviations from means, which must be computed as a starting point for either correlation or regression analysis. Specifically,

$$b_{12} = \frac{\sum x_1 x_2}{\sum x_2{}^2} \quad \text{and} \quad r_{12} = \frac{\sum x_1 x_2}{\sqrt{\sum x_1{}^2 \cdot \sum x_2{}^2}}$$

Hence,

$$b_{12} = r_{12}\left[\frac{\sum x_1 x_2}{\sum x_2{}^2} \cdot \frac{(\sum x_1{}^2 \sum x_2{}^2)^{\frac{1}{2}}}{\sum x_1 x_2}\right] = r_{12}\left[\frac{(ns_1{}^2 \cdot ns_2{}^2)^{\frac{1}{2}}}{ns_2{}^2}\right]$$

$$= r_{12}\left(\frac{ns_1 s_2}{ns_2{}^2}\right) = r_{12}\left(\frac{s_1}{s_2}\right)$$

Since s_1 and s_2 are exact numbers in any given sample, we can carry through a complex series of calculations in terms of correlation coefficients and translate the end results back into regression coefficients, simply multiplying by the appropriate ratios of standard deviations.

Correlation coefficients are pure numbers. The facts that the diagonal elements of a correlation matrix are 1 and all the off-diagonal elements range between -1 and 1 mean that the coefficients are all of the same general order of magnitude; the same number of decimal places for each coefficient means roughly the same number of significant figures, and a given level of accuracy can be attained while carrying calculations to fewer decimal places than would usually be required with variables stated in their original units and with different numbers of decimal points.

The effects of errors on the multiple regression results may be shown by various paired comparisons.

(7.12) $\hat{X}_1 = 0.0753 + 0.9475 X_2$ $\bar{S}_{1.2} = 4.192$
           (1.2701)   (0.6291) $r_{12}{}^2 = 0.185$

(7.12a) $\hat{X}_{1e} = -0.4642 + 0.0977 X_{2e}$ $\bar{S}_{1e.2e} = 4.761$
           (1.3842)   (0.7096) $r_{1e,2e}^2 = 0.002$

(7.13) $\hat{X}_1 = -0.6119 + 0.9868 X_3$ $\bar{S}_{1.3} = 2.106$
           (0.6083)   (0.1589) $r_{13}{}^2 = 0.794$

(7.13a) $\hat{X}_{1e} = -0.5751 + 0.8992 X_{3e}$ $\bar{S}_{1e.3e} = 2.530$
           (0.7307)   (0.1782) $r_{1e,2e}^2 = 0.718$

(7.14) $\hat{X}_1 = 0.0000 + 1.0000 X_2 + 1.0000 X_3$ $\bar{S}_{1.23} = 0$
           (0)   (0)   (0) $R^2_{1.23} = 1.0000$

(7.14a) $\hat{X}_{1e} = -0.3725 + 0.9539 X_{2e} + 1.0696 X_{3e}$ $\bar{S}_{1e.2e,3e} = 1.793$
           (0.5213)   (0.2886)   (0.1363) $R^2_{1e.2e,3e} = 0.873$

The simple correlation between X_1 and X_2 is only moderate, and the regression coefficients b_0 and b_2 in (7.12) are both nonsignificant. The random components in (7.12a) have increased the standard error of estimate and the standard errors of the regression coefficients and reduced the coefficient of determination.

The correlation between X_1 and X_3 is quite high. The error components again reduce r^2 (from 0.794 to 0.718) and increase $\bar{S}$ (from 2.106 to 2.530); there is a related increase in the standard errors of the regression coefficients from (7.13) to (7.13a).

The coefficient b_3 is reduced moderately, from 0.9868 to 0.8992. We note also that b_{2e} was reduced from b_2 in the preceding pair of equations. This *bias toward zero* is characteristic of all *simple* regression coefficients when a random error component is added to the *independent* variable.

This bias toward zero does not necessarily carry through into the net or partial regression coefficients in equations involving two or more independent variables, as evidenced by (7.14) and (7.14a). Thus b_{3e} is greater than b_3, whereas b_{2e} is smaller than b_2. The standard error of estimate, $\bar{S}_{1e.2e,3e} = 1.793$, is a combination of the random components in all three of the variables X_{1e}, X_{2e}, and X_{3e}.

To see how the individual variables are affected by the addition of the error components, we may regress X_{1e} on X_1, X_{2e} on X_2, and X_{3e} on X_3, with the following results:

$$(7.15) \qquad \hat{X}_{1e} = 0.0171 + 0.9960X_1 \qquad \bar{S}_{1e.1} = 1.153$$
$$(0.3351) \quad (0.0785) \qquad r^2_{1e,1} = 0.941$$

$$(7.16) \qquad \hat{X}_{2e} = 0.2727 + 0.8196X_2 \qquad \bar{S}_{2e.2} = 1.233$$
$$(0.3735) \quad (0.1850) \qquad r^2_{2e,2} = 0.663$$

$$(7.17) \qquad \hat{X}_{3e} = -0.0154 + 1.0576X_3 \qquad \bar{S}_{3e.3} = 0.711$$
$$(0.2053) \quad (0.0536) \qquad r^3_{3e,3} = 0.975$$

The independent variables are error-free, as is assumed in regression theory. Random errors in the *dependent* variable in a pair do not *bias* the simple regression coefficient, but "bias" refers to the average or expected result in many samples and not to any one sample. The formula for the regression coefficient $b_{1e,1}$ in (7.15) may be written as

$$(7.18) \quad b_{1e,1} = \frac{\sum (x_{1e}x_1)}{\sum x_1^2} = \frac{\sum (x_1 + z_1)x_1}{\sum x_1^2} = \frac{\sum x_1^2 + \sum z_1x_1}{\sum x_1^2} = 1 + \frac{\sum z_1x_1}{\sum x_1^2}$$

Let us define

$$b_{z_1x_1} = \frac{\sum z_1x_1}{\sum x_1^2} = r_{z_1x_1}\left(\frac{s_{z_1}}{s_{x_1}}\right)$$

The correlation matrix of z_1, z_2, and z_3 with X_1, X_2, and X_3 is

$$
\begin{array}{c}
\\
z_1 \\
z_2 \\
z_3
\end{array}
\begin{array}{ccc}
X_1 & X_2 & X_3 \\
\left[\begin{array}{ccc}
-0.02 & -0.32 & 0.14 \\
-0.56 & -0.29 & -0.48 \\
0.05 & -0.52 & 0.32
\end{array}\right]
\end{array}
$$

Then the departures of the regression slopes in (7.15), (7.16) and (7.17) from 1 may be explained as follows:

$$(7.19) \qquad b_{z_1x_1} = -0.02\left(\frac{1.0524}{4.234}\right) = -0.02(0.25) = -0.005$$

$$(7.20) \qquad b_{z_2x_2} = -0.29\left(\frac{1.178}{1.924}\right) = -0.29(0.62) = -0.1798$$

$$(7.21) \qquad b_{z_3x_3} = 0.32\left(\frac{0.686}{3.828}\right) = 0.32(0.18) = 0.0576$$

(In these formulas the s_{z_i} and s_{x_i} are calculated with 12 degrees of freedom.) Hence,

$$b_{1e,1} = 1 - 0.005 = 0.995$$
$$b_{2e,2} = 1 - 0.180 = 0.820$$
$$b_{3e,3} = 1 + 0.058 = 1.058$$

These agree with the coefficients of (7.15), (7.16), and (7.17) except for rounding errors.

Because of the way in which z_1, z_2, and z_3 were drawn, the *expected* or population values in the correlation matrix just cited would be

$$
\begin{array}{c c}
 & \begin{array}{c c c} X_1 & X_2 & X_3 \end{array} \\
\begin{array}{c} z_1 \\ z_2 \\ z_3 \end{array} &
\left[\begin{array}{c c c}
0 & 0 & 0 \\
0 & 0 & 0 \\
0 & 0 & 0
\end{array} \right]
\end{array}
$$

But in our sample of 12 observations the corresponding coefficients range from -0.56 to 0.32. No one of these is significantly different from zero at the 5% level for samples with ten degrees of freedom, so we cannot reject the hypothesis that each pair of variables is uncorrelated in the parent population. We may also observe the following equations.

$$(7.22) \quad \hat{X}_1 = 0 + 1.0000X_2 + 1.0000X_3 \qquad \bar{S}_{1.23} = 0$$
$$R^2_{1.23} = 1.0000$$

$$(7.23) \quad \hat{X}_{1e} = -0.0916 + 0.8259X_2 + 1.0373X_3 \qquad \bar{S}_{1e.23} = 1.139$$
$$\phantom{(7.23) \quad \hat{X}_{1e} = } (0.3451) \quad (0.1710) \qquad (0.0859) \qquad R^2_{1e.23} = 0.959$$

$$(7.24) \quad \hat{X}_1 = -0.3733 + 1.0265X_{2e} + 1.0530X_{3e} \qquad \bar{S}_{1.2e,3e} = 1.577$$
$$\phantom{(7.24) \quad \hat{X}_1 = } (0.4586) \quad (0.2539) \qquad (0.1200) \qquad R^2_{1.2e,3e} = 0.896$$

$$(7.25) \quad \hat{X}_{1e} = -0.3725 + 0.9539X_{2e} + 1.0696X_{3e} \qquad \bar{S}_{1e.2e,3e} = 1.793$$
$$\phantom{(7.25) \quad \hat{X}_{1e} = } (0.5213) \quad (0.2886) \qquad (0.1363) \qquad R^2_{1e.2e,3e} = 0.873$$

Starting from the perfectly correlated set of variables X_1, X_2, and X_3, we let into the system successively larger amounts of random error. Equation (7.23) contains one source of error, z_1; (7.24) has two sources of error, z_2 and z_3; and (7.25) has three sources of error, z_1, z_2, and z_3. Each of the z's was drawn from a population with unit variance, so in large samples z_1, z_2, and z_3 should contribute about equally to the total random variance of any system to which they are added.

The standard errors of estimate of the three equations just cited are, respectively, 1.139, 1.577, and 1.793. Squaring, we obtain the corresponding variances 1.297, 2.487, and 3.215 which stand in *roughly* the ratios we should expect for one, two, and three sources of random error with equal population variances. The variances depart from the expected values of 1, 2, and 3 because (1) the *sample* variances are 1.11, 1.39, and 0.47 for z_1, z_2, and z_3 rather than 1, 1, and 1 as in the population; (2) the *sample* correlation coefficients among the z's are not zero, as in the population, but are equal to 0.27, -0.11, and 0.03, respectively, for z_1 and z_2, z_1 and z_3, and z_2 and z_3; and (3) the *sample* correlation coefficients between the errors z_1, z_2, and z_3 and the independent variables X_1, X_2, and X_3 are not zero, but form the matrix

$$\begin{array}{c} \\ z_1 \\ z_2 \\ z_3 \end{array} \begin{array}{ccc} X_1 & X_2 & X_3 \end{array} \\ \begin{bmatrix} -0.02 & -0.32 & 0.14 \\ -0.56 & -0.29 & -0.48 \\ -0.05 & -0.52 & 0.32 \end{bmatrix}$$

as we have seen.

In the error-free system, the matrix of adjusted sums of squares and cross products would be, in lower triangular form,

$$\begin{bmatrix} \sum x_1^2 & & \\ \sum x_2 x_1 & \sum x_2^2 & \\ \sum x_3 x_1 & \sum x_3 x_2 & \sum x_3^2 \end{bmatrix}$$

In the system X_{1e}, X_{2e}, and X_{3e} the corresponding matrix is

$$\begin{bmatrix} \sum (x_1 + z_1)^2 & & \\ \sum (x_2 + z_2)(x_1 + z_1) & \sum (x_2 + z_2)^2 & \\ \sum (x_3 + z_3)(x_1 + z_1) & \sum (x_3 + z_3)(\sum x_2 + z_2) & \sum (x_3 + z_3)^2 \end{bmatrix}$$

or

$$\begin{bmatrix} (\sum x_1^2 + \sum z_1^2 \\ \quad + 2 \sum x_1 z_1) & & \\ (\sum x_2 x_1 + \sum x_2 z_1 \\ \quad + \sum x_1 z_2 + \sum z_2 z_1) & (\sum x_2^2 + \sum z_2^2 \\ \quad + 2 \sum x_2 z_2) & \\ (\sum x_3 x_1 + \sum x_3 z_1 \\ \quad + \sum x_1 z_3 + \sum z_3 z_1) & (\sum x_3 x_2 + \sum x_3 z_2 \\ \quad + \sum x_2 z_3 + \sum z_3 z_2) & (\sum x_3^2 + \sum z_3^2 \\ \quad + 2 \sum x_3 z_3) \end{bmatrix}$$

The first matrix contains only six distinct summation terms, whereas the third matrix contains 21. In a random sample of infinite size, all of the nine cross-product terms $\sum_{i=1}^{3} \sum_{j=1}^{3} x_i z_j$ would approach zero and so would the three cross-product terms $\sum z_1 z_2$, $\sum z_1 z_3$, and $\sum z_2 z_3$. The terms $\sum z_1^2$, $\sum z_2^2$, and $\sum z_3^2$ would, of course, remain in the system and would approach

n times the population variance. (In our example the population variances all equal 1, so each $\sum z_i^2$ would approach n.)

It is the $\sum z_i^2$ terms which justify the statement that "random errors in the *independent* variable bias a simple regression coefficient toward zero."

We may simply contrast

$$(7.26) \qquad b_{12} = \frac{\sum x_1 x_2}{\sum x_2^2}$$

with

$$(7.27) \qquad b_{1,2e} = \frac{\sum x_1 x_2 + \sum x_1 z_2}{\sum x_2^2 + \sum z_2^2 + 2 \sum x_2 z_2}$$

If $\sum x_1 z_2$ and $\sum x_2 z_2$ both equal zero, (7.27) becomes simply

$$(7.28) \qquad b_{1,2e} = \frac{\sum x_1 x_2}{\sum x_2^2 + \sum z_2^2} = \frac{\dfrac{\sum x_1 x_2}{\sum x_2^2}}{1 + \dfrac{\sum z_2^2}{\sum x_2^2}}$$

or

$$b_{1,2e} = b_{12}\left(\frac{1}{1 + (\sum z_2^2 / \sum x_2^2)}\right)$$

One reason for the greater stability of b_{13} than b_{12} in our example was that

$$\frac{\sum z_2^2}{\sum x_2^2} = \frac{16.64}{44.40} = 0.375$$

whereas

$$\frac{\sum z_3^2}{\sum x_3^2} = \frac{5.64}{175.86} = 0.032$$

In this sample, these factors operating alone would have influenced the regression coefficients as follows:

$$b_{1,2e} \cong b_{12}\left(\frac{1}{1 + 0.375}\right) = 0.727 b_{12}$$

$$b_{1,3e} \cong b_{13}\left(\frac{1}{1 + 0.032}\right) = 0.969 b_{13}$$

The actual results in the sample were also influenced by the cross-product terms which disappear in infinite samples but not in small ones.

7.4.2 Comments on the Very Special Nature of the Present Constructed Example

It is only because we specified X_1, X_2, and X_3 and then added z_1, z_2, and z_3 as distinct numerical values that we are able to make many of the comparisons and comments in this section. The following array of correlation matrices may help to emphasize this:

	X_1	X_2	X_3	z_1	z_2	z_3	X_{1e}	X_{2e}	X_{3e}
X_1	1.00 X^2								
X_2	0.43	1.00							
X_3	0.89	0.03	1.00						
z_1	−0.02	−0.32	0.14	1.00 z^2					
z_2	−0.56	−0.29	−0.48	0.27	1.00				
z_3	0.05	−0.52	0.32	−0.11	0.03	1.00			
X_{1e}	0.97	0.34	0.90	0.23	−0.49	0.03	1.00 $(X+z)^2$		
X_{2e}	0.84	0.81	−0.32	−0.16	0.32	−0.50	0.04	1.00	
X_{3e}	0.84	−0.11	0.99	0.12	−0.44	0.47	0.85	−0.38	1.00

Typically, the real world presents us with data of the type $X + z$, with z, an error component. Error components are not necessarily random, but we will confine our comments here to random errors. The computation methods of correlation and regression analysis then give us the correlation matrix $(X + z)^2$ and all the regression measures that flow from it.

The method of least squares forcibly separates the total variation in the dependent variable into a portion that is linearly associated with the specified independent variables and a remainder which is uncorrelated with any or all of the independent variables. The residuals from the regression equation obtained in a particular sample are not the true errors that existed in and were drawn from the population but simply *estimates* of the population values.

The errors z_2 and z_3 affecting the independent variables are not supposed to exist. Carefully controlled experiments in most sciences should be able to keep such errors as z_2 and z_3 quite small relative to the standard deviations of X_2 and X_3. In nonexperimental data the investigator has to make such tests and inquiries as he can to form some judgment as to the magnitudes of z_2 and z_3.

The effects of superimposing successive increments of random error on the initial perfectly correlated set X_1, X_2, and X_3 are reflected in the correlation matrices:

	X_1	X_2	X_3
X_1	1.00		
X_2	0.43	1.00	
X_3	0.89	0.03	1.00

	X_{1e}	X_2	X_3
X_{1e}	1.00		
X_2	0.34	1.00	
X_3	0.90	0.03	1.00

$$
\begin{array}{cccc}
 & X_{1e} & X_2 & X_{3e} \\
X_{1e} & 1.00 & & \\
X_2 & 0.34 & 1.00 & \\
X_{3e} & 0.85 & -0.11 & 1.00
\end{array}
$$

$$
\begin{array}{cccc}
 & X_{1e} & X_{2e} & X_{3e} \\
X_{1e} & 1.00 & & \\
X_{2e} & 0.04 & 1.00 & \\
X_{3e} & 0.85 & -0.38 & 1.00
\end{array}
$$

Since the diagonal elements are always 1, we can summarize the comparison solely in terms of r_{12}, r_{13}, and r_{23}, as follows:

		(1)	(2)	(3)	(4)
Variables		X_1	X_{1e}	X_{1e}	X_{1e}
		X_2	X_2	X_2	X_{2e}
		X_3	X_3	X_{3e}	X_{3e}
Correlation coefficients	r_{12}	0.43	0.34	0.34	0.04
	r_{13}	0.89	0.90	0.85	0.85
	r_{23}	0.03	0.03	-0.11	-0.38
Sum of absolute values of differences of coefficients from Column (1)		−	0.10	0.27	0.84

For comparison, the regression measures are presented in columns in the same order:

$$
\begin{array}{cccc}
\bar{S}_{1.23} & 0 & 1.14 & 1.79 \\
R^2_{1.23} & 1 & 0.96 & 0.87
\end{array}
$$

$$
\begin{array}{cccc}
b_0 & 0 & -0.09 & -0.37 \\
b_{12} & 1 & 0.83 & 0.95 \\
b_{13} & 1 & 1.04 & 1.07
\end{array}
$$

$$
\begin{array}{cccc}
s_{b_0} & 0 & 0.34 & 0.52 \\
s_{b_{12}} & 0 & 0.17 & 0.29 \\
s_{b_{13}} & 0 & 0.09 & 0.14
\end{array}
$$

Clearly, each source of error reduces the quality of the results. If we had some basis for assigning a dollar value to a reduction in the standard error of estimate from (say) 1.79 to 1.14 we could also assign a rough dollar value to improvements in the accuracy with which X_2 and X_3 are measured—and also X_1 if we regard z_1 as partly attributable to errors of measurement.

If we had a basis for assigning dollar values to more accurate estimates of b_0, b_{12}, and b_{13}—that is, to better knowledge of the structural relationship between X_1, X_2, and X_3 we could also assign a dollar value to the reductions in s_{b_0}, $s_{b_{12}}$, and $s_{b_{13}}$ that could be achieved by increasing the size n of the sample, since the square root of $n - 3$ appears in the denominator of their formulas. If the sample size was increased from 12 to 39, or from 9 to 36 degrees of freedom in the residuals from the sample regression, we would *expect* the standard errors of the coefficients to be cut in half.

7.5 EFFECTS OF INTERCORRELATION ON MULTIPLE CORRELATION AND REGRESSION MEASURES IN THE THREE-VARIABLE CASE

Since correlation coefficients are pure numbers and can vary only from $+1$ to -1, they are often useful in comparing some properties of different populations even when these do not satisfy the assumptions of the correlation model. In this instance, correlation coefficients have only descriptive and not inferential significance. We shall use one kind of coefficient in this section that has not been discussed previously, namely, the beta coefficient. If each variable is divided by its standard deviation, regression equations can be calculated in terms of these standardized or *normalized* variables. As each observation in (say) X_1 is divided by the same constant (s_1), the normalized series (X_1/s_1) will correlate perfectly with X_1. The same applies to each of the other variables, so the simple, multiple, and partial correlation coefficients among the transformed variables are identical with those among the original variables. However, the regression coefficients are changed by a multiplicative factor representing the ratio of two standard deviations. Thus we may write

$$b_{12} = \frac{\sum x_1 x_2}{\sum x_2^2}$$

In contrast, the normalized variables X_1/s_1 and X_2/s_2 give us

$$\beta_{12} = \frac{\sum \left(\frac{x_1}{s_1}\right)\left(\frac{x_2}{s_2}\right)}{\sum \left(\frac{x_2^2}{s_2^2}\right)} = \frac{\sum x_1 x_2}{\sum x_2^2} \frac{s_2}{s_1} = b_{12}\left(\frac{s_2}{s_1}\right)$$

Conversely,

$$b_{12} = \beta_{12}\left(\frac{s_1}{s_2}\right)$$

It should be noted that the simple correlation coefficient between two variables is equal to the corresponding beta coefficient, so it is clear that any calculations carried on in terms of correlation coefficients can be translated into corresponding calculations and results in terms of beta coefficients or simple regression coefficients.

We have commented on unexpected correlations in small random samples drawn from noncorrelated populations. We have also noted the manner in which our production function experiment was designed to give zero intercorrelation between N and P, $\sqrt{N}$ and P, N and $\sqrt{P}$, and $\sqrt{N}$ and $\sqrt{P}$.

In these ways we have avoided dealing with very high correlation coefficients between independent variables. But this is one of the most vexing and perplexing problems in the multiple regression analysis of nonexperimental observations. It is particularly acute in economic time series. So the problem of high intercorrelation must be faced.

Economic statisticians have known the effects of intercorrelation in a general way for some 70 years. They have given particular attention to the extreme case ("multicollinearity") in which two or more independent variables are so highly correlated that their separate effects upon the dependent variable cannot be distinguished. At the other extreme, where there is no intercorrelation, the effects of the different independent variables are strictly additive.

Trained statisticians are also aware that increasing levels of intercorrelation are reflected in increasing standard errors of net regression coefficients—that is, high intercorrelation tends to mean lowered reliability for the individual regression constants. But most students of elementary statistics and many persons who make regression analysis as an occasional adjunct to their applied work have only a vague idea of the effects of intercorrelation and frequently get results from multiple regression analyses that they are unable to explain. More concrete information on the effects of intercorrelation through its whole range of variation and not merely at the points 0 and 1 should therefore be useful. This information for the three-variable case is shown by means of charts and tables for a number of pairs of values of the simple correlation coefficients between the dependent variable and each of the two independent variables.

The general problem of three-variable regression analysis is to estimate the values of a dependent variable X_1 based on given values of two independent variables X_2 and X_3. Assume that we have already calculated the direct correlation coefficients (r_{12} and r_{13}) between X_1 and X_2 on the one hand and X_1 and X_3 on the other for a number of different problems. Suppose that several of the analyses, based on entirely different sets of data, have yielded the same values of r_{12} and r_{13}. Nevertheless, in each instance, we may obtain different values for the multiple and partial correlation coefficients and for the net regression, or beta, coefficients. The coefficient of multiple determination $R^2_{1.23}$ may vary from almost 1.0 down to 0.5, or lower.

Why do these differences occur? In the three-variable case, these variations can be wholly explained by variations in the value of the intercorrelation coefficient r_{23} between the independent variables X_2 and X_3.

7.5.1 Basic Formulas

Some standard methods of calculating multiple correlation and regression coefficients start out from the determinant of simple correlation coefficients, which for the three-variable case is as follows:

$$(7.29) \quad \triangle_3 = \begin{vmatrix} 1 & r_{12} & r_{13} \\ r_{12} & 1 & r_{23} \\ r_{13} & r_{23} & 1 \end{vmatrix} = 1 + 2r_{12}r_{13}r_{23} - r_{12}^2 - r_{13}^2 - r_{23}^2$$

All the basic correlation and regression measures in the three-variable case can be derived from the values of the three simple correlation coefficients, with the following exceptions which are trivial in the present context. First, if we wish to talk about net regression coefficients in terms of original units (pounds, dollars, and so on) rather than normalized or standard deviation units we must multiply the beta coefficients by the ratio of the standard deviation of the dependent variable to that of the particular independent variable concerned. Second, the standard error of the beta coefficient, or of the corresponding net regression coefficient, is affected by the number of observations in the sample.

Equations (7.30) through (7.37) define the various correlation and regression measures in terms of the three simple correlation coefficients:

$$(7.30) \quad R^2_{1.23} = \frac{r_{12}^2 + r_{13}^2 - 2r_{12}r_{13}r_{23}}{1 - r_{23}^2}$$

$$(7.31) \quad \beta_{12.3} = \frac{r_{12} - r_{13}r_{23}}{1 - r_{23}^2}$$

$$(7.32) \quad b_{12.3} = \beta_{12.3} \cdot \frac{S_1}{S_2}$$

where S_1 and S_2 are the standard deviations of X_1 and X_2, respectively.

$$(7.33) \quad \beta_{13.2} = \frac{r_{13} - r_{12}r_{23}}{1 - r_{23}^2}$$

$$(7.34) \quad b_{13.2} = \beta_{13.2} \cdot \frac{S_1}{S_3}$$

where S_3 is the standard deviation of X_3.

$$(7.35) \qquad r_{12.3} = \frac{r_{12} - r_{13}r_{23}}{[(1 - r_{23}{}^2)(1 - r_{13}{}^2)]^{\frac{1}{2}}}$$

$$(7.36) \qquad r_{13.2} = \frac{r_{13} - r_{12}r_{23}}{[(1 - r_{23}{}^2)(1 - r_{12}{}^2)]^{\frac{1}{2}}}$$

$$(7.37) \qquad S_{\beta_{12.3}} = S_{\beta_{13.2}} = \left[\frac{1 + 2r_{12}r_{13}r_{23} - r_{12}{}^2 - r_{13}{}^2 - r_{23}{}^2}{[(N-3)(1 - r_{23}{}^2)]} \right]^{\frac{1}{2}}$$

$$= \left(\frac{1 - R_{1.23}^2}{(1 - r_{23}{}^2)(N-3)} \right)^{\frac{1}{2}}$$

$$(7.38) \qquad S_{b_{12.3}} = S_{\beta_{12.3}} \cdot \frac{S_1}{S_2}$$

and

$$(7.39) \qquad S_{b_{13.2}} = S_{\beta_{13.2}} \cdot \frac{S_1}{S_3}$$

These formulas show that once we have fixed the values of r_{12} and r_{13}, the various measures can be expressed simply as functions of r_{23}. In the charts and tables that follow, the value of each correlation measure was calculated for series of values of the intercorrelation coefficient r_{23} covering all or nearly all of the range of possible values of that coefficient, *given* the stated values of r_{12} and r_{13}.[5]

7.5.2 Discussion of Charts and Tables

In Figure 7.1 the values of r_{12} and r_{13} were chosen in such a way that the coefficient of multiple determination is 0.98 when the intercorrelation coefficient is zero. As r_{23} increases, the value of $R_{1.23}^2$ declines continuously, approaching a lower limit of 0.49 as r_{23} approaches 1. At this point the

---

[5] In the charts and tables that follow, r_{12} and r_{13} are always taken as positive, and the corresponding values of r_{23} and other measures are predominantly positive. If the same absolute values of r_{12} and r_{13} are taken with negative signs, the corresponding values of $R_{1.23}^2$, r_{23}, $S_{\beta_{12.3}}$, and $S_{\beta_{13.2}}$ are the same as before; *absolute* values of $\beta_{12.3}$, $\beta_{13.2}$, $r_{12.3}$, and $r_{13.2}$ are the same as before but with the opposite sign. If we take r_{12} positive and r_{13} negative, r_{23} will be predominantly negative. Values of $R_{1.23}^2$, $S_{\beta_{12.3}}$, $S_{\beta_{1.23}}$, $\beta_{12.3}$, and $r_{12.3}^2$ will be the same as in the first case (r_{12} and r_{13} both positive); and the *absolute* values of $\beta_{13.2}$ and $r_{13.2}$ will be the same as in the first case but with opposite sign. Finally, if we take r_{12} negative and r_{13} positive, the values of r_{23} will be predominantly negative; those of $R_{1.23}^2$, $S_{\beta_{12.3}}$, $S_{\beta_{13.2}}$, $\beta_{13.2}$, and $r_{13.2}$ will be the same as in the first case; and the *absolute* values of $\beta_{12.3}$ and $r_{12.3}$ will be the same as in the first case but with opposite sign. Since the *absolute* values of all the measures are unchanged by these interchanges of signs, the figures tabulated below each chart can be used for all four cases with appropriate changes in signs.

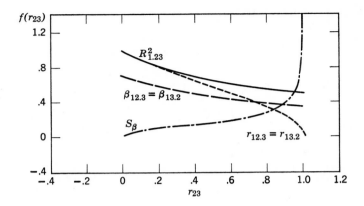

Figure 7.1 Effects of intercorrelation—3-variable case: $r_{12} = 0.7$; $r_{13} = 0.7$; $N = 20$. (From U.S. Department of Agriculture)

Table 7.10 Data for Case in Which $r_{12} = 0.7$, $r_{13} = 0.7$, and $N = 20$

							t-ratio for	
r_{23}	$R^2_{1.23}$	$\beta_{12.3}$	$\beta_{13.2}$	$r_{12.3}$	$r_{13.2}$	S_β [a]	$\beta_{12.3}$	$\beta_{13.2}$
-0.020 [b]	1.0000	0.7143	0.7143	1.0000	1.0000	0	–	–
0	0.9800	0.7000	0.7000	0.9803	0.9803	0.0346	20.2312	20.2312
0.100	0.8909	0.6364	0.6364	0.8866	0.8866	0.0806	7.8958	7.8958
0.200	0.8167	0.5833	0.5833	0.8003	0.8003	0.1058	5.5132	5.5132
0.300	0.7538	0.5385	0.5385	0.7193	0.7193	0.1261	4.2704	4.2704
0.400	0.7000	0.5000	0.5000	0.6417	0.6417	0.1449	3.4507	3.4507
0.500	0.6533	0.4667	0.4667	0.5659	0.5659	0.1649	2.8302	2.8302
0.600	0.6125	0.4375	0.4375	0.4901	0.4901	0.1887	2.3185	2.3185
0.700	0.5765	0.4118	0.4118	0.4118	0.4118	0.2209	1.8642	1.8642
0.800	0.5444	0.3889	0.3889	0.3267	0.3267	0.2728	1.4256	1.4256
0.900	0.5158	0.3684	0.3684	0.2249	0.2249	0.3872	0.9514	0.9514
0.950	0.5026	0.3590	0.3590	0.1570	0.1570	0.5478	0.6553	0.6553
0.980	0.4949	0.3535	0.3535	0.0985	0.0985	0.8655	0.4084	0.4084
0.990	0.4925	0.3518	0.3518	0.0695	0.0695	1.2278	0.2865	0.2865
0.999	0.4902	0.3502	0.3502	0.0219	0.0219	3.1623	0.1107	0.1107
1.000 [c]	–	–	–	–	–	–	0	0

[a] Identical for each β.
[b] Lowest possible value of r_{23}.
[c] Highest possible value of r_{23}.

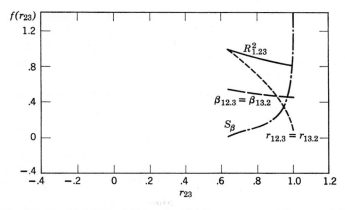

Figure 7.2 Effects of intercorrelation—3-variable case: $r_{12} = 0.9$; $r_{13} = 0.9$; $N = 20$. (From U.S. Department of Agriculture)

variable X_3 adds nothing to the explanation of X_1 that is not already given by the single independent variable X_2. The partial correlation coefficient $r_{12.3}$ decreases continuously as r_{23} increases, approaching zero as r_{23} approaches 1. The beta coefficient also decreases through this entire range and its standard error increases. By the time r_{23} exceeds 0.7, the beta coefficient (based on an assumed 20 observations) is no longer significantly different from zero at the commonly used 5% probability level.

Figure 7.2 illustrates the fact that the values of r_{12} and r_{13} set certain

Table 7.11 Data for Case in Which $r_{12} = 0.9$, $r_{13} = 0.9$, and $N = 20$

r_{23}	$R_{1.23}^2$	$\beta_{12.3}$	$\beta_{13.2}$	$r_{12.3}$	$r_{13.2}$	S_β[a]	t-ratio for $\beta_{12.3}$	t-ratio for $\beta_{13.2}$
0.620[b]	1.0000	0.5556	0.5556	1.0000	1.0000	0	–	–
0.700	0.9529	0.5294	0.5294	0.8710	0.8710	0.0735	7.2073	7.2073
0.800	0.9000	0.5000	0.5000	0.6883	0.6883	0.1277	3.9154	3.9154
0.900	0.8526	0.4737	0.4737	0.4737	0.4737	0.2135	2.2183	2.2183
0.950	0.8308	0.4615	0.4615	0.3306	0.3306	0.3195	1.4444	1.4444
0.980	0.8182	0.4545	0.4545	0.2076	0.2076	0.5193	0.8752	0.8752
0.990	0.8141	0.4523	0.4523	0.1463	0.1463	0.7431	0.6087	0.6087
0.999	0.8000	0.4500	0.4500	0.0462	0.0462	2.0000	0.2250	0.2250
1.000[c]	–	–	–	–	–	–	–	–

[a] Identical for each β.
[b] Lowest possible value of r_{23}.
[c] Highest possible value of r_{23}.

limits upon the range of values which r_{23} may take. Obviously, if X_2 and X_3 are both closely correlated with X_1 they have some degree of correlation with each other. The exact nature of the limits set upon r_{23} by the values of r_{12} and r_{13} is shown in Appendix A, note 1. In this particular instance, r_{23} cannot be lower than 0.62.

Figure 7.3 shows a result that may be surprising. As intercorrelation increases beyond a certain level, the "weaker" of the two partial regression coefficients changes sign from positive to negative. This change in sign occurs at a value of r_{23} somewhat above the value of the lower of the two simple correlation coefficients r_{12} and r_{13}. Within a considerable range of values of r_{23} in the region of this sign change, the value of the corresponding beta coefficient would not differ significantly from zero. Other features illustrated in Figure 7.3 are (1) the "stronger" of the two regression coefficients increases for a time as the intercorrelation increases, and (2) the coefficient of multiple determination trends down to a minimum at some value of r_{23} greater than the lower of the two direct coefficients and then increases again.

The characteristics of Figure 7.3 are repeated in the data shown in Tables 7.13 and 7.14 and in Figure 7.4. Each shows minimum values[6] for the co-

Table 7.12   Data for Case in Which $r_{12} = 0.9$, $r_{13} = 0.7$, and $N = 20$

							t-ratio for	
r_{23}	$R^2_{1.23}$	$\beta_{12.3}$	$\beta_{13.2}$	$r_{12.3}$	$r_{13.2}$	S_β[a]	$\beta_{12.3}$	$\beta_{13.2}$
0.3187[b]	1.0000	0.7535	0.4599	1.0000	1.0000	0	–	–
0.4000	0.9488	0.7381	0.4048	0.9473	0.8511	0.0599	12.3222	6.7579
0.4500	0.9191	0.7335	0.3695	0.9172	0.7578	0.0772	9.5013	4.7863
0.5000	0.8933	0.7333	0.3333	0.8892	0.6623	0.0917	7.9967	3.6347
0.5500	0.8703	0.7384	0.2939	0.8635	0.5632	0.1046	7.0593	2.8098
0.6000	0.8500	0.7500	0.2500	0.8402	0.4588	0.1175	6.3830	2.1277
0.6500	0.8329	0.7706	0.1991	0.8200	0.3472	0.1305	5.9050	1.5257
0.7000	0.8196	0.8039	0.1373	0.8039	0.2249	0.1442	5.5749	0.9521
0.7500	0.8114	0.8571	0.0571	0.7938	0.0867	0.1592	5.3838	0.3587
0.8000	0.8111	0.9444	−0.0556	0.7935	−0.0765	0.1758	5.3720	−0.3163
0.8500	0.8252	1.0991	−0.2342	0.8107	−0.2831	0.1925	5.7096	−1.2166
0.9000	0.8737	1.4211	−0.5789	0.8673	−0.5789	0.1977	7.1882	−2.9282
0.9413[c]	1.0000	2.1149	−1.2912	1.0000	−1.0000	0	–	–

[a] Identical for each β.

[b] Lowest possible value of r_{23}.

[c] Highest possible value of r_{23}.

[6] That is, minima in the mathematical sense of points at which the slope with respect to r_{23} is zero and becomes positive as r_{23} increases and negative as r_{23} decreases. Further information on these minimum values is given in Appendix A, note 2.

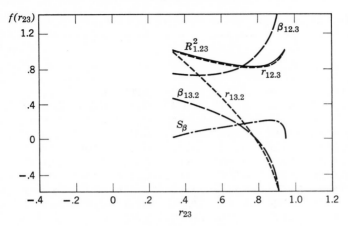

Figure 7.3 Effects of intercorrelation—3-variable case: $r_{12} = 0.9$; $r_{13} = 0.7$; $N = 20$. (From U.S. Department of Agriculture)

efficient of multiple determination $R^2_{1.23}$, the stronger partial correlation coefficient $r_{12.3}$, and the stronger regression coefficient $\beta_{12.3}$, and each shows a sign change for the weaker coefficients $\beta_{13.2}$ and $r_{13.2}$. As the spread between r_{12} and r_{13} increases, so also does the range of permissible values of r_{23}. When r_{13} falls to 0.3, r_{23} can take on small negative values as well as positive values. If r_{13} equals 0.1, then r_{23} can take values slightly lower than -0.3.

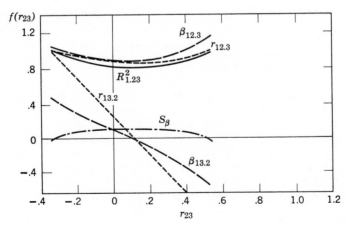

Figure 7.4 Effects of intercorrelation—3-variable case: $r_{12} = 0.9$; $r_{13} = 0.1$; $N = 20$. (From U.S. Department of Agriculture)

Table 7.13   Data for Case in Which $r_{12} = 0.9$, $r_{13} = 0.5$, and $N = 20$

r_{23}	$R^2_{1.23}$	$\beta_{12.3}$	$\beta_{13.2}$	$r_{12.3}$	$r_{13.2}$	S_β[a]	t-ratio for $\beta_{12.3}$	t-ratio for $\beta_{13.2}$
0.0725[b]	1.0000	0.8684	0.4371	1.0000	1.0000	0	–	–
0.1000	0.9798	0.8586	0.4141	0.9864	0.9454	0.0346	24.8150	11.9682
0.2000	0.9167	0.8333	0.3333	0.9428	0.7492	0.0714	11.6709	4.6681
0.3000	0.8681	0.8242	0.2527	0.9079	0.5532	0.0922	8.9393	2.7408
0.4000	0.8333	0.8333	0.1667	0.8819	0.3504	0.1082	7.7015	1.5407
0.5000	0.8133	0.8667	0.0667	0.8667	0.1325	0.1208	7.1747	0.5522
0.6000	0.8125	0.9375	−0.0625	0.8661	−0.1147	0.1311	7.1510	−0.4767
0.7000	0.8431	1.0784	−0.2549	0.8892	−0.4176	0.1345	8.0178	−1.8952
0.8000	0.9444	1.3889	−0.6111	0.9623	−0.8413	0.0954	14.5587	−6.4057
0.8275[c]	1.0000	1.5428	−0.7766	1.0000	−1.0000	0	–	–

[a] Identical for each β.
[b] Lowest possible value of r_{23}.
[c] Highest possible value of r_{23}.

The summary tables contain values of the "*t*-ratios," that is, ratios of the respective net regression coefficients to their standard errors. Since in each of the last four cases $\beta_{12.3}$ has a minimum and $S_{\beta_{12.3}}$ has a maximum, the corresponding *t*-ratio has a minimum beyond which it rises again with further increases in r_{23}.

Table 7.14   Data for Case in Which $r_{12} = 0.9$, $r_{13} = 0.3$, and $N = 20$

r_{23}	$R^2_{1.23}$	$\beta_{12.3}$	$\beta_{13.2}$	$r_{12.3}$	$r_{13.2}$	S_β[a]	t-ratio for $\beta_{12.3}$	t-ratio for $\beta_{13.2}$
−0.1458[b]	1.0000	0.9642	0.4406	1.0000	1.0000	0	–	–
−0.1000	0.9636	0.9394	0.3939	0.9798	0.8992	0.0465	20.2022	8.4710
0	0.9000	0.9000	0.3000	0.9435	0.6882	0.0767	11.7340	3.9113
0.1000	0.8545	0.8788	0.2121	0.9166	0.4842	0.0930	9.4495	2.2806
0.2000	0.8250	0.8750	0.1250	0.8987	0.2810	0.1035	8.4541	1.2077
0.3000	0.8110	0.8901	0.0330	0.8901	0.0722	0.1105	8.0552	0.2986
0.4000	0.8143	0.9286	−0.0714	0.8921	−0.1502	0.1141	8.1385	−0.6258
0.5000	0.8400	1.0000	−0.2000	0.9079	−0.3974	0.1120	8.9286	−1.7857
0.6000	0.9000	1.1250	−0.3750	0.9439	−0.6883	0.0959	11.7310	−3.9103
0.6858[c]	1.0000	1.3107	−0.5988	1.0000	−1.0000	0	–	–

[a] Identical for each β.
[b] Lowest possible value of r_{23}.
[c] Highest possible value of r_{23}.

Table 7.15 Data for Case in Which $r_{12} = 0.9$, $r_{13} = 0.1$, and $N = 20$

							t-ratio for	
r_{23}	$R^2_{1.23}$	$\beta_{12.3}$	$\beta_{13.2}$	$r_{12.3}$	$r_{13.2}$	S_β[a]	$\beta_{12.3}$	$\beta_{13.2}$
-0.3437[b]	1.0000	1.0595	0.4641	1.0000	1.0000	0	–	–
-0.3000	0.9604	1.0220	0.4066	0.9798	0.8899	0.0510	20.0392	7.9725
-0.2000	0.8917	0.9583	0.2917	0.9437	0.6556	0.0812	11.8017	3.5924
-0.1000	0.8465	0.9192	0.1919	0.9192	0.4381	0.1010	9.1010	1.9000
0	0.8200	0.9000	0.1000	0.9045	0.2294	0.1030	8.7379	0.9709
0.1000	0.8101	0.8990	0.0101	0.8990	0.0231	0.1122	8.0125	0.0900
0.2000	0.8167	0.9166	-0.0833	0.9027	-0.1873	0.1058	8.6635	-0.7873
0.3000	0.8418	0.9560	-0.1868	0.9166	-0.4089	0.1010	9.4653	-1.8495
0.4000	0.8930	1.0000	-0.3023	0.9319	-0.6432	0.0854	11.7096	-3.5398
0.5000	0.9733	1.1333	-0.4667	0.9864	-0.9272	0.0458	24.7445	-10.1900
0.5237[c]	1.0000	1.1680	-0.5116	1.0000	-1.0000	0	–	–

[a] Identical for each β.
[b] Lowest possible value of r_{23}.
[c] Highest possible value of r_{23}.

7.6   HIDDEN EXTRAPOLATION

Suppose that two independent variables X_2 and X_3 are highly intercorrelated, so that the scatter diagram of X_2 and X_3 forms a long narrow ellipse indicating a highly significant linear regression relationship between them. Suppose further that we were to draw a rectangle which completely enclosed the scatter of actual observations, the two vertical lines representing the smallest and largest values, respectively, of X_3 and the two horizontal lines representing the largest and smallest values of X_2. The major axis of the ellipse will lie approximately on the diagonal of this rectangle. Most of the observations will be clustered fairly close to this diagonal, and there may be no observations at all in substantial areas near the other two corners of the enclosing rectangle.

Obviously, it would be quite possible to choose values of X_2 and values of X_3, *each of which lies within the previously experienced range of its own sample values*; yet the two values in combination would place the observation in a portion of the rectangle for which no previous experience is available.

This situation is sometimes referred to as "hidden extrapolation." If there are only two independent variables and a small number of observations, it is not too difficult to check this graphically. However, if there are three independent variables having substantial intercorrelations among themselves, the sample observations will form an ellipsoid or football-shaped cluster in three dimensions. This ellipsoid can be enclosed by a rectangular parallelepiped or box. Given high intercorrelation, the observations will tend to cluster around one of the four corner-to-corner diagonals of this box, although the space near six of the eight corners of the box contains no observations at all. Here is the same basic problem of hidden extrapolation; a new observation falling near one of these six corners is outside of the range of experience covered by our original sample. Unless the regression relationship with which we are concerned is known to follow a definite "law" or functional form, hidden extrapolation may lead us into projections as poorly founded as were some of our linear approximations to the parabolic relationship between alfalfa yields and irrigation water in Chapter 6.

Fortunately, the formula for the standard error of the function, which can be generalized to any number of variables, automatically takes into account the problem of hidden extrapolation. The coefficients of terms involving $(x_2 x_3)$, $(x_2 x_4)$, and $(x_3 x_4)$ allow for the sample intercorrelations among all the independent variables. If we consider the parabolic yield and irrigation water function of Chapter 6, it is clear that W^2 is very closely correlated with W. There is, of course, an exact curvilinear relationship between W^2 and W, but the sample values of W^2 will deviate from a *straight-line* regression of one upon the other. A more common instance might be that the price of a commodity shows a high positive correlation with disposable personal income, so that a very low price in a year with very high income would take us outside the range of our previous experience in "explaining" consumption of the commodity as a function of price and income.

7.7 CUMULATIVE EFFECTS OF RUNNING MANY REGRESSION EQUATIONS OF SIMILAR FUNCTIONAL FORM ON DIFFERENT APPLICATIONS IN A SPECIALIZED FIELD

Multiple regression analysis can be used by a skilled investigator almost as a tool may be used by a skilled craftsman. Often, although it may not be possible to represent and estimate a complex economic structure in a rigorous way, the fitting of a considerable number of simple and multiple regression equations may throw much light on the structure as a whole.

If a research worker who is well trained in statistics and thoroughly competent in economics performs many regression analyses in a certain field of application, he may build up cumulative knowledge and judgment in this field which cannot readily be duplicated by persons who run only one or two regression studies in the area. Two examples of such potential cumulative effects are presented here.

7.7.1 *Multiple Regression Equations for Estimating Retail and Farm Prices of Food Products*

Table 7.16 presents some results of an extensive investigation of the demand, supply, and price structures for farm products and foods in the United States.[7] Although nearly all of the specific regression equations underlying the table were computed during a three-month period in 1950–1951, they reflected the author's experience with quantitative analysis of food and agricultural data over a period of several years. All of the equations were fitted to first differences (year-to-year changes) of the logarithms of the original time series variables.

The first column of Table 7.16 presents the standard errors of estimate associated with some of those equations in which price was used as the dependent variable. The percentages shown in Column (1) are based on antilogs of the original standard errors of estimate which were, of course, logarithmic. About two-thirds of the prices actually experienced during 1922–1941 were within one standard error of estimate of the corresponding prices estimated from the regression equation. Thus the correspondence between actual and estimated retail prices of most food livestock products was considerably closer than 5% in two years out of three. This level of accuracy was rarely attained at the farm price level. Error levels between 5 and 10% for farm prices of livestock and livestock products were fairly typical; for hogs, the standard error of estimate was about 15%.

Table 7.16 also shows some of the factors contributing to differences in the precision with which prices of the various commodities could be estimated at different market levels. A small standard error of estimate requires high correlation between price and the independent variables and relatively small variability in the price itself. These measures are shown in Columns (3) and (2), respectively. Their effects can be seen by comparing the results for beef and apples, where the difference in standard errors results solely from the difference in price variability, and those for meat at retail and dairy products at the farm level, where the difference in standard errors is due almost entirely to a difference in the level of correlation between price and the explanatory variables.

Columns (4), (5), and (6) show some factors accounting for differences in the basic variability of the various price series as indicated in Column (2). Farm prices of crops (in the absence of price supports) are more variable than farm prices of livestock products, mainly because of the greater year-to-year variation in crop supplies noted in Column (4).

The price of potatoes is more variable than that of hogs because the former responds more violently to a given change in supply [Column (5)]. In other

[7] First reported in Karl A. Fox, "Factors Affecting Farm Income, Farm Prices and Food Consumption," *Agricultural Economics Research*, pp. 65–82 (July 1951).

Table 7.16 Selected Farm and Food Products: Factors Affecting the Accuracy of Price Estimates, United States, 1922–1941

Commodity[a]	(1) Standard Error of Estimate, Percent of Expected Price[b]	(2) Standard Deviation of Actual Prices, Percent[c]	(3) Coefficient of Determination[d]	(4) Standard Deviation of Supply, Percent[e]	(5) Effect on Price of 1% Change in Supply, Percent	(6) Effect on Price of 1% Change in Demand, Percent[f]	(7) Ratio of Standard Error to Standard Deviation of Prices[g]
Retail prices
All meat	2.1	13.2	0.98	7.3	−1.07	0.86	0.16
Pork	4.9	17.8	0.92	13.2	−0.85	0.93	0.28
Beef	2.4	12.3	0.96	7.1	−0.83	0.83	0.20
Evaporated milk[h]	3.3	7.7	0.84	4.8	–	0.59	0.43
Butter[h]	5.3	13.6	0.84	3.3	–	1.01	0.39
Farm Prices
All meat animals	7.9	23.3	0.88	7.3	−1.60	1.43	0.34
Hogs	14.8	36.1	0.82	13.2	−1.54	1.63	0.41
Cattle	7.4	18.8	0.90	7.1	−1.19	1.27	0.39
Condensed milk[h]	9.7	19.6	0.76	4.8	–	1.34	0.49
Butterfat[h]	7.4	19.2	0.85	3.3	–	1.28	0.39
All dairy products	4.4	13.4	0.87	1.8	–	0.98	0.33
Apples	6.7	36.3	0.96	44.0	−0.79	1.04	0.18
Peaches	16.6	37.8	0.80	54.6	−0.67	0.96	0.44
Oranges	14.0	61.5	0.93	31.1	−1.61	1.34	0.23

Grapefruit	33.0	67.0	0.72	26.4	−1.77	1.29	0.49
All lemons	36.2	59.8	0.61	23.2	−1.69	0.78	0.61
Potatoes	16.3	72.9	0.93	15.0	−3.51	1.20	0.22
All onions	15.2	50.1	0.89	17.5	−2.27	1.00	0.30
Late summer	27.0	77.9	0.85	21.4	−2.90	0.72	0.35
Corn	17.9	48.3	0.85	21.4	−1.93	0.89	0.37
Hay	8.6	28.8	0.90	13.6	−1.63	0.96	0.30

[a] The supply variables used are total or per capita production unless otherwise noted.

[b] Represents minimum error range attainable two years out of three under most favorable possible conditions, *given* the particular regression equation used. In some instances, smaller standard errors could be obtained by using original values of all variables instead of first differences. Also, improvements could be obtained in some instances by further refinement of the basic data, the construction of special series, or the use of additional or different explanatory variables.

[c] Standard deviations of price for a few crops might be smaller than this in terms of original values, rather than the first differences actually used.

[d] Unadjusted. Represents the percentage of total year-to-year variation in retail price during 1922–1941 which was "explained" by the combined effects of the independent variables.

[e] Standard deviations of supply for a number of crops would probably be smaller in terms of original values (effectively, deviations from 1922–1941 averages) than in terms of the first differences (year-to-year changes) used here. For corn, for example, the standard deviation of the supply variable used would be only 18% based on logarithms of original values. The inertia in livestock production means that variation from one year to the next is usually smaller than variation around a 20-year average.

[f] The demand variable used in all analyses except those for corn and hay is disposable personal income. The standard deviation of this variable during 1922–1941, based on logarithmic first difference, was 12.3%.

[g] Standard error of estimate divided by standard deviation of actual prices.

[h] Supply variable used is per capita consumption of the end product.

Source: Karl A. Fox, *Econometric Analysis for Public Policy* (Ames: Iowa State University Press), p. 132, 1958.

269

words, the demand for potatoes is much less elastic than the demand for hogs. Some differences in price variability also result from differences in price responses to consumer income [Column (6)], the average year-to-year variability of which was about 12% during the 1922–1941 period. Farm prices are more variable in regard to percentage than retail prices because of the presence of relatively stable or even fixed elements in marketing charges. This is reflected in Columns (5) and (6), where price responses to both supply and income changes are indicated to be sharper in logarithmic or percentage terms at the farm than at the retail level.

Column (7) gives a measure of the over-all efficiency of each regression equation in terms of the ratio of the standard error of estimate to the original price variability. In a few instances, the standard error of estimate is only a fifth as large as the standard deviation; more commonly it is closer to a third as large for the analyses shown.

7.7.2 *Multiple Regression Analyses of Family Expenditures in Several Countries*

Table 7.17 is reproduced from an extensive study by H. S. Houthakker published, quite appropriately, on the hundredth anniversary of Engel's generalization about food expenditures taking up a declining percentage of income as family income rises—now known as "Engel's law."[8]

Family expenditures for each of four categories of consumer goods and services (food, clothing, housing, and miscellaneous) were regressed upon (1) total family expenditures and (2) family size. Total expenditures were used rather than total income because of differences among studies in the definition and measurement of family income. The equations were fitted to logarithms of the three variables, so the regression coefficients in Table 7.17 are *elasticities* of expenditures for particular categories of goods with respect to (1) total expenditures and (2) family size. The weighted sum of the four elasticities with respect to total expenditures is one; the weighted sum of the four elasticities with respect to family size is zero. Elasticities are pure numbers and those from different studies can be compared readily with one another even though the original data were in many different monetary units and quantity measures.

Let us now look at the elasticities with respect to total family expenditure in Table 7.17. (The numbers in parentheses are standard errors of the elasticity coefficients directly above them.) The elasticities for food are all

[8] A. S. Houthakker, "An International Comparison of Household Expenditure Patterns, Commemorating the Centenary of Engel's Law," *Econometrica* 25, pp. 532–551 (October 1957).

Table 7.17 Partial Elasticities for Four Expenditure Groups with Respect to Total Expenditure (1) and Family Size (2)

Country	Food		Clothing		Housing		Miscellaneous	
	1	2	1	2	1	2	1	2
Austria	0.554	0.351	1.767	−0.350	0.741	−0.210	1.620	−0.392
	(0.019)	(0.022)	(0.055)	(0.064)	(0.038)	(0.044)	(0.022)	(0.025)
Canada [a]	0.647	0.292	1.337	−0.114	1.114	−0.447	1.131	−0.061
	(0.008)	(0.007)	(0.092)	(0.081)	(0.043)	(0.038)	(0.036)	(0.032)
Finland	0.621	0.272	1.622	−0.310	0.802	0.008	1.445	−0.367
	(0.026)	(0.019)	(0.063)	(0.047)	(0.077)	(0.056)	(0.048)	(0.036)
France [b]	0.483	0.466	1.158	0.232	1.098	−0.652	1.656	−0.536
	(0.020)	(0.029)	(0.024)	(0.034)	(0.048)	(0.068)	(0.029)	(0.041)
Germany 1907	0.537	0.261	1.498	0.061	0.913	−0.154	1.604	−0.358
	(0.018)	(0.015)	(0.045)	(0.038)	(0.026)	(0.022)	(0.046)	(0.039)
Germany 1927–28 manual workers	0.598	0.291	1.297	−0.014	1.056	0.476	1.474	−0.481
	(0.035)	(0.019)	(0.054)	(0.029)	(0.483)	(0.262)	(0.334)	(0.181)
Germany 1927–28 clerical workers	0.501	0.274	1.035	0.226	0.881	−0.052	1.469	−0.298
	(0.030)	(0.025)	(0.059)	(0.049)	(0.070)	(0.058)	(0.089)	(0.074)
Germany 1927–28 govern. officials	0.385	0.319	0.918	0.149	0.887	−0.023	1.606	−0.335
	(0.027)	(0.027)	(0.079)	(0.081)	(0.054)	(0.055)	(0.069)	(0.071)
Germany 1927–28 all 3 groups [c]	0.473	0.295	1.049	0.102	0.906	0.196	1.447	0.034
	(0.020)	(0.015)	(0.047)	(0.036)	(0.045)	(0.035)	(0.082)	(0.063)
Ireland [g]	0.597	0.323	1.177	0.009	0.705	−0.221	1.478	−0.219
	(0.019)	(0.024)	(0.307)	(0.382)	(0.021)	(0.026)	(0.025)	(0.032)
Italy [d]	0.602	0.346	1.042	−0.733	[e]		[e]	
	(0.096)	(0.312)	(0.196)	(0.733)				
Japan 1955	0.556	0.309	1.593	−0.051	0.861	−0.383	1.416	−0.178
	(0.025)	(0.027)	(0.119)	(0.128)	(0.023)	(0.024)	(0.040)	(0.043)
Latvia [f]	0.430	0.482	1.094	−0.065	1.024	0.002	1.567	−0.516
	(0.030)	(0.033)	(0.077)	(0.084)	(0.059)	(0.062)	(0.037)	(0.040)

Continued

271

Table 7.17 *(continued)*

Country	Food 1	Food 2	Clothing 1	Clothing 2	Housing 1	Housing 2	Miscellaneous 1	Miscellaneous 2
Mexico[g]	0.657 (0.017)	0.248 (0.014)	e		e		e	
Netherlands manual workers	0.714 (0.050)	0.237 (0.014)	1.634 (0.097)	−0.110 (0.027)	0.514 (0.129)	0.021 (0.036)	1.273 (0.106)	−0.241 (0.029)
Netherlands white-collar workers	0.490 (0.025)	0.304 (0.019)	1.059 (0.043)	0.034 (0.034)	0.619 (0.044)	−0.016 (0.035)	1.403 (0.045)	−0.157 (0.036)
Netherlands both groups[c]	0.502 (0.022)	0.291 (0.014)	1.088 (0.045)	0.001 (0.029)	0.613 (0.036)	−0.001 (0.023)	1.406 (0.041)	−0.200 (0.026)
Norway[h]	0.515 (0.048)	0.131 (0.030)	1.266 (0.237)	−0.044 (0.149)	0.800 (0.144)	0.031 (0.091)	1.524 (0.050)	−0.296 (0.032)
Poland[i]	0.731 (0.030)	0.213 (0.027)	1.784 (0.041)	−0.497 (0.036)	0.662 (0.026)	−0.068 (0.022)	1.774 (0.030)	−0.534 (0.026)
Sweden	0.631 (0.048)	0.311 (0.048)	1.119 (0.138)	0.003 (0.138)	0.803 (0.085)	−0.008 (0.084)	1.446 (0.047)	−0.269 (0.046)
Switzerland	0.460 (0.036)	0.397 (0.026)	1.445 (0.075)	0.044 (0.055)	0.824 (0.242)	−0.137 (0.178)	1.879 (0.118)	−0.629 (0.086)
United Kingdom working class	0.594 (0.021)	0.294 (0.019)	1.042 (0.029)	0.143 (0.026)	0.553 (0.026)	−0.072 (0.023)	1.793 (0.026)	−0.390 (0.023)
United Kingdom middle class	0.344 (0.019)	0.386 (0.021)	1.342 (0.154)	−0.111 (0.169)	0.346 (0.031)	0.145 (0.034)	1.488 (0.016)	−0.221 (0.018)
United Kingdom both groups[c]	0.519 (0.027)	0.330 (0.032)	1.096 (0.057)	0.139 (0.067)	0.477 (0.023)	−0.045 (0.027)	1.640 (0.027)	−0.358 (0.032)
United States 1901[h]	0.712 (0.004)	0.158 (0.002)	1.435 (0.019)	0.016 (0.012)	0.839 (0.016)	−0.111 (0.010)	1.561 (0.045)	−0.241 (0.028)
United States 1950, large cities, North	0.693 (0.017)	0.224 (0.016)	1.399 (0.059)	0.016 (0.054)	0.764 (0.011)	−0.155 (0.010)	1.367 (0.011)	−0.111 (0.010)

272

United States 1950, suburbs, North	0.664 (0.029)	0.280 (0.030)	1.303 (0.090)	0.135 (0.092)	0.978 (0.115)	−0.236 (0.117)	1.255 (0.108)	−0.125 (0.112)
United States 1950, small cities, North	0.653 (0.029)	0.258 (0.028)	1.367 (0.079)	0.074 (0.076)	0.810 (0.054)	−0.237 (0.052)	1.370 (0.049)	−0.068 (0.047)
United States 1950, large cities, South	0.685 (0.015)	0.213 (0.015)	1.231 (0.055)	0.134 (0.055)	0.789 (0.040)	−0.271 (0.040)	1.245 (0.021)	−0.097 (0.021)
United States 1950, suburbs, South	0.698 (0.037)	0.190 (0.034)	1.147 (0.062)	0.175 (0.057)	0.974 (0.085)	−0.292 (0.078)	1.178 (0.036)	−0.090 (0.033)
United States 1950, small cities, South	0.687 (0.031)	0.235 (0.032)	1.068 (0.055)	0.287 (0.057)	1.122 (0.081)	−0.543 (0.083)	1.217 (0.033)	−0.151 (0.034)
United States 1950, large cities, West	0.682 (0.023)	0.193 (0.021)	1.410 (0.048)	−0.111 (0.045)	0.654 (0.032)	−0.182 (0.029)	1.243 (0.011)	−0.044 (0.010)
United States 1950, suburbs, West	0.709 (0.031)	0.225 (0.028)	1.285 (0.087)	0.124 (0.061)	0.933 (0.031)	−0.401 (0.028)	1.081 (0.010)	−0.111 (0.010)
United States 1950, small cities, West	0.645 (0.029)	0.292 (0.029)	1.195 (0.064)	0.145 (0.063)	0.766 (0.059)	−0.292 (0.059)	1.286 (0.038)	−0.187 (0.038)
United States 1950, all classes of cities	0.692 (0.002)	0.221 (0.002)	1.280 (0.006)	0.080 (0.006)	0.895 (0.013)	−0.287 (0.012)	1.248 (0.006)	−0.082 (0.006)

a Direct taxes (which are excluded from total and miscellaneous expenditure) estimated from other data in source.

b Based on breakdown by city (Paris, Rennee, and 17 others combined) and total expenditure.

c Allowing for possible social-class differences in levels of Engel curves (see text).

d Based on breakdown by region (North vs. South), farm vs. nonfarm, and total expenditure.

e Not computed because of insufficient data.

f Family size estimated from number of equivalent adults.

g Unweighted (see text).

h "Normal" families only, consisting of two adults and young children.

i Based on figures for individual households.

273

significantly less than one and therefore strongly confirm Engel's law.[9] The range, however, is substantial; the highest figure is 0.731 for Poland and the lowest 0.344 for the British middle-class survey. Since the standard errors are quite small, the differences between the various estimates are mostly significant.

The elasticities for clothing with respect to total expenditure are all, with one statistically nonsignificant exception, greater than unity, and with five exceptions, less than 1.5. For housing (which includes fuel and light, but not furniture) the elasticities are mostly below one. The elasticities for miscellaneous expenditures are all well above one; indeed, those for the Dutch manual workers, Canada, and the United States are the only ones below 1.4.

As has been pointed out, the elasticities for the four-commodity groups are not independent of each other. The sum of the four elasticities, each being weighted by the expenditure on the commodity concerned, must always equal unity. If the income elasticity of food expenditures for one country is higher than for another but the elasticities for clothing and housing in the two countries are about the same, the elasticity for miscellaneous items must be lower in the first country than in the second (except for possible differences in the weights given to different expenditure categories in the two countries).

The effects of increasing family size upon the allocation of a given amount of total family expenditures are measured by the coefficients under Column (2) of each category in Table 7.17. In every instance increasing family size means that a larger percentage of total expenditure is allocated to food. The effect of increasing family size is generally to increase the percentage of total expenditures for clothing, although the elasticities are usually much smaller than those for food and are often not significantly different from zero. Increasing family size means smaller percentages of total expenditures allocated (1) to housing and (2) to miscellaneous items in almost every instance.

Houthakker's article is an outstanding example of cumulative research in the field of household expenditures, drawing directly on economic theory and estimating the empirical counterparts of the theoretical relationships by means of multiple regression techniques.

[9] Engle's law, strictly speaking, refers to income elasticities, but these are normally smaller than elasticities with respect to total expenditure (since the elasticity of total expenditure with respect to income is normally less than one), and the strict form of the law is therefore also confirmed.

APPENDIX A

NOTE 1   LIMITS IMPOSED ON VALUES OF r_{23} BY GIVEN VALUES OF r_{12} AND r_{23}

By definition, no simple or multiple correlation coefficient can exceed 1 in absolute value.

We repeat (7.30)

$$(7.30) \qquad R^2_{1.23} = \frac{r_{12}{}^2 + r_{13}{}^2 - 2r_{12}r_{13}r_{23}}{1 - r_{23}{}^2}$$

noting that $R^2_{1.23}$ must lie between 1 and 0.

If $R^2_{1.23} = 1$, we have

$$(A.1) \qquad 1 - r_{23}{}^2 = r_{12}{}^2 + r_{13}{}^2 - 2r_{12}r_{13}r_{23}$$

Rearranging terms, we have

$$(A.2) \qquad r_{23}{}^2 - 2r_{12}r_{13}r_{23} + (r_{12}{}^2 + r_{13}{}^2 - 1) = 0$$

and, using a standard formula of elementary algebra, we obtain

$$(A.3) \qquad r_{23} = r_{12}r_{13} \pm \sqrt{(1 - r_{12}{}^2)(1 - r_{13}{}^2)}$$

If $r_{12} = 0.9$ and $r_{13} = 0.7$, as in Figure 7.3, we have

$$r_{23} = 0.63 \pm \sqrt{(0.19)(0.51)} = 0.63 \pm 0.3113$$

hence $r_{23} = 0.3187$ or 0.9413. Substituting these values back into (7.30) we obtain $R^2_{1.23} = 1$ in each instance.

Only if $r_{12} = r_{13}$ can r_{23} reach the maximum value of 1. But when $r_{23} = 1$, $R^2_{1.23} = r_{12}{}^2$, which is, in general, less than 1. This is shown in Figures 7.2 and 7.3.

Thus if $r_{12} = r_{13} = 0.7$, (A.3) gives us

$$r_{23} = 0.49 \pm 0.51 = 1 \qquad \text{or} \quad -0.02$$

Substituting -0.02 for r_{23} in (7.30) we obtain

$$R^2_{1.23} = \frac{0.98 - 0.98(-0.02)}{1 - (-0.02)^2} = \frac{0.9996}{0.9996} = 1$$

But if we substitute $r_{23} = 1$ we obtain

$$R^2_{1.23} = \frac{0.98 - 0.98(1)}{1 - (1^2)} = \frac{0}{0}$$

an indeterminate value.

This indeterminacy can be resolved by applying L'Hospital's rule,[1] from which we obtain

$$R^2_{1.23} = \frac{-0.98}{-2(1)} = 0.49 \ (= r_{12}{}^2)$$

NOTE 2   MINIMUM VALUES OF SPECIFIED CORRELATION AND REGRESSION MEASURES

Assume that we are given the values of r_{12} and r_{13} and wish to obtain the values of r_{23} at which various coefficients reach their minimum values within the permissible ranges in which $R^2_{1.23}$ is equal to or less than 1 and r_{23} is equal to or less than 1 in absolute value. A necessary condition for a minimum is that the partial derivative with respect to r_{23} of a measure that is a function of r_{23} be zero.

Starting with (7.30),

$$(7.30) \qquad R^2_{1.23} = \frac{r_{12}{}^2 + r_{13}{}^2 - 2r_{12}r_{13}r_{23}}{1 - r_{23}{}^2}$$

we find that $R^2_{1.23}$ reaches a minimum when

$$(A.4) \qquad r_{23} = \frac{(r_{12}{}^2 + r_{13}{}^2) \pm (r_{12}{}^2 - r_{13}{}^2)}{2r_{12}r_{13}}$$

that is, when $r_{23} = r_{12}/r_{13}$ or r_{13}/r_{12}.

When $r_{12} = r_{13}$ (as in Figures 7.1 and 7.2), $R^2_{1.23}$ reaches its minimum value when $r_{23} = 1$. When $r_{13} \neq r_{12}$, only one of the two values of r_{23} given by Eq. (A.4) will be less than 1, and hence a permissible value. In Figure 7.3 we have $r_{23} = 0.7/0.9 = 0.78$; in the data shown in Table 7.13, $r_{23} = 0.56$, and so on. It is clear that these are minimum rather than maximum values.

Using the same approach, the minima for the beta coefficients, $\beta_{12.3}$ $\beta_{13.2}$, respectively, are given at the points where

$$(A.5) \qquad r_{23} = \frac{r_{12} \pm \sqrt{r_{12}{}^2 - r_{13}{}^2}}{r_{13}}$$

and

$$(A.6) \qquad r_{23} = \frac{r_{13} \pm \sqrt{r_{13}{}^2 - r_{12}{}^2}}{r_{12}}$$

If $r_{12} = r_{13}$, the two beta coefficients are identical and reach their low point when $r_{23} = 1$. If $r_{13} > r_{12}$, the low point for $\beta_{12.3}$ is imaginary, whereas that for $\beta_{13.2}$ occurs at a value somewhat greater than r_{13}/r_{12}. The converse

[1] See pp. 15–16 of Frederick S. Woods, *Advanced Calculus*, new ed., illus. (New York), 397 pp., 1934, or other standard calculus texts.

is true if $r_{12} > r_{13}$. In the data shown in Table 7.13, for example, $\beta_{13.2}$ has no minimum value in the permissible range; $\beta_{12.3}$ has a minimum value at the point

$$r_{23} = \frac{0.9 \pm \sqrt{0.81 - 0.25}}{0.5} = \frac{0.900 \pm 0.748}{0.5} = 0.304$$

The second value of r_{23} is outside the permissible range.

A prominent feature of the cases illustrated in Tables 7.12 through 7.15 is the fact that $\beta_{13.2}$ changes sign at a value of r_{23} somewhat greater than that of r_{13}. Referring to (A.7)

(A.7)
$$\beta_{13.2} = \frac{r_{13} - r_{12}r_{23}}{1 - r_{23}^2}$$

we see that the sign is determined by the numerator only.

If

$$r_{23} = \frac{r_{13}}{r_{12}}, \qquad \beta_{13.2} = 0$$

if

$$r_{23} < \frac{r_{13}}{r_{12}}, \qquad \beta_{13.2} > 0$$

and if

$$r_{23} > \frac{r_{13}}{r_{12}}, \qquad \beta_{13.2} < 0$$

The minima for the partial correlation coefficients $r_{12.3}$ and $r_{13.2}$, respectively, are given at the points where

(A.8)
$$r_{23} = \frac{r_{13}}{r_{12}}$$

and

(A.9)
$$r_{23} = \frac{r_{12}}{r_{13}}$$

In Tables 7.12 through 7.15, $r_{13} < r_{12}$ and $r_{13.2}$ has no minimum in the permissible range of values for r_{23}. However, $r_{12.3}$ has a minimum at the level indicated by (A.8).

When $r_{12} = r_{13}$, $r_{12.3}$ and $r_{13.2}$ are equal and reach their lowest point in the permissible range when $r_{23} = 1$.

Finally, the minimum value of the standard errors of the beta coefficients can be obtained easily from formula (A.10)

(A.10)
$$S_{\beta_{12.3}} = S_{\beta_{13.2}} = \left[\frac{1 - R_{1.23}^2}{(N - 3)(1 - r_{23}^2)} \right]^{1/2}$$

When $R^2_{1.23} = 1$, $S_{\beta_{12.3}} = 0$ (provided $r_{23}{}^2$ is less than 1). Thus in Tables 7.12 through 7.15, $S_{\beta_{12.3}} = 0$ at two points, one at each end of the permissible range of values of r_{23}. In Figures 7.2 and 7.3, $S_{\beta_{12.3}} = 0$ at one point, the lowest permissible value of r_{23}.

Figures 7.1 and 7.2 indicate that, if $r_{13} = r_{12}$, $S_{\beta_{12.3}}$ approaches infinity as r_{23} approaches 1. This follows readily from (A.9), since if $R^2_{1.23}$ is less than 1 at the point where $r_{23} = 1$, we have a real number divided by zero.

If we set $\partial S_{\beta_{12.3}}/\partial r_{23} = 0$, we obtain

(A.11) $r_{23}{}^3 - 3r_{12}r_{13}r_{23}{}^2 + [2(r_{12}{}^2 + r_{13}{}^2) - 1]r_{23} - r_{12}r_{13} = 0$

For given values of r_{12} and r_{13} this can be solved most readily by plotting the values of the function for a range of values of r_{23}. Thus, for Table 7.14, the expression (A.11) becomes

$$r_{23}{}^3 - 0.81r_{23}{}^2 + 0.8r_{23} - 0.27 = 0$$

This equals zero when r_{23} is approximately 0.424. It is clear from the table that this is a maximum, or upper turning point, rather than a minimum.

APPENDIX B

MULTIPLE REGRESSION THEORY IN MATRIX NOTATION

The formulas that have been spelled out so laboriously in the text can be derived and expressed very compactly by the matrix methods described in Appendix A of Chapter 6. A little sampling theory is also woven into the derivation. Appendix A of Chapter 6 provides a further foundation for what follows.

We assume that the dependent variable y contains a *systematic* part that depends linearly on a number m of other variables and, in addition, a *random* part z. We need a notation to indicate that a given observation on y is associated with specified observations on $x_1, x_2, \ldots, x_m$; let us assume that the observations take the form of a time series and use the index t, where t runs from 1 to n, n being the total number of observations in the sample. We may then write

(B.1) $y(t) = \sum_{j=1}^{m} \beta_j x_{j(t)} + z(t)$

to denote any particular observation drawn from a population with regression parameters $\beta_j, j = 1, 2, \ldots, m$.

In matrix notation, (B.1) becomes

(B.2) $$y = X\beta + z$$

where

$$y = \begin{bmatrix} y(1) \\ y(2) \\ \vdots \\ y(n) \end{bmatrix} \qquad X = \begin{bmatrix} x_1(1) & \cdots & x_m(1) \\ x_1(2) & \cdots & x_m(2) \\ \vdots & & \vdots \\ x_1(n) & \cdots & x_m(n) \end{bmatrix} \qquad z = \begin{bmatrix} z(1) \\ z(2) \\ \vdots \\ z(n) \end{bmatrix} \qquad \beta = \begin{bmatrix} \beta_1 \\ \beta_2 \\ \vdots \\ \beta_m \end{bmatrix}$$

Least squares theory is based on the following assumptions:

1. The errors and/or disturbances in y have an expected or mean value of zero: $E(z) = 0$.

2. The z's are not correlated with one another and have the same expected variance for all possible sets of values of the x's: $E(zz') = \sigma^2 I$. Note that z' is the row vector $[z(1), z(2), \ldots, z(n)]$.

We cannot actually measure the variance of $z(t)$ in the sample for each time period; constant variance is simply an assumption we make about the population as a whole. If we *could* measure the population variances of z at each point $[x_1(t), x_2(t), \ldots, x_m(t)]$ and the covariances between the disturbances at all possible pairs of x_j's for different time periods, the variance-covariance matrix would be

(B.3) $$= \begin{bmatrix} \sigma_{11}^2 & 0 & \cdots & 0 \\ 0 & \sigma_{22}^2 & \cdots & 0 \\ \vdots & \vdots & & \vdots \\ 0 & 0 & \cdots & \sigma_{nn}^2 \end{bmatrix}$$

or, since $\sigma_{11}^2 = \sigma_{22}^2 = \cdots = \sigma_{nn}^2$,

(B.3a) $$= \begin{bmatrix} \sigma^2 & 0 & \cdots & 0 \\ 0 & \sigma^2 & \cdots & 0 \\ \vdots & \vdots & & \vdots \\ 0 & 0 & \cdots & \sigma^2 \end{bmatrix} = \sigma^2 \begin{bmatrix} 1 & 0 & \cdots & 0 \\ 0 & 1 & \cdots & 0 \\ \vdots & \vdots & & \vdots \\ 0 & 0 & \cdots & 1 \end{bmatrix} = \sigma^2 I$$

The matrix of sums of squares and products of the random variables z_1, z_2, and z_3, mentioned previously, is based on identical assumptions concerning the parent population. The matrix, even though based on only 12 observations of each z_i, is strongly "diagonal dominant" and the off-diagonal terms are relatively small. In the present notation, the matrix of terms in z_1, z_2, and z_3 is equivalent to a sample estimate of matrix (B.3) for only three observations.

3. The $m \times n$ values of $x_j(t)$ are real numbers containing no random errors or disturbances.

The method of least squares gives us an estimate b of the β in (B.1) which minimizes the sum of squares of the estimated disturbances. Here b is the column vector,

$$b = \begin{bmatrix} b_1 \\ b_2 \\ \vdots \\ b_m \end{bmatrix}$$

The vector of estimated disturbances is $z = y - Xb$, so the sum of squares is

(B.4) $\quad ns^2 = (y - Xb)'(y - Xb) = y'y - 2y'Xb + b'X'Xb$

where s^2 is the variance of the estimated disturbances.

We may differentiate (B.4) with respect to b in a generalization of the method described in Chapter 4, obtaining the m normal equations

(B.5) $\qquad\qquad\qquad\qquad X'y = X'Xb$

from which we derive

(B.6) $\qquad\qquad\qquad\qquad b = (X'X)^{-1}X'y$

The term $(X'X)^{-1}$ is the inverse of the matrix of sums of squares and products.

How is our estimate b related to β? From (B.1), we obtain

(B.2) $\qquad\qquad\qquad\qquad y = X\beta + z$

where X is a matrix with n rows and m columns. The matrix of sums of squares and products is $(X'X)$, so we multiply (B.2) by X' to obtain

(B.7) $\qquad\qquad\qquad\qquad X'y = X'X\beta + X'z$

Then multiplying (B.7) by the inverse $(X'X)^{-1}$ we obtain

(B.8) $\quad (X'X)^{-1}X'y = (X'X)^{-1}X'X\beta + (X'X)^{-1}X'z$

The coefficient of β is equal to I, the identity matrix, so

(B.9) $\qquad\qquad \beta = (X'X)^{-1}X'y - (X'X)^{-1}X'z$

Substituting from (B.6), we have

(B.10) $\beta = b - (X'X)^{-1}X'z$

or

(B.10a) $b = \beta + (X'X)^{-1}X'z$

Since the expected value of $X'z$ is zero—that is, the population z's are not correlated with the x_j's—the expected value of b, $Eb = \beta$. From (B.10a) we obtain

(B.11) $E[(b - \beta)(b - \beta)'] = E[(X'X)^{-1}X'zz'X(X'X)^{-1}] = \sigma^2(X'X)^{-1}$

The foregoing operation is analogous to squaring both sides of the equation. The left-hand side is now an m by m matrix of estimated variances and covariances of the regression coefficients, b $(= b_1, b_2, \ldots, b_m)$. Note that $\sigma^2 I = E(zz')$, and that $X'X(X'X)^{-1} = I$.

From (B.11) it is evident that the covariance matrix of the least squares estimator of β—that is, of the whole set of m regression coefficients, $b = (b_1, b_2, \ldots, b_m)$—is equal to the inverse of the matrix of sums of squares and products of the explanatory variables multiplied by the (population) variance of the disturbances, z. By assumption, the x_j's are all exact (population) values with no random components. Then the variance of disturbances in the sample, adjusted for m degrees of freedom used up in determining m regression coefficients, is taken as our best estimate of σ^2.

The sums of squares and products in $(X'X)$ can be doubled by repeating each of the $x_j(t)$ observations twice or, more generally, can be multiplied by k if we replicate each set of $x_j(t)$'s k times for all $t = 1, 2, \ldots, n$. If we are at liberty to increase the sample size in this way we can make the variances and covariances of our regression coefficients as small as we like. For as the elements of $(X'X)$ become very large the corresponding elements of its inverse become very small.

In particular, the variance of an estimated value of y, $\hat{y}$, may be written

(B.12) $V(\hat{y}) = \bar{S}_{y.12,\ldots,m}^2 \left[\dfrac{1}{n} + \sum_{j=1}^{m} \sum_{k=1}^{m} c_{jk}(x_j - \bar{x}_j)(x_k - \bar{x}_k) \right]$

where c_{jk} is the element at the intersection of the jth row and the kth column of the inverse $(X'X)^{-1}$. If the values of all the x_j's are set at their respective means,

(B.13) $V(\hat{y}) = \dfrac{1}{n} (\bar{S}_{y.12,\ldots,m}^2)$

the squared standard error of the mean of y *given* the information contained in the regression equation.

It is quite possible to include a dummy variable, $X_0 = 1$ for all values of t, in the original list of x_j's; the coefficient corresponding to this variable, b_0, is the constant term of the regression equation and its variance can be estimated like that of any other coefficient.

We can, of course, extend (B.12) to give us the standard error of forecast of an individual value of y not included in the original sample:

$$(B.14) \quad V(y) = \bar{S}^2_{y.12,\ldots,m}\left[1 + \frac{1}{n} + \sum_{j=1}^{m} \sum_{k=1}^{m} c_{jk}(x_j - \bar{x}_j)(x_k - \bar{x}_k)\right]$$

Returning to (B.12), we may rearrange terms to provide a computational scheme for the terms involving the c_{jk}'s and $(x_j - \bar{x}_j)$'s, noting that $s_{b_j}^2 = \bar{S}^2_{y.12,\ldots,m}c_{jj}$ and $s_{b_j b_k} = \bar{S}^2_{y.12,\ldots,m}c_{jk}$:

$$(B.15) \quad V(\hat{y}) - \frac{\bar{S}^2_{y.12,\ldots,m}}{n} = \begin{bmatrix} s_{b_1}^2 & s_{b_1 b_2} & \cdots & s_{b_1 b_j} \\ s_{b_1 b_2} & s_{b_2}^2 & \cdots & s_{b_2 b_j} \\ \vdots & \vdots & & \vdots \\ s_{b_1 b_j} & s_{b_2 b_j} & \cdots & s_{b_j}^2 \end{bmatrix}$$

$$\times \begin{bmatrix} x_1^2 & x_1 x_2 & \cdots & x_1 x_j \\ x_1 x_2 & x_2^2 & \cdots & x_2 x_j \\ \vdots & \vdots & & \vdots \\ x_1 x_j & x_2 x_j & \cdots & x_j^2 \end{bmatrix}$$

where the x's are deviations from their respective means. The matrix of x_i^2 and $x_i x_j$'s will involve a different set of numerical values for *each observation*. In particular, if we can specify a set of values for the x's for observation $n + 1$ (or $T + 1$ in a time series context), the product of the two matrices in (B.15) gives us that portion of $V(\hat{y})$ which is associated with the variances and covariances of the regression slopes. The term $(\bar{S}^2_{y.12,\ldots,m})/n$ is, of course, the variance or squared standard error of $\bar{y}$. For two independent variables, this calculation is illustrated in (A.33) of Chapter 6, Appendix A.

APPENDIX C

MULTIPLE REGRESSION ANALYSIS BY THE SHORT CUT GRAPHIC METHOD

In the 1920s and 1930s, relatively few economists had access to well-organized computing facilities. Careful training and close professional supervision were required if clerical workers were to carry through multiple regression analyses on desk calculators without serious danger of numerical errors. Only a few large government and private research agencies maintained good "computing room" staffs.

Under these circumstances, many economists and business statisticians felt obliged to run their regression analyses themselves; to persons in this position, Louis H. Bean's shortcut graphic method of multiple regression analysis was particularly appealing. It also forced the investigator to become thoroughly acquainted with his data as a byproduct of plotting scatter diagrams and carrying out other aspects of the subsequent analysis himself. In addition, some professors of economic statistics found the shortcut graphic method very useful for establishing in the minds of their students the basic concepts of multiple regression. The logic and expository value of the shortcut graphic method will be indicated with an example.

Table 7.18 presents annual average values of the price of pork, the per capita consumption of pork, and disposable personal income per capita in the United States during 1922–1941. These three variables logically belong in a consumer demand function for pork (probably supplemented by prices or supplies of competing meats), so we are interested in estimating the multiple regression of the price of pork upon pork consumption and disposable income.

In the first step of the shortcut graphic method we plot a scatter diagram between pork price and consumption, Figure 7.5a, containing all 20 observations. Next, *we select certain pairs of years* in which disposable personal income was about the same but in which pork consumption was appreciably different.

For example, income was $651 in 1926 and $653 in 1928. Clearly, this difference in income (which is probably smaller than the measurement errors in the two income figures) cannot account for a significant change in retail price between the two years. However, pork consumption in 1928 was fully 10% higher than in 1926, and price of pork was nearly 12% lower. The negative relationship is characteristic of a demand curve relating the price and consumption variables. Therefore we draw a straight line connecting the price-quantity observations for 1926 and 1928.

Similarly, we find that disposable income was not markedly different from that between certain other pairs of years; for each such pair we connect the price-quantity observations with a straight line. The four "drift lines" shown in Figure 7.5a have rather similar slopes. Having first computed the means of price and per capita consumption (a fairly simple calculation even with a desk calculator or a pencil and paper), we draw through the point of means a straight line whose slope is approximately an average of the slopes of the four drift lines. This is our first approximation to the net regression of price upon consumption.

Table 7.18 Pork: Basic Data on Retail Price and Consumption and on Disposable Personal Income, United States, 1922–1941

	Original Values			First Differences		
Year	Retail Price of Pork (Cents per lb)	Pork Consumption (lb per Capita)	Disposable Personal Income (Dollars per Capita)	Price	Consumption	Income
1922	26.8	65.7	541	–	–	–
1923	25.3	74.2	616	−1.5	8.5	75
1924	25.3	74.0	610	0	−0.2	−6
1925	31.1	66.8	636	5.8	−7.2	26
1926	33.3	64.1	651	2.2	−2.7	15
1927	31.2	67.7	645	−2.1	3.6	−6
1928	29.5	70.9	653	−1.7	3.2	8
1929	30.3	69.6	682	0.8	−1.3	29
1930	29.1	67.0	604	−1.2	−2.6	−78
1931	23.7	68.4	515	−5.4	1.4	−89
1932	15.6	70.7	390	−8.1	2.3	−125
1933	13.9	69.6	364	−1.7	−1.1	−26
1934	18.8	63.1	411	4.9	−6.5	47
1935	27.4	48.4	459	8.6	−14.7	48
1936	26.9	55.1	517	−0.5	6.7	58
1937	27.7	55.8	551	0.8	0.7	34
1938	24.5	58.2	506	−3.2	2.4	−45
1939	22.2	64.7	538	−2.3	6.5	32
1940	19.3	73.5	576	−2.9	8.8	38
1941	24.7	68.4	697	5.4	−5.1	121
Means	25.33	65.795	558.1			

Next, we measure the vertical deviations of each of the 20 observations from this approximate regression line and (if we choose to) record each price residual beside the original value of disposable personal income associated with that particular observation. Since we have drawn our price-consumption line through the point of means of price and consumption, the arithmetic mean of the price residuals will be zero. Having computed the mean of disposable income, we plot this value on a horizontal line corresponding to a zero price residual. A scatter diagram is then formed by plotting the 20 residuals against disposable income in Figure 7.5b. There appears to be a strong positive relationship between the price residuals and disposable personal income. If the relationship appears linear (or if we wish to restrict

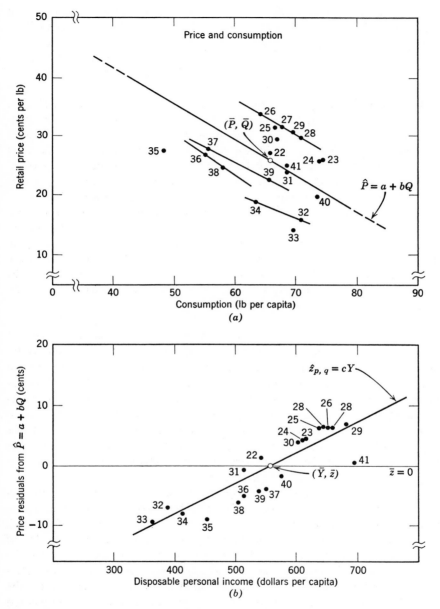

Figure 7.5 Short cut graphic method applied to price, consumption, and income relationship for pork, United States, 1922–41.

ourselves to linear relationships), we draw a straight line through the point $(0, \overline{Y})$ in such a way as to make the sum of the squared residuals as small as our eyesight and judgment permit.

Residuals from this line $\hat{z}_{p.q} = cY$ are a first approximation to the random component in pork price, $z_{p.qy}$, that is not linearly associated with either pork consumption or disposable income.

A full-fledged use of the shortcut graphic method would involve successive approximations. The first approximation line $\hat{P} = a + bQ$ from the price-consumption section of Figure 7.5a could be reproduced on another sheet of graph paper and the residuals $z_{p.qy}$ plotted at appropriate distances above or below this line for the values of pork consumption per capita experienced in each specified year. If the pattern of residuals suggested that a smaller sum of squares could be obtained by changing the slope of the original price-consumption line, this would be done. Actually, residuals from two or more alternative positions of the price-consumption line could be measured, squared, and summed to check the accuracy of the next approximation. The price residuals from this second approximation to the price-consumption line would again be plotted against disposable personal income to see if the slope of this relationship might also be "improved" in the sense of yielding a reduced sum of squared residuals.

Intuitively it seems clear that, if the investigator limits himself to linear relationships, the shortcut graphic method will converge in successive iterations upon the mathematical solution. If there is very little intercorrelation between Q and Y, the second approximation may make no appreciable improvement over the first; however, if the two independent variables are highly intercorrelated, there may be a fairly wide range of slopes of the price-consumption line which yield approximately the same sums of squared residuals. Uncertainty concerning the "least squares" position of the regression line means that the standard error of the regression slope is rather large; its size might be due in part to intercorrelation and in part to the limited number of observations available.

The shortcut graphic method does not yield standard errors of the regression coefficients in any easy way. One could, of course, make all measurements with a ruler, and then do some supplementary arithmetic with pencil and paper or a desk calculator, applying the standard error formulas of arithmetical regression analysis. However, it seems rather pointless to insist on *not* using mechanical aids in the form of either desk calculators or electronic computers. Once a particular functional form has been chosen for the multiple regression equation, the exact numerical procedures emphasized in Chapters 4, 6, and 7 might as well be applied.

In economic time series, it is possible to obtain some of the advantages of visualization and realism associated with the shortcut graphic method by transforming the original values into first differences and inspecting the latter rather carefully. Thus in Table 7.18, suppose we compare year-to-year changes in price and consumption, simply looking for the inverse or negative relationship characteristic of a demand curve. We find that 15 of the 19 pairs of first differences (ΔP, ΔQ) have opposite signs and that a 16th involves a zero change in one variable and an extremely small one in the other. This leaves only three observations out of 19 for which price and quantity change in the same (wrong) direction. But in 1930 a sharp decline in income may have more than offset the effects on price of a reduction in the quantity of pork available. The change in income from 1932 to 1933 and from 1936 to 1937 probably accounted for at least part of the nonconformity of the price with the quantity changes in those years.

If the analysis stopped with such a visual inspection, we might find ourselves rationalizing each failure of price and quantity changes to conform and overlooking other instances in which the signs of the two first differences happen to be "right" but in which the associated change in disposable income *might* (if properly allowed for) leave us with nonconforming signs. After a visual inspection of the first differences, an investigator with access to a good computing facility would proceed to have the regression equation computed numerically.

In most multiple regression analyses of economic time series, the observations are relatively few and therefore precious. A rather intensive mining and interpretation of these few observations is indicated, since additional observations usually cannot be generated at will. The making of time series charts and scatter diagrams with the aid of auxiliary equipment in a computer installation may be quite helpful with such data; otherwise, it may be well worthwhile to have scatter diagrams and time series charts produced manually by clerks. Only rarely, if at all, would more than one or two iterations of the shortcut graphic method be justified if good computing facilities are at hand.

EXERCISES

1. If we have a demand function of the form:

$$q_{1t} = a_1 + b_{11}p_{1t} + b_{12}p_{2t} + c_1 y_t + z_t$$

show that when we transform the function into natural logarithms, that is,

$$\ln q_{1t} = a_1^* + b_{11}^* \ln p_{1t} + b_{12}^* \ln p_{2t} + c_1^* \ln y_t + z_{1t}^*$$

that b_{11}^*, b_{12}^*, and c_1^* are own-price elasticity, cross-price elasticity, and income elasticity of demand, respectively.

2. Houthakker's results show that for food,

$$\log Y_1 = a_1 + 0.693 \log X_1 + 0.224 \log X_2$$

This illustrates Engel's law, which roughly states that as a household's income increases, it spends a smaller proportion of its income on food. Trace through the implications of Engel's law for the agricultural sector of the U.S. economy over the last 50 years and over the next 50 years.

3. For a regression model:

$$y_i = b_0 + b_1 X_{1i} + b_2 X_{2i} + z_i$$

show that the t-value of each of the least squares estimators b_0, b_1, and b_2, where we are testing the null hypotheses that b_0, b_1, and b_2 are equal to zero, is equal to the ratio of the least squares estimator to its own standard error.

4. Suppose we have a multiplicative production function of the form:

$$Y = AK^a L^b \qquad \text{(Cobb-Douglas production function)}$$

(a) If we want to estimate a and b by linear regression methods, in what form will we estimate the production function?

(b) How would we test for the following?

  (i) Diminishing marginal productivity of labor.

  (ii) Diminishing marginal productivity of capital.

  (iii) Increasing, constant, or decreasing returns to scale.

5. The assumptions of the regression model are discussed in Section 7.2.2. Take each of these assumptions and explain why they are necessary, if they are, in order to obtain best, linear, unbiased estimates by least squares techniques.

6. Typically, the aggregate Keynesian consumption function, $C = a + bY$, is estimated under the assumption that income Y is measured without error. However, Milton Friedman, an economist at the University of Chicago, takes the position that income should also be measured with error, that is, there is a random component associated with income. If this position is true, show carefully the effects of it on:

(a) the estimate of the Marginal Propensity to Consume over time,

(b) the "multiplier."

7. Summarize and compare the effects of multicollinearity in the three-variable case under the assumptions of (1) Table 7.10 and Figure 7.1, and (2) Table 7.12 and Figure 7.3 on:

(a) $R^2_{1.23}$ (e) $r_{13.2}$

(b) $\beta_{12.3}$ (f) t-value for $\beta_{12.3}$

(c) $\beta_{13.2}$ (g) t-value for $\beta_{13.2}$

(d) $r_{12.3}$

REFERENCES

1. Aitken, A. C., *Determinants and Matrices*, Edinburgh: Oliver and Boyd, 1954.
2. Duesenberry, J. S., O. H. Eckstein, and Gary Fromm, "A Simulation of the United States Economy in Recession," *Econometrica* **28**, No. 4, pp. 749–809, October 1960.

3. Ezekiel, Mordecai and Karl A. Fox, *Methods of Correlation and Regression Analysis*, Third edition, New York: John Wiley and Sons, 1959.
4. Ferber, R. and P. J. Verdoorn, *Research Methods in Economics and Business*, New York: The Macmillan Co., 1962.
5. Fox, Karl A., *Econometric Analysis for Public Policy*, Ames: Iowa State University Press, 1958.
6. Fox, Karl A., "Factors Affecting Farm Income, Farm Prices and Food Consumption," *Agricultural Economics Research*, pp. 65–82, July 1951.
7. Fox, Karl A. and J. F. Cooney, "Effects of Intercorrelation Upon Multiple Correlation and Regression Measures," Washington: U.S. Department of Agriculture, *Agricultural Marketing Service Bulletin*, April 1954, reissued October 1959.
8. Houthakker, H. S. "An International Comparison of Household Expenditure Patterns, Commemorating the Centenary of Engel's Law," *Econometrica* 25, pp. 532–551, October 1957.
9. Williams, E. J., *Regression Analysis*, New York: John Wiley and Sons, 1959.

CHAPTER 8

The Analysis of Variance

In earlier chapters we have distinguished between the "correlation model" and the "regression model" with particular reference to the different interpretations of the correlation coefficient in each. We have noted that regression coefficients and standard errors of estimate, however, have the same interpretation in both models.

The correlation model was originally applied to nonexperimental data—random samples from a universe in which all variables were normally distributed. The regression model grew out of applications in which the values of the independent variables could be selected as part of an experiment. Particularly in connection with agricultural and biological experiments, an extensive theory of experimental design developed. Part of this theory related to situations in which the independent factors were qualitatively rather than quantitatively different. For example, does one variety of wheat have a significantly higher yield than another? Is one insecticide significantly more effective than another? Regression analysis is not adapted to such situations. However, from the problem of comparing the effects of qualitatively different "independent" factors grew a very powerful tool called "analysis of variance." Moreover, the theory underlying analysis of variance is sufficiently general to include regression analysis as a special instance. In this chapter we shall consider only certain aspects of variance analysis that are closely related to regression problems.

8.1 BASIC PRINCIPLES OF VARIANCE ANALYSIS

The sum of squares of a set of observations about their mean can be represented as the sum of two independent sums of squares—specifically,

290

in simple linear regression analysis, a sum of squares of deviations of regression values from their mean and a sum of squares of deviations about the regression line. We have also noted that the first sum of squares has a single degree of freedom, and the second has $n - 2$ degrees of freedom—n is the total number of observations to which the regression line is fitted.

In discussing tests of significance, we introduced the t-ratio, or ratio of a coefficient to its standard error.[1] For the simple regression coefficient, this ratio can be written as follows [from (4.5), (4.3), and Appendix A, Chapter 6]:

$$t_b = \frac{b}{s_b} = \frac{\sum xy}{\sum x^2} \div \frac{\bar{S}_{yx}}{s_x \sqrt{n}}$$

(8.1)
$$t_b = \frac{\sum xy}{\sum x^2} \div \frac{\sqrt{\dfrac{\sum z^2}{n - 2}}}{\sqrt{\dfrac{\sum x^2 n}{n}}} = \frac{\sum xy}{\sum x^2} \frac{\sqrt{\sum x^2}}{\sqrt{\dfrac{\sum z^2}{n - 2}}}$$

$$= \frac{\sum xy}{\bar{S}_{yx} \sqrt{\sum x^2}}$$

In this form, the t-ratio is used to estimate the probability that an observed value of b might have been obtained by chance in random sampling from a population in which the true regression coefficient was zero.

A closely related measure is basic to the analysis of variance. A "variance" is equal to a sum of squares divided by the appropriate number of degrees of freedom. In simple regression, the sum $\sum y^2$ can be divided into two parts or components, $b^2 \sum x^2$ and $\sum z^2$—that is, $\sum y^2 = b^2 \sum x^2 + \sum z^2$. The first component has a single degree of freedom and the second has $n - 2$ degrees of freedom, so the corresponding variances are $b^2 \sum x^2$ and $\sum z^2/(n - 2)$, or $\bar{S}_{yx}^2$. It is intuitively plausible that a measure of the significance of the regression relationship between y and x can be based upon the ratio of these two variances.

$$F = \frac{b^2 \sum x^2}{\bar{S}_{yx}^2}$$

Substituting $b = \sum xy/\sum x^2$ in this expression we obtain

(8.2)
$$F = \frac{(\sum xy)^2 \sum x^2}{(\sum x^2)^2 \bar{S}_{yx}^2} = \frac{(\sum xy)^2}{\bar{S}_{yx}^2(\sum x^2)} = t^2$$

It will be noted at once that F is equal to t^2 or $t = \sqrt{F}$.

[1] See Chapter 3, p. 70.

The equality $t = \sqrt{F}$ holds only when the total sum of squares is divided into two, and only two, parts. This occurs in simple linear regression analysis and in testing the significance of the difference between two means, two standard deviations, and so on. But the F-ratio is also applicable to situations in which a total sum of squares is divided into three or more components. The question asked in each instance is: Could the variances under comparison have been obtained by random sampling from the same population? This question is answered, of course, on the basis of probability rather than certainty. Values of F covering a wide range of paired values of degrees of freedom have been tabulated by Snedecor and are reproduced here with the kind permission of Dr Snedecor and the Iowa State University Press.

8.1.1 *Applications of Variance Analysis*

Difference between the Effects of Two "Treatments." The following data are taken from the study by Heady, Pesek, and Brown,[2] which was referred to in Chapter 7. Assume that 28 plots of ground are selected at random in a field and are planted to corn of a single variety. Eighteen of the plots receive no fertilizer, and ten receive nitrogen fertilizer at the rate of 40 pounds N per acre. The yield of corn obtained on each plot is carefully measured. Our problem is to discover whether the application of fertilizer at the specified rate has a significant effect upon corn yields.

The values resulting from the experiment are tabulated below; the symbol Y is used to represent an actual yield and y a deviation from the mean yield for a specified group.

Item	Treatment 1, No Fertilizer	Treatment 2, Nitrogen (40 lb per acre)	Total, Treatments 1 and 2
Observations, n	18	10	28
Mean yield, M	26.65	60.66	38.7964
$\sum Y^2$	14,794.71	43,982.22	58,776.93
nM^2	12,784.00	36,796.36	42,144.56
$\sum y^2$	2,010.71	7,185.86	16,632.37
Degrees of freedom	17	9	27

[2] Earl O. Heady, John T. Pesek, and William G. Brown, "Crop Response Surfaces and Economic Optima in Fertilizer Use," *Iowa State College Agricultural Experiment Station Research Bulletin 424*, p. 330 (March 1955).

The analysis of variance for these data follows:

Source of Variation	Degrees of Freedom	Sum of Squares	Mean Square
Total	27	16,632.37	–
Difference between treatments	1	7,435.80	7435.80
Variation within treatments	26	9,196.57	353.71

$$F = \frac{7435.80}{353.71} = 21.02$$

The total sum of squares about the mean of the 28 observations is 16,632.37. The sums of squares about the individual means are 2010.71 and 7185.86, totaling 9196.57. The difference of 7435.80 (equals 16,632.37 − 9196.57) is due to the departures of the two group means from the mean of the entire set of 28 observations. According to the logic of the experiment, this term is an estimate of the effect of the difference in treatment—nitrogen versus no nitrogen—accorded to the two groups of plots. The variation *within* each group is presumably due to a large number of factors of essentially random incidence independent of the fertilizer treatment.

As it happens the *sum* of squares within groups exceeds that arising from the difference in treatments. But the mean square column shows that the effect of the difference in treatments *per degree of freedom* is 21.02 times as large as the corresponding variation within groups. Referring to Table 8.1 we find that for degrees of freedom $n_1 = 1$ and $n_2 = 20$, an F-ratio greater than 8.10 would occur by chance only one time in 100 experiments if the treatment actually had no effect upon corn yields. The probability of obtaining an F-ratio as great as 21.02 if the treatment were ineffective is negligibly small; we conclude therefore that nitrogen fertilizer applied at the rate of 40 pounds per acre has a highly significant effect upon corn yields.

The expected value of F would be 1.0 if the difference in treatments had no systematic effect upon yields. For in that event the variance of the group means about the general mean would reflect the same random forces as does the variance of each subset of observations about its group mean. The classification of observations on the basis of the amount of nitrogen applied would then be irrelevant; it would not contribute significantly to an explanation of the variance of all the observations about the general mean.

The analysis-of-variance table suggests certain obvious analogies with regression analysis. The total sum of squares has been partitioned into "explained" and "unexplained" components. If the two treatments were two different varieties of corn we could say that 45% of the observed variation in yields was attributable to the difference in varieties. In the current instance

Table 8.1 Five Per Cent and 1% Points for the F-Distribution,[a] 5% in light face, 1% in bold face

n_1, Degrees of Freedom for Numerator

n_2, Degrees of freedom for denominator	1	2	3	4	5	6	8	10	12	20	50	100
1	161	200	216	225	230	234	239	242	244	248	252	253
	4052	**4999**	**5403**	**5625**	**5764**	**5859**	**5981**	**6056**	**6106**	**6208**	**6302**	**6334**
2	18.51	19.00	19.16	19.25	19.30	19.33	19.37	19.39	19.41	19.44	19.47	19.49
	98.49	**99.01**	**99.17**	**99.25**	**99.30**	**99.33**	**99.36**	**99.40**	**99.42**	**99.45**	**99.48**	**99.49**
3	10.13	9.55	9.28	9.12	9.01	8.94	8.84	8.78	8.74	8.66	8.58	8.56
	34.12	**30.81**	**29.46**	**28.71**	**28.24**	**27.91**	**27.49**	**27.23**	**27.05**	**26.69**	**26.35**	**26.23**
4	7.71	6.94	6.59	6.39	6.26	6.16	6.04	5.96	5.91	5.80	5.70	5.66
	21.20	**18.00**	**16.69**	**15.98**	**15.52**	**15.21**	**14.80**	**14.54**	**14.37**	**14.02**	**13.69**	**13.57**
5	6.61	5.79	5.41	5.19	5.05	4.95	4.82	4.74	4.68	4.56	4.44	4.40
	16.26	**13.27**	**12.06**	**11.39**	**10.97**	**10.67**	**10.27**	**10.05**	**9.89**	**9.55**	**9.24**	**9.13**
6	5.99	5.14	4.76	4.53	4.39	4.28	4.15	4.06	4.00	3.87	3.75	3.71
	13.74	**10.92**	**9.78**	**9.15**	**8.75**	**8.47**	**8.10**	**7.87**	**7.72**	**7.39**	**7.09**	**6.99**
7	5.59	4.74	4.35	4.12	3.97	3.87	3.73	3.63	3.57	3.44	3.32	3.28
	12.25	**9.55**	**8.45**	**7.85**	**7.46**	**7.19**	**6.84**	**6.62**	**6.47**	**6.15**	**5.85**	**5.75**
8	5.32	4.46	4.07	3.84	3.69	3.58	3.44	3.34	3.28	3.15	3.03	2.98
	11.25	**8.65**	**7.59**	**7.01**	**6.63**	**6.37**	**6.03**	**5.82**	**5.67**	**5.36**	**5.05**	**4.96**

df												
10	4.96	4.10	3.71	3.48	3.33	3.22	3.07	2.97	2.91	2.77	2.64	2.59
	10.04	**7.56**	**6.55**	**5.99**	**5.64**	**5.39**	**5.06**	**4.85**	**4.71**	**4.41**	**4.12**	**4.01**
12	4.75	3.88	3.49	3.26	3.11	3.00	2.85	2.76	2.69	2.54	2.40	2.35
	9.33	**6.93**	**5.95**	**5.41**	**5.06**	**4.82**	**4.50**	**4.30**	**4.16**	**3.86**	**3.56**	**3.46**
14	4.60	3.74	3.34	3.11	2.96	2.85	2.70	2.60	2.53	2.39	2.24	2.19
	8.86	**6.51**	**5.56**	**5.03**	**4.69**	**4.46**	**4.14**	**3.94**	**3.80**	**3.51**	**3.21**	**3.11**
16	4.49	3.63	3.24	3.01	2.85	2.74	2.59	2.49	2.42	2.28	2.13	2.07
	8.53	**6.23**	**5.29**	**4.77**	**4.44**	**4.20**	**3.89**	**3.69**	**3.55**	**3.25**	**2.96**	**2.86**
18	4.41	3.55	3.16	2.93	2.77	2.66	2.51	2.41	2.34	2.19	2.04	1.98
	8.28	**6.01**	**5.09**	**4.58**	**4.25**	**4.01**	**3.71**	**3.51**	**3.37**	**3.07**	**2.78**	**2.68**
20	4.35	3.49	3.10	2.87	2.71	2.60	2.45	2.35	2.28	2.12	1.96	1.90
	8.10	**5.85**	**4.94**	**4.43**	**4.10**	**3.87**	**3.56**	**3.37**	**3.23**	**2.94**	**2.63**	**2.53**
30	4.17	3.32	2.92	2.69	2.53	2.42	2.27	2.16	2.09	1.93	1.76	1.69
	7.56	**5.39**	**4.51**	**4.02**	**3.70**	**3.47**	**3.17**	**2.98**	**2.84**	**2.55**	**2.24**	**2.13**
40	4.08	3.23	2.84	2.61	2.45	2.34	2.18	2.07	2.00	1.84	1.66	1.59
	7.31	**5.18**	**4.31**	**3.83**	**3.51**	**3.29**	**2.99**	**2.80**	**2.66**	**2.37**	**2.05**	**1.94**
50	4.03	3.18	2.79	2.56	2.40	2.29	2.13	2.02	1.95	1.78	1.60	1.52
	7.17	**5.06**	**4.20**	**3.72**	**3.41**	**3.18**	**2.88**	**2.70**	**2.56**	**2.26**	**1.94**	**1.82**
100	3.94	3.09	2.70	2.46	2.30	2.19	2.03	1.92	1.85	1.68	1.48	1.39
	6.90	**4.82**	**3.98**	**3.51**	**3.20**	**2.99**	**2.69**	**2.51**	**2.36**	**2.06**	**1.73**	**1.59**
1000	3.85	3.00	2.61	2.38	2.22	2.10	1.95	1.84	1.76	1.58	1.36	1.26
	6.66	**4.62**	**3.80**	**3.34**	**3.04**	**2.82**	**2.53**	**2.34**	**2.20**	**1.89**	**1.54**	**1.38**

[a] Abridged, with permission of author and publisher, from George W. Snedecor, *Statistical Methods*, 5th ed., Iowa State College Press, Ames, 1956.

the treatments can be quantified (as zero and 40 pounds of nitrogen, respectively) and we can actually fit a regression line to the 28 observations or draw a freehand line between the two points (26.65, 0) and (60.66, 40) with a slope of 0.85025 bushels per pound of nitrogen.

A more complete understanding of the relation between variance analysis and regression analysis can be gained by actually fitting the regression line just mentioned. The basic data are given in Table 8.2.

The discontinuous values of X are quite typical in controlled experiments. The required values are

$$\sum Y = 1086.3 \qquad M_y = 38.7964$$
$$\sum X = 400 \qquad M_x = 14.2857$$
$$\sum YX = 24,264 \qquad \sum X^2 = 16,000$$

From these we find that

$$b_{yx} = \frac{24,264 - 15,518.56}{16,000 - 5,714.28} = 0.85025,$$

Table 8.2   Corn Yields Related to Quantity of Nitrogen Fertilizer Applied

Corn Yield, Y, Bushels per Acre	Nitrogen Fertilizer Applied, X, Pounds per Acre	Corn Yield, Y, Bushels per Acre	Nitrogen Fertilizer Applied, X, Pounds per Acre
24.5	0	32.4	0
6.2	0	27.4	0
26.7	0	5.3	0
29.6	0	17.9	0
22.1	0	23.9	40
30.6	0	11.8	40
44.2	0	60.2	40
21.9	0	82.5	40
12.0	0	96.2	40
34.0	0	80.7	40
37.7	0	81.1	40
34.2	0	51.0	40
38.0	0	79.5	40
35.0	0	39.7	40

Source: Heady et al., *op. cit.*

the same value obtained by simply drawing a line through the points previously indicated. The constant a is given by

$$a = 38.7964 - 0.85025(14.2857)$$
$$= 26.65$$

This is the mean of the 18 observations for plots which received no fertilizer ($X = 0$). When $X = 40$, $Y = 26.65 + 40(0.85025) = 60.66$, the mean of the ten observations for plots which received 40 pounds of nitrogen.

In the analysis of variance table, it is clear that the variation within treatments is identical with the sum of squared deviations about the regression line and the variation due to the difference between treatments is equal to that "explained" by the regression line. The sum of squares about the general mean has 27 degrees of freedom. Since the regression line must pass through this general mean, only one additional degree of freedom is used up in determining the *slope* of the regression line b. Hence the 26 degrees of freedom shown for "variation within treatments" check with the 26 degrees of freedom left in the residuals about a least squares regression line fitted to 28 observations.

Differences among the Effects of Three or More "Treatments." Suppose now that, in addition to the 28 plots already noted, we have applied 80 pounds of nitrogen per acre to ten other randomly selected plots. We can again use variance analysis to answer a question that is more appropriate where the treatments are *qualitatively* different. Do variations in the amount of nitrogen applied have a significant effect upon corn yields?

The appropriate analysis of variance in this instance follows:

Source of Variation	Degrees of Freedom	Sum of Squares	Mean Square
Total	37	46,476.79	–
Differences among treatments	2	24,288.06	12,144.02
Variation within treatments	35	22,188.73	633.96

$$F = \frac{12,144.03}{633.96} = 19.16$$

Referring to Table 8.1, we note that for $n_1 = 2$ and $n_2 = 30$ degrees of freedom an F-ratio greater than 5.39 would be expected to occur by chance only one time in 100 experiments if, in reality, there were no relationship between corn yields and amounts of nitrogen applied.

The analogy with regression analysis can also be extended to this instance. We could fit a second-degree parabola precisely to the three points (26.65, 0), (60.66, 40), and (86.62, 80), 86.62 bushels being the mean yield obtained on the ten plots which received 80 pounds of nitrogen. The "variation within treatments" would be identical with the sum of squared deviations about this parabola, and the difference between this amount and the sum of squared deviations about the general mean would be "accounted for" by the parabolic relation between group-mean yields and quantity of nitrogen applied. This analogy could obviously be extended to any number k of groups receiving quantitatively different "treatments" of a single factor *if* we are willing to conceive of a kth-order parabola passing through the k points of group means. (The significance of such a parabola would be no greater than that of a series of straight lines connecting each successive group mean to the one preceding it, since all the yield observations would be concentrated at the k discrete levels of fertilizer application.)

Testing the Significance of Additional Terms in a Regression Equation. Suppose that we have the data presented in the first and third columns of Table 8.3; we assume for the present purposes that the X and Y values represent only nine individual observations. We have successively fitted a

Table 8.3   Relation between Average Yields of Corn Obtained and Quantities of Nitrogen Fertilizer Applied

Nitrogen Applied, X, Pounds per Acre	Number of Plots	Average Yield of Corn, Y, Bushels per Acre	Sum of Squared Yields, $\sum Y_i^2$ [a]
0	18	26.65	14,794.71
40	10	60.66	43,982.22
80	10	86.62	88,022.40
120	10	103.59	123,820.19
160	18	104.09	218,485.05
200	10	97.66	117,912.18
240	10	101.79	124,570.93
280	10	106.03	133,183.85
320	18	105.27	222,421.15

[a] Based on the individual observations.

Source: Heady et al., *op. cit.*

straight line and a second-order parabola, and wish to determine whether the new term in X^2 has significantly increased the proportion of variance attributable to regression.

The least squares regression line and parabola are, respectively,

Straight line: $\hat{Y} = 56.37 + 0.19792X$
Parabola: $\hat{Y} = 34.54 + 0.66598X - 0.0014627X^2$

The following values are also obtained:

$$\sum X = 1440 \qquad\qquad M_x = 160$$
$$\sum Y = 792.36 \qquad\qquad M_y = 88.04$$
$$\sum X^2 = 326,400 \qquad\qquad M_x^2 = 36,272$$
$$\sum Y^2 = 75,681.3122 \qquad\qquad \sum YX = 145,777.60$$
$$\sum YX^2 = 33,669,728$$

These result in the following adjusted sums of squares and cross products:

$$\sum y^2 = 5921.94$$
$$\sum yx = 19,000$$
$$\sum yx^2 = 4,929,248$$

The variance in yields explained by the straight line regression may be calculated as $0.19792 \sum yx = 3760.48$, and the variance explained by the parabolic regression curve may be computed as

$$0.66598(\textstyle\sum yx) - 0.0014627(\textstyle\sum yx^2) = 12,653.62 - 7210.01 = 5443.61$$

The difference between either of these values and $\sum y^2$ would be the sum of squared deviations around the corresponding regression function, whereas the difference between 5433.61 and 3760.48 is the additional variance explained by the parabolic regression.

The analysis of variance to determine the significance of the new term in X^2 in the parabolic equation is conducted as follows:

Source of Variation	Degrees of Freedom	Sum of Squares	Mean Square
Total	8	5,921.94	–
Linear regression	1	3,760.48	3,760.48
Additional variation accounted for by parabolic regression	1	1,683.13	1,683.13
Variation around parabolic regression	6	478.33	79.2

$$F = \frac{1,683.13}{79.72} = 21.11$$

Referring to Table 8.1 for $n_1 = 1$ and $n_2 = 6$ degrees of freedom, we find that the probability of a value of F greater than 13.74 occurring by chance would be less than 0.01 (1%) if the regression of yield upon the additional term in the universe were really zero. It also follows that the parabola gives a significantly better representation of the relationship between Y and X than does the straight line. This process could be extended to determine whether a third-order parabola gives a significantly better fit than the second-order parabola already fitted.

Testing for Curvilinearity of Regression. We now note that each Y value in Table 8.3 is an average of 10 or 18 observations. Assume that we have fitted a straight line to the nine mean values, weighting each of the nine corresponding values of Y, Y^2, X, X^2, and XY by the number of observations (10 or 18) represented by the particular group mean. As a result of the weighting pattern, this line differs slightly from that of the preceding section; the new equation is

$$\hat{Y} = 52.11514 + 0.212208X$$

The variance due to regression is obtained by computing the squared deviations of the nine possible values of $\hat{Y}$ about the general mean and weighting each of them by the number of individual cases (10 or 18) located at that particular value of X.

The analysis of variance for the current example is

Source of Variation	Degrees of Freedom	Sum of Squares	Mean Square
Total	113	242,707	–
Within groups	105	149,366	1,422.53
Due to linear regression	1	61,676	61,676
Deviation of means about linear regression	7	31,665	4,523.57

$$F = \frac{4523.57}{1422.53} = 3.18$$

Referring to Table 8.1 we note that for $n_1 = 6$ and $n_2 = 100$, a value of F greater than 2.99 would be obtained by chance only one time in 100 samples if the true regression in the universe were linear.

The logic of the foregoing test may need some clarification. The variance within groups is the "pooled" variance of individual yields about their respective group means. This variance presumably results from random factors independent of the quantity of nitrogen applied. If the group means deviated from the regression line only because of these same random factors, the expected variance of the means about the regression line would be equal to the variance of individual yields about the group means.[3] In this instance, the expected sum of squares due to deviations of group means about the regression line would be $7(\bar{S}_y)^2$ or $7(1422.53) = 9957.71$. Their actual contribution was 31,665, or 3.18 times the expected value.

Since such a value would be highly improbable under our present assumption, we conclude that other, nonrandom factors are primarily responsible for the deviations of group means about the regression line. In other words, the expected mean values of Y for given values of X *in the population* follow some (unspecified) curvilinear pattern. We might then proceed to fit an appropriate type of curve to the data.

Significance of Two or More "Principles of Classification." In certain types of experiments, we are interested in determining whether each of two or more factors is significantly associated with a given variable. In some instances the factors are qualitative rather than quantitative—for example, we might have three varieties of corn and three different insecticides, and apply each insecticide to each variety. A complete experiment might then involve nine plots or some multiple of nine. We wish to analyze the nine observed yields to determine whether either or both of the two "principles of classification" —differences in varieties and differences in insecticides—are significantly associated with differences in yields.

Some assumed data corresponding to such an experiment are shown in Table 8.4.

The total variation is the sum of squared deviations of the nine individual yields about the general mean $M_y = 85.078$. The variation due to differences in insecticides is measured by the squared deviations of the three group means in the right-hand column about the general mean. (Each of these squared deviations must be multiplied by three, since each group mean represents three individual observations.) The variation due to differences in varieties is measured by the squared deviations of the three group means in the bottom row about the general mean, multiplied by three as before. The computation of these values will be left to the reader.

---

[3] Note again that a variance is a sum of squares divided by the appropriate number of degrees of freedom. Although the group means would cluster more closely around the regression line than would the individual observations according to the relation $S_m{}^2 = (S_y/n)^2$, the squared deviation of each group mean from the regression line would be multiplied by n, the number of observations on which it was based, to arrive at the contribution of their deviations to the total sum of squares. On the average, then, each mean might be expected to contribute approximately $(S_y)^2$ to this sum of squares. But two degrees of freedom are taken up in fitting the regression line to the nine group means, so the exact expected contribution of the group means would be $7(S_y)^2$.

The analysis of variance for this example follows:

Source of Variation	Degrees of Freedom	Sum of Squares	Mean Square
Total	8	11,012.38	–
Differences among insecticides	2	4,973.42	2,486.71
Differences among varieties	2	4,928.94	2,464.47
Residual, or "interaction"	4	1,110.02	277.50

$$\text{For insecticides} \quad F = \frac{2,486.71}{277.50} = 8.96$$

$$\text{For varieties} \quad F = \frac{2,464.47}{277.50} = 8.88$$

In Table 8.1 we note that for $n_1 = 2$ and $n_2 = 4$ degrees of freedom, values of F larger than 6.94 would occur by chance only five times in 100 if either of the "principles of classification" were in reality not associated with corn yields. To reduce this probability to one in 100 ($P = 0.01$), F would have to be 18.00 or larger, so the results of our experiment are significant at the 5%, but not at the 1%, level for each of the two factors.

The foregoing example is analogous to multiple regression with two independent variables. One could, of course, apply each of three different fertilizers to each of the insecticide-and-variety combinations of our example and apply each of two or more different methods of plowing to each of the 27 combinations of three factors, and so on. These experiments would be analogous to multiple regression with three or four independent variables.

One peculiarity of the analysis of variance just summarized is the use of the so-called interaction term in the denominator of the F-ratio. Presumably random factors not related to insecticides or varieties are responsible for a

Table 8.4 Hypothetical Data on Corn Yields Resulting from Combinations of Three Varieties and Three Insecticides

Insecticides	Varieties			Totals	Means
	B_1	B_2	B_3		
A_1	40.60	55.88	59.07	155.55	51.849
A_2	58.63	119.83	123.75	302.21	100.736
A_3	56.72	128.15	123.07	307.94	102.646
Totals	155.95	303.86	305.89	765.70	
Means	51.986	101.286	101.962		85.078

portion of the observed variation in yields. If the effects of insecticides and of varieties upon yield are strictly independent of one another, the interaction term gives us an estimate of the level of other (random) effects. But it may be that there are *joint* effects of insecticides and varieties in addition to the independent ones; if so, the true random component would be smaller than the interaction term. Hence use of the interaction term in the foregoing fashion gives a conservative estimate of the *F*-ratio. If we replicated our experiment two or more times we could gain a better estimate of the random component from the variance of individual yields about the mean obtained for each of the nine combinations of insecticides and varieties.

Table 8.5 Experimental Yields of Corn for Varying Levels of Fertilizer Application on Calcareous Ida Silt-Loan Soil in Western Iowa in 1952 (Yields are in Bushels per Acre)[a]

P_2O_5, lb	Nitrogen, lb								
	0	40	80	120	160	200	240	280	320
0	24.5	23.9	28.7	25.1	17.3	7.3	16.2	26.8	25.1
	6.2	11.8	6.4	24.5	4.2	10.0	6.8	7.7	19.0
40	26.7	60.2			96.0	95.4			81.9
	29.6	82.5			107.0	95.4			76.4
80	22.1		99.5		115.9		112.4		129.0
	30.6		115.4		72.6		125.6		82.0
120	44.2			119.4	113.6			114.9	124.6
	21.9			97.3	102.1			129.2	83.0
160	12.0	96.2	102.2	133.3	129.7	105.7	130.5	123.6	135.6
	34.0	80.7	108.5	124.4	116.3	115.5	124.3	142.5	122.7
200	37.7	81.1			128.7	140.3			136.0
	34.2	51.0			109.3	142.2			118.2
240	38.0		97.2		127.6		121.1		130.9
	35.0		107.8		125.8		114.2		144.9
280	32.4			129.5	134.4			130.0	124.8
	27.4			125.2	127.6			141.9	114.1
320	5.3	79.5	116.9	135.7	122.9	138.7	127.3	131.8	127.9
	17.9	39.7	83.6	121.5	122.7	126.1	139.5	111.9	118.8

[a] Two figures are shown in each cell since the treatments were replicated (that is, two plots received the same fertilizer quantities and ratios).

Source: Earl O. Heady, John T. Pesek, and William G. Brown, "Crop Response Surfaces and Economic Optima in Fertilizer Use," *Iowa State College Agricultural Experiment Station Research Bulletin 424*, March 1955, p. 330 (March 1955).

Relation to Multiple Regression. The following experimental study by Heady, Pesek, and Brown (referred to earlier in Chapter 7) is classically suited to our present purpose. The complete set of 114 observations is included in Table 8.5, the structure of which clearly suggests a multiple regression of yields upon two different plant nutrients, which we will refer to as nitrogen N and phosphate P. Since each combination of quantities of N and P was applied to two different plots, the variance of these two yields about their mean, with one degree of freedom for each of the 57 combinations, provides an estimate of the random error component in yields, independent of the effects (additive, joint, or both) of the fertilizer elements.

The meaning of partial or net regression is also implicit in Table 8.5. For each of nine levels of phosphate application, a net regression line or curve can be fitted to the observations on corn yield and quantity of nitrogen applied. Similar net regression curves can be derived for the other plant nutrient. That this is a *regression* rather than a *correlation* model is evidenced by the selection of widely spaced values of the independent factors and a heavy concentration of observations toward the extreme ends of their ranges. A random sample from a normal trivariate universe would give a large number of observations near the point of means of the two independent factors and a very small number near the extremes.

The authors proceeded to fit the following multiple curvilinear regression function by least squares:

$$Y = -5.682 - 0.316N - 0.417P + 6.3512\sqrt{N} + 8.5155\sqrt{P} + 0.3410\sqrt{NP}$$
$$\qquad\quad (0.040) \quad (0.040) \quad (0.8676) \quad (0.8680) \quad (0.0385)$$

The figures in parentheses are standard errors of the regression coefficients. The *t*-ratios range from 7.32 to 10.44, all highly significant at the 1% level.

The analysis of variance associated with the complete experiment follows:

Source of Variation	Degrees of Freedom	Sum of Squares	Mean Square
Total	113	242,707	–
Treatments	56	233,811	4,175
Due to regression	5	222,828	44,566
Deviations from regression	51	10,983	215
Among plots treated alike	57	8,896	156

$$F = \frac{44,566}{156} = 286$$

The regression is, of course, highly significant. The variance of deviations of treatment means about the regression is small enough to be accounted for by the same forces responsible for variation among plots treated alike. Thus there is no point in searching for a better regression surface; although another just as good *might* be found, it would be impossible to show that it gave a *significantly* better fit to the data.

By way of contrast, the authors had fitted a different curvilinear joint regression surface about which the variance of treatment means was 625; the variance among plots treated alike remained, of course, at 156. The corresponding F-ratio, 4.01, would occur slightly less often than one time in 100 experiments if the deviations of treatment means from the regression surface were due exclusively to the same random factors that caused yields to vary among plots treated alike. It followed logically that one or more other regression surfaces might be found that would better express the true (population) relationship between corn yields and applications of nitrogen and phosphate.

8.1.2 *Summary of Variance Analysis of Experimental Data*

The methods of variance analysis can be used to break down the sum of squared deviations of a variable about its mean into a number of additive components. Ordinarily these methods are used in connection with experimental data, and the design of the experiment determines the number of relevant components and the logical significance of each. Variance analysis is particularly suited to situations in which the independent "variables" or "principles of classification" are qualitative.

Until the 1950s variance analysis was applied chiefly to discontinuous or grouped data. When the principles of classification were quantitative, the analysis generally stopped (explicitly or implicitly) with discontinuous "lines of averages" connecting the group means. *All* the variation of group averages of the dependent variable about its general mean was presumed to be explained by the independent variables. A continuous regression function fitted to the same data would not pass precisely through all the group averages (except in rare or trivial cases), so the proportion of total variation "explained" by the regression function would be somewhat smaller than that attributed in variance analysis to differences among group means.

The historical distinction between variance and regression analysis is not required by the underlying statistical theory, and today statisticians dealing with data from controlled experiments often fit regression functions to the group means and appraise the goodness of fit of the functions using significance tests customary in variance analysis. These tests lead to the same estimates of probability levels as do the standard-error formulas applicable to regression constants. Both approaches may be regarded as based upon the same general theory of least squares estimation. As in regression analysis, attempts to measure the separate contributions of the different independent factors to total variance often encounter the difficulty of *covariance*, which is essentially intercorrelation among the independent variables.

The methods of variance analysis may also be used to test the significance of the improvement in fit shown by a curved regression over a linear one, of additional constants in fitting a curve, or of an additional variable in a multiple regression analysis.

8.2 VARIANCE ANALYSIS ASPECTS OF SOME EXAMPLES TREATED IN EARLIER CHAPTERS

We made a number of uses of variance analysis concepts in Chapters 4 to 7 and the reader will no doubt have noted some analogies between the earlier examples and those of this chapter.

The zero-one variables employed in our regression equation in Chapter 5, to estimate the seasonal component of a time series are frequently used in variance analysis when part of the total variance is believed to be associated with the *qualitatively* different categories into which the observations are subdivided. In our time series example we treated Januarys as qualitatively different from Julys, and about two-thirds of the original variance was attributed to differences between months. Roughly speaking, another 10% of the variance was attributed to trend, 15% to cycle, 4 or 5% to the random component, and 4 or 5% to the interaction terms.[4]

Chapter 4 on simple regression mechanics introduced the concept of explained versus unexplained variance, and showed that the simple least squares straight line separated the original variance of the dependent variable into two additive components, variance explained by the regression equation and variance of the residuals about the regression equation. In Chapter 6 we again spoke of pooling variances from two or more sets of observations, made some references to degrees of freedom, and showed one table indicating the extent to which the parabolic regression had improved upon the straight line regression equation. In Chapter 7 we used an *F*-test in connection with the regression analysis of yields and fertilizer inputs. We also showed how random error components in both independent and dependent variables increase the total amount of variance in the dependent variable which cannot be explained by the (simple) regression equation. It should be clear that the principles of *variance* analysis ramify very widely through economic statistics wherever *regression* analysis is used.

---

[4] The sum of squares of differences between years (annual averages) in this example should have given us an estimate of the variance attributable to trend and cyclical factors combined.

Even in the conventional methods of univariate analysis of economic time series, variance concepts may provide useful insights. Two or three examples and suggestions will be made.

8.2.1 *Variance Analysis Concepts and Seasonal Patterns*

Suppose we obtain the following estimates of average monthly temperatures in a city:

Month	Average Monthly Temperature	Deviation of Monthly Average from General Mean	Variance of Average Monthly Temperatures
January	30°F	−25	625
February	35	−20	400
March	45	−10	100
April	55	0	0
May	65	+10	100
June	75	+20	400
July	80	+25	625
August	75	+20	400
September	65	+10	100
October	55	0	0
November	45	−10	100
December	35	−20	400
Total	660	0	3250
Mean	55	0	

Assume that these averages refer to a period of ten years or 120 months. Then the variance of the average monthly temperatures around the general mean must be multiplied by ten years, giving a total variance of 32,500 for the decade.

One degree of freedom is used in calculating the general mean. Deviations of the monthly averages from the general mean use up 11 degrees of freedom, leaving a total of 108 for deviations of actual monthly temperatures year by year from their respective ten-year averages. As the ten-year average for a given month takes up one of the ten original degrees of freedom, there are nine degrees of freedom left for variations of the ten January temperatures (for example) around the January average.

Let us assume further that the standard deviations of actual monthly temperatures around the long-term averages are 4°F in each of the 12 months, implying a common variance of 16. If we multiply this variance by its 108 degrees of freedom, we obtain 1728 as the total variance of the deviations about the ten-year means for each month.

Thus the total variance of the 120 monthly temperatures would be 34,228. The mean squares would have been 2954 for differences among the ten-year average temperatures for different months and only 16 for deviations of actual observations around the appropriate monthly averages. The F-ratio is 185, indicating, of course, a highly significant seasonal pattern.

8.2.2 Reduction of Variance in Passing from Monthly to Quarterly Observations

The monthly temperature data are simply illustrative of the phenomenon of seasonal variation which characterizes many economic time series. Some of the most important time series in our national economic data system are on a quarterly basis, particularly the gross national product and income accounts. For many kinds of quantitative analysis, if other time series published on a monthly basis must be correlated with components of the national income accounts, it is necessary to convert these monthly series into quarterly averages or totals.

It is intuitively clear that some information is lost when we convert the 12 monthly figures into four quarterly averages. If we contemplate using the series as the dependent variable in a regression analysis, we leave less total variation to be explained (although perhaps the averaging of three monthly figures removes mostly short-term random fluctuations or "noise" and leaves the majority of the variation, which may be systematically related to other economic variables). If the series is to be used as an *independent* variable, a reduction in the systematic component of its variance will tend to increase the standard errors of the regression coefficients of dependent variables upon it.

Let us consider what happens specifically when we convert our monthly temperature series (which could just as well represent monthly sales of a commodity) into quarterly averages. The results for a single year are summarized in the following tabulation:

Quarter	Quarterly Average	Variance of Monthly Average around Quarterly Average	Deviation of Quarterly Average from General Mean	Variance of Quarterly Averages about the General Mean
Jan.–Mar.	36.667°F	116.667	−18.3	1008.333
Apr.–June	65.000	200.000	10.0	300.000
Jul.–Sept.	73.333	116.667	18.3	1008.333
Oct.–Dec.	45.000	200.000	−10.0	300.000
Total	220.000	633.334	0	2616.667
Mean	55.000			

There are ten years, so the variances in the tabulation must be multiplied by ten.

Our time series of 120 monthly observations has now been compressed into one of 40 quarterly observations. One degree of freedom is used up in calculating the general mean and three degrees of freedom are taken up by the deviations of quarterly averages from the general mean. This leaves 36 degrees of freedom for variations of the ten observations for each quarter of the year about the appropriate ten-year average for that quarter. For comparison with the variance of the original monthly observations, we must remember that there are 80 degrees of freedom (two for each of 40 quarters) in the variations of the monthly observations about the respective quarterly averages.

Hence, of the 32,500 total variance of the original monthly averages around the general mean, we lose 6333 by suppressing the variations of monthly averages around the quarterly averages. The variance remaining in the deviations of quarterly averages from the general mean is 26,167, or 80.5% as large as that in the original monthly averages. Our estimates of standard errors of regression coefficients will rise in the ratio $1/\sqrt{0.805}$ if all other factors remain the same.

In most economic times series the seasonal amplitudes will be smaller than in our temperature series, the seasonal patterns may be less regular, and the individual monthly values will also show much greater variation about the long-term monthly averages than we have assumed here.

Similar information losses occur when small areas with distinctly different values of some variable (such as per capita income) are aggregated into larger areas. The "losses" to which we refer are of course the losses of parts of the *systematic* variation reflected in the monthly data or small area data.

EXERCISES

1. Show that

$$\sum y^2 = b^2 \sum x^2 + \sum z^2$$

where our simple regression model is

$$y = \alpha + \beta x + z$$

and b is the least squares estimate of β.

2. Suppose we have three types of fertilizer, A, B, and C, and that we apply equal amounts of fertilizer A to ten plots of land, fertilizer B to eight plots of land,

and fertilizer *C* to six plots of land. The yields of these plots of land are as follows:

A	B	C
23	30	15
26	24	19
13	28	26
17	31	21
47	32	19
37	30	15
29	36	
40	30	
33		
28		

(a) Set up the analysis of variance and test whether there is a significant difference between the mean yields of fertilizers *A* and *B*.

(b) Set up the analysis of variance and test whether there is a significant difference among the mean yields of the three fertilizers. Does your answer conflict with your findings of part (a)?

3. Now suppose we are interested not only in testing the fertilizers, but also in whether there is any difference between two different types of land. Therefore we apply five units of fertilizers *A*, *B*, and *C* to four different plots of each of the two types of land. The results of this follow:

	Fertilizers		
	A	B	C
Type I land	19	26	27
	27	34	36
	32	29	31
	24	41	36
Type II land	17	24	25
	24	29	28
	26	28	30
	18	34	37

Set up the analysis of variance and test (1) whether there is any significant difference among the three fertilizers and (2) whether there is any difference between the two types of land.

REFERENCES

1. Ezekiel, Mordecai and Karl A. Fox, *Methods of Correlation and Regression Analysis*, Third edition, New York: John Wiley and Sons, 1959.
2. Fisher, R. A., *Statistical Methods for Research Workers*, Thirteenth revised edition, New York: Hafner Publishing Co., 1963.

CHAPTER 9

The Logical or Structural Analysis
of Economic Time Series

In Chapter 5 we discussed time series analysis from descriptive and statistical points of view. We partitioned the total variance of a time series into trend, seasonal, cyclical, and random components on the basis of their different time paths without much regard to any economic reasons for their existence.

In this chapter we shall concentrate on interpreting the systematic components of economic time series in logical or structural terms. The key word in such interpretations is *why*. *Why* does a particular variable trace out a certain time path? What causes the seasonal pattern? What causes the trend? In what ways, if any, can knowledge of these causes improve the decisions of a business firm, a public agency, or one who makes government policy?

9.1 AN APPROACH THROUGH MICROANALYSIS

Some of the early advances in automation and assembly-line production methods were stimulated by time and motion studies. A worker packing apples in wooden boxes, if asked what he was doing, would most likely say "packing apples." A time and motion expert would answer the question differently in terms of basic units of motion, perception, and decision. Through visual perception and some kind of thought process, the worker selects an apple that seems to him an appropriate candidate, moves his hand to the vicinity of the next vacant spot in the box, places it in the desired position, spreads his fingers and releases the apple. One of the most imaginative of the early scientific managers, Frank Gilbreth, coined the word "therbligs" (an approximation to Gilbreth spelled backwards) to describe these basic units of human motion and action.

Once an activity such as packing apples had been reduced to its basic "therbligs," two sorts of response were possible. The first would be to devise an alternative sequence of therbligs which would enable an average worker to pack more boxes per hour with the same effort. The other would be to consider whether a machine could be devised to execute an appropriate sequence of therbligs which would accomplish the desired result at a still lower cost. Even if the machine did a less tasteful job, so that boxes packed by machine brought a slightly lower price than those packed by hand, construction of the machine would still be warranted from a firm's standpoint if the reduction in costs were expected to be greater than the reduction in market price.

To avoid both the mysticism and the empiricism that tends to invade most introductory discussions of economic times series, it may be helpful to build up a structural model of an aggregative economic time series starting virtually at the "therblig" level of concreteness.

9.1.1 *A Household's Demand for Electricity*

Figure 9.1 schematically describes the demand for electricity by a particular household in terms of the smallest basic units of action.[1] Suppose we were to take an inventory of the installed and/or ready-to-use electrical equipment in a private home at a particular moment. We would note the wattage of each light bulb and a corresponding measure of current required for each plate of the electric stove, each electric fan, the electric toaster, the airconditioner, the washing machine, the clothes dryer, the refrigerator, and every other device in the house which used electric current.

All of these appliances would (when in use) be connected by the electric wiring to an outside source of current which would pass through a metering device. If we had accurate specifications of the current utilized by each appliance (and for each position of the control knob on appliances with several different settings), we could set out a synthetic model of the electrical system of the house and from it estimate the total amount of current which must pass through the meter for any conceivable combination of appliances simultaneously in use.

For experimental purposes, one could attach to each appliance an instrument which would record graphically on time series paper the volume of current used by that appliance at any and every minute of the day.

Figure 9.1a is the sort of time series graph we might expect such an instrument to show for current used by a particular electric light bulb. On a December day, this light bulb might be turned on for an hour and a half in

---

[1] The seasonal differences shown in Figure 9.1 are appropriate for United States cities at about the latitudes of New York City and Chicago.

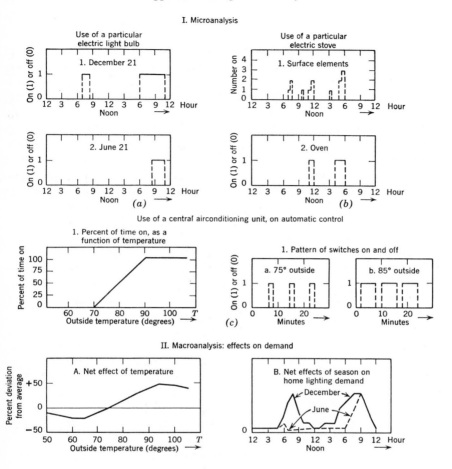

Figure 9.1 Structural analysis of household demand for electricity (schematic).

the morning and as much as five hours in the evening. In June the same light bulb might be required for only two or three hours in the evening. Part *b* is the sort of time series graph that might be recorded by a meter which intercepts all current used by the surface elements of an electric stove. (It is a very primitive kind of electric stove in which each element is either on or off and has only one setting for the "on" position.) We may visualize this pattern, if we like, in terms of a simple breakfast, a morning coffee break, a fairly simple lunch, an afternoon coffee break, and a substantial evening meal. Another meter connected to the electric oven might show utilization for an hour or less before lunch and as much as two hours before dinner.

Figure 9.1c shows a hypothetical relationship between the outside temperature and the percentage of the time which a central airconditioning unit on automatic control might actually be turned on. The diagram implies a linear relationship connecting the number of minutes per hour the unit must be turned on to the difference between the outside temperature and the desired inside temperature at which the automatic control is set. (The diagram also assumes away other important factors such as variations in humidity which might be important under real operating conditions.) If the desired inside temperature is 70 degrees and the control is set at that figure, the right-hand diagrams in Part c imply that an outside temperature of 75 degrees would cause the airconditioner to run for two minutes and stop for six minutes in an eight-minute cycle. With an outside temperature of 85 degrees, the cycle might be six minutes on and two minutes off. If the thermostat was extremely sensitive the pattern of use for each of the two temperature levels might involve a shorter cycle, but the *proportions* of time on within the cycle should not be affected. Hence to explain the proportions of "on" and "off" time for the automatic air conditioner shown on the time series chart, it would be helpful to plot the outside temperature on the same chart.

Given accurate measuring and recording devices, we should be able to add up the flows of current through each electrical appliance in the house minute by minute and arrive at an aggregative time series for total use of current by the household. If there are significant power losses in the household wiring between individual appliances and the meter connected to the outside source, the time series graph recorded at the outside source would run at a somewhat higher level than the sum of the rates of current consumption measured at the individual appliances.

One could approach this problem either synthetically in terms of actual measurements of power loss over each segment of wiring or on an empirical basis. For example, given extremely sensitive recording devices, one might turn off all appliances except one. Then, when light bulb A is turned on, the flow of current measured at the outside meter box could be compared with the flow recorded at the light bulb itself. Similar measurements could be made at the two locations for every appliance in the house and for combinations of appliances. If the power loss in the household wiring were a small percentage of the total current flowing into the house, we might ignore detailed questions as to which particular light bulbs are turned on at a given moment and simply compute the regression equation of total current required at the meter box upon the *sum* of currents used at the appliances. That is, for practical purposes we might assume that the total current which must enter the house depends only upon the total amount of current passing through all appliances and is independent of the particular combinations of appliances which might be in use at the time.

9.1.2 *Demand for Electricity by an Aggregate of Households*

We now proceed to a different level of aggregation. Let us suppose that the particular household is one of a thousand households which collectively constitute the household demand for electricity from a municipal power plant. Suppose further that (ignoring details as to which appliances are used in each household) we record as time series minute by minute the total amount of current entering each household.

Each of the household curves might show some fairly sharp jumps and discontinuities, but the graph of total current use by a household would be much smoother than that for many of the individual appliances. The one thousand time series for households could be added to obtain a measure minute by minute of the total amount of electricity entering household circuits served by the power plant.

Since there are power losses between the plant's generating equipment and the household meter boxes, the time series of current demanded at the generator will be at a somewhat higher level than the simple aggregate of demands at the household meter boxes. Here again, the plant manager could approach the analysis of this phenomenon either synthetically (by measuring separately the power losses along each section of each transmission line) or empirically.

Theoretically, he could enlist the cooperation of each individual household and estimate for each household separately the regression relationship of current required at the generator to current required at that household's meter box. If power losses of this sort were fairly small relative to the total output of current at the generator, however, the plant manager might be willing to use the regression equation of total current demanded at the generator upon total current recorded at all household meter boxes as a measure of the relationship between the two.

The hour-by-hour operating problems at the power plant probably depend only upon the total amount of electricity required at the generators. For this purpose, information about which households are using the most electricity at a given moment is irrelevant. The manager is interested in having sufficient generator capacity to meet household requirements at whatever peak load may occur during the day; during slack periods, if one generator can be operated at a lower unit cost than another, he will be interested in seeing that the required flow of current is produced at minimum in-plant cost.[2]

---

[2] The municipal plant might find it cheaper to buy ("import") power from a large private utility at peak load periods than to maintain enough generator capacity of its own to meet all contingencies.

9.1.3 *A Model of Household Demand for Electric Power*

This discussion may already seem quite elaborate, but a further extension of the example will prove useful.

Let us suppose that we have accurate information on the technological characteristics of each microelement in the system just described: a complete inventory of the electrical appliances in each household; the power loss properties of each segment of each household's internal wiring; and the power loss characteristics of each unit or segment of the distribution system between the households and the generators. The total power requirement at the generators might then be predicted in advance from estimates of the *proportions* of the total numbers of appliances of each type which were likely to be turned on at each minute of the day.

A model of household consumption of electric power in this system might be as follows: An outer limit on possible demand would be set by the complete inventory of appliances installed and/or ready for use. If each appliance of a particular type i ($i = 1, 2, 3, \ldots, m$) has only one setting while turned on, we may write the total power demand on the system as

$$D = \sum_{i=1}^{m} d_i = \sum_{i=1}^{m} n_i \lambda_i p_i$$

where n_i is the total number of appliances of the ith type; λ_i is the number of kilowatts required by each unit of the ith type; and p_i is the proportion of the total number of units of the ith type turned on at a given moment.

At any given date, the n_i and λ_i are constants, presumed known. If the plant manager is to predict electricity requirements anywhere from one hour to several months in advance of need, he is interested (implicitly) in predicting the time paths of each of the p_i's.

The proportion of central air conditioners turned on should be primarily a function of outside temperature and humidity. The proportion of room air conditioners turned on might be a function of temperature, humidity, and the number of family members likely to be in the house rather than elsewhere at particular times of day. The proportion of all electric lights turned on should be a function of the time of day and a seasonal factor reflecting times of sunrise and sunset. Different within-day patterns would be found for Saturday, for Sunday, and for the other days of the week.

The proportion of surface elements and ovens of electric stoves turned on might be a function of the hour of the day, a seasonal factor representing differences between (say) summer and winter cooking habits, and of departures of outside temperature from the seasonal norm for the given date. Similar functions might be postulated and (if desired) empirically estimated for other types of electrical appliances in the community.

Once the plant manager had worked out equations (or rules of thumb) for predicting the time paths of each p_i he could estimate the time paths of each d_i and then aggregate the d_i to obtain the estimated time path for D.

If the plant manager is responsible for long-run investment and expansion plans, he must also try to project the *trend* of power demand. Logically, this trend may be broken down into (1) a trend in the number of households and (2) a trend in the average consumption of electric power per household. The latter trend in turn may be broken down into the effects of changes in each of the variables n_i, λ_i, and p_i. The trend in a particular n_i (that is, the total number of units of a particular kind of appliance installed) could in some instances follow a logistic curve and approach an upper limit or saturation point relative to any given total number of households. A λ_i might trend downward over time if there were an increase in the efficiency of that kind of appliance; it could perhaps trend upward if standards of appliance capacity or intensity of illumination increased. The p_i would be matters of consumer behavior, recognizing that the relevant consumers had already committed themselves to a certain broad pattern or type of electric power consumption by having purchased a particular kind of electrical appliance.

Trends in the local household demand for electricity will also depend upon trends in income per wage earner and per household and perhaps upon the stability of employment in the community. We might postulate that the total number of units of each kind of appliance owned in the community per 1000 households will depend upon (1) the average income per household, (2) the proportions of households in each of five or ten income classes, (3) the stability of employment, and (4) the expectations of members of the community concerning its economic prospects over the next several years. For example, households with a high degree of confidence in their economic prospects in the locality would be more likely to invest in central air conditioning than households that expected to have to move within two or three years to better or even maintain their economic positions.

9.2 POLICY IMPLICATIONS OF A STRUCTURAL ANALYSIS OF ECONOMIC TIME SERIES FOR BUSINESS FIRMS

So far, we have considered only *what* consumers do and not *why* they do it. Household members turn on lights because they want to do things that require or are facilitated by light and turn on stoves because they want hot beverages and cooked food. Other household wants are clean clothes, a cool house, well-refrigerated (or simply well-preserved) food, and perhaps certain types of television and radio programs. If some of these wants can be satisfied in alternative ways, through commercial laundries, laundromats, gas stoves, and irradiated food—the prices of electrical appliances and electric power relative to the prices of commercial services and the operating costs of gas stoves will be relevant to the demand for electric power.

Hence the plant management may wish to influence the behavior of its household customers by means of its rate schedules and other policy instruments. Price schedules might be altered in order to reduce the peak load and achieve a somewhat less variable pattern of current use within a day. In principle, it would be possible to install household meters which measured not only the total amount of electricity consumed but the amount consumed in particular time periods. If the peak use of air conditioners occurs in the early afternoon and present peak load on the generators occurs in the late afternoon, favorable rates for households having central air conditioning units could be used to encourage their purchase. On the other hand, if air conditioners became sufficiently numerous to shift the peak load on the system from late afternoon to early afternoon, the plant management might decide to withdraw the favorable rates for households with central air conditioners or (theoretically) even charge higher than average rates to those households which install central air conditioners after a specified date.

To the extent that the number of appliances owned n_i, the average power or rate of current consumption required to operate a unit of each appliance λ_i, and the proportion of the total number of appliances in use at a given moment p_i can be influenced by the average price or price schedule charged for electricity, a private power company would be justified in estimating the probable effects on household demand for power of a wide range of possible variations in its prices. If there were only two kinds of appliances and if adjustments of n_i, λ_i, and p_i to changes in P_i (the price charged for current used in the ith type of appliance) were instantaneous, the economic framework in which the firm operated could be characterized as follows:

$$(9.1) \qquad \hat{n}_1 = n_{01} + b_1 P_1 + g_1 N + \gamma_1 y$$

$$(9.2) \qquad \hat{\lambda}_1 = \lambda_{01} + c_1 P_1$$

$$(9.3) \qquad \hat{p}_1 = p_{01} + f_1 P_1 + \delta_1 y$$

$$(9.4) \qquad \hat{n}_2 = n_{02} + b_2 P_2 + g_2 N + \gamma_2 y$$

$$(9.5) \qquad \hat{\lambda}_2 = \lambda_{02} + c_2 P_2$$

$$(9.6) \qquad \hat{p}_2 = p_{02} + f_2 P_2 + \delta_2 y$$

$$(9.7) \qquad d_1 = n_1 \lambda_1 p_1$$

$$(9.8) \qquad d_2 = n_2 \lambda_2 p_2$$

$$(9.9) \qquad D_T = d_1 + d_2$$

(9.10) $\text{TR} = d_1 P_1 + d_2 P_2$

(9.11) $\text{TC} = \text{TFC} + \text{MC}(D_T)$

(9.12) $\text{TNR} = d_1 P_1 + d_2 P_2 - \text{TFC} - \text{MC}(D_T)$

where N is the total number of households in the community and y is the average income per household, TR is the firm's total revenue, TC its total cost, TFC its total fixed cost, and MC its marginal cost per unit, TNR is the firm's total net revenue.

If the power company takes N and y as given, and *if* it can make satisfactory estimates of the coefficients of the six equations (9.1) through (9.6), it can estimate the effects of changes in each of its prices, P_1 and P_2, upon its total net revenue. The profit-maximizing values of P_1 and P_2 will also depend upon the values of N and y.

Because n_1 is the total stock of units of appliance 1 owned by households and since the appliance no doubt has a working life of several years, n_1 will not adjust instantaneously to a new level of P_1 (or of y). Hence (9.1) should probably include terms in $P_{1(t-1)}, P_{1(t-2)}, \ldots, P_{1(t-k)}$ and perhaps in $y_{(t-1)},$ $y_{(t-2)}, \ldots, y_{(t-r)}$. Equations (9.1) and (9.4) become *stock adjustment* or *ownership adjustment* equations rather than short-run demand equations and λ_1 and λ_2 may change simply because the new units added to n_1 and n_2 use more power than the older models (a "trading-up" in quality or performance standards of appliances purchased when the price of electricity is reduced, for example). Equations (9.3) and (9.6), the proportions of existing appliances actually turned on at a given moment, would probably contain most of the short-run or instantaneous response of power consumption to a change in price.[3]

We will not embellish the model further for its own sake. We will use it instead to illustrate the differences between economic time series analysis directed toward empirical forecasting and time series analysis oriented toward policy uses. We assume that the power company has no control over N and y; hence its interest in them is limited to a desire for accurate *forecasts* of their future values. However, the company has a policy interest in P_1 and P_2, which it can set on its own initiative (within limits usually prescribed by a utility commission). The company also has a *policy* interest in d_1 and d_2 to the extent that it can influence them through changes in its prices P_1 and P_2. The two prices and the two quantities, d_1 and d_2, all enter into the total net revenue function which is the criterion by which success is measured in the theory of the firm.

---

[3] Koyck's method of distributed lags appears to be one of the most practical approaches to the estimation of reactions extending over several units of time. See Appendix A to this chapter.

To the extent that P_1 and P_2 were used by the power company to influence n_1 and n_2, the situations of electric appliance dealers in the area would also be affected. If there were many small dealers and the city is large, each dealer would have to accept the changes in P_1 and P_2 as facts of his external environment. *Forecasts* of n_1 and n_2 for the city as a whole would be useful to a dealer in gauging the state of the market, but the variables of interest to him from a *policy* standpoint would include his own volumes of sales and the selling prices and other instruments available to him for influencing his sales and net revenue.

9.3   STRUCTURAL ANALYSIS OF SEASONAL, TREND, AND CYCLICAL COMPONENTS OF ECONOMIC TIME SERIES

The present section extends a structural approach to the analysis of various components of economic time series. Seasonal, trend, and cyclical movements will be discussed in turn. In each instance it appears that the movements in one time series can hardly be explained without pointing to movements in other time series and a model—sometimes a rather loose and intuitive one—relating these series to the series of primary concern.

Interestingly enough, although seasonal variation seems to be the most promising area of application of *spectral analysis* to economic time series, our analysis of the seasonal pattern of prices of a storable commodity suggests that multivariate models may be more illuminating than univariate models even in the seasonal domain.[4]

9.3.1 *Structural Analysis of Seasonal Patterns*

During the 1950–1956 period pork production in the United States showed a seasonal pattern running from 134% of the annual average in December down to 78% in July. The corresponding seasonal index for prices received by farmers for hogs moved inversely, rising from a low of 90% of the annual average in December to a high of 108% in August.

In this section, we wish to consider *why* seasonal patterns of particular timing and amplitudes have developed; we are no longer content simply with measuring *what* they may have been in some past period. The relationship between the seasonal patterns of hog prices and hog production has the inverse or negative sign we expect to find in a demand curve. If the 12 seasonal price and production index values all lay on or near a demand curve,

---

[4] For an excellent introduction to spectral analysis and its application to the seasonal component of economic time series, see Marc Nerlove, "Spectral Analysis of Seasonal Adjustment Procedures," *Econometrica* **32**, No. 3, pp. 241–286 (July 1964).

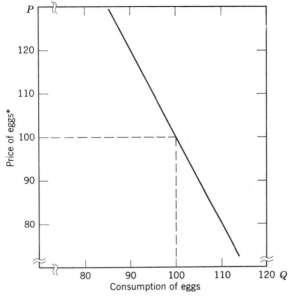

*Annual average level equals 100.

Figure 9.2 Consumer demand function for eggs (schematic).

we might take the ratio of the percentage range in production to the percentage range in price as an estimate of its elasticity. The resulting estimate of "demand elasticity" would be $(134 - 78)/(90 - 108) = 56/-18 = -3.1$. However, several careful analyses have all given estimates of the price elasticity of demand for pork of -0.6 to -0.8 at the retail level.[5] The corresponding *derived demand* at the farm price level should be less elastic than the demand at retail. Hence our "elasticity" estimate of -3.1 must result primarily from factors other than a relationship in consumer demand, although consumer demand may still contribute something to the observed effect.

Figure 9.2 shows a hypothetical consumer demand function for eggs which has an elasticity of -0.5 at the point $(100,100)$ which we will take as the point of annual averages or means. According to this relationship, a 10% decrease in the retail price of eggs is associated with a 5% increase in

[5] These are calendar year averages. B. F. Stanton obtained estimates of about -0.5 in summer and about -1.1 in winter seasons during 1953–1959. [See B. F. Stanton, "Seasonal Demand for Beef, Pork and Broilers," *Agricultural Economics Research*, USDA, pp. 1–14 (January 1961). Figures 4.5, 4.6, and 4.7 (pp. 70, 70, and 71) were reproduced from this article.]

consumption. It is assumed that this consumer demand function applies equally to all 12 months of the year.

Suppose that there is no storage activity for eggs so that the quantity of eggs offered to consumers by retailers in a given month is precisely equal to the farm production of eggs for that month. Let us further assume the following monthly pattern of egg production:

Month	Production, Units	Price in Absence of Storage, Cents per Unit
January	97.5	105
February	102.5	95
March	107.5	85
April	112.5	75
May	112.5	75
June	107.5	85
July	102.5	95
August	97.5	105
September	92.5	115
October	87.5	125
November	87.5	125
December	92.5	115
Average	100.0	100.0

The specific formula for the demand function in Figure 9.2 is $P_i = 300 - 2Q_i$; if consumption is equal to production, retail prices must move in the manner shown in the third column of the foregoing table. The ratio of the extreme ranges is $(112.5 - 87.5)/(75 - 125) = -25/50 = -0.5$, which in the present symmetrical and straight line pattern of price-quantity points is identical with the elasticity of demand at the point of means. These particular sets of monthly consumption (equals production) and monthly prices are shown as the solid lines in Figure 9.3.

Suppose that there are some firms engaged in the seasonal storage of eggs. For simplicity we assume that the eggs do not deteriorate in quality while in storage but will sell at the same price as the current month's production. If the cost of storing a unit of eggs is two cents a month, and if storage operators have a clear knowledge of the seasonal pattern of egg production and of the consumer demand curve, the resulting price and consumption patterns should be as indicated in the dashed line in Figure 9.3.[6]

Obviously, storage operators would be buying eggs in the months in which production is large and prices are low and they would be selling eggs in months

---

[6] We assume the storage firms are operating under pure competition.

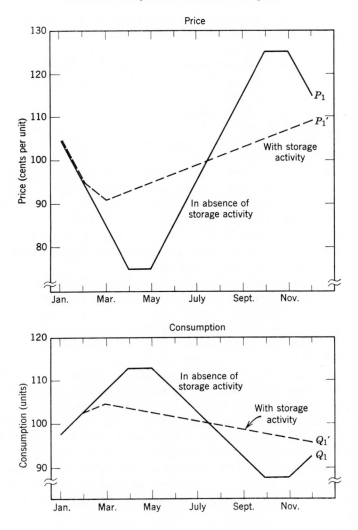

Figure 9.3 Seasonal patterns of price and consumption of eggs, with and without a storage activity (schematic).

of below average production and above average price. In equilibrium, since the marginal cost of storage is assumed to be two cents a month, the expected selling price of eggs must increase by two cents a month to justify a storage operation. The price pattern resulting under the conditions of our particular problem is one in which prices rise by two cents a month from a low of

91 cents in March to a high of 109 cents in December. Conversely, consumption (as distinct from production) would decline from a high of 104.5 units in March to a low of 95.5 units in December.

The paired observations of price and *consumption* fall on the demand function shown in Figure 9.2; the ratio of consumption range to price range is $(104.5 - 95.5)/(91 - 109) = -9/18 = -0.5$, as before. However, the ratio of the seasonal range in *production* to the new seasonal range in price becomes $(112.5 - 87.5)/(91 - 109) = -25/18 = -1.4$. This ratio or "pseudo-elasticity" is about three times as large as the true elasticity of consumer demand.

Intuitively, it appears that (except for discontinuities and special circumstances) a reduction of the storage cost to one cent per month would reduce the amplitude of seasonal price variation from 18 cents to about nine cents; with the amplitude of seasonal variation in production unchanged, the "pseudo-elasticity" would rise to -2.8. An increase in storage costs to three cents or four cents a month would clearly increase the amplitude of price variation and reduce the "pseudo-elasticity."

A complete explanation of Figures 9.3 and 9.4 would involve some simple operations research considerations. Figure 9.4 indicates that the consumer demand function for eggs, the seasonal pattern of egg production, and the level of storage costs collectively result in a strong and regular seasonal pattern of storage stocks and of net movements of eggs into and out of storage if all disturbances and uncertainty are ruled out.

The traditional approach to seasonal analysis would have applied the same routine methods of determining seasonal indices to each of the five time series of (1) egg production, (2) egg consumption, (3) retail price, (4) total storage holdings, and (5) net movements of eggs into and out of storage. In effect, the process of data adjustment would have treated each of these series as if it were completely independent of the others.

Our analysis implies that the seasonal patterns in the five series are closely bound together by means of a consumer demand function and a storage cost function, operating in conjunction with a predetermined pattern of egg production.

Given a structural analysis of seasonal variation, we should be able to estimate the effects of changes in individual elements of the structure. For example, if monthly storage costs increased successively from two cents to three cents and from three cents to four cents, the amplitude of seasonal price variation would increase from 18 cents to 27 cents to 30 cents; peak storage stocks would fall from 30.00 units to 22.75 units to 19.00 units; the total number of "unit-months" of storage would fall from 160.00 to 117.75 to 91.00; and the gross income to all storage operators would rise from 320.00 "cents" to 353.25 to 364.00.

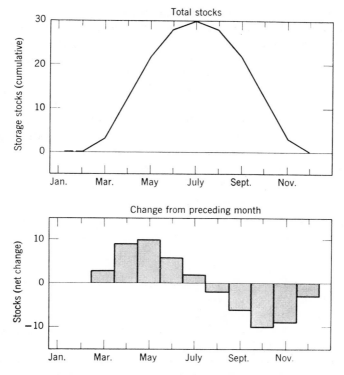

Figure 9.4 Seasonal variations in storage holdings of eggs (schematic).

This level of precision is, of course, not found in the real world. Actually, seasonal patterns of egg storage, like seasonal patterns of many other economic time series, have changed considerably in recent years. A structural analysis of these changes can largely explain them, whereas an empirical analysis can only describe them or extrapolate them on the basis of unanalyzed assumptions that certain trends will continue.

Obviously, a reduction in the seasonal amplitude of egg production would also reduce the seasonal amplitude of price variations and storage holdings. If an egg producer takes any particular seasonal pattern of egg prices as given, he is faced with the problem of choosing a seasonal pattern of egg production which maximizes his net profits. It would be an oversimplification to say that the cost of egg production varied from month to month. It might be more realistic to regard the egg producer as being confronted with a number of alternative activities or processes for producing eggs, each requiring a different seasonal pattern of labor inputs, feed purchases, short-term credit costs, and costs of buildings and equipment. From the complete range of activities available and the limitations upon his labor supply, his line of credit, and his aversion to debt (or preference for liquidity), the "rational" egg producer would be viewed as selecting that level and seasonal pattern of production which maximized his expected profits, given the expected seasonal pattern of egg prices.

Changes in the array of production techniques available set forces in motion which tend to rearrange the seasonal pattern of egg production. If the rest of the demand and storage cost mechanism remains as indicated in our example, these changes in the seasonal pattern of production will be associated with changes in the seasonal patterns of prices, consumption, and storage activity.

9.3.2 Structural Analysis of Trends

We have already suggested some logical principles of trend analysis in earlier sections of this chapter. First, the trend in a particular variable Y may logically be separable into the net effects of trends in certain other variables X_1, X_2, ..., X_m. If this is so, Y is evidently a dependent or *endogenous* variable, whereas at least some of the X_i's may be independent or *exogenous* variables. If none of the X_i's are subject to influence by the firm or agency interested in explaining the trend in Y, the problem of projecting or predicting Y in the future becomes one of projecting or predicting the time paths of each of the relevant X_i's.

If the historical relationships between Y and each of the X_i's have been straight lines, a serious technical difficulty is encountered in trying to estimate the coefficients relating Y to each of the X_i's. Estimation of trends might take the form either of statistical regression analysis or of a logical synthesis of engineering relationships and/or institutional relationships *with* regression analysis.[7]

Input-Output Relationships and Trend Analysis. The input-output mechanism often helps to explain trends in aggregative production variables which are too highly intercorrelated to be separated by regression analysis. Consider the following model in which the gross outputs X_1 and X_2 are expressed as linear functions of the deliveries to final demand F_1 and F_2:

(9.13) $$X_1 = 1.8F_1 + 0.1F_2$$

(9.14) $$X_2 = 0.4F_1 + 1.6F_2$$

In an expanding economy, both categories of final demand, F_1 and F_2, tend to increase strongly. Through the input-output mechanism, a unit increase in F_1 tends to raise X_1 by 1.8 units and X_2 by 0.4 units. Similarly, a unit increase in F_2 tends to raise X_1 by 0.1 units and X_2 by 1.6 units.

[7] See Chapter 13.

In the following tabulation, F_1 and F_2 both follow exactly linear trends and are therefore perfectly correlated:

Year	F_1	F_2	$X_{1.1} + X_{1.2} = X_1$	$X_{2.1} + X_{2.2} = X_2$
0	10	20	$(18.0 + 2.0) = 20.0$	$(4.0 + 32.0) = 36.0$
1	11	21	$(19.8 + 2.1) = 21.9$	$(4.4 + 33.6) = 38.0$
2	12	22	$(21.6 + 2.2) = 23.8$	$(4.8 + 35.2) = 40.0$
3	13	23	$(23.4 + 2.3) = 25.7$	$(5.2 + 36.8) = 42.0$
4	14	24	$(25.2 + 2.4) = 27.6$	$(5.6 + 38.4) = 44.0$
5	15	25	$(27.0 + 2.5) = 29.5$	$(6.0 + 40.0) = 46.0$

The input-output mechanism causes X_1 to move according to the sum of two linear trends, $X_1 = X_{1.1} + X_{1.2}$, where $X_{1.1} = 1.8F_1$ and $X_{1.2} = 0.1F_2$. Also, X_2 moves as the sum of the two linear trends, $X_{2.1} = 0.4F_1$ and $X_{2.2} = 1.6F_2$. The sum of the two linear trend components of X_1 is a linear trend; the same is true for X_2. The result is that X_1, X_2, F_1, and F_2 are *all* perfectly correlated; it is impossible to separate out the net effects of F_1 and F_2 upon X_1 and X_2, respectively, by any statistical technique.

If F_1 and F_2 have short-run deviations from trend which are not perfectly correlated, these deviations will be propagated through the input-output mechanism of the economy into X_1 and X_2. The expected deviation in X_1 will be $x_1 = 1.8f_1 + 0.1f_2$, and the expected deviation in X_2 will be $x_2 = 0.4f_1 + 1.6f_2$. The deviations in X_1 and X_2 will not be perfectly correlated with each other or with either f_1 or f_2. If there are errors of measurement or aggregation in all variables, the regression of x_1 on f_1 and f_2 may give a good approximation to the input-output coefficient connecting x_1 to f_1, but the net regression coefficient of x_1 upon f_1 might appear to be of borderline significance.

In the conventional input-output model, the deliveries to final demand F_1 and F_2 are independent or exogenous variables and X_1 and X_2 are dependent or endogenous. Equations (9.13) and (9.14) permit us to make conditional forecasts of X_1 and X_2 *given* F_1 and F_2. If we were free to choose sets of values of F_1 and F_2 which were completely uncorrelated with one another and which covered wide ranges (as in the designed experiment of Chapters 6 and 7), we could regress the resulting values of X_1 and X_2 on the assigned values of F_1 and F_2 and obtain quite good estimates of all four coefficients along with their standard errors.[8]

---

[8] As we have seen in Chapter 8, experimental designs are often contrived so as to give zero intercorrelations between all pairs of independent variables, so that the net effects of the individual variables can simply be added to one another to obtain their total effect.

Figure 9.5 illustrates the net input-output effects of changes in production in the machinery and equipment industry in the United States upon required production of steel and electric power over the 1947–1961 period, *assuming* that (1) the value of purchases of steel and electric power per dollar of machinery sales remains constant at the 1947 level and (2) the complete

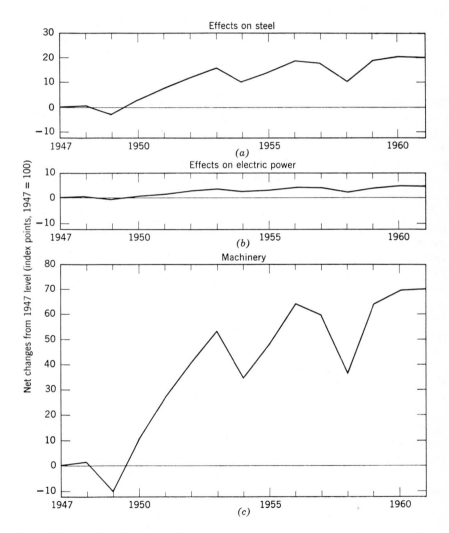

Figure 9.5 Net interindustry effects of changes in production of machinery upon required production of steel and electric power, 1947–61.

structure of technological relationships connecting other industries in the economy either remains as in 1947 or changes tend to be offsetting and neutral with respect to the interactions among machinery production, steel, and electric power.

In 1947, the machinery industry purchased about 0.12 dollar worth of steel and 0.0047 dollar worth of electric power per dollar of machinery output or sales. The machinery industry used about 1% of total electric power production in 1947.

If, for illustration purposes, we regard the production of machinery as an exogenous or independent variable, the direct and indirect effects of an increase of one index point (1947 = 100) in machinery output would require an increase of about 0.3 index point in steel production and perhaps 0.07 index point in the production of electric power. (These figures are not precise, but the orders of magnitude as of 1947 are approximated from the 1947 interindustry relations study for the United States.)

On these assumptions, the time path of machinery production in Figure 9.5c would have accounted for an increase of 20 points in the index of steel production and five points in the index of electric power production between 1947 and 1961. If each of the two series in Figure 9.5a and b were regressed on the index of machinery production in part c, all observations would fall on the regression lines, the squared correlation coefficients would equal one, and the slopes of the regression lines would be 0.3 for steel and 0.07 for electric power; the constant terms would be zero in each instance.

Trends in Population. One of the most important variables in economic projections and trend analysis is population. For a large country such as the United States with a limited amount of immigration and emigration, the general inclination of economists is to treat population growth as an exogenous, noncontrollable factor.

Figure 9.6 shows three "population pyramids" or percentage distributions by age and sex. A striking feature of the United States population pyramid in 1960 was the fact that the numbers in the age groups 20–24 and 25–29 were smaller than the numbers in age groups 30–34, 35–39, and 40–44. Working backward, the proximate cause is found in the fact that the number of babies born in the 1930s was smaller than the number born in each of the two preceding decades. This was largely due to the depressed economic circumstances of the 1930s during which many adults were unemployed and many young people delayed marrying and starting families because of the difficulties and uncertainties of finding jobs.

Hence, in a broad sense, human population even at the national level is an endogenous or dependent variable influenced by political and economic conditions.

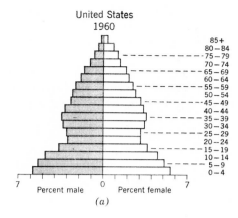

United States
1960

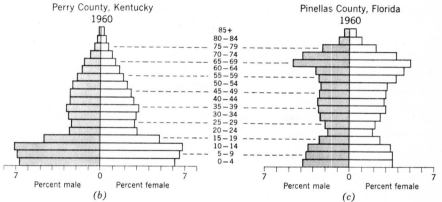

Perry County, Kentucky
1960

Pinellas County, Florida
1960

Figure 9.6 Population pyramids, selected countries and areas, 1954–60. (From Bureau of the Census, U.S. Census of Population: 1960. General Population Characteristics, Washington: U.S. Government Printing Office, 1961.)

Population changes in small subdivisions of a country are highly endogenous. Projections for a particular county must take into account the array of economic and other forces which are tending to redistribute jobs and people among areas. Perry County, Kentucky, shows evidence of a very high birth rate and a very high rate of out-migration. Apparently, job opportunities in Perry County had not expanded rapidly enough to accommodate (on a net basis) more than half of their young people as they reached working age. Pinellas County, Florida, evidently serves in part as a retirement area for elderly people. The number of persons aged 65–69 is larger than the number in any other five-year age group.

Thus, in forecasting population, routine and empirical methods may prove to be exceedingly unreliable. Only when we understand economic and other variables that influence people in their decisions do we begin to find satisfying explanations for past population trends or convincing support for future projections.

Trends in the Stock of Capital and Production Capacity. Changes in the stock of capital (plant and equipment) result from the difference between gross investment (new construction and installation of new machines and equipment) and depreciation plus other forms of capital consumption.

The technological characteristics and efficiency of machinery produced in 1966 are different and generally better than those of machinery produced in 1956. Therefore the age distribution of the nation's stock of machinery and equipment is relevant to projections of (1) total productive capacity and (2) the time path of investment demand. For example, a high rate of investment in new machinery during one five year period might be followed by a low rate in the succeeding five years and an increased rate in the third five-year period owing to a bunching of replacement demand.

Analogously, young people entering the labor force in the middle 1960s have different kinds of educations (at least in matters of emphasis and detail) than workers educated in previous decades and have different implications for the potential gross national product at full employment.

Growth Models and Decision Models—Trends or Targets? Since World War II, governments in most democratic nations have assumed increased responsibility for economic growth as well as for economic stability. Most modern economies are "mixed economies" in the sense that government agencies and enterprises (schools, post offices, the defense establishment, and so on) account for a significant fraction of production and final demand. Moreover, many of the activities of private firms and individuals operate within constraints (tax policies, anti-trust laws, pure food and drug laws, and others) which are subject to change by legislative or administrative bodies. As awareness of the importance of government actions for the behavior of the private economy grows and as measurement of structural relationships in the economy becomes more dependable, there will be a greater tendency for public bodies to consider the effects of alternative policies upon the probable future course of the private economy.

A knowledge of the structure of the private economy would enable us to project economic trends in it under the assumption that government policies are unchanged or are changed in specified ways. In contrast, *unconditional forecasts* of the values of certain economic variables in 1975 would also imply unconditional forecasts as to the actions that will be undertaken by government and the degree of success of these actions in achieving their intended objectives.

In particular, many countries and groups of countries are concerned with increasing their rates of economic growth and are evaluating their economic policies in relation to this objective. Logically, we may think of a regression equation connecting the national income or the gross national product in future years with (1) each variable which might be used directly or indirectly as a policy instrument and (2) each of the more important noncontrollable factors.

The implementation of realistic means for accelerating economic growth in any country entails some economic and/or social costs in addition to benefits. The approach of economic theory is fairly clear—each method of increasing the growth rate should be extended to that point at which the last billion dollars of cost is expected to produce a future income stream with a discounted present value of a billion dollars. This implies difficult problems of measurement to which economists should nevertheless address themselves, and even more difficult problems of obtaining political and social consensus as to the values of different targets and the full costs of proposed means of implementation.

9.3.3 *Structural Analysis of Cyclical Fluctuations*

The input-output or interindustry relations effects underlying Figure 9.5 help to explain cyclical fluctuations as well as trends in economic time series of production. In the 1950s and early 1960s, economists gave increasing attention to the analysis of inventory fluctuations in individual firms and industries, and for the national economy as a whole. If there are random or irregular variations in the final demand for a product, retailers, wholesalers, and manufacturers of the product respond to these changes partly through offsetting fluctuations in inventories. During a business recession, however, partly as a result of technical input-output relationships, the final sales of many firms in many industries level off or decline simultaneously.

If many firms have as one of their policy targets the maintenance of a desired ratio of inventories to sales, a decline in final sales will be followed by a larger absolute decline in factory production. In effect, the "market" for inventories becomes supersaturated. When sales increase again, the desired level of inventories also rises and production is increased sufficiently to meet the increased final demand and also the desired increase in inventories.

The following tables illustrate a few important aspects of the structure of the United States economy which influence the cyclical patterns of major macroeconomic variables.

Table 9.1 indicates that production of durable manufactures declined an average of 15% in the three recessions, whereas nondurable manufactures declined only 5%. If we make a special grouping of the industrial production components into metal manufactures, miscellaneous manufactures, and manufactures of consumer nondurable goods, we find that the average

Table 9.1   Industrial Production: Changes in Major Groups of Industries from Peak to Trough during Three Cyclical Episodes, United States, 1948–1958

Industry Group [b]	Average Percentage Changes [a] Peak to Trough, Three Cycles, Percent
Industrial production total	− 11.0
Durable manufactures	− 15.2
Nondurable manufactures	− 5.0
Minerals	− 12.1
Manufacturers: special groupings	
Metal manufactures	− 16.8
Consumer nondurables	− 3.8
Miscellaneous manufactures	− 10.4

[a] Averages for the three special groups of manufacturing industries are based on simple arithmetic averages of published index numbers for five, six, and nine industries, respectively; figures for the "total," "durable manufactures," "nondurable manufactures," and "minerals" indices are as officially published.

[b] Relative importance of the components may be estimated from 1956 figures on "production and related workers" employed: all manufacturing industries, 13.2 million; metal manufactures, 5.6 million; consumer nondurables, 4.2 million; and miscellaneous manufactures, 3.4 million. (About 0.8 million wage and salary workers were engaged in minerals production.)

Sources: Computed from basic data in *Business Statistics, 1957 Biennial Edition* (a supplement to the *Survey of Current Business*); and various issues of *Survey of Current Business and Federal Reserve Bulletin.*

decline in the production of metal manufactures was more than four times as large in regard to percentage as the average decline in the output of consumer nondurables. This latter fact tallies with the relative stability of personal consumption expenditures during these recessions primarily as a result of various built-in stabilizers and patterns of corporate behavior as well as some special counter-cyclical actions by government.

Table 9.2 shows the absolute and percentage changes in nonagricultural employment from peak to trough in each of the three recessions, by broad

Table 9.2 Nonagricultural Employment: Absolute and Percentage Changes from Peak to Trough in Three Recessions, by Industry Group, United States, 1948–1958[a]

Industry Group	Actual employment Aug. 1957	Absolute Changes (Thousands)				Percentage Changes (Percent)			
		Average, Three recessions	Nov. 1948 to July 1949	July 1953 to July 1954	Aug. 1957 to April 1958	Average, Three Recessions	Nov. 1948 to July 1949	July 1953 to July 1954	Aug. 1957 to April 1958
Total[b]	52,457	−1,948	−1,692	−1,749	−2,403	−4.0	−3.8	−3.5	−4.6
Manufacturing	16,826	−1,655	−1,629	−1,753	−1,583	−10.0	−10.6	−10.0	−9.4
Durable goods industries	9,863	−1,248	−1,070	−1,376	−1,297	−13.2	−12.9	−13.4	−13.2
Nondurable goods industries	6,963	−392	−514	−377	−286	−5.5	−7.3	−5.2	−4.1
Mining	820	−78	−59	−79	−97	−9.0	−5.9	−9.3	−11.8
Contract construction	2,805	−97	−114	3	−181	−3.8	−5.1	0.1	−6.5

Transportation and public utilities	4,184	−249	−202	−250	−294	−5.9	−4.8	−5.9	−7.0
Wholesale and retail trade	11,402	−173	−132	−35	−352	−1.6	−1.4	−0.3	−3.1
Finance, insurance and real estate	2,354	32	17	78	2	1.6	1.0	3.8	0.1
Service and miscellaneous	6,477	0	−5	130	−125	0.1	−0.1	2.3	−1.9
Government	7,694	123	90	157	122	1.9	1.6	2.4	1.6

[a] Seasonally adjusted. Includes all full- and part-time wage and salary workers in nonagricultural establishments. Excludes proprietors, self-employed persons, domestic servants, and personnel of the armed forces.

[b] Annual figures for this series on "nonagricultural employment" have borne the following relationships to "total civilian employment" as published in *Monthly Reports on the Labor Force*, USDC: 1948, 74.9%; 1953, 80.2%; 1957, 80.2%; average of the three peak years, 78.4%. If the "total" percentage changes were adjusted to a "total civilian employment basis," the figures in this row (last four columns) would become, respectively, −3.1, −2.8, −2.8, and −3.7%.

Sources: Survey of Current Business, selected monthly issues (1949 to 1958); *Business Statistics, 1957 Biennial Edition* (a supplement to the *Survey of Current Business*), p. 59.

Table 9.3 Nonagricultural Employment: Actual Employment, Average Percentage Change from Peak to Trough, and Number of Recessions in Which Employment Decreased, Remained Stable, or Increased, by Industry Group, United States, 1948–1958

Industry Group	Actual Employment, August 1957, Millions	Average Change from Peak to Trough in Three Recessions, Percent	Number of Recessions during Which Employment		
			Decreased	Remained Stable[a]	Increased
Total	52.5	−4.0[b]	3	—	—
Manufacturing	16.8	−10.0	3	—	—
Mining	0.8	−9.0	3	—	—
Transportation and public utilities	4.2	−5.9	3	—	—
Contract construction	2.8	−3.8	2	1	—
Wholesale and retail trade	11.4	−1.6	2	1	—
Service and miscellaneous	6.5	0.1	1	1	1
Finance, insurance, and real estate	2.4	1.6	—	1	2
Government	7.7	1.9	—	—	3

a Changed less than 0.5%.

b Equivalent to −3.1% in terms of total civilian employment, including self-employed persons, persons engaged in agriculture, and certain other categories not included in "nonagricultural employment." Note, however, that total civilian employment had a long-run growth trend of slightly more than 1% a year, or approximately 0.8% during the average recession period of nine months from peak to trough.

Source: Calculated from Table 9.2.

industry groups. On a net basis, the declines were concentrated in manufacturing and predominantly in the durable goods industries.

Table 9.3 reflects the interaction of cyclical variations and trends in employment in major industry groups. Thus employment in manufacturing, mining, transportation, and public utilities decreased during each of the three recessions. Employment in contract construction and wholesale and retail trade decreased slightly in two of the recessions and remained stable in one. Employment in service and miscellaneous industries showed extremely small changes in the three recessions; employment in finance, insurance, and

Table 9.4 Nonagricultural Employment: Regional Variations in Employment Change Related to Degree of Regional Concentration in Durable Goods Industries, United States, July 1953 to July 1954

Geographic Division	(1) Percentage of Nonagricultural Workers Employed in Durable Goods Industries, July 1953	(2) Percentage Change in Total Nonagricultural Employment, July 1953 to July 1954	(3) Percentage Change in Total Nonagricultural Employment, March–April 1940 to March 1953
	Percent		
United States	16.8[a]	−3.7[a,b]	69.2[a]
East North Central	32.8	−7.0	69.4
New England	23.1	−4.6	41.7
Middle Atlantic	20.3	−4.4	48.3
Pacific	18.6	−3.1	98.9
East South Central	14.5	−3.7	59.7
West North Central	13.4	−2.5	61.0
South Atlantic	10.8	−3.1	66.7
West South Central	9.8	−1.9	85.8
Mountain	7.8	−3.0	90.9

[a] Simple arithmetic averages of regional figures.
[b] Simple regression of Column (2) upon Column (1) follows:

$$X_1 = -0.763 - 0.175 X_2; \quad r^2 = 0.84$$
$$(0.029)$$

Source: Based on data prepared by Edmond L. Kanwit in connection with his article, "Patterns of Recent Employment Changes—Area and National," *Survey of Current Business*, pp. 15–20 (June 1955).

real estate actually increased during two of them and government employment (state, local, and federal combined) increased during each of the three recessions.

Table 9.4 shows for the 1953–1954 recession the relationship between regional variations in employment change and the degree of regional concentration of employment in the durable goods manufacturing industries. In this recession, the decline in employment in durable goods manufactures accounted for nearly 80% of the decline in total nonagricultural employment. As might be expected, regions having a large proportion of their labor forces engaged in durable goods manufactures showed much larger than average percentage declines in total nonagricultural employment.

Regression equations expressing percentage changes in nonagricultural employment from July 1953 to July 1954 as functions of the percentage of workers employed in durable goods industries and the percentage increase in total nonagricultural employment from 1940 to 1953 were also computed for three different population size groups of standard metropolitan areas. There is some indication that the larger metropolitan areas, with their more diversified economies, were more homogeneous in their recession behavior than the less populous areas. For each of the three size groups differences in the local impacts of a national business cycle were significantly related to differences in the industrial structures of the metropolitan areas.

9.4 IMPLICATIONS OF A STRUCTURAL ANALYSIS OF TIME SERIES FOR MACROECONOMIC POLICY

The rapid advance of knowledge about the structure and functioning of a national economy has made it impossible for a modern government to ignore the effects of its own policies upon output, employment, and income in the private as well as the public sectors of the economy. A Dutch economist, Jan Tinbergen, formulated the nature of the relation of a modern government to the national economy in what appears to be a particularly fruitful way.

Tinbergen published his conceptualization of the nature of national economic policy in 1952 and more elaborately in 1956. Figure 9.7 summarizes Tinbergen's approach in graphic form.

Tinbergen classified macroeconomic variables into four groups from the standpoint of an official responsible for national economic policy. First, there are some variables which are beyond his power to influence. These must be taken simply as facts of life and as neither instruments nor targets of economic policy. It is important, however, for the policy maker to obtain the best forecasts he can of the future values of these *noncontrollable variables*.

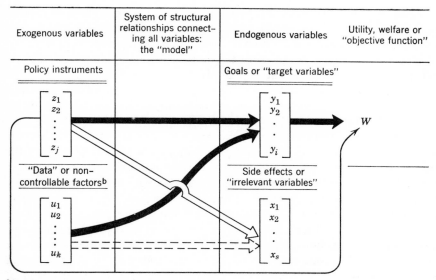

a Classification of variables based on J. Tinbergen.

b Not subject to control by the policy maker or level of government
that sets the goals and uses the policy instruments in question.

Figure 9.7 The theory of economic policy.

Prices of imports and the level of demand for exports from a given country would be examples of noncontrollable factors.

The policy maker also sees one set of variables as the primary *target* or objective of economic policy. These variables enter into the policy maker's preference function W which is analogous to the indifference surface of an individual consumer. The policy maker is assumed to be capable of ranking different combinations of values of such target variables as the level of employment, the real gross national product, the rate of change in the consumer price level, and others, and stating that in his judgment one combination of values is better than, as good as, or worse than other specified alternative combinations.

The third group of variables in Tinbergen's conceptualization consists of the *instruments* available to the policy maker for influencing the economy in the direction of the desired targets. These instruments may include the level of government purchases of goods and services, changes in tax rates, changes in the instruments of monetary policy (excess reserve requirements, rediscount rates, and so on), and many others. (The usability or practical availability of different instruments varies considerably from country to country and from one decade to another in a given country.)

There is a fourth group of economic variables which, for a particular policy maker at a particular time, is regarded as *irrelevant* or neutral in their implications for policy. Some of these may be regarded simply as by-products of achieving the primary targets; for example, if target levels are achieved for (1) the gross national product in constant dollars and (2) the price level or implicit price deflator for the gross national product, the *money value* of the gross national product is automatically determined as the product of the two target variables.

The essence of the problem of macroeconomic policy is this: to use the available instruments of economic policy in such a way as to achieve the desired levels of the target variables as closely as possible despite the fact that the time paths of the target variables are strongly influenced by factors which are, for the policy maker, noncontrollable. Formally, this problem has the same structure as does statistical decision theory.

This conceptualization of the policy maker as a decision maker and steerman for the economy by no means implies rigid or sweeping government controls over the economy and the individuals and firms in it. In selecting instruments such as a reduction in income tax rates or an acceleration of investment in a national highway network, one of the considerations would typically be the avoidance of needlessly detailed controls over individual firms or citizens.

The active role played by modern governments in promoting economic growth and reducing cyclical fluctuations inevitably affects the approach of economic statisticians to the analysis of the cyclical and trend components of time series. A lagging growth rate brings forth efforts to stimulate growth; forecasts of a recession bring forth efforts to avert it or at least to reduce its depth and shorten its duration. Univariate approaches to trend and cycle analysis are becoming increasingly vulnerable to the more and more sophisticated use of national income and product accounts and macroeconomic models as bases for government efforts to change trends and cycles.

APPENDIX A

A NOTE ON THE "TIME-SHAPE OF ECONOMIC REACTIONS" AND KOYCK'S METHOD OF DISTRIBUTED LAGS [1]

In the text we discussed multivariate analysis of economic time series for the most part as if the current value of a dependent variable y was a function only of the current values of one or more other variables—x_1, x_2,

[1] L. M. Koyck, *Distributed Lags and Investment Analysis*, Amsterdam: North-Holland Publishing Company, 111 pp. 1954.

and so on. In discussing univariate approaches in Chapter 5, we referred briefly to the *autoregressive* model in which the current value of a given variable would be regressed on its own values for one or more previous time periods. In other words, our multivariate time series analysis model had the form

(A.1) $$y_t = a + b_1 x_{1t} + b_2 x_{2t} + \cdots + b_m x_m$$

whereas our autoregressive model could be written as

(A.2) $$y_t = a + b_1 y_{t-1} + b_2 y_{t-2} + \cdots + b_n t_{t-n}$$

As a rule, the autoregressive model is rationalized simply as an empirical attempt to take into account the inertia or nonrandomness in a time series in order to improve forecasts of the value of the same variable in a succeeding time period y_{t+1}.

The time unit employed in an economic analysis may be rather arbitrary in some instances, depending upon the time units for which official data are published. Some economic reactions may run their full course within a single time unit. For example, most households in the United States shop for food at least once a week. It seems reasonable to expect that the reactions of consumers in adjusting their purchases to changes in the relative prices of different foods would be essentially completed within a limited number of weeks and almost certainly in less than a year.

However, for producers' investment in plant and equipment and consumer demand for major durable goods and housing, it seems likely that the full adjustments to changes in income and relative prices may be spread out over a number of years. If so, the purchases of an investment good or a major consumer durable good in year t, although most strongly influenced by the current value of an independent variable, will also show progressively smaller effects of the values of the independent variable in previous time periods.

The basic idea of an economic reaction which is spread out over a number of time units is intuitively obvious and has been put forward by various economists. Unless the units are extremely short, it has also seemed safe to assume in most practical instances that the largest adjustment to a change in an independent variable would take place in the first time period, a smaller one in the second time period, and so on until the remaining adjustments (if any) became imperceptible. Irving Fisher (1937) proposed a linearly decreasing adjustment pattern, so that if the adjustment in the first period amounted to (say) five units, the further adjustment to the initial stimulus would be four units in the second period, three units in the third period, and so on.[2]

---

[2] Irving Fisher, "Note on a Short-Cut Method for Calculating Distributed Lags," *Bulletin de l'Institut International de Statistique*, La Haye (1937). Cited by Koyck, *op. cit.*, p. 30ff.

Fisher suggested a procedure along these lines. Write the following sequence of functions:

$$y_t = 1x_t$$
$$y_t = 2x_t + 1x_{t-1}$$
$$y_t = 3x_t + 2x_{t-1} + 1x_{t-2}$$
$$y_t = 4x_t + 3x_{t-1} + 2x_{t-2} + 1x_{t-3}$$

and so on. The right-hand side of each successive equation was converted into a single composite variable, and y_t was regressed upon this variable. An example of such a regression would be

$$y_t = a + b(4x_t + 3x_{t-1} + 2x_{t-2} + 1x_{t-3})$$

The coefficient b amounted to an adjustment factor which would be multiplied by the original weight assigned to each of the lagged values of x. Different weighting patterns for the x_{t-i}'s would lead to different correlation coefficients between y_t and the composite lagged variable. Fisher would select that equation which yielded the highest r^2 as his best estimate of the actual time path of the adjustment of y to x.

L. M. Koyck (1954) made a different assumption about the time-shape of economic reactions and obtained a very elegant and efficient result. Whereas Fisher had assumed a linearly decreasing response, Koyck assumed a *geometrically* or exponentially decreasing response, so that the response in year 1 was equal to a certain percentage of the response in year 0, and so on.

The general expression for a dependent variable as a linear function of current and lagged values of another (independent) variable is

(A.3) $$y_t = \alpha_0 x_t + \alpha_1 x_{t-1} + \alpha_2 x_{t-2} + \alpha_3 x_{t-3} + \cdots + \alpha_n x_{t-n}$$

Koyck makes the specific assumption that $\alpha_1 = \lambda\alpha_0$, where the value of λ is between 0 and 1. This same common geometric factor λ connects the responses for successive years, as follows:

$$\alpha_1 = \lambda\alpha_0$$
$$\alpha_2 = \lambda\alpha_1 = \lambda^2\alpha_0$$
$$\alpha_3 = \lambda\alpha_2 = \lambda^2\alpha_1 = \lambda^3\alpha_0$$
$$\alpha_4 = \lambda\alpha_3 = \lambda^2\alpha_2 = \alpha^3\alpha_1 = \lambda^4\alpha_0$$
$$\vdots$$
$$\alpha_n = \lambda\alpha_{n-1} = \lambda^2\alpha_{n-2} = \alpha^3\alpha_{n-3} = \lambda^4\alpha_{n-4} = \cdots = \lambda^n\alpha_0$$

The cumulative effect or total reaction after a number of time periods is indicated in (A.4):

(A.4) $$\sum_{j=0}^{n} \alpha_0\lambda^j = \alpha_0(1 + \lambda + \lambda^2 + \lambda^3 + \lambda^4 + \cdots + \lambda^n)$$

For example, if $\lambda = \frac{1}{2}$, (A.4) becomes

(A.5) $$\sum_{j=0}^{n} \alpha_0 \left(\frac{1}{2}\right)^j = \alpha_0 \left(1 + \frac{1}{2} + \frac{1}{4} + \frac{1}{8} + \frac{1}{16} + \cdots + \frac{1}{2^n}\right)$$

The first five terms within parentheses add to $1\frac{15}{16}$ and all the remaining terms to $n = \infty$ would total only $\frac{1}{16}$. This suggests, incidentally, that a combination of only three or four lagged values of x would, in most instances with $\lambda = \frac{1}{2}$ or less, capture the majority of the total long-term effect.

Koyck's demonstration proceeds as follows: We may write the value of y_{t+1} in the form of (A.6):

(A.6) $$y_{t+1} = \alpha_0 x_{t+1} + \alpha_0 \lambda x_t + \alpha_0 \lambda^2 x_{t-1} + \alpha_0 \lambda^3 x_{t-2} + \cdots$$

Since we have assumed that $\alpha_1 = \lambda \alpha_0$, $\alpha_2 = \lambda^2 \alpha_0$, and so on, we may rewrite (A.3) as

(A.7) $$y_t = \alpha_0 x_t + \alpha_0 \lambda x_{t-1} + \alpha_0 \lambda^2 x_{t-2} + \cdots$$

The next few steps represent the application of a common method of manipulating power series, such as $\lambda + \lambda^2 + \lambda^3 + \cdots + \lambda^n$. We multiply both sides of (A.7) by λ, obtaining

(A.8) $$\lambda y_t = \alpha_0 \lambda x_t + \alpha_0 \lambda^2 x_{t-1} + \alpha_0 \lambda^3 x_{t-2} + \cdots$$

Then, subtracting (A.8) from (A.6) we obtain (A.9):

(A.9) $$y_{t+1} - \lambda y_t = \alpha_0 x_{t+1}$$

To express y in first difference form we may add $(-y_t)$ to both sides of the equation and rearrange terms:

(A.10) $$y_{t+1} - y_t = \alpha_0 x_{t+1} + \lambda y_t - y_t$$

and

(A.11) $$y_{t+1} - y_t = \alpha_0 x_{t+1} - (1 - \lambda) y_t$$

or

(A.12) $$\Delta y_t = \alpha_0 x_{t+1} - \gamma y_t \quad \text{where} \quad \gamma = 1 - \lambda$$

Equation (A.12) is very economical in the use of data, in that only the two coefficients α_0 and γ must be estimated by least squares regression. Using the first difference of y, $\Delta y_t = y_{t+1} - y_t$, since the dependent variable also implicitly combines the current period value or starting point for adjustment y_t with the next period value y_{t+1} into a single time series variable.

If we follow through a single adjustment process until it reaches equilibrium, we arrive at the point at which $\Delta y_t = 0$, $y_{t+1} = y_t$, and

$$(A.13) \qquad\qquad y_t^* = \frac{\alpha_0}{\gamma} x_t$$

If we think of investment goods or consumer durable appliances and automobiles, we might think of y_t^* as the *desired level of stocks* of y, if x stabilizes over successive periods at the value of x_t.

The coefficient for the complete long-run reaction of y to x is

$$(A.14) \qquad\qquad \alpha_L = \frac{\alpha_0}{\gamma} = \frac{\alpha_0}{1 - \lambda}$$

For example, if $\lambda = 0$, the long-run coefficient is identical with the short-run coefficient, and we have instantaneous adjustment which may well apply to consumer demand for foods, other perishable commodities, and frequently purchased services when the time unit is one year.

With a little algebra, we can express the actual change in y_t from time t to $t + 1$ as

$$(A.15) \qquad\qquad \Delta y_t = \gamma(y_{t+1}^* - y_t) \qquad 0 \le \gamma < 1$$

(Since we know the value of y_t, we can obtain an estimate of y_{t+1} simply by adding Δy_t to y_t itself.)

Some implications of (A.15) follow. If $\gamma = 1$, inasmuch as $\lambda = 1 - \gamma = 0$,

$$\Delta y_t = y_{t+1} - y_t = y_{t+1}^* - y_t, \qquad \text{and} \quad y_{t+1} = y_{t+1}^*$$

If $\gamma = 1$, $\lambda = 0$, and we have the instantaneous adjustment just described for foods, other perishables, and some services.

$$(A.16) \qquad \text{If } \gamma = \tfrac{1}{2}, \ \lambda = 1 - \gamma = \tfrac{1}{2} \qquad \text{and} \quad \Delta y_t = \tfrac{1}{2}(y_{t+1}^* - y_t)$$

In this instance, the actual adjustment from the value of y_t to that of y_{t+1} will be one-half of the final or complete adjustment to the desired level of stocks, y_{t+1}^*. And

$$(A.17) \qquad \text{If } \gamma = \tfrac{2}{3}, \ \lambda = 1 - \gamma = \tfrac{1}{3} \qquad \text{and} \quad \Delta y_t = \tfrac{2}{3}(y_{t+1}^* - y_t)$$

Koyck's method looks quite promising and is certainly attractive from a conceptual viewpoint. It seems likely to be of most use in the analysis of the demand for investment goods, including business plant and equipment and housing, and for major consumer durable goods.

EXERCISES

1. A very important time series in monetary economics is the demand deposits (checking accounts) in the hands of the public. Using the successive aggregation technique employed in Section 9.1, construct a (hypothetical) structural analysis of this time series, showing the factors underlying the seasonal, trend, and cyclical patterns of the series. (*Hint*: A good place to start would be with the habits of an individual depositor in a single bank and proceed from there.)

Demand Deposits (in Billions)

	1963	1964
January	121.2	125.4
February	117.9	121.5
March	116.9	120.3
April	118.9	122.3
May	116.5	119.4
June	116.9	120.3
July	117.7	121.5
August	117.3	121.3
September	118.6	123.1
October	120.4	124.8
November	122.1	125.9
December	124.1	128.7

Source: Economic Report of the President, Table B-47, p. 246, 1965.

2. Since demand deposits are the most important part of the total money supply, which in turn plays an important role in our national economy, indicate some possible uses in formulating policy in your structural analysis in Question 1.

3. Define carefully the four different types of macroeconomic variables discussed by Tinbergen. Assume that you are a policymaker for the United States. Set up a classification of economic variables into the four groups with discussion of the relative importance of the variables within each group, and the potential conflicts among the variables within each group. For example, if we desire one thing, do we have to sacrifice another thing we desire in order to achieve it?

REFERENCES

1. Davis, H. T., *The Analysis of Economic Time Series*, Bloomington, Indiana: The Principia Press, 1941.
2. Fisher, Irving, "Note on a Short-Cut Method for Calculating Distributed Lags," *Bulletin de l'Institut International de Statistique*, La Haye, 1937.
3. Granger, C. W. J. and M. Hatanaka, *Spectral Analysis of Economic Time Series*, Princeton: Princeton University Press, 1964.

4. Grenander, W. F. and M. Rosenblatt, *Statistical Analysis of Stationary Time Series*, New York: John Wiley and Sons, 1957.
5. Hannan, E. J., *Time Series Analysis*, New York: John Wiley and Sons, 1960.
6. Koopmans, T. C., *Linear Regression Analysis of Economic Time Series*, Haarlem: Deerven F. Bohn, 1937.
7. Koyck, L. M., *Distributed Lags and Investment Analysis*, Amsterdam: North-Holland Publishing Co., 111 pp., 1954.
8. Nerlove, Marc, "Spectral Analysis of Seasonal Adjustment Procedures," *Econometrica* **32**, No. 3, pp. 241–286, July 1964.
9. Rosenblatt, M. (ed.), *Symposium on Time Series Analysis*, New York: John Wiley and Sons, 1963.
10. Wold, Herman, *A Study in the Analysis of Stationary Time Series*, Second edition, Stockholm: Almquist and Wiksell, 1954.

CHAPTER 10

The Construction of Large-Scale Economic Models: A Proving Ground for Economic Statistics

We have devoted several chapters to the analysis of relationships between two or more variables. We have also discussed the measurement of economic aggregates (mainly by means of index numbers) and the analysis of time series.

The chapters on index numbers and time series have a somewhat different emphasis than would have been likely in an economic statistics textbook written a few years ago. However, the economic concepts reviewed in Chapter 2 have been widely used in textbooks for two decades. The mechanics of correlation and regression analysis have been available in textbooks of economic statistics for at least 40 years.

The distinction between regression and correlation models was not widely recognized in undergraduate statistics texts until the late 1930s, and the probability interpretation of economic time series, along with tests for autocorrelation in the residuals from time series regressions, entered the advanced scientific literature of economics in the late 1930s and early 1940s. However, it remains true that virtually every concept demonstrated in Chapters 4, 6, 7, and 8 on simple and multiple regression analysis and the analysis of variance existed in the literature of economic statistics by the end of World War II.

All of these methods have been well tested. They have, and will continue to have, very wide areas of practical application in economics.

However, the revolution in macroeconomics which has occurred since the middle 1930s presents new challenges to economic statistics. These challenges have come particularly from attempts, beginning with Tinbergen (1939), to develop quantitative models of the functioning of national economies. Interest in the construction of large-scale macroeconomic models grew very rapidly after World War II. By 1965 government agencies in several countries were using multiequation models of their economies as one basis for appraising alternative economic policies and/or for economic forecasting. The Netherlands' Central Planning Bureau, under the direction of Tinbergen during the late 1940s and early 1950s, was the first official agency to make extensive practical use of such a model—again, let us stress, not as the exclusive basis for either forecasting or policy, but as *one* basis to supplement and check against other bases for judgment.

Large-scale macroeconomic models are here to stay. Every well-trained economist should know how they are constructed, their advantages as compared with other analytical alternatives, their present limitations, and, in a general way, the principal means of improving them for forecasting and for policy analysis.

The attempts to build large-scale economic models of this type have raised problems of estimation which did not exist at all in the regression model based on controlled experiments. The basic problem is that in an economic model containing n equations the traditional method of regression analysis would require us to use dependent variables from some equations as independent variables in others. In regression analysis of experimental data it is quite clear that biases would result if we used the dependent variable from the experiment as an independent variable in a second regression equation. At the least, the dependent variable from the first experimental regression would contain random errors which would cause it to behave differently in the second regression equation than would a controlled variable, the values of which were fixed by the experimenter and contained no stochastic elements.

Moreover, multicollinearity, a serious problem in single equation analysis of economic times series, appears in even more acute form when we deal with systems of several equations. Aggregation problems (see Chapter 14) are multiplied when many structural coefficients between aggregative variables must be estimated consistently in a multiple equation model.

It is very difficult to discuss these new problems in a vacuum. Therefore we will present an actual macroeconomic model of the United States in some detail. This will be supplemented by a partial description of a much larger model of the United States economy which was published in 1965. These two models will illustrate problems or clusters of related problems with which the modern economic statistician must cope.

We will list and summarize these problems at the end of this chapter. In Chapters 11, 13, and 14 we will treat the individual problems more intensively. The topics in Chapter 11 will include identification, causal ordering, and estimation in multiple equation models. In Chapter 13 we will consider multicollinearity and the use of *a priori* or "extraneous" information in economic models. Chapter 14 will deal with the measurement of economic aggregates.

10.1 THE KLEIN–GOLDBERGER MODEL OF THE UNITED STATES ECONOMY, 1929–1952

Jan Tinbergen constructed a macroeconomic model of the United States in the late 1930s, taking advantage of some then recently published national income accounts for the United States covering the 1919–1932 period.[1] However, Lawrence R. Klein was the first United States economist to follow up on Tinbergen's trail blazing work with a cumulative program of research and development on econometric models of the United States. Klein published a 12-equation model of the United States economy in 1950, using annual data for the period 1921–1941.[2] In collaboration with Arthur S. Goldberger, Klein also published a 20-equation model in 1955, using annual data for 1929–1952.[3]

The list of variables and equations included in the Klein–Goldberger model is taken from pp. 4–8 of Goldberger's book, *Impact Multipliers and Dynamic Properties of the Klein–Goldberger Model.*[4] The appraisal of the model and its least squares counterpart is based on a review article published by Karl A. Fox in 1956.[5]

10.1.1 Basic Logic of the Klein–Goldberger Model

The Klein–Goldberger model attempts to describe the workings of the United States economy from 1929 through 1952 in terms of 20 simultaneous equations. Collectively, these equations describe the interrelationships existing among 20 jointly dependent economic variables and among these and a larger number of "predetermined" factors. The jointly dependent variables include components of GNP, such as consumption expenditures, gross private capital formation, and capital consumption allowances. The various components of GNP on both the expenditure and the income side are bound together by a set of accounting identities which are implicit in the national income accounts. Other equations express the determination of money wage

---

[1] Jan Tinbergen, *Statistical Testing of Business-Cycle Theories*, Vol. I: *A Method and Its Application to Investment Activity*, Vol. II: *Business Cycles in the United States of America, 1919–1932*, League of Nations Economic Intelligence Service, Geneva, 1939.

[2] Lawrence R. Klein, *Economic Fluctuations in the United States, 1921–1941*, Cowles Commission Monograph No. 11 (New York: John Wiley and Sons), 174 pp., 1950.

[3] Lawrence R. Klein and Arthur S. Goldberger, *An Econometric Model of the United States, 1929–1952* (Amsterdam: North-Holland Publishing Company), 165 pp., 1955.

[4] Arthur S. Goldberger, *Impact Multipliers and Dynamic Properties of the Klein–Goldberger Model* (Amsterdam: North-Holland Publishing Company), 138 pp., 1959.

[5] Karl A. Fox, "Econometric Models of the United States," *Journal of Political Economy* **64**, No. 2, pp. 128–142 (April 1956). Also published as Chapter 12 in Karl A. Fox, *Econometric Analysis for Public Policy* (Ames: Iowa State University Press), 288 pp., 1958.

rates, prices of farm products, long- and short-term interest rates, employ-ment, the general price level, the stock of fixed capital, and liquid assets held by individuals and businesses.

Fifteen of the 20 equations are fitted by statistical means. These 15 equa-tions do not form a complete and self-contained system; if they did, they would be sufficient to determine the values of 15 of the jointly dependent variables. Actually, the five remaining equations—the accounting identities previously referred to—are needed to "close" the basic statistical set; at the same time they give, by addition and subtraction, the values of five more jointly dependent variables.

The model as published in 1955 contained 39 distinct economic variables. However, 26 of these variables also appeared in lagged form, such as prices or wages in one or more previous years. From the standpoint of statistical properties and calculations, each lagged series functions as a distinct variable in addition to the original current series. In the statistical sense, then, the 20 equations included 65 variables, which may be classified as follows:

Endogenous	20
Predetermined	
Lagged endogenous	19
Exogenous	19
Lagged exogenous	7
Total	65

Endogenous and predetermined variables are analogous, respectively, to the dependent and independent variables of least squares regression analysis. Values of the predetermined variables are given in advance; they do not have to be explained by the equations. Current values of the endogenous variables are to be estimated on the basis of their statistical relationships to the pre-determined variables.

10.1.2 *The Model Itself: Variables and Equations*

The Klein–Goldberger model was slightly revised and rearranged after 1955 so that Goldberger (1959) lists 38 economic variables of which 21 are classified as endogenous and 17 as exogenous. However, the 15 statistically estimated equations are identical with those published in 1955. The 1959 version contains six identities or definitional equations compared with five in 1955. This is a minor change, and our discussion, in any event, is focused on the 15 statistically estimated functions.

The 38 variables of the 1959 version are listed and classified in Table 10.1 and the 21 equations of the 1959 version are shown in Table 10.2. As Gold-berger remarks, "This system of twenty-one behavioral, technological, and

Table 10.1 List of Variables in the Klein–Goldberger Model

New Symbol, 1959	Brief Definition	Category	Old Symbol, 1955
C	Consumption	Endogenous	
D	Depreciation	Endogenous	
F_I	Imports	Endogenous	
F_R	Farm exports	Exogenous	F_A
G	Government expenditures and exports	Exogenous	$G + F_E$
h	Hours of work	Exogenous	
I	Investment	Endogenous	
i_L	Long-term interest rate	Endogenous	
i_S	Short-term interest rate	Endogenous	
K	Capital stock	Endogenous	
L_1	Household liquid assets	Endogenous	
L_2	Business liquid assets	Endogenous	
L_B	Percentage excess reserves	Exogenous	R
M	National income	Endogenous	Y
N_E	Entrepreneurs	Exogenous	$N_E + N_F$
N_G	Government employees	Exogenous	N
N_L	Labor force	Exogenous	
N_P	Population	Exogenous	
N_W	Employees	Endogenous	
P	Nonwage, nonfarm income	Endogenous	
P_C	Corporate profits	Endogenous	
p	Price level	Endogenous	
p_F	Import price level	Exogenous	p_I
p_R	Farm price level	Endogenous	p_A
Q	Gross national product	Endogenous	$Y + T + D$
R_1	Farm income	Endogenous	A_1
R_2	Farm subsidies	Exogenous	A_2
S_B	Corporate surplus	Endogenous	B
S_C	Corporate savings	Endogenous	S_P
t	Time trend	Exogenous	
T_C	Corporate taxes	Exogenous	
T_E	Indirect taxes	Exogenous	T
T_N	Nonwage, nonfarm, noncorporate taxes, less transfers	Exogenous	$T_P - T_C$
T_R	Farm taxes, less transfers	Exogenous	T_A
T_W	Wage taxes, less transfers	Exogenous	
w	Wage rate	Endogenous	
W_1	Private wage bill	Endogenous	
W_2	Government wage bill	Exogenous	

Source: Arthur S. Goldberger, *Impact Multipliers and Dynamic Properties of the Klein–Goldberger Model* (Amsterdam: North-Holland Publishing Company), pp. 5–6, 1959.

Table 10.2   List of Equations in the Klein–Goldberger Model

(10.1) $C = -22.26 + 0.55(W_1 + W_2 - T_W) + 0.41(P - T_C - T_N - S_C)$
$+ 0.34(R_1 + R_2 - T_R) + 0.26C_{-1} + 0.072(L_1)_{-1} + 0.26N_P$

(10.2) $I = -16.71 + 0.78(P - T_C - T_N + R_1 + R_2 - T_R + D)_{-1}$
$- 0.073K_{-1} + 0.14(L_2)_{-1}$

(10.3) $S_C = -3.53 + 0.72(P_C - T_C) + 0.076(P_C - T_C - S_C)_{-1} - 0.028(S_B)_{-1}$

(10.4) $P_C = -7.60 + 0.68P$

(10.5) $D = 7.25 + 0.10 \dfrac{K + K_{-1}}{2} + 0.044(Q - W_2)$

(10.6) $W_1 = -1.40 + 0.24(Q - W_2) + 0.24(Q - W_2)_{-1} + 0.29t$

(10.7) $(Q - W_2) = -26.08 + 2.17[h(N_W - N_G) + N_E]$
$+ 0.16 \dfrac{K + K_{-1}}{2} + 2.05t$

(10.8) $w - w_{-1} = 4.11 - 0.74(N_L - N_W - N_E) + 0.52(p_{-1} - p_{-2}) + 0.54t$

(10.9) $F_I = 0.32 + 0.0060(M - T_W - T_C - T_N - T_R)\dfrac{p}{p_F} + 0.81(F_I)_{-1}$

(10.10) $R_1(p/p_R) = -0.36$
$+ 0.054(W_1 + W_2 - T_W + P - T_C - T_N - S_C)(p/p_R)$
$- 0.007[(W_1 + W_2 - T_W + P - T_C - T_N - S_C)(p/p_R)]_{-1}$
$+ 0.012F_R$

(10.11) $p_R = -131.17 + 2.32p$

(10.12) $L_1 = 0.14(M - T_W - T_C - T_N - S_C - T_R) + 76.03(i_L - 2.0)^{-0.84}$

(10.13) $L_2 = -0.34 + 0.26W_1 - 1.02i_S - 0.26(p - p_{-1}) + 0.61(L_2)_{-1}$

(10.14) $i_L = 2.58 + 0.44(i_S)_{-3} + 0.26(i_S)_{-5}$

(10.15) $100 \dfrac{i_S - (i_S)_{-1}}{i_S} = 11.17 - 0.67L_B$

(10.16) $K - K_{-1} = I - D$

(10.17) $S_B - (S_B)_{-1} = S_C$

(10.18) $W_1 + W_2 + P + R_1 + R_2 = M$

(10.19) $C + I + G - F_I = M + T_E + D$

(10.20) $h(w/p)N_W = W_1 + W_2$

(10.21) $Q = M + T_E + D$

Source: Goldberger, *op. cit.*, pp. 4, 6, and 7.

definitional equations . . . constitutes a quantitative characterization of the economy of the United States. It provides a self-contained explanation of economic behavior in view of the fact that it is a complete system, that is to say, there are just enough equations to determine the values of the 'unknowns' —the endogenous variables."

Exogenous variables are treated as logically independent variables which do not have to be explained inside of the 21-equation model. The *endogenous* variables are logically dependent upon the exogenous variables and must be explained by them.

The novelty involved in the concept of endogenous variables is that a single equation in the Klein–Goldberger model might contain two or more "endogenous" variables. Regression analysis can tolerate only a single dependent variable. Hence if the economic theory underlying the model requires that two logically dependent variables must both appear in each of two structural equations, new methods must be devised for estimating the coefficients of these variables in the two equations in a consistent manner.[6]

Two equations are logically sufficient (except in special instances) to determine the values of two endogenous variables, three equations are sufficient to determine the values of three endogenous variables, and so on. The economic logic of the Klein–Goldberger model, at the level of aggregation at which the authors chose to work, called for 21 endogenous or jointly dependent variables whose values were to be estimated by means of the equation system *given* the values of the exogenous or logically independent variables. The 21 endogenous variables require a total of 21 equations for their explanation and estimation.

Fifteen of the equations are estimated statistically. They may be grouped in the following way:

1. Equations (10.1), (10.2), and (10.9) represent final demands for components of the gross national product: consumption, investment, and imports.

2. Equation (10.7) constitutes a production function or supply equation for the total gross national product (less the government wage bill).

3. The allocation of the gross national *income* (which is equal in value to the gross national product) by distributive shares is described in part by the private sector labor demand equation (10.6), the farm income equation (10.10), and the depreciation equation (10.5).

4. The important role of the corporate sector in the United States economy is represented in the corporate profits equation (10.4) and in the corporate savings equation (10.3).

5. A set of four equations relates to the money and securities market: (10.12) and (10.13) describe the demand for liquid assets by households and businesses, respectively; the money supply situation is indicated in terms of long-term interest rates in (10.14), and short-term interest rates in (10.15).

6. Equation (10.8) relates to the labor market where the money wage rate is, in the immediate sense, determined. This variable is critical in the determination of the absolute general price level, and hence, via (10.11), the level of farm prices. The final demand, production, and income allocation equations refer to real, not money, magnitudes.

---

[6] The basic problem here (the *identification problem*) was first encountered in connection with the estimation of a demand curve and a supply curve, each of which contains both the price and the quantity of a given commodity (see Chapter 11).

10.1.3 *Statistical Properties of the Klein–Goldberger Model*

Theoretically, the Klein–Goldberger model (as published in 1955) could have included as many as 1300 coefficients since there were 20 equations in 65 variables, including lagged variables. The actual number of nonzero coefficients in their 1929–1952 model (including 98 coefficients based on accounting identities) was 151; only 51 coefficients were statistically estimated from time series. Two coefficients were estimated from family budget data.

The meaning of the coefficients based on accounting restrictions may be clarified with an example. One of the variables used in the statistical analysis is "disposable income of nonfarm people," which, in the 1955 Klein–Goldberger notation, was written $(W_1 + W_2 - T_w + P - T_p - S_p)$. Each element in this composite variable had an "internal" coefficient of 1 or -1. The relationship between farm income and disposable income of nonfarm people involved a single statistically estimated coefficient, but this coefficient, multiplied by each of the "internal" ones, accounted for six of the 151 nonzero coefficients mentioned previously.

Of the 51 coefficients estimated from time series, 15 are constant terms which indicate the value of a given variable (the dependent variable in least squares terminology) when all other variables in the equation have zero values. The remaining 36 coefficients express net relationships between economic variables.

If econometric models of this general type are to be used as a basis for appraising economic policies, the reliability of the coefficients expressing relationships between economic variables is of great importance. Klein and Goldberger laid considerable stress upon the statistical method by which their coefficients were estimated—the "limited information maximum likelihood method." Actually, the general theory that underlies the limited information method often leads one to single equation least squares estimation as a special case. For example, the authors noted on page 50 of their 1955 book that "equation (14) . . . and equation (15) . . . are both written in a form immediately adapted to single-equation least-squares estimation."

Some light may be shed on the reliability and stability of the Klein–Goldberger coefficients and upon the limited importance (in this instance) of differences in statistical method by the comparison summarized in Table 10.3. Klein and Goldberger first fitted their model to observations from 1929 through 1950 (omitting the war years 1942–1945); subsequently they fitted it to the same observations plus those for the years 1951 and 1952. If the coefficients for the earlier period were firmly grounded in economic behavior, one would not expect the addition of two more years to change the coefficients significantly. As a check upon the importance of the statistical method used, we also had each of the 15 equations (other than identities) fitted to the 1929–

1952 data by the method of least squares. The three sets of results are shown in detail in Table 10.4.

Table 10.3 compares the effects upon the model of differences in time periods and methods of estimation. Differences among the three sets of coefficients are expressed in multiples of the standard errors of the respective 1929–1952 limited information coefficients. If the 1929–1950 and 1929–1952

Table 10.3 Klein–Goldberger Model: Comparison of Differences between (1) Limited Information Coefficients, 1929–1950 and 1929–1952, and (2) Limited Information and Least Squares Coefficients, both for 1929–1952

Ratio of Differences to Standard Error of 1929–1952 Limited Information Coefficients[a]	No. of Differences between Limited Information Coefficients, 1929–1950 and 1929–1952	No. of Differences between Limited Information and Least Squares Coefficients, 1929–1952
Constant terms		
0 –0.49	4	7
0.50–0.99	4	5
1.00–1.49	3	2
1.50–1.99	1	1
2.00–2.99	0	0
3.00 and over	2	0
Total	14[a]	15
Average ratio[b]	1.28	0.57
Net regression coefficients		
0 –0.49	13	14
0.50–0.99	5	6
1.00–1.49	5	8
1.50–1.99	6	2
2.00–2.99	3	4
3.00 and over	2	2
Total	34[c]	36
Average ratio[b]	1.13	0.96

[a] Equation (10.11) is omitted from the 1929–1950 model.

[b] Without regard to sign.

[c] The limited-information model for 1929–1952 includes 36 net regression coefficients. The 1929–1950 model contained one less variable in (10.5), (10.11), containing a single predetermined variable, was omitted entirely, hence the 1929–1950 model included only 34 net regression coefficients.

Table 10.4 Klein–Goldberger Model: Regression Coefficients, Standard Errors, and Other Measures Based on Limited Information Method for 1929–1950 and 1929–1952 and on Least Squares Method for 1929–1952

Equation and Variable	Coefficients[a]			Standard Errors			Von Neumann's Ratio[b]			Other Least Squares Measures 1929–1952	
	Limited Information 1929–1950	1929–1952	Least Squares 1929–1952	Limited Information 1929–1950	1929–1952	Least Squares 1929–1952	Limited Information 1929–1950	1929–1952	Least Squares 1929–1952	R^2[c]	S[d]
	(1)	(2)	(3)	(4)	(5)	(6)	(7)	(8)	(9)	(10)	(11)
1. Consumer expenditures											
Constant term	−34.5	−22.26	−21.06	7.7	9.66	n.a.[e]	2.2	1.98	2.02	0.998	1.03
Wage and salary income	0.62	0.55	0.62	0.04	0.06	0.06	–	–	–	–	–
Nonfarm proprietors' income	0.46	0.41	0.46	0.03	0.05	0.04	–	–	–	–	–
Farm operators' income	0.39	0.34	0.39	0.025	0.04	0.04	–	–	–	–	–
Consumer expenditures ($t-1$)	0.23	0.26	0.21	0.05	0.075	0.07	–	–	–	–	–
Consumer liquid assets ($t-1$)	0.024	0.072	0.063	0.02	0.025	0.023	–	–	–	–	–
Population	0.36	0.26	0.25	0.08	0.10	0.10	–	–	–	–	–
2. Gross capital formation											
Constant term	−16.8	−16.71	−16.70	4.5	4.74	4.76	2.3	2.08	2.06	0.863	3.32
Nonwage income, after taxes plus capital consumption allowances	0.76	0.78	0.78	0.17	0.18	0.18	–	–	–	–	–
Stock of capital ($t-1$)	−0.14	−0.073	−0.073	0.08	0.067	0.067	–	–	–	–	–
Business liquid assets ($t-1$)	0.14	0.14	0.14	0.10	0.11	0.11	–	–	–	–	–

3. Corporate savings											
Constant term	−2.42	−3.53	−2.59	0.81	1.02	0.75	1.9	0.99	1.84	0.977	0.47
After-tax corporate income	0.86	0.72	0.85	0.04	0.06	0.04	—	—	—	—	—
Dividends paid (t − 1)	−0.30	0.076	−0.24	0.20	0.254	0.181	—	—	—	—	—
Accumulated corporate savings (t − 1)	−0.014	−0.028	−0.014	0.016	0.019	0.015	—	—	—	—	—
4. Corporate profits (before tax)											
Constant term	−8.34	−7.60	−8.51	0.53	0.54	0.42	1.4	1.28	1.59	0.989	0.70
Nonwage, nonfarm income	0.71	0.68	0.72	0.02	0.02	0.02	—	—	—	—	—
5. Depreciation											
Constant term	11.46	7.25	6.47	0.36	0.80	0.77	0.30	0.94	1.02	0.954	0.73
Stock of capital (July 1)	0.14	0.10	0.09	0.08	0.01	0.01	—	—	—	—	—
Private GNP	—	0.044	0.052	—	0.008	0.007	—	—	—	—	—
6. Private wage bill											
Constant term	−2.70	−1.40	−3.15	1.05	1.46	n.a.	2.0	2.45	1.77	0.998	0.79
Private GNP	0.36	0.24	0.38	0.04	0.07	0.03	—	—	—	—	—
Private GNP (t − 1)	0.14	0.24	0.13	0.03	0.06	0.03	—	—	—	—	—
Time trend	0.16	0.29	0.12	0.08	0.125	0.07	—	—	—	—	—
7. Private GNP											
Constant term	−31.98	−26.08	−22.31	7.3	7.27	n.a.[e]	1.4	1.09	1.09	0.995	2.50
Man-years worked	2.31	2.17	2.02	0.18	0.18	0.15	—	—	—	—	—
Stock of capital (July 1)	0.076	0.16	0.18	0.06	0.05	0.05	—	—	—	—	—
Time trend	1.90	2.05	2.15	0.15	0.16	0.14	—	—	—	—	—
8. Change in wage rates [t − (t − 1)]											
Constant term	4.11	4.11	6.73	4.83	4.85	4.83	2.4	2.38	2.29	0.794	5.32
Unemployment	−0.75	−0.74	−1.20	0.63	0.61	0.58	—	—	—	—	—

357

continued

Table 10.4 (continued)

Equation and Variable	Coefficients[a] Limited Information 1929–1950 (1)	Limited Information 1929–1952 (2)	Least Squares 1929–1952 (3)	Standard Errors Limited Information 1929–1950 (4)	Limited Information 1929–1952 (5)	Least Squares 1929–1952 (6)	Von Neumann's Ratio[b] Limited Information 1929–1950 (7)	Limited Information 1929–1952 (8)	Least Squares 1929–1952 (9)	Other Least Squares Measures 1929–1952 R^{2c} (10)	S^d (11)
Price change											
$(t-1)-(t-2)$	0.56	0.52	0.41	0.30	0.28	0.27	–	–	–	–	–
Time trend	0.56	0.54	0.48	0.26	0.24	0.24	–	–	–	–	–
9. Value of imports											
Constant term	2.09	0.32	0.29	0.65	0.49	1.10	1.6	2.33	2.05	0.817	0.39
Disposable income	0.0087	0.0060	0.0200	0.0057	0.0084	0.0067	–	–	–	–	–
Value of imports $(t-1)$	0.24	0.81	0.54	0.12	0.21	0.17	–	–	–	–	–
10. Farm operators' income											
Constant term	−4.53	−0.36	0.33	1.48	2.12	2.02	1.5	0.85	0.76	0.269	1.03
Nonfarm disposable income	0.25	0.054	0.010	0.09	0.045	0.041	–	–	–	–	–
Nonfarm disposable income $(t-1)$	−0.13	−0.007	0.026	0.11	0.043	0.040	–	–	–	–	–
Value of agricultural exports	0.0096	0.012	0.013	0.014	0.006	0.006	–	–	–	–	–
11. Farm prices											
Constant term	n.a.	−131.17	−113.36	n.a.	15.3	14.0	n.a.	0.74	0.83	0.961	1802
General price level	n.a.	2.32	2.18	n.a.	0.11	0.10	–	–	–	–	–

12. Liquid assets of individuals											
Constant term	75.0	76.03	71.27	16.6	15.31	n.a.	0.73	0.73	0.71	0.823	0.088[f]
Long-term interest rate	−0.84	−0.84	−0.74	0.03	0.03	0.09	–	–	–	–	–
13. Liquid assets of businesses											
Constant term	−0.77	−0.34	0.40	1.43	0.99	n.a.	2.0	1.72	1.87	0.991	1.13
Private wage bill	0.24	0.26	0.22	0.05	0.03	0.03	–	–	–	–	–
Short-term interest rate	−0.69	−1.02	−0.45	0.31	0.19	0.22	–	–	–	–	–
Price change $[t − (t − 1)]$	−0.27	−0.26	−0.10	0.09	0.06	0.06	–	–	–	–	–
Liquid assets of businesses $(t − 1)$	0.64	0.61	0.60	0.08	0.06	0.05	–	–	–	–	–
14. Long-term interest rate											
Constant term	2.66	2.58	2.58	0.17	0.15	0.15	0.9	0.84	0.84	0.897	0.40
Short-term interest rate $(t − 3)$	0.46	0.44	0.44	0.10	0.10	0.10	–	–	–	–	–
Short-term interest rate $(t − 5)$	0.33	0.26	0.26	0.10	0.09	0.09	–	–	–	–	–
15. Short-term interest rate											
Constant term	6.42	11.17	11.17	8.52	7.81	7.81	1.3	1.59	1.59	0.220	23.52
Excess reverses of banks	−0.55	−0.67	−0.67	0.31	0.30	0.30	–	–	–	–	–

[a] Except for constant term, these indicate estimated changes in the dependent variable associated with unit changes in the specified explanatory variables.

[b] Values below 1.25 indicate significant correlation between successive residuals or "disturbances."

[c] Coefficient of multiple determination. Measures percentage of total variation in dependent variable associated with variations in the independent variables.

[d] Standard error of estimate. Describes a range about the regression surface which includes about two-thirds of the 1929–1952 observations.

[e] Not available.

[f] Applies to logarithmic form of the residuals.

359

limited information models were based on independent samples from the same universe, we should expect about two-thirds of the differences to be less than 1.4 standard errors.[6] Actually, about four-fifths of the differences between constant terms and two-thirds of those between net regression coefficients fall within this range.

Differences between the least squares and limited information coefficients for the same time period (1929–1952) are even smaller; all but one of those for constant terms and three-fourths of those for net regression coefficients are less than 1.4 standard errors. The average differences between the 1929–1952 coefficients derived by alternative methods are also smaller than those between the limited information coefficients for alternative time periods.

Although more rigorous tests of the significance of these differences would be desirable, they are not crucial for our immediate purpose. On page 93 of their 1955 book, Klein and Goldberger summarized a comparison of their 1929–1950 and 1929–1952 limited information models by saying, "the majority of differences in parameter estimates obtained from the revised and augmented sample are not large and can be accounted for by the presence of sampling error." If this generalization were accepted, it would follow quite clearly that the still smaller differences between the limited information and the least squares models for 1929–1952 would be well within the range of sampling error attaching to the limited information coefficients. (The differences themselves are, of course, due to methods of computation rather than to sampling error.)

It appears that the authors gained little of economic importance in this particular model by using the limited information method rather than least squares. The similarity between the least squares and the limited information results also extended to measures of autocorrelation. Seven of the limited information equations for 1929–1952 showed significant autocorrelation; the least squares versions of six of these seven equations also showed significant autocorrelation. Table 10.4 presents the coefficients and other statistics for each of the 15 equations for the different time periods and different methods of estimation just described.

10.1.4 *Economic Evaluation*

The usefulness of a model for appraising economic policies depends upon the variables included and the accuracy with which their interrelations are measured. Economic theory is largely concerned with explaining the behavior of firms and consumers in terms of demand curves, supply curves, production

---

[6] A narrower range should be applicable here, since the two models differ only by the addition of two observations (plus changes in the specifications of two equations).

functions, and so on. It is difficult to think about economic policies systematically without drawing upon these basic concepts. From this viewpoint, the Klein–Goldberger model is disappointing, since several of its equations are frankly empirical. For example, corporate profits before taxes are expressed simply as a function of nonwage, nonfarm income, of which corporate profits constitute a major share. Changes in wage rates are expressed as functions of time and of earlier changes in the general price level. Net farm income is expressed as a function of real disposable income and the volume of agricultural exports, and farm prices are expressed as a function solely of the general price level. Long-term interest rates are expressed as a function of short-term rates three years and five years previous.

These relationships find little support in economic theory. Other equations, such as those explaining consumption expenditures, gross domestic capital formation, and corporate savings are more in accord with theoretical considerations. The authors were fully aware of these variations in the theoretical appropriateness of the different equations, but some of the expected relationships failed to show up significantly in the data either because they did not in fact hold in the real economy or because the data were inadequate to reflect them.

The level of aggregation in the model is extremely high. This means that we do not have obvious "handles" or points of entry into the equation system for the analysis of some major (and many minor) economic policies. For example, we cannot show the effects on other sectors of the economy of a reduction in support prices for basic crops; we cannot show the effects of a change in aggregate supplies of livestock products (or, for that matter, of all farm products) upon the level of farm prices; we cannot show the effects of changes in down payments and amortization periods upon the volume of residential construction.

The Klein–Goldberger model shares other problems with time series analysis in general, including so-called "latent variables" and intercorrelation. In a few instances coefficients are not statistically significant in 1929–1950 but appear to be so when the period is extended by two years. This phenomenon cannot, of course, be explained on the basis of economic theory but only on the basis of technical statistical considerations. For example, the variable "liquid assets of consumers," which did not vary a great deal before World War II, does not show up as statistically significant in the earlier period but does when two more observations reflecting the huge World War II accumulations of consumer assets are added. The effect of interest rates upon investment is somewhat parallel; although some theories accord it great importance (if properly measured), statistical studies have usually disclosed little or no significant effect.

The high level of intercorrelation in the Klein–Goldberger model creates a hazard from the standpoint of accurate specification of the variables to be included in a given equation. In the consumption equation for example, the coefficient of multiple determination is 0.998, but the largest simple coefficient is 0.991, and three other simple coefficients range from 0.90 to 0.98. Two of the independent variables—lagged consumption expenditures and current disposable income—are correlated to the extent of 0.96. The simple regression of consumer expenditures upon current disposable income fits the historical data quite closely; a combination of disposable income with any or all of the other variables also yields a good forecasting equation, but one with considerably different net regression coefficients. Specifically, the simple least squares regression coefficient of consumer expenditures upon a specially adjusted disposable income variable is 1.035; the corresponding net regression coefficient in the five-variable equation is 0.617.[7] Such differences are highly important if a given policy impinges directly upon only one of the independent variables in an equation.

It should be stressed that many interesting and constructive aspects of the 1955 book by Klein and Goldberger have not been mentioned here. The authors carried out an elaborate reasoning process as well as an elaborate set of statistical computations, and most students of economics would profit by reading the book and following the steps of this reasoning process.

10.1.5 *Suggestions for Further Adaptation of Econometric Models to the Appraisal of Economic Policies*

The chief limitation of the Klein–Goldberger model is its level of aggregation. Many applied economists in business and government are sector specialists who take pride in their alertness to a large number of indicators and pressure gauges within their areas of specialization. If models of the economy as a whole are to be useful to such economists and eventually to justify their full acceptance, they must be designed so as to incorporate readily detailed information concerning developments within individual sectors.

The sector specialist tends to be weak in interpreting the effects upon other parts of the economy of developments within his particular area. To measure these effects, we need models which reflect interactions among the different major sectors of the economy. If alternative policies are under consideration in each of several sectors, we should be concerned not only with the effects of each policy upon the area of its immediate application but also with the

---

[7] The simple regression coefficient exceeds 1.0 because certain components of disposable income were scaled down in making the special adjustment alluded to. The coefficient is therefore not comparable with estimates of the marginal propensity to consume based on unadjusted income data.

effects of the group of policies as a whole upon the level of activity achieved by the economy as a whole and in each individual sector.

The impatience of sector specialists with such highly aggregative models as those of the Klein and Goldberger type can be understood in terms of the wealth of detailed sector information which is available and which they see no ready way of incorporating into models of the general economy. For example, the United States Department of Agriculture conducts an extensive program of crop and livestock estimates, many of which have forecasting value in relation to supplies, marketings, and prices for from several months to a year ahead. The department's economists have also built up a considerable repertoire of statistical demand-and-supply analyses for individual farm products and related groups. These formal analyses are supplemented by the continuous observation of market developments by commodity specialists, who interpret them in regular quarterly or bimonthly reports.

Relationships among different farm products are reviewed continuously in connection with the preparation of a monthly report, *The Demand and Price Situation*, and awareness of interrelationships is further stimulated by the periodic calculation of indices of prices received by farmers, farm output, farm marketings, and civilian food consumption, based on detailed estimates by various commodity specialists.

Thus leading economists in the Department of Agriculture have at their disposal an elaborate network of economic and statistical intelligence concerning the agricultural sector. The Klein–Goldberger model, with its single equation expressing the determination of farm income and one other expressing the determination of farm prices, ignores the great bulk of this information.

Similarly, the housing specialist might be interested in such factors as population growth, shifts in age distribution, new family formation, geographical shifts in population, the strength of motivations underlying the movement from central cities to suburbs, and the influence of disposable income, liquid assets, down-payment requirements, amortization periods, and mortgage interest rates upon the demand for housing. For some purposes the demand for labor and construction materials by builders (reflected in such series as the number of housing starts) might be considered separately in point of time and price implications from the demand for finished houses on the part of prospective owners or tenants. The housing expert, like the agricultural economist, might use a host of geographical breakdowns, price and construction-cost indices, wage and interest rates, and other factors in order to forecast developments in the housing sector or to appraise the consequences of proposed changes in policies. Here, too, it may be fairly easy to see the direct impact of policy changes upon the housing sector but very difficult to appraise their effects upon other sectors.

We might readily conceive of a model representing the major lines of influence of a set of housing policies upon various economic magnitudes. This model would include wage rates, price indices, disposable personal income, GNP, and perhaps other variables which would also appear, for example, in a model relating agriculture to the nonfarm economy. To the extent that a housing program stimulated employment and raised disposable income, it would lead to a secondary increase in the demand for housing. But it would also increase the demand for farm products, leading to a change in the original situation in that sector. The adjustments involving agriculture might produce still another increase in disposable income, which would result in a further increase in the demand for housing. Thus we could visualize an iterative process whereby two sectors would be brought into a new equilibrium relationship with each other and with the rest of the economy.[8] Prices of building materials would influence the index of prices paid by farmers, increases in farm prices of food products would tend to raise wage rates and construction costs, and so on. The resulting model of two interacting sectors, including some variables relating to the economy as a whole, could be converted into a formally complete system analogous to that of Klein and Goldberger. However, many of the coefficients would have been built up by aggregation from more detailed relationships, and many of the time lags would be based on special analyses. The model as a whole would be built up synthetically from sound components; it would not be limited by the resolving power of a single process of statistical estimation.

This same approach could, of course, be carried out for more than two sectors. Presumably, the model for each sector could be developed in such a way as to leave "handles" or points of entry for each type of policy intervention that might be regarded as worthy of appraisal. The major channels of communication among sectors would also be represented. The logical outcome of this approach would be a model which would permit the advance appraisal of any set of economic policies and programs in relation to any initial positions and trends of the various sectors of the economy. Technical coefficients, which are the mainstay of the interindustry model, would also appear in the model conceived here but would represent only one of several channels of economic interaction.

If we think in terms of the coordination of economic policies and the appraisal of economic developments by the federal establishment as a whole, it is obviously desirable to use the detailed knowledge and skills of specialists in particular economic sectors. At the same time, a more comprehensive and internally consistent model than any now available is needed to anticipate

---

[8] This "iterative process" is described only for purposes of exposition. In actual practice this "process" would be embodied in a single set of aggregative equations that would be solved simultaneously.

the interactions among sectors and their cumulative effects upon the economy as a whole.

In summary, it seems clear that progress in economic forecasting and the appraisal of economic policies can be hastened by the development of a model or models of the general economy which can encompass our detailed knowledge of the individual sectors. In doing this, we cannot afford to be tied down to a single type of statistical estimation or confined to time series observations drawn from a single limited period. We should not be afraid of the statistical implications of a partly synthetic model if we know the reliability of its basic components. The latter will continue to be useful for intrasector analysis as at present. The major new achievement would lie in the synthesis of these basic components into a model adequately reflecting the interactions among sectors.

Most of the preceding discussion is reproduced verbatim from the 1956 review article mentioned at the beginning of this section.[9] During the late 1950s books and scientific papers by Tinbergen (1956), Theil (1958), Duesenberry, Eckstein, and Fromm (1960), and by other economists in several countries testified to a growing professional interest and sophistication in the construction, interpretation, and use of large-scale macroeconomic models.

In 1960, Klein and Duesenberry, under the sponsorship of the Social Science Research Council's Committee on Economic Stability, organized a major research effort which brought together a number of economists to collaborate on a much larger and more sophisticated model of the United States economy than had heretofore been attempted. A brief description of this research effort and the resulting model should provide a sufficient background and setting for our discussions of particular problems in Chapters 11, 13, and 14.

10.2 THE BROOKINGS INSTITUTION–SOCIAL SCIENCE RESEARCH COUNCIL MODEL OF THE UNITED STATES

As of 1965, the most elaborate economic model with a short-run stabilization focus was the Brookings–SSRC econometric model of the United States. The initial development of this model was sponsored by the Social Science Research Council during 1961–1963 under a grant from the National Science Foundation. Beginning in September 1963, responsibility for completing the model and for testing and improving it over a period of years was transferred to the Brookings Institution.

[9] Karl A. Fox, "Econometric Models of the United States," *op. cit.*

A major volume on the Brookings–SSRC model was published in 1965, so only a few of its features will be mentioned here.[10] The model is based on quarterly rather than annual data. It is larger than other models thus far developed. In its initial form, the Brookings–SSRC model includes more than 150 equations. An expanded version, in terms of 32 producing sectors rather than the seven sectors provided for in the basic model, has been discussed. If implemented, it would involve 300–400 equations.

The large size of even the basic model is the outcome of a deliberate research strategy. Previous models of the United States economy had been carried out by one or two principal investigators. Treatment of individual sectors of the economy was highly aggregative. Much empirical knowledge and many sources of data available to experts in particular sectors were overlooked.

During 1961–1963, the SSRC group sought to overcome these limitations by dividing the exploratory and developmental work on the model among approximately 20 economists. Each major block of equations in the model was made the responsibility of an economist with special knowledge and previous research experience in that area. The various tasks or sectors included the following: (1) consumption, (2) inventories, (3) residential construction, (4) business investment realization, (5) business investment anticipation, (6) foreign trade, (7) production and final demand, (8) price conversion, (9) price mark-up, (10) wage rates, (11) production and manhours, (12) dividends and other factor shares, (13) labor force, (14) interest and money, (15) agricultural submodel, and (16) government. Functional tasks cutting across sectors included consistent statistical estimation of all equations and simulation tests of various subsystems and the model as a whole.

The work of the sector specialists was coordinated by means of a three-week workshop in August 1961 and another two-week workshop in August 1962. In addition to securing standardization on technical points, the workshop discussions generated a number of insights which could scarcely have emerged from a one- or two-man project.

Figure 10.1 presents a flow diagram of the Brookings–SSRC model. This includes the various components of final GNP demand and behavior equations reflecting the purchasing decisions of consumers, the investment decisions of producers, and the investment decisions of home builders. These decisions express themselves as purchases by consumers and as new orders by business firms, including builders. The demand for finished goods are transmitted by means of an input-output "translator" into the producing sectors of the economy. The producing sectors respond to changes in the demands for their

[10] James S. Duesenberry, Gary Fromm, Lawrence R. Klein, and Edwin Kuh (eds.), *A Quarterly Econometric Model of the United States Economy* (Chicago: Rand McNally and Amsterdam: North-Holland Publishing Company), 776 pp., 1965.

outputs by changing their levels of employment and capacity utilization, which in turn lead to changes in the levels and distribution of payments to labor and other factors of production. Tax functions and transfer payments further influence the disposable personal income available for consumption expenditures and the after-tax profits available to business firms. These income streams, of course, influence the final demand decisions of consumers and firms in the next time period. The impacts of changes in production upon income payments, changes in income payments upon expenditures, and changes in expenditures upon production constitute the core of this as well as of other econometric models.

Further study of the flow diagram will disclose other features of the Brookings–SSRC model. Each arrow, in general, represents several equations. Many of the relationships in the model operate with time lags.

The use of quarterly data should throw more light on the mechanisms of inventory cycles and of monetary and fiscal policy than would be possible with annual data. Several sectors of the economy, including agriculture, foreign trade, housing, money and finance, government, and the labor force, are treated in greater detail than in previous econometric models. This permits a clearer and more operational definition of policy instruments than in previous models of the United States economy. For example, the equations for the government sector use tax *rates* rather than the amount of tax receipts as the true policy variables; they show that some government expenditures (for example, transfer payments) are endogenously determined; and they clearly separate federal expenditures from those of state and local governments.

An interesting by-product of the workshop discussions in 1961 and 1962 was a greatly increased awareness by the participants of the logical and operational differences between a policy model and a forecasting model. The previous emphasis of most of the individual participants had been either upon forecasting or upon analyzing the effects of policies in particular sectors of the economy. Only gradually did a consensus develop that the model as a whole should be to the fullest extent possible structural and policy-oriented. By the end of the 1962 workshop, there appeared to be general agreement that appropriate equations in the model should express the mechanisms by which specific policy instruments did in fact influence other variables, including those which were the targets of stipulated policies. The model should, of course, forecast adequately, but this was by no means its sole or even its primary objective.

The Brookings Institution research program includes a good many applications of the model to simulating the probable economic effects of alternative policy measures. The simulation experiments may be expected to elucidate what the model implies as to the consequences of (1) various

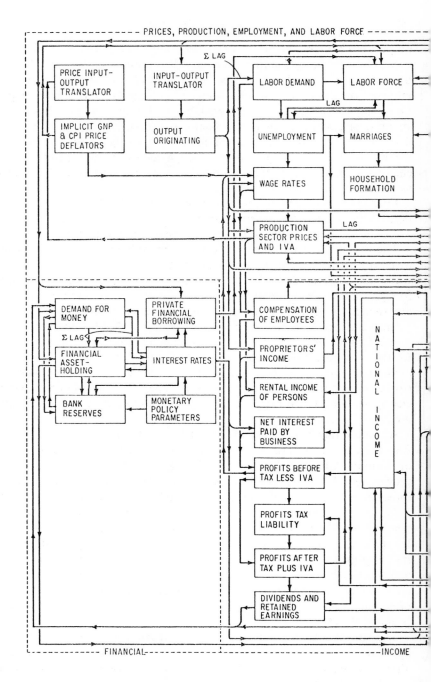

Figure 10.1 Condensed flow diagram of the Brookings–SSRC econometric model. (*Source:* J. S. Duesenberry, G. Fromm, L. R. Klein, and E. Kuh (editors) *The Brookings*

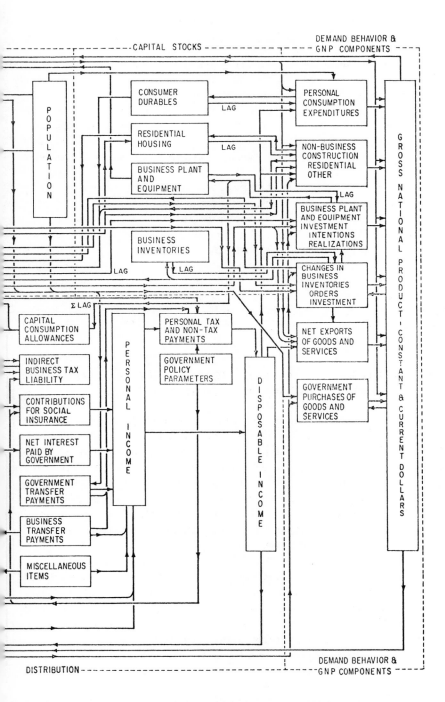

Quarterly Econometric Model of the United States (Chicago: Rand McNally, and Amsterdam: North-Holland Publishing Company), pp. 24–25, 1965.

combinations of initial conditions, (2) specified sequences of policy actions or specified "decision rules" for manipulating policy instruments, and (3) specified sequences of values of the noncontrollable variables. Simulation tests of this type offer almost endless opportunities for exploring the compatibility and joint effectiveness of combinations of economic policies. Over the coming decade, they should greatly improve the level of understanding of both academic economists and public officials concerning short-run economic policies.

The Brookings–SSRC model is so designed that further disaggregation by sectors of the economy and/or by regions and local areas is possible. The model has also raised many interesting problems of statistical estimation.

In his exploratory work, each of the participating economists had used ordinary least squares estimates for virtually all of his equations. All variables which were determined outside of a particular sector were taken as exogenous or predetermined in the exploratory work on that sector, even though they might prove to be endogenous from the standpoint of the model as a whole. The final version of the basic model, published in 1965, eliminated inconsistencies of this kind.

10.3   A SORTING-OUT OF STATISTICAL PROBLEMS ASSOCIATED WITH LARGE-SCALE ECONOMIC MODELS

A number of problems appear to stand out in the discussions of both the Klein–Goldberger and the Brookings–SSRC models.

First, we have the *identification problem*, which is associated with the appearance of two or more endogenous or logically dependent variables in a single equation. In principle, any given endogenous variable could appear in several or many equations, and a given pair of endogenous variables, such as the retail price and consumption of a commodity, could both appear in at least two equations, for example, a consumer demand function and a retailers' supply function. The identification problem precipitated a number of technical developments in the estimation of interrelated structural equations. The *limited information maximum likelihood* method was the first proposed and tried for estimating truly simultaneous or interdependent structural equations. However, other methods, such as *two-stage* least squares, *three-stage* least squares, and a whole category of so-called *k-class* estimators were also developed during the 1950s and early 1960s to deal with problems of consistent estimation of multiple economic relationships.

The concept of *causal ordering* has been used fruitfully in recent years to sort out and classify different kinds of economic models in terms of the direction of influence from one variable to another and the implications of this for the correct choice of a method of statistical estimation for each kind of economic structure.

These three topics, identification, causal ordering, and estimation in multiple equation models, form a logical cluster and will be treated together in Chapter 11. A somewhat different kind of estimation problem, the use of *a priori* or *extraneous information*, is treated in Chapter 13. *Multicollinearity* is treated in Chapter 13 also, since in some instances high intercorrelation among the independent or exogenous variables of a model cannot be resolved at all by statistical means. In such cases, it seems essential to use information from other sources and to impose numerical values (or ranges of values) on certain coefficients in a model, leaving the remaining coefficients to be estimated by statistical means *given* the values of the coefficients imposed on the basis of other or "outside" information.

Finally, *aggregation* problems appear in a new light when we try to apply the principle of "perfect aggregation" (see Chapter 14) to the statistical estimation of relationships from economic time series. In imposing coefficients on the basis of *a priori* information, we may sometimes apply the concept of perfect aggregation in the pure mathematical and functional sense. However, in other instances we may have no alternative but to use aggregative time series, including index numbers, as the basis for estimating regression coefficients or related structural parameters. This adds statistical problems to the purely mathematical and functional ones. Both will be dealt with in Chapter 14.

EXERCISES

1. Suppose we have the following "Keynesian" model:

(a) $Y = C + I$
(b) $C = a + bY$
(c) $I = d + eY$

(i) Classify each of the equations as to whether it is definitional, behavioral, or technological.

(ii) Classify all variables occurring in the model into

jointly dependent	current endogenous
	$\lceil$ lagged endogenous
predetermined	$\{$ current exogenous
	$\lfloor$ lagged exogenous

2. Classify each of the equations in the Klein–Goldberger model into definitional, behavioral, and technological.

3. Represent the Klein–Goldberger model in matrix notation of the form:

$$Y\Gamma + XB = E$$

where Y = matrix of jointly dependent variables
  Γ = matrix of the coefficients of the jointly dependent variables
  X = matrix of predetermined variables
  B = matrix of the coefficients of the predetermined variables
  E = matrix of the error terms.

REFERENCES

1. Duesenberry, J. S., G. Fromm, L. R. Klein, and Edwin Kuh (eds.), *The Brookings Quarterly Econometric Model of the United States*, Chicago: Rand McNally and Co., and Amsterdam: North-Holland Publishing Co., 776 pp., 1965.
2. Fox, Karl A., "Econometric Models of the United States," *Journal of Political Economy* **64**, No. 2, pp. 128–142, April 1956.
3. Goldberger, A. S., *Impact Multipliers and Dynamic Properties of the Klein–Goldberger Model*, Amsterdam: North-Holland Publishing Co., 1959.
4. Klein, L. R., *Economic Fluctuations in the United States, 1921–1941*, Cowles Commission Monograph No. 11, New York: John Wiley and Sons, 174 pp., 1950.
5. Klein, L. R. and A. S. Goldberger, *An Econometric Model of the United States, 1929–1952*, Amsterdam: North-Holland Publishing Co., 165 pp., 1955.
6. Tinbergen, Jan, *Statistical Testing of Business-Cycle Theories, Vol. I: A Method and Its Application to Investment Activity, Vol. II: Business Cycles in the United States of America, 1919–1932*, Geneva: League of Nations Economic Intelligence Service, 1939.

CHAPTER 11

Identification, Causal Ordering and Estimation in Economic Models

At the end of Chapter 10 we mentioned several clusters of problems which have been encountered in the construction of large-scale economic models. This chapter will treat a number of these which are rather closely related, namely *identification, causal ordering*, and appropriate methods of *estimation* in economic models consisting of several equations.

Although experience with models of national economies has played an important part in focusing professional discussion on these problems, they are also found in simpler models with which most readers of this book are familiar. We will discuss the identification problem with the aid of examples from demand, supply, and price structures for particular commodities. The principles can then be generalized to other economic contexts.

11.1 THE IDENTIFICATION PROBLEM IN ECONOMIC MODELS

In Chapter 7 we indicated that multiple regression analysis can, in principle, be extended to include any number of *independent* variables. And, as far as the computations are concerned, any one of the variables may be placed in the dependent position. For example, we may express the retail price of beef as a function of the quantity of beef available for consumption, along with other variables. But we can also express the quantity of beef available for consumption (and purchased by consumers) as a function of the retail price of beef, along with the other variables in the preceding equation.

It may be argued that there is a logical inconsistency between these two equations. In the first equation, we use quantity consumed to "explain" retail price and in the second we use retail price to "explain" quantity consumed. If we are indeed interested in cause and effect relationships, one of these equations would seem to be preferable to the other.

We might also argue that there is a structural relationship between price and consumption—that they are connected by a consumer demand curve. A demand curve is an exact mathematical construct. It is immaterial whether we write it as $P = a + bQ$ or as $Q = -a/b + (1/b)P$. We know, however, that if P and Q are statistical time series subject to the disturbances and measurement errors of the real world, our least squares estimate of b obtained by regressing P on Q will in general not equal the reciprocal of the coefficient $1/b$ when the latter is estimated as the least squares regression of Q on P.

If for reasons of logic or exposition we must manipulate a "reversible" demand curve, we could choose either the regression of P on Q or the regression of Q on P and treat it as if it were reversible. Or we may choose as our reversible demand curve one with a slope somewhere between the two regression lines. For example, in the 1920s Henry Schultz used a reproducible mathematical procedure to arrive at reversible "weighted regressions" in demand analysis.[1]

It should be noted that any procedure by which we arrive at a reversible demand curve somewhere in between the two least squares regressions implies that both variables are on the same logical footing—that is, both partake of the characteristics of dependent variables. If only the relation between price and consumption is logically required to be reversible, the remaining variables in the multiple regression equation may be treated as independent variables in the usual sense.

However, if price and consumption are both logically dependent upon the remaining variables in the equation, we are faced with a contradiction: We have only one equation with which to determine the values of two variables. Logically, the values of retail price and consumer purchases in any time period represent the point of intersection of a consumer demand curve and a producers' (or dealers') supply curve. If the independent variables in the equation we have considered thus far clearly belong in a consumer demand curve but not in a producers' supply curve, it appears that we should specify a supply curve with equal care, including in it variables (raw material costs, unit labor costs, and so on) which would influence the quantity that producers would offer for sale at a given retail price.

Now we are clearly beyond the domain of conventional least squares methods. We need to estimate two different relationships between two jointly dependent variables—one relationship is a reversible demand curve and the other is a reversible supply curve (by "reversible" here we simply mean that in the demand curve the "slope" of consumption on price is the reciprocal

---

[1] Henry Schultz, *Statistical Laws of Supply and Demand* (Chicago: The University of Chicago Press), 1928.

of the "slope" of price on consumption; a similarly reciprocal relationship should exist between the price-quantity slope and the quantity-price slope in the supply curve).

The requirement that we estimate *two* relationships between price and consumption for the same time period raises a certain uneasiness. How will we be able to identify one regression coefficient (or similar measure) with the slope of the demand curve and another regression coefficient (or related measure) with the slope of the simultaneous supply curve? The answer is not self-evident. It will be elaborated in the following section.

11.1.1 *The Identification Problem: The Same Two Endogenous Variables in Each of Two Equations; No Exogenous Variables*

Suppose we are simply given two time series on retail price P and consumption Q for a specified commodity. The P and Q values for each year are points of intersection of a demand curve and a supply curve. If we consider only three observations, we therefore have three points on a supply curve; we also have three points on a demand curve. Two points are sufficient to determine a straight line; with three points we can also detect deviations from a simple (or at least a stable) straight line relationship.

Figures 11.1a and 11.1b will clarify our estimation problem. If both the supply curve and the demand curve had remained absolutely fixed for three years, our three observations should be identical. In the diagrams, the "average" positions of both the supply curve and the demand curve pass through the point at which $P = 100$ and $Q = 100$.

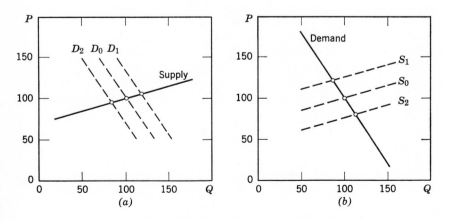

Figure 11.1   The identification problem: one function fixed, the other shifting. (a) Supply curve fixed, demand curve shifting; (b) demand curve fixed, supply curve shifting.

If the supply curve has remain fixed but the demand curve has shifted each year (perhaps because of changes in consumer income), our three observations will lie on the supply curve, as in Figure 11.1a. If, on the other hand, the demand curve has remained fixed for three years and the supply curve has shifted (perhaps as a result of fluctuations in the price of a major raw material), the three points will lie on the demand curve as in Figure 11.1b.

Clearly, we cannot obtain this information from the observations on P and Q alone. If the three observations fall along a positively sloping line, we may be encouraged to believe that we are approximating the supply curve. Conversely, if the three points indicate a negatively sloping relationship, we are encouraged to believe we are approximating the demand curve. Note, however, that if supply has remained stable, our observations will give us no information about the slope of the demand curve. And if the demand curve has remained fixed, our observations give us no information about the slope of the supply curve.

In general, both the demand curve and the supply curve will have shifted from year to year. In Figure 11.2a we assume that the shifts are positively associated, with the highest position of the supply curve occurring in the same year as the highest position of the demand curve. The line joining these observations, $P = f_1(Q)$, has a steep positive slope. The positive sign suggests that we have an approximation to the supply curve, and the steepness of the slope suggests that supply must be highly inelastic. But it is not enough simply to have the correct sign. If a producer thought that other producers

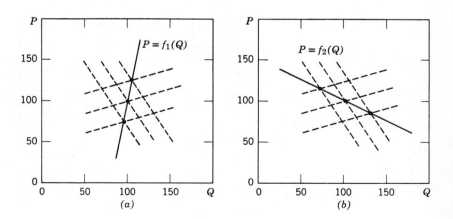

Figure 11.2 The identification problem: both functions shifting—with shifts in the two functions highly correlated. (a) Shifts positively correlated; (b) shifts negatively correlated.

in the aggregate would make only negligible increases in output in response to a substantial increase in retail price, his own production and marketing strategy might go awry.

Figure 11.2*b* shows the results of negatively correlated shifts in the two functions—that is, the highest position of the supply curve occurs in the same year as the lowest position of the demand curve and vice versa. In this instance, the three observations lie on a negatively sloping line. The negative slope is characteristic of demand functions, so we may be led to believe that the line $P = f_2(Q)$ approximates the demand curve, and that demand is quite elastic (a 25% drop in price is associated with a 50% increase in consumption). But in fact the demand curve is moderately *inelastic* (a 25% decrease in retail price will result in only a 15 or 16% increase in consumption). If interpreted as *the* demand curve, $P = f_2(Q)$ suggests that total revenue could be increased considerably by reducing price when in fact total revenue would be reduced by a price cut.[2]

The three observations in Figure 11.2*a* fall on a straight line because we have assumed a perfect positive linear association between disturbances in the demand and the supply functions. Similarly, the three points in Figure 11.2*b* lie on a straight line because we have assumed a perfect negative linear association between the disturbances. If the actual correlation between the disturbances is somewhere between 1 and −1, and if we assume that the demand curve and the supply curve can take only the three distinct positions indicated, any three of the nine points of intersection might turn up as the P and Q observations for the three years of our sample.

Three points could be selected from the total of nine points in 84 different combinations.[3] Of these, three combinations would lie along a demand curve, three combinations would lie along a supply curve, and 78 would yield regression lines which did not coincide with either a demand curve or a supply curve.

Two of these "nonstructural" regressions might be particularly attractive since the three observations would lie on straight lines, implying perfect positive or negative correlation between the observed values of P and Q. These are shown in Figures 11.2*a* and *b*. In the remaining 76 possible instances, the three observations would not lie on a straight line. If it were known that P and Q were estimated without error or with only negligible errors, the relatively low correlations between P and Q in many of the 76 instances would perhaps serve to warn us that all was not well.

[2] This would be true of an individual producer who had essentially a monopoly, within a limited price range, in a given trade area. Otherwise, if the demand function applies to the total sales of an industry including several or many firms, its inelasticity implies that an industrywide price cut would reduce industrywide gross revenue.

[3] See Chapter 3, p. 46 on combinations.

The simple two-equation economic model represented in Figures 11.1 and 11.2 can be stated in algebraic form as follows:

(11.1)   *Demand:* $P = a_1 + b_1 Q + u$
(11.2)   *Supply:* $P = a_2 + b_2 Q + v$

Assume we have a specific number of time series observations on P and Q from which we hope to derive a supply curve and a demand curve. We can then express P and Q as deviations from their means as follows:

(11.3) $$p = b_1 q + u$$

and

(11.4) $$p = b_2 q + v$$

Since the two functions are shifted by the disturbances u and v, we may solve for p and q as functions of u and v, using Cramer's rule (see Chapter 4, Appendix A):
    Write

$$p - b_1 q = u$$

and

$$p - b_2 q = v$$

Then

$$p = \frac{\begin{vmatrix} u & -b_1 \\ v & -b_2 \end{vmatrix}}{\begin{vmatrix} 1 & -b_1 \\ 1 & -b_2 \end{vmatrix}} = \frac{-b_2 u + b_1 v}{-b_2 + b_1} = \frac{b_1 v - b_2 u}{b_1 - b_2}$$

$$q = \frac{\begin{vmatrix} 1 & u \\ 1 & v \end{vmatrix}}{\begin{vmatrix} 1 & -b_1 \\ 1 & -b_2 \end{vmatrix}} = \frac{v - u}{-b_2 + b_1} = \frac{v - u}{b_1 - b_2}$$

Suppose we regress p on q by least squares. The formula for the least squares regression coefficient of p on q is

(11.5) $$B_{pq} = \frac{\sum pq}{\sum q^2} = \frac{\sum \left(\dfrac{b_1 v - b_2 u}{b_1 - b_2} \right) \left(\dfrac{v - u}{b_1 - b_2} \right)}{\sum \left(\dfrac{v - u}{b_1 - b_2} \right)^2}$$

Hence canceling out $1/(b_1 - b_2)^2$ in numerator and denominator, we obtain

$$B_{pq} = \frac{\sum (b_1 v^2 - b_1 uv - b_2 uv + b_2 u^2)}{\sum (v^2 - 2uv + u^2)}$$

The summations are taken over the number of observations to which the regression is fitted. Dividing both numerator and denominator by the number of observations, we obtain

(11.6) $$B_{pq} = \frac{b_1 s_v^2 - (b_1 + b_2) r_{uv} s_u s_v + b_2 s_u^2}{s_v^2 - 2 r_{uv} s_u s_v + s_u^2}$$

From (11.6) we know a number of things.[4] First, if the supply curve has not shifted, $s_v = 0$; two terms in both numerator and denominator vanish, and $B_{pq} = b_2 s_u^2 / s_u^2$ or b_2. In other words, the least squares regression coefficient is the slope of the supply curve, as in Figure 11.1a.

Conversely, if the demand curve has not shifted, $s_u = 0$; two terms in both numerator and denominator vanish, and $B_{pq} = b_1 s_v^2 / s_v^2$ or b_1. The least squares regression coefficient in this instance is the slope of the demand curve, as in Figure 11.1b.

In brief, if we set out to estimate a demand curve and a supply curve with no more information than a series of paired observations on P and Q the most likely outcome is that we do not obtain a good estimate of either curve; if we are lucky, we may get a good estimate of one; but in no case can we obtain good estimates of both curves.[5]

11.1.2 *The Identification Problem: Two Endogenous Variables in Each of Two Equations and a Different Exogenous Variable in Each Equation*

There is a way to continue, however, if the disturbances u and v are thought to result from fluctuations in certain other specific and quantifiable variables. For example, we might have a good basis in experience and in economic theory for thinking that a considerable portion of the disturbances in the demand function result from changes in the disposable income of consumers, Y. And, we may know that a large proportion of the shifts in the supply function results from fluctuations in the cost of some major raw material, say Z.

[4] The value of B_{pq} would not be changed if we divided both numerator and denominator by the number of observations *minus one*, so that s_u and s_v would be properly adjusted for degrees of freedom.

[5] We rule out the "cobweb" model in this statement and insist that the P and Q observations to be correlated refer to the same time interval—their values emerge simultaneously and not in sequence.

If we have times series on Y and Z, an obvious procedure is to rewrite (11.1) and (11.2) as

$$Demand: \quad P = a_1 + b_1Q + c_1Y + e_1$$
$$Supply: \quad P = a_2 + b_2Q + c_2Z + e_2$$

We might then run the least squares regression of P on Q and Y (or of Q on P and Y) and take the resulting equation as an approximation to the demand function. Similarly, we might run the least squares regression of P on Q and Z (or of Q on P and Z) and take this equation as an approximation to the supply function.

At this point it will advance our discussion if we present the model from which the actual observations in Figures 11.1 and 11.2 were generated.

The demand and supply equations are

(11.7)   Demand: $P = 260 - 1.6Q + 0.8(Y - 100)$
(11.8)   Supply: $P = 70 + 0.3Q + 0.6(Z - 100)$

Thus the disturbances in (11.1) and (11.2) are

(11.9) $u = 0.8(Y - 100)$

and

(11.10) $v = 0.6(Z - 100)$

Each unit change in Y above or below 100 changes the constant term a_1 of the demand curve $P = a_1 + b_1Q$ by 0.8 units. Similarly, each change of one unit in Z changes the constant term a_2 in the supply curve $P = a_2 + b_2Q$ by 0.6 units.

Knowing the complete model of (11.7) and (11.8), we can generate the observations in Figure 11.2a in the following manner:

Y	Demand Curve	Z	Supply Curve
140	$P = 292 - 1.6Q$	140	$P = 94 + 0.3Q$
100	$P = 260 - 1.6Q$	100	$P = 70 + 0.3Q$
60	$P = 228 - 1.6Q$	60	$P = 46 + 0.3Q$

Using Cramer's rule, we solve for P and Q for each pair of values of Y and Z (we first transpose $-1.6Q$ and $0.3Q$ to the left sides of the equations and change their signs):[6]

[6] The two equations are written as

$$P + 1.6Q = 292$$

and

$$P - 0.3Q = 94$$

See Chapter 4, Appendix A, for a statement of Cramer's rule.

$$\underline{Y = Z = 140}$$

$$P = \frac{\begin{vmatrix} 292 & 1.6 \\ 94 & -0.3 \end{vmatrix}}{\begin{vmatrix} 1 & 1.6 \\ 1 & -0.3 \end{vmatrix}} = \frac{-87.6 - 150.4}{-0.3 - 1.6} = \frac{238.0}{1.9} = \underline{125.3}$$

$$Q = \frac{\begin{vmatrix} 1 & 292 \\ 1 & 94 \end{vmatrix}}{\begin{vmatrix} 1 & 1.6 \\ 1 & -0.3 \end{vmatrix}} = \frac{94 - 292}{-1.9} = \frac{198}{1.9} = \underline{104.2}$$

$$\underline{Y = Z = 60}$$

$$P = \frac{\begin{vmatrix} 228 & 1.6 \\ 46 & -0.3 \end{vmatrix}}{\begin{vmatrix} 1 & 1.6 \\ 1 & -0.3 \end{vmatrix}} = \frac{-68.4 - 73.6}{-1.9} = \frac{142}{1.9} = \underline{74.7}$$

$$Q = \frac{\begin{vmatrix} 1 & 228 \\ 1 & 46 \end{vmatrix}}{\begin{vmatrix} 1 & 1.6 \\ 1 & -0.3 \end{vmatrix}} = \frac{46 - 228}{-1.9} = \frac{182}{1.9} = \underline{95.8}$$

When $Y = Z = 100$, it is clear by inspection of the equations $P = 260 - 1.6Q$ and $P = 70 + 0.3Q$ that they are satisfied by $P = 100$, $Q = 100$.

The slope of the line connecting the three points just derived is

$$b_{f1} = \frac{125.3 - 100}{104.2 - 100} = \frac{25.3}{4.2} = 6$$

and the full equation is $P - 100 = 6(Q - 100) = 6Q - 600$, or $P = -500 + 6Q$, which bears little resemblance to either the true supply curve or the true demand curve.

The *range* of u is 64 and the *range* of v is 48. We could divide both the numerator and the denominator of (11.6) by s_v^2 without affecting B_{pq}; that is, the ratio of s_u/s_v is the important factor, not their absolute magnitudes. In the present instance,

$$s_u^2 = \frac{(32)^2 + 0 + (-32)^2}{(3 - 1)} \quad \text{and} \quad s_v^2 = \frac{(24)^2 + 0 + (-24)^2}{(3 - 1)}$$

so $s_u = 32$ and $s_v = 24$. The ratio is $4/3$, so we will take $s_u = 4$ and $s_v = 3$ when substituting into (11.6):

$$(11.11) \qquad B_{pq} = \frac{-1.6(9) - (-1.6 + 0.3)(1)(12) + 0.3(16)}{9 - 2(1)(12) + 16}$$

$$= \frac{-14.4 + 15.6 + 4.8}{25 - 24} = \frac{1.2 + 4.8}{1} = 6$$

This checks with the slope already obtained for $P = f_1(Q)$ and confirms the algebra underlying (11.6).

If $r = -1$ but b_1, b_2, s_u, and s_v are unchanged, (11.11) becomes

$$(11.12) \qquad B_{pq} = \frac{-14.4 - 15.6 + 4.8}{25 + 24} = \frac{-25.2}{49} = -0.5143$$

Algebraic generation of the three observations in Figure 11.2b gives us approximately

$$B_{pq} = \frac{115.2 - 100}{70.5 - 100} = \frac{15.2}{-29.5} = -0.515$$

the slight discrepancy from -0.5143 is the result of rounding errors. This is only about one-third as steep as the slope of the true demand curve.

11.1.3 Identification through Experimental Control of One or More Variables

If we were free to experiment, we could readily solve the identification problem. On the one hand, we could vary the price P in a number of stores according to a carefully planned experimental design (we might have to "partial out" the effects of differences in average incomes among the customers of the different stores) and obtain estimates of the consumer demand function as a regression (simple or partial) of per capita quantities purchased by consumers upon the predetermined retail prices. The supply curve of producers would simply not be relevant for this experiment. As a practical matter, it would be hard to carry out a corresponding experiment with producers since their sophistication would quickly tell them that something peculiar was going on. *Possibly* interviews could be conducted with a number of producers who would enter into the spirit of the inquiry and tell us quite accurately how they would change their outputs in response to specified changes in retail price and the cost of their principal raw material (P and Z, respectively). There would be no way for consumers to influence the results of this hypothetical experiment in production response.

Wold and Strotz (1960) have argued that in principle all identification problems involving the behaviors of two groups of economic agents can be eliminated if we measure our prices, quantities, and other relevant variables in terms of the appropriate time unit. For example, suppose that retailers change the price of a perishable commodity to consumers once a week. If consumers generally use up any particular purchase of the commodity within the same week, accurate weekly observations on the price charged by producers and the quantities purchased by consumers should enable us to estimate the consumer demand curve.

Similarly, dealers may look at their raw material costs and sales for the preceding week in determining the price they will charge during the current week. In each instance, that of consumers and that of producers, if we choose the proper time unit and make observations on the proper variables (including time lags, where they exist) we should be able to make a clear-cut identification of the consumer demand functions and the producer supply functions. Wold and Strotz have argued that the kind of identification problem represented in Figures 11.1 and 11.2 is the result of "aggregation over time" so that several supply response cycles (with coefficient b_2) and several demand response cycles (with coefficient b_1) are averaged together in the annual or quarterly observations for P and Q.

11.1.4 *Estimation by the Method of Reduced Forms*

The identification problem was formulated quite clearly by E. J. Working in 1927. Ezekiel (1928) demonstrated that this problem could be solved for most agricultural products because this year's supply was determined by *previous* prices and not by the current year's price.

However, it remained for Haavelmo (1943) to generalize the identification problem and to develop a method based on modern probability theory for solving it in a good many situations. In the situation which Haavelmo characterized as the "just-identified" case the solution is simple and precise but at the same time most ingenious. The procedure is called the method of *reduced forms*.

Equations (11.7) and (11.8) can be rewritten, incorporating $0.8(-100)$ and $0.6(-100)$ into their respective constant terms:

(11.13)   *Demand:* $P = 180 - 1.6Q + 0.8Y$

(11.14)   *Supply:* $P = 10 + 0.3Q + 0.6Z$

We will arbitrarily transpose Q into the "dependent" position for the ensuing discussion:

(11.15)   *Demand:* $Q = 112.5 - 0.625P + 0.5Y$

(11.16)   *Supply:* $Q = -33.3 + 3.33P - 2Z$

For notational convenience, we will write the coefficients of (11.15) as $a_1 = 112.5$, $b_1 = -0.625$, and $c_1 = 0.5$, and those of (11.16) as $a_2 = -33.3$, $b_2 = 3.33$, and $c_2 = -2$.

Note that both equations are exact functions, with no disturbances or errors, for the mysterious disturbances of the two-variable equations (11.1) and (11.2) have been revealed to be exact functions of Y and Z.

There is a logical difference between Y and Z on the one hand and P and Q on the other. The values of Y and Z are determined independently of or before P and Q in a causal sense. If we *could* directly control the values of P and Q, we would find that they had no discernible effects upon the current period values of Y and Z. We may call Y and Z *exogenous* variables in the present model, meaning that their values are determined *outside of* the model.

In contrast, we may call P and Q *endogenous* variables since their values are determined *inside of* the model; P and Q are *jointly dependent* upon the values of the exogenous variables Y and Z.

From a mathematical standpoint, the values of Y and Z in any time period can be taken as given numbers; the two equations are then logically sufficient to determine the values of the two jointly dependent variables P and Q. It is quite possible to solve (11.15) and (11.16) for P and Q as functions of Y and Z; we will do this on the intuition that this procedure will throw some light on the identification problem.

For general purposes, we will deal with the algebraic forms of (11.15) and (11.16):

(11.17)   *Demand:* $Q = a_1 + b_1 P + c_1 Y$

(11.18)   *Supply:* $Q = a_2 + b_2 P + c_2 Z$

We bring $b_1 P$ and $b_2 P$ to the left sides of the equations and apply Cramer's rule to

$$Q - b_1 P = a_1 + c_1 Y + 0.Z$$
$$Q - b_2 P = a_2 + 0.Y + c_2 Z$$

The zeros are inserted for formal reasons.[7] Then

$$Q = \frac{\begin{vmatrix} a_1 + c_1 Y + 0.Z & -b_1 \\ a_2 + 0.Y + c_2 Z & -b_2 \end{vmatrix}}{\begin{vmatrix} 1 & -b_1 \\ 1 & -b_2 \end{vmatrix}} = \frac{(-a_1 b_2 - c_1 b_2 Y) + a_2 b_1 + c_2 b_1 Z}{-b_2 + b_1}$$

or

(11.19) $Q = \left(\dfrac{-a_1 b_2 + a_2 b_1}{b_1 - b_2} \right) - \left(\dfrac{b_2 c_1}{b_1 - b_2} \right) Y + \left(\dfrac{b_1 c_2}{b_1 - b_2} \right) Z$

[7] The entire right-hand side of each equation, namely $[a_1 + c_1 Y + 0.Z]$ and $[a_2 + 0.Y + c_2 Z]$, is treated as the constant term in this adaptation of Cramer's rule.

Also,

$$P = \frac{\begin{vmatrix} 1 & a_1 + c_1 Y + 0.Z \\ 1 & a_2 + 0.Y + c_2 Z \end{vmatrix}}{\begin{vmatrix} 1 & -b_1 \\ 1 & -b_2 \end{vmatrix}} = \frac{a_2 + c_2 Z - a_1 - c_1 Y}{b_1 - b_2}$$

or

(11.20) $$P = \left(\frac{a_2 - a_1}{b_1 - b_2}\right) - \left(\frac{c_1}{b_1 - b_2}\right) Y + \left(\frac{c_2}{b_1 - b_2}\right) Z$$

Equations (11.19) and (11.20) are known as *reduced form equations* or, taken together, as the *reduced form* of the model represented by (11.17) and (11.18). Each reduced form equation contains a single endogenous variable, so there is no logical reason why we should not estimate the coefficients of each equation separately by least squares. Since (in the present illustration) P and Q are exact linear functions of Y and Z, each equation when fitted to time series observations will yield an R^2 of one and the standard errors of the regression coefficients will be zero.

For convenience, let us rewrite (11.20) as

(11.21) $$P = A_1 + B_1 Y + C_1 Z$$

and (11.19) as

(11.22) $$Q = A_2 + B_2 Y + C_2 Z$$

where the coefficients of (11.21) and (11.22) are assumed to have been estimated by least squares. Statistically, these equations give us minimum variance estimates of P and Q. In a certain sense they contain the maximum amount of information concerning the determination of the jointly dependent variables that can be extracted from the data.

The real value of our reduced form equations becomes apparent when we look more closely at the coefficients of (11.19) and (11.20). First, we note that $b_1 = C_2/C_1$. For,

$$\frac{C_2}{C_1} = \frac{\left(\dfrac{b_1 c_2}{b_1 - b_2}\right)}{\left(\dfrac{c_2}{b_1 - b_2}\right)} = \frac{b_1 c_2}{c_2} = b_1$$

Next, we see that $b_2 = B_2/B_1$, for,

$$\frac{B_2}{B_1} = \frac{\left(\dfrac{b_2 c_1}{b_1 - b_2}\right)}{\left(\dfrac{c_1}{b_1 - b_2}\right)} = \frac{b_2 c_1}{c_1} = b_2$$

These two coefficients give us the value of $(b_1 - b_2)$, which appears in the denominators of all the terms.

Then $c_1 = B_1[-(b_1 - b_2)]$, and $c_2 = C_1(b_1 - b_2)$. Only a_1 and a_2 remain to be determined. From (11.19) and (11.20), respectively, we obtain

$$(11.23) \qquad -a_1b_2 + a_2b_1 = A_2(b_1 - b_2)$$

and

$$(11.24) \qquad -a_1 + a_2 = A_1(b_1 - b_2)$$

Multiplying the second equation by $-b_2$ and adding, we have

$$-a_1b_2 + a_2b_1 = A_2(b_1 - b_2)$$
$$\underline{a_1b_2 - a_2b_2 = A_1(b_1 - b_2)(-b_2)}$$
$$(11.25) \qquad a_2(b_1 - b_2) = (b_1 - b_2)(A_2 - b_2A_1)$$

so $a_2 = A_2 - b_2A_1$. Finally, from (11.24), $a_1 = a_2 - A_1(b_1 - b_2)$. This completes the solution. From the numerical values of the least squares regression coefficients A_1, B_1, C_1 and A_2, B_2, C_2 we have succeeded in deriving the numerical values of the structural coefficients of our demand curve (a_1, b_1, c_1) and of our supply curve (a_2, b_2, c_2).

The demonstration that reduced form equations which could be used to derive consistent and reversible estimates of structural relations between jointly dependent or endogenous variables was perhaps Haavelmo's major contribution. The procedure is by no means obvious to an economist who has grown up in the tradition of least squares regression analysis. Although a knowledge of matrix algebra is not necessary in order to understand the relation of structural coefficients to reduced form coefficients in a two-equation model, matrix algebra is almost essential in generalizing the identification problem and the reduced form method of estimation for models of three equations or more.

Furthermore, we have taken the simplest case—the model represented by (11.7) and (11.8) is mathematically exact. In real situations there would be some variation in P and Q which could not be explained by Y and Z. Suppose that Y and Z, although logically distinct entities, happened to be highly correlated during the sample period. It is clear from (11.21) and (11.22) that usually the R^2's will be less than 1, the regression coefficients will have standard errors, and if Y and Z are highly intercorrelated, these standard errors may be rather large. In other words, we do not escape the problems of intercorrelation or (in the extreme) multicollinearity by using the method of reduced forms.

Two other situations are possible with respect to identification in our two-equation model. In one of these, the model is said to be *underidentified*.

This would be true if, for example, the variable Z did not appear in the supply equation. In that instance, Z would not appear in either of the reduced form equations. The coefficient b_2 could be estimated as the ratio of the coefficients of Y in (11.19) and (11.20) (the terms in Z are omitted). However, it would be impossible to determine the remaining coefficients b_1, c_1, a_1, and a_2 from information provided by this revised model.

The *overidentified* case may be illustrated by adding another variable, W, to the demand equation (11.7) and leaving the supply equation (11.8) as it is, with P expressed as a function of Q and Z. In this instance, a term in W (perhaps an index number of supplies or prices of competing commodities) would be added to both (11.19) and (11.20). Thus if we add a term $D_1 W$ to (11.21) and $D_2 W$ to (11.22),

$$D_1 = \frac{d_1}{(b_1 - b_2)}$$

and

$$D_2 = \frac{b_2 d_1}{(b_1 - b_2)}$$

we can obtain an estimate of b_2 as follows:

$$b_2 = \frac{D_2}{D_1}$$

But we can also obtain an estimate of b_2 as

$$b_2 = \frac{C_2}{C_1}$$

Since the reduced form coefficients D_2, D_1, C_2, and C_1 are all subject to sampling errors and the two reduced form equations are estimated independently of one another, the two estimates of b_2 will usually differ. This ambivalence cannot be confined to the coefficient b_2 alone, for the expression $(b_1 - b_2)$ constitutes the denominator of every other reduced form coefficient. Hence some reproducible method is required for reconciling the two divergent sets of estimates and arriving at some rational compromise.

If the standard errors of the reduced form coefficients are fairly small, one would intuitively expect some kind of weighted average of the two sets of estimates for the coefficients to yield a reasonable solution. In models of three equations or more, overidentification may be of a multiple character; three or more alternative means of estimating the coefficients may be available. A reproducible method of arriving at a unique set of estimates is virtually indispensable, and such a procedure has in fact been devised.

Before going further, we should indicate the numerical values of the reduced form coefficients derived from (11.17) and (11.18); they are

(11.26) $$P = 36.84214 + 0.12632\,Y + 0.50526Z$$

(11.27) $$Q = 89.47375 + 0.42105\,Y - 0.31579Z$$

Referring to the detailed structure of the reduced form coefficients in (11.19) and (11.20), we calculate

$$b_1 = \frac{-0.31605}{0.50568} = -0.62500$$

$$b_2 = \frac{0.42225}{0.12642} = 3.33320$$

$$c_1 = 3.955(0.12642) = 0.50002$$

$$c_2 = -3.955(0.50568) = -1.99999$$

$$a_2 = 89.47375 - 36.84214(3.33333) = -33.33326$$

and

$$a_1 = -33.33333 + 145.83335 = 112.50002$$

These values reproduce coefficient by coefficient the original values of the structural coefficients in (11.17) and (11.18).

In the overidentified instance, the computations originally developed by Haavelmo and his colleagues in the 1940s are extremely laborious when carried out with nothing more than desk calculators. More recently, standard routines have been developed for carrying out these calculations on electronic computers. The computations in the overidentified case are more expensive than certain alternative methods, but not sufficiently so to warrant avoiding the complex method if it seems to be indicated by the nature of an applied problem.

One of the simpler methods that has been proposed is the method of *two-stage least squares*. Assume that, for some logical reason, it seems best to write P in the dependent position in the demand function, $P = f(Q, Y)$. We regress Q upon Y and Z, which are all of the exogenous variables in the present model; this gives us the reduced form equation (11.19). The values of Q estimated from this equation, $\hat{Q}$, are exact functions of the exogenous variables Y and Z. Therefore the *statistical* properties of $\hat{Q}$ must be the statistical properties of the exogenous variables; the disturbances in the two equations (if we recognize the existence of disturbances in addition to the exogenous variables) are by hypothesis uncorrelated with $\hat{Y}$ and $\hat{Z}$. The time series of $\hat{Q}$ is substituted for the times series of the original Q's; we then calculate the least squares regression of P on $\hat{Q}$ and Y as an estimate of our structural demand function.

Similarly, if it seems logical to put Q in the dependent position in our structural supply function, we may calculate the least squares regression of P upon Y and Z, obtaining the estimate $\hat{P}$. We then calculate the least squares regression of Q on $\hat{P}$ and Z, taking the result as an estimate of the structural supply curve.

Advocates of this method feel that it is equally applicable to both the just-identified and the overidentified equations of multiple equation models. A numerical example of two-stage least squares estimation will be presented in a later section.

11.2   SOME MULTIPLE EQUATION MODELS IN WHICH LEAST SQUARES ESTIMATION PERFORMS WELL

In Chapter 10 we noted that the least squares counterparts of the Klein–Goldberger equations were quite similar to those obtained by the limited information maximum likelihood method. The limited information method was designed by Haavelmo to deal with true simultaneity which gives rise to the identification problem. In the Klein–Goldberger model we found that the differences in 1929–1952 coefficients estimated by (1) limited information and (2) least squares averaged slightly smaller than the differences in limited information coefficients obtained for (1) 1929–1952 and (2) 1929–1950.

This comparison does not demonstrate the general superiority of either method of estimation. It does suggest that true simultaneity is less prevalent or at least less damaging to least squares estimation in macroeconomic models than one might expect, given the theoretical interrelationships among all commodities and decision makers in an economic system.[8] It also suggests that an attempt to explain *why* least squares estimation appears to work well in particular situations may be enlightening. We shall once again draw some examples from demand analysis.

Examples from the food and agricultural sectors are of interest because many of them show close approximations to the cobweb or *recursive* model even in annual data. Until the 1950s very little econometric work had been done with quarterly data. Many sectors of the United States economy appear to provide examples of recursives in terms of quarterly data, which have become widely available since 1950. The heavy emphasis on interdependent models maintained by leading econometricians in the 1940s and 1950s may have been based partly on an implicit assumption that the most important

---

[8] But note the argument of Wold and Strotz (mentioned previously in this chapter) that the basic decision-making processes of firms and consumers are essentially of a *recursive* or stimulus-response character, involving time lags, and not simultaneous in the sense of general equilibrium theory.

economic time series were, and would continue to be, available only on an annual basis. Monthly data should disclose an even larger proportion of recursive models than do quarterly data. Hence the methodological implications of the following pages are applicable to situations in any sector of the economy (and for any selections of time units) which are characterized by recursive structures or close approximations of them.

Figure 4.15 expresses a hypothesis about the economic structure or model responsible for generating time series observations on a number of major variables which logically belong to consumer demand, producers' supply, and other relationships in the hog and pork economy. The directions of the arrows express our hypothesis about the direction of causal relations *given* the time unit (one year) and the market (the United States as a whole) to which our time series data refer. The widths of the arrows reflect our expectations that fluctuations in specified variables will cause large changes in the variables to which arrows lead but that fluctuations in other variables will have only moderate effects. Similar diagrams could be drawn for any other food product.

Let us assume that our primary objective is to obtain a structural estimate of the consumer demand function for a food product. Equation (11.28) is typical of the simpler demand functions for food products which have been estimated by economists in the United States:

(11.28) $$X_1(t) = a_0 + b_0 X_2(t) + c_0 X_3(t) + d_1(t)$$

where X_1 is the retail price and X_2 the per capita consumption of the product, X_3 is the per capita disposable income of consumers, d_1 is a random disturbance, and a_0, b_0, and c_0 are "true" values of structural coefficients.[9] In order to show (within the framework of simultaneous equations theory) that this demand function can be approximated by a single least squares equation, we must show on logical grounds that the disturbances are distributed independently of the explanatory variables, consumption and disposable income. If this is true, we may regard consumption and disposable income as predetermined variables. Since the disturbances are then reflected only in retail price, the demand function must logically be fitted with price in the dependent position. A demand function with these attributes may be called a *uniequational complete model* to indicate that it contains only one genuinely endogenous variable and can properly be estimated by ordinary least squares.[10]

---

[9] The following pages are adapted from Karl A. Fox, "Structural Analysis and the Measurement of Demand for Farm Products," *Review of Economics and Statistics* **37**, No. 1, pp. 57–66 (1954).

[10] We may think of a complete model as being a "closed set"; the internal relations of variables forming the set are essentially unaffected by variables excluded from the set.

The argument in the following pages is directed toward showing that demand functions for a number of food products approximately meet the statistical specifications of the uniequational complete model. It is impossible to show affirmatively that the disturbances in a given instance are distributed independently of the explanatory variables because the disturbances are (by definition) not directly observable. Thus it is *possible* that a non-economic variable such as summer temperature, which affects consumer demand for lemons, will be correlated with disturbances arising from minor economic factors. Similarly, it is *possible* that apple production, although causally determined by weather and economic influences before harvest, will somehow be correlated with nonmeasurable disturbances in the demand function for apples during the subsequent marketing season. But there is certainly no *a priori* reason to expect that the disturbances will be dependent (in a probability sense) upon the variables in question.

In general, we shall argue that relevant variables whose values are determined before the current time period or outside a given model may be used as explanatory variables in the estimation of demand functions by the method of least squares. Such variables are independently determined or predetermined in the usual or logical sense in which this word is used. The nonanswerable question of whether the disturbances are distributed independently of the explanatory variables will be disregarded.[11] Instead we shall concentrate on the answerable question of whether certain variables entering into demand functions for foods are predetermined in a logical sense, or nearly enough so to be used as explanatory variables without leading to seriously biased estimates of demand elasticities.

11.2.1 *Is Aggregate Consumption of the Given Commodity Predetermined?*

For perishable food products, production in the United States is very nearly equal to domestic consumption. It will facilitate the exposition to consider first the logical status of production as a variable determined independently of the current price of the commodity, assuming for the moment that production and consumption are identical.

If production is not predetermined, its current value must be influenced by the current values of other endogenous variables, particularly price. This at once implies the existence of a second structural equation in which production is expressed as a function of current price in addition to other relevant variables. Since production is now dependent on price, it can no longer be regarded as distributed independently of the disturbances affecting price. A least squares regression of price upon production (equals consumption) and consumer income would give biased estimates of the

---

[11] The small sample aspects of this question are treated in Chapter 7.

structural demand coefficients, as we have seen earlier in this chapter. Thus the alternative to treating production as a predetermined variable is the simultaneous fitting of two equations, a supply curve and a demand curve.

For many farm products it is clear on logical grounds that production is a predetermined variable. The production of a crop is the product of planted acreage, which is influenced by economic and other considerations before planting time, and yield, which in any given year is strongly influenced by weather. For livestock products, the question might be approached on a partly statistical basis: What part of the observed variance in production can be explained by (1) variables whose values were actually known before the beginning of the current period, (2) variables whose values, although not *known* in advance, must clearly have been *determined* before the current period,[12] (3) exogenous or noneconomic variables, such as weather and disease, and (4) errors of measurement? If by such a procedure we can explain 95% or so of the observed variation in production we may conclude that, for practical purposes, production is a predetermined variable. The residual variation sets an upper limit to the possible endogenous or jointly determined element in production and to the bias which might be involved in the least squares regression of price on production.

If production of a perishable commodity is predetermined and if consumption is identically equal to production, consumption itself can obviously be treated as a predetermined variable. But can consumption be so treated under more general conditions?

United States consumption of many farm products differs from (predetermined) production due to variations in exports, imports, or stocks but is still highly correlated with production. For example, during 1922–1941 the correlation coefficient between year-to-year changes in production and consumption of meat was 0.98 ($r^2 = 0.95$). If the disturbance or unexplained residual in the relationship between consumption and production is random, intuitively it seems clear that the degree of bias in the least squares estimate of b_0 in (11.28) will not exceed the percentage of total variance in consumption which is uncorrelated with variations in production.[13]

Thus it appears that consumption may be treated as an explanatory variable in this instance also, although perhaps with certain minor adjustments. One

---

[12] For example, the number of milk cows on farms on January 1 is causally determined as of that date but is not reported until mid-February.

[13] This would be strictly true if X_2 and X_3 were uncorrelated during the sample period. We have noted in Chapter 7 that random errors in an independent variable bias the *simple* regression coefficient b_{12} toward zero. This effect may not carry through into the partial or net regression coefficient $b_{12.3}$ if X_2 and X_3 are correlated. But if $r_{23} = 0$, $b_{12.3} = b_{12}$, and $b_{12.3}$ is biased toward zero by the random errors in X_2.

of these would be to regard not actual consumption but consumption as estimated from its regression upon production as a predetermined variable. The remaining variation in actual consumption would be regarded as a random disturbance-and-error component attaching to the consumption variable itself. The least squares regression of price upon consumption would tend to be biased toward zero by the random measurement error component.

This may be shown as follows. Let

$$(11.28a) \qquad\qquad Y = \alpha + \beta X + u$$

where X is a fixed or "true" value and u is a random disturbance, $E(u) = 0$. If we estimate β by fitting the least squares regression of Y on X we obtain

$$(11.29) \qquad\qquad b = \frac{\sum xy}{\sum x^2} = \frac{\beta \sum x^2 + \sum xu}{\sum x^2}$$

small letters denoting deviations from means. Since $E(\sum xu) = 0$, we have

$$(11.30) \qquad\qquad E(b) = \beta$$

Suppose, however, that in place of the "true" value, X, we have an estimated value, $X' = X + \Delta$, in which Δ is an error considered fixed. Then the least squares regression of Y on X gives us

$$(11.31) \qquad b' = \frac{\sum yx'}{\sum x'^2} = \frac{\beta(\sum x^2 + \sum x\delta) + \sum xu + \sum u\delta}{\sum x^2 + \sum \delta^2 + 2\sum x\delta}$$

in which small letters again denote deviations from means. Since $E(\sum xu)$ and $E(\sum u\delta)$ are both zero,

$$(11.32) \qquad E(b') = \beta \frac{\sum x^2 + \sum x\delta}{\sum x^2 + \sum \delta^2 + 2\sum x\delta}$$

In particular, if

$$(11.33) \qquad\qquad \sum \delta^2 > -\sum x\delta$$

it follows that

$$(11.34) \qquad\qquad |E(b')| < |\beta|$$

Condition (11.33) does not appear to be particularly restrictive.

Under the special assumption that the δ's are random and independent of the true x's, $E(\sum x\delta) = 0$, and we have

$$(11.35) \qquad\qquad E(b') = \beta\left(\frac{\sum x^2}{\sum x^2 + \sum \delta^2}\right)$$

In this instance

$$(11.36) \qquad |E(b')| < |\beta| \qquad \text{for all possible values of } \sum \delta^2 \neq 0$$

The bias in the least squares regression coefficient of price upon consumption arising from the *disturbances* reflected in the consumption variable is less obvious, and could be either positive or negative depending upon their correlation with the disturbances attaching to the "true" demand function.

The possible "disturbance bias" in the situation under discussion may be shown as follows:

Assume a "true" demand function

$$(11.37) \qquad p = \beta q + u$$

and a consumption-production relationship

$$(11.38) \qquad q = \gamma z + v$$

where p, q, and z are, respectively, price, consumption, and production, all in deviation form; u and v are random disturbances distributed independently of z, which is a predetermined variable; $E(u)$ and $E(v) = 0$.

If we attempt to estimate β by fitting the least squares regression of p on q, we obtain

$$(11.39) \qquad b = \frac{\sum pq}{\sum q^2} = \frac{\sum (\beta q + u)q}{\sum q^2} = \frac{\beta \sum q^2 + \sum qu}{\sum q^2} = \beta + \frac{\sum qu}{\sum q^2}$$

Substituting $(\gamma z + v)$ for q in the numerator we have

$$(11.40) \qquad b = \beta + \frac{\sum (\gamma z + v)u}{\sum q^2} = \beta + \frac{\sum \gamma zu + \sum vu}{\sum q^2}$$

Under our assumptions z and u are not correlated, so $E(\sum zu) = 0$ and the term $(\sum \gamma zu / \sum q^2)$ will vanish when we take expectations. If we define $b_{uv} = E(\sum uv / \sum v^2)$, we may write

$$(11.41) \qquad E\left(\frac{\sum vu}{\sum q^2}\right) = E\left(\frac{\sum vu}{\sum q^2} \frac{\sum v^2}{\sum v^2}\right) = E\left(\frac{\sum uv}{\sum v^2} \frac{\sum v^2}{\sum q^2}\right)$$

or

$$E\left(\frac{\sum vu}{\sum q^2}\right) = b_{uv} E\left(\frac{\sum v^2}{\sum q^2}\right)$$

Hence,

$$(11.42) \qquad E(b) = \beta + b_{uv}\left(\frac{\sigma_v^2}{\sigma_q^2}\right)$$

where σ_v^2 and σ_q^2 are the population variances of v and q, respectively.

If the disturbances u and v are not correlated, $b_{uv} = 0$, and b is an unbiased estimate of β. Alternatively, if σ_v^2 is small relative to σ_q^2 the bias in b will generally be small, since it seems unlikely that the regression of *disturbances* in (11.37) upon disturbances in (11.38), b_{uv}, will be as large in absolute value as the structural coefficient β relating p and q.

In the present model, β might also be estimated as follows. By least squares, fit the reduced-form equations

$$(11.43) \qquad\qquad p = dz + u'$$

$$(11.44) \qquad\qquad q = cz + v$$

in which u' is the random disturbance $(u + \beta v)$. If we substitute $(\gamma z + v)$ for q in (11.37), we obtain $p = \beta \gamma z + (u + \beta v)$. Since d is an estimate of $(\beta \gamma)$ and c is an estimate of γ, the estimate of the structural parameter, β, is given by d/c. This estimate should be asymptotically unbiased even if q contains random measurement errors as well as the effects of disturbances.

11.2.2 *Is Aggregate Consumer Income Predetermined?*

If this question is answered in the negative, we are implying that the applicable model includes an equation "explaining" the disposable personal income of consumers as a function of other variables. In an article by Girshick and Haavelmo,[14] disposable income was treated as a function only of predetermined variables, so that the equation explaining income could be fitted independently by the method of least squares. This did not preclude the possibility that disturbances in this equation were correlated with disturbances in other equations.

A more interesting possibility for present purposes is that disposable income may also be a function of one or more other endogenous variables, such as price and possibly consumption of a given commodity. If this is so, we are immediately confronted with the problem of deriving this equation simultaneously with the demand function (and also with a supply function if the consumption variable is not wholly or approximately predetermined). This alternative should be kept in mind during the following discussion.

First, if the commodity in question is relatively unimportant—that is, if total expenditures for it are very small relative to the national income—even relatively large (percentage) gyrations in the value of the commodity can have little effect on the level of aggregate consumer income.

Pork, beef, and fluid milk are the three most important farm food products in terms of retail value. Expenditures for each of these products are equivalent to 2 or 3% of disposable personal income. It is difficult to see how variations in the supply of one of these commodities, operating chiefly through the coefficients of consumer demand functions, could account for more than 2 or

---

[14] M. A. Girshick and T. Haavelmo, "Statistical Analysis of the Demand for Food: Examples of Simultaneous Estimation of Structural Equations," *Econometrica* **15**, pp. 79–111 (April 1947).

3% of the total variation in disposable income. In fact, since the bulk of the variation in disposable income is usually attributed to changes in investment and government expenditures, the 2 or 3% figure is almost certainly too high.

Various factors may be cited in support of this proposition. Among these are the relative stability of agricultural production, especially that of livestock products, and the apparently limited degree of competition (in demand) among major farm products on a short-run or year-to-year basis. The fact that consumer demand elasticities for pork and beef are between -0.5 and -1.0 tends to restrict the income effects which might otherwise flow from these commodities. It seems doubtful therefore that "feedback effects" on disposable income resulting from variations in the price of pork, beef, or fluid milk would stand out above the errors of measurement in the published disposable income series, even if the latter were assessed at not more than 1% of the observed variance. If this conclusion is justified with respect to the major foods and farm products, it applies even more strongly to the minor ones.

In the preceding paragraphs we have rejected on intuitive grounds the hypothesis that an equation expressing the generation of consumer income must be fitted simultaneously with the consumer demand function. This hypothesis can also be treated formally.

If disposable income y is determined jointly with the price of the given commodity p_1 we may write our structural equations as follows:

(11.45)   *Demand:* $p_1 = cy + bq_1 + u$ or $p_1 - cy = (bq_1 + u)$

(11.46)   *Income:* $y = \gamma p_1 + \delta z + v$ or $y - \gamma p_1 = (\delta z + v)$

where q_1 is (predetermined) consumption of the given commodity and z is an aggregate of all the predetermined elements in disposable income. We wish to test the hypothesis that y is an endogenous variable which must be estimated simultaneously with p_1. If this is true, y is not independent of u, and (11.45) is not a uniequational complete model.

Applying Cramer's rule, we solve for p_1 and y as functions of q_1, z, u, and v, obtaining the reduced form equations

(11.47) $$p_1 = \left(\frac{b}{1 - \gamma c}\right)q_1 + \left(\frac{c\delta}{1 - \gamma c}\right)z + \left(\frac{u + cv}{1 - \gamma c}\right)$$

and

(11.48) $$y = \left(\frac{\gamma b}{1 - \gamma c}\right)q_1 + \left(\frac{\delta}{1 - \gamma c}\right)z + \left(\frac{\gamma u + v}{1 - \gamma c}\right)$$

Each of these equations may be fitted separately by the method of least squares. An estimate of the structural coefficient γ is then derived by dividing the coefficient of q_1 in (11.48) by the corresponding coefficient in (11.47).

The latter regression coefficient (of p_1 upon q_1) will be statistically significant in most analyses for farm and food products. But it seems quite unlikely that the regression of y upon q_1 will be significantly different from zero for any commodity which absorbs (say) 3% or less of disposable income. Therefore, the estimate of γ will also be nonsignificant, and we may assume $\gamma = 0$ without serious loss of statistical accuracy.

If $\gamma = 0$, the reduced-form equations become

(11.49) $$p_1 = bq_1 + c\delta z + (cv + u)$$

(11.50) $$y = \delta z + v$$

The structural coefficient b is estimated without significant bias in the least squares fitting of (11.49). The coefficient c might still be estimated as the ratio $c\delta/\delta$. However, if y is very highly correlated with z, the regression of p_1 upon y in a least squares fitting of (11.45) will give a value of c not materially different from the foregoing ratio.

For these reasons, it appears safe to ignore (11.46) in demand analyses for individual foods and to take a least squares fitting of (11.45) as an estimate of the structural demand function (assuming that q_1 is predetermined).

11.2.3 Applications to Pork and Beef

The complication which seems most likely in estimating demand functions for food livestock products is the existence of a simultaneous supply function. Suppose that consumption *is* determined simultaneously with price. Then the two structural equations are identical with (11.17) and (11.18) except for the addition of disturbance terms u and v:

(11.51)   *Demand:* $Q = a_1 + b_1P + c_1Y + u$

(11.52)   *Supply:* $Q = a_2 + b_2P + c_2Z + v$

where P is retail price, Q is consumption, Y is disposable consumer income, and Z is an estimate of production based wholly on exogenous and predetermined variables.[15] If the variables are in logarithmic form, b_1 is the elasticity of consumer demand and b_2 is the elasticity of producer supply.

We have noted before that these equations form a just-identified model. The corresponding reduced-form equations may be written precisely as in (11.21) and (11.22). The only difference is that Z stands for another variable now but with the same statistical properties as the Z of our hypothetical example.

---

[15] The author chose this procedure on logical grounds in 1951 or 1952. This is also the basic principle of two-stage least squares estimation, to be described later in this chapter.

Table 11.1 Basic Data for "Just-Identified" Model of Supply and Demand for Pork, United States, 1922–1941

| Year, T | Original Arithmetic Values | | | | Logarithms | | | | First Differences of Logarithms | | | |
	Retail Price of Pork, P_t, Cents per lb	Consumption of Pork, Q_t, Pounds per lb	Disposable Personal Income, Y_t, Dollars per lb	"Predetermined Elements in Pork Production," Z_t, Pounds per lb	P_t	Q_t	Y_t	Z_t	P_t	Q_t	Y_t	Z_t
1922	26.8	65.7	541	74.0	1.428	1.818	2.733	1.869	—	—	—	—
1923	25.3	74.2	616	84.7	1.403	1.870	2.790	1.928	-0.025	0.052	0.057	0.059
1924	25.3	74.0	610	80.2	1.403	1.869	2.785	1.904	0.000	-0.001	-0.005	-0.024
1925	31.1	66.8	636	69.9	1.493	1.825	2.803	1.844	0.090	-0.044	0.018	-0.060
1926	33.3	64.1	651	66.8	1.522	1.807	2.814	1.825	0.029	-0.018	0.011	-0.019
1927	31.2	67.7	645	71.6	1.494	1.831	2.810	1.855	-0.028	0.024	-0.004	0.030
1928	29.5	70.9	653	73.6	1.470	1.851	2.815	1.867	-0.024	0.020	0.005	0.012
1929	30.3	69.6	682	71.2	1.481	1.843	2.834	1.852	0.011	-0.008	0.019	-0.015
1930	29.1	67.0	604	69.6	1.464	1.826	2.781	1.843	-0.017	-0.017	-0.053	-0.009
1931	23.7	68.4	515	68.0	1.375	1.835	2.712	1.833	-0.089	0.009	-0.069	-0.010
1932	15.6	70.7	390	74.8	1.193	1.849	2.591	1.874	-0.182	0.014	-0.121	0.041
1933	13.9	69.6[a]	364	73.6[b]	1.143	1.843	2.561	1.867	-0.050	-0.006	-0.030	-0.007
1934	18.8	63.1[a]	411	70.2[b]	1.274	1.800	2.614	1.846	0.131	-0.043	0.053	-0.021
1935	27.4	48.4	459	46.5	1.438	1.685	2.662	1.667	0.164	-0.115	0.048	-0.179
1936	26.9	55.1	517	57.6	1.430	1.741	2.713	1.760	-0.008	0.056	0.051	0.093
1937	27.7	55.8	551	58.7	1.442	1.747	2.741	1.769	0.012	0.006	0.028	0.009
1938	24.5	58.2	506	58.0	1.389	1.765	2.704	1.763	-0.053	0.018	-0.037	-0.006
1939	22.2	64.7	538	67.2	1.346	1.811	2.731	1.827	-0.043	0.046	0.027	0.064
1940	19.3	73.5	576	73.7	1.286	1.866	2.760	1.867	-0.060	0.055	0.029	0.040
1941	24.7	68.4	697	66.5	1.393	1.835	2.843	1.823	0.107	-0.031	0.083	-0.044

[a] Excludes quantities purchased and distributed under government emergency programs. Per capita consumption including these ... as 70.7 pounds in 1933 and 64.4 pounds in 1934.

Table 11.1 provides data for four time series relating to pork which meet the requirements of the foregoing model.

Since no new *statistical* calculations are involved in the just-identified instance, we shall present only the final equations obtained in an attempt to derive simultaneous demand and supply equations for pork. The same symbols are used as in (11.34) and (11.35); the basic data were first difference of logarithms of annual observations for the period 1922–1941 (see Table 11.1).

The reduced-form equations are

$$\hat{P} = -0.0101 + 1.0813\,Y - 0.8320Z \qquad R^2 = 0.893$$
$$\phantom{\hat{P} = -0.0101 +} (0.1339) \quad\;\; (0.1159)$$

$$\hat{Q} = 0.0026 - 0.0018\,Y + 0.6839Z \qquad R^2 = 0.898$$
$$\phantom{\hat{Q} = 0.0026 -} (0.0673) \quad\;\; (0.0582)$$

The numbers in parentheses are standard errors of the net regression coefficients. The coefficients of the structural equations are calculated as follows:

$$b_2 = \frac{-0.0018}{1.0813} = -0.0017$$

$$b_1 = \frac{0.6839}{-0.8320} = -0.8220$$

$$c_1 = 1.0813\{-[-0.8220 - (-0.0017)]\} = 1.0813(0.8203) = 0.8870$$

$$c_2 = -0.8320(-0.8203) = 0.6825$$

To compute the constant terms a_1 and a_2, we solve the following two simultaneous equations:

$$0.0017a_2 - 0.0017a_1 = (-0.0108)(-0.8203)(0.0017) = 0.0000$$

$$-0.8220a_2 - (-0.0017)a_1 = (0.0026)(-0.8203) = -0.0021$$

Adding the two equations, we obtain

$$-0.8203a_2 = -0.0021 + (0.0017)(0.0089) = -0.0021$$

$$a_2 = \frac{-0.0021}{-0.8203} = 0.0026$$

Then substituting $a_2 = 0.0026$ into the first equation divided by 0.0017, we have $0.0026 - a_1 = 0.0089$, or $a_1 = -0.0063$. This completes the set of coefficients for the two structural equations. Consequently, the structural equations can be written as follows:

Demand function: $Q = -0.0063 - 0.8220P + 0.8870\,Y + u$

Supply function: $Q = 0.0026 - 0.0017P + 0.6825Z + v$

Because the data were in logarithmic form, the coefficients represent *approximately* the percentage changes in Q associated with changes of 1% in each of the other variables. In particular, the coefficients of P are estimates of the elasticities of demand and (simultaneous or concurrent) supply for pork. Although standard errors of the structural coefficients are not presented here, such errors (appropriate for large samples) can be computed.

For each observation values of u and v are computed from the following forms of the last two equations:

$$u_t = Q_t + 0.0063 + 0.8220P_t - 0.8870Y_t$$

$$v_t = Q_t - 0.0026 + 0.0017P_t - 0.6825Z_t$$

The subscript t simply refers to the particular year for which the disturbances are being calculated. The von Neumann ratios for the disturbances prove to be

Demand function: $\quad \delta = \left(\dfrac{0.008017}{0.003553}\right)\left(\dfrac{19}{18}\right)$

$$= 2.256403(1.055556) \doteq 2.381760$$

Supply function: $\quad \delta = \left(\dfrac{0.007122}{0.003181}\right)\left(\dfrac{19}{18}\right)$

$$= 2.238919(1.055556) = 2.363304$$

Referring to Tables 6.5 and 11.2 for $N = 19$ observations, we find no evidence of significant autocorrelation in either set of disturbances.

It is interesting to compare the equations just derived with their least squares counterparts. The demand function for pork has been fitted by least squares in two different ways. When Q is treated as the dependent variable we obtain

Least squares: $\quad \hat{Q} = -0.0049 - 0.7205P + 0.7646Y \qquad R^2 = 0.903$
$$\qquad\qquad\qquad (0.0594) \quad (0.0967)$$

Structural: $\quad Q = -0.0063 - 0.8220P + 0.8870Y + u$

When P is treated as the independent variable, we obtain

Least squares: $\quad \hat{P} = -0.0070 - 1.2518Q + 1.0754Y \qquad R^2 = 0.956$
$$\qquad\qquad\qquad (0.1032) \quad (0.0861)$$

For easier comparison, we divide all terms in the structural demand equation by the coefficient of P (using the positive sign) and transpose P and Q to opposite sides of the equality sign, obtaining

Structural: $\quad P = -0.0077 - 1.2165Q + 1.0791Y + \left(\dfrac{u}{0.8220}\right)$

Table 11.2   Disturbances Computed from Structural Equations

Year	Disturbances in Demand Function		Disturbances in Supply Function	
	u_t	$u_{t+1} - u_t$	v_t	$v_{t+1} - v_t$
1923	−0.013	−	0.009	−
1924	0.010	0.023	0.013	0.004
1925	0.020	0.010	−0.005	−0.018
1926	0.002	−0.018	−0.008	−0.003
1927	0.011	0.009	0.001	0.009
1928	0.002	−0.009	0.009	0.008
1929	−0.010	−0.012	0.000	−0.009
1930	0.022	0.032	−0.014	−0.014
1931	0.003	−0.019	0.013	0.027
1932	−0.022	−0.025	−0.017	−0.030
1933	−0.014	0.008	−0.004	0.013
1934	0.024	0.038	−0.031	−0.027
1935	−0.016	−0.040	0.005	0.036
1936	0.010	0.026	−0.010	−0.015
1937	−0.003	−0.013	−0.003	0.007
1938	0.014	0.017	0.019	0.022
1939	−0.007	−0.021	0.000	−0.019
1940	−0.014	−0.007	0.025	0.025
1941	−0.010	0.004	−0.003	−0.028

The coefficients of the last two equations are almost identical—they differ by small fractions of one standard error. Evidently the least squares equation with price dependent gives an excellent approximation to the structural demand function. And the logic of the simultaneous equations approach supports the choice of price as the dependent variable in our least squares demand function *if* there is no simultaneous response of supply to price.

The corresponding comparison for the supply function (with Q dependent in the least squares equation) is

Least squares: $Q = 0.0022 - 0.0788P + 0.6090Z$ $R^2 = 0.910$
$$(0.0522)   (0.0734)$$

Structural: $Q = 0.0026 - 0.0017P + 0.6825Z + v$

The coefficient of P in the least squares supply function is nonsignificant according to the usual criteria and has a negative sign, whereas normally we would expect a true supply function to show a positive response of quantity to price.

If we discard the price variable from the least squares supply function as nonsignificant, we obtain simply

$$\textit{Least squares:} \quad Q = 0.0025 + 0.6841Z \qquad R^2 = 0.898$$
$$(0.0857)$$

This is almost identical with the structural equation, recognizing that the coefficient of P in the latter is negligibly small and would prove to be statistically nonsignificant if its standard error were calculated.

In the simple two-equation model for pork the similarity of the least squares demand function to the corresponding structural equation has both theoretical and statistical explanations. First, 90% or more of the variation in pork *production* was attributable either to variables which were predetermined as of January 1 or to exogenous factors, such as the effects of weather and disease upon the number of pigs saved per litter. Under 1922–1941 conditions, most hogs were marketed at the age of eight or nine months; the gestation period for pigs is about four months. With this built-in lag of 12 or 13 months between sow breeding and hog slaughter (equals pork production), hog producers had very little latitude to change the *current* year's production in response to the current year's price of pork or hogs. Hence there was little reason to expect a significant net regression coefficient between the current price of pork and the current quantity of pork in the supply equation. Actually, this structural coefficient was nonsignificant, being based on a nonsignificant coefficient in the reduced form of the model. Moreover, as already noted, the structural coefficient was negative, whereas one would ordinarily expect an increase in price to induce an increase in supply.

If we discard P from the supply equation as nonsignificant, we are left with the least squares equation

$$Q = 0.0025 + 0.6841Z$$
$$(0.0857)$$

as a basis for estimating current pork consumption from a composite of predetermined factors affecting the production of pork. This new estimating equation also helps to explain why the least squares demand function is so much like its structural counterpart. For if 90% of the variation in Q is associated with a predetermined variable its statistical properties will be very similar to those of a predetermined variable.

Applying this argument, our least squares demand equation fitted with price, for the dependent variable is roughly consistent with the theory underlying the simultaneous equations method.

Simultaneous Equations Methods for "Overidentified" Models. The basic problem of *overidentification* can be illustrated in a two-equation demand and supply model for beef. The structural equations are assumed to be

(11.53)   *Demand:* $Q = a_1 + b_1 P + c_1 Y + d_1 W + u$

(11.54)   *Supply:* $Q = a_2 + b_2 P + c_2 Z + v$

where Z is an estimate of beef production based on wholly predetermined variables and W is consumption of other meats, assumed predetermined for present purposes. The reduced form of this model is

$$(11.55) \quad P = \left(\frac{a_2 - a_1}{b_1 - b_2}\right) - \left(\frac{c_1}{b_1 - b_2}\right)Y + \left(\frac{c_2}{b_1 - b_2}\right)Z$$

$$- \left(\frac{d_1}{b_1 - b_2}\right)W + \left(\frac{v - u}{b_1 - b_2}\right)$$

$$(11.56) \quad Q = \left(\frac{a_2 b_1 - a_1 b_2}{b_1 - b_2}\right) - \left(\frac{c_1 b_2}{b_1 - b_2}\right)Y + \left(\frac{c_2 b_1}{b_1 - b_2}\right)Z$$

$$- \left(\frac{d_1 b_2}{b_1 - b_2}\right)W + \left(\frac{b_1 v - b_2 u}{b_1 - b_2}\right)$$

We can estimate b_1 as a ratio of the coefficients of Z in the two equations. But b_2 can be estimated in two ways, one as a ratio of the coefficients of Y and the other as a ratio of the coefficients of W. If the two estimates of b_2 differ, we can also obtain different estimates for a_1, a_2, c_1, c_2, and d_1.

The reduced-form equations fitted to logarithms of the variables during 1922–1941 by least squares are as follows, neglecting the constant terms:

$$P = A_1 + 0.8185\,Y - 0.8521Z - 0.4346W + f_1(u, v) \qquad R^2 = 0.87$$
$$\quad\;\; (0.1061) \quad\;\; (0.1877) \quad\;\; (0.1631)$$

$$Q = A_2 + 0.0509\,Y + 0.8801Z - 0.0899W + f_2(u, v) \qquad R^2 = 0.87$$
$$\quad\;\; (0.0545) \quad\;\; (0.0964) \quad\;\; (0.0838)$$

Then $b_1 = 0.8801/-0.8521 = -1.0329$; this is our structural estimate of the elasticity of demand for beef. The two alternative values of b_2 are

$$b_{2(y)} = \frac{0.0509}{0.8185} = 0.0622$$

and

$$b_{2(w)} = \frac{-0.0899}{-0.4346} = 0.2068$$

Some pragmatic comments are also warranted in the present instance. First, neither of the reduced-form coefficients in the numerators of the ratios from which b_2 is calculated differ significantly from zero; one is slightly smaller than its standard error and the other is only slightly larger. Starting from such unpromising materials it seems likely that any compromise estimate of b_2, which must be analogous to a weighted average of $b_{2(y)}$ and $b_{2(w)}$, will also be nonsignificant. If we discard Y and W from the second reduced-form equation, we obtain a least squares estimate of Q as a function of the composite predetermined variable Z:

$$Q = A'_2 + 0.8878Z + f'_2(u, v) \qquad r^2 = 0.85$$
$$(0.0900)$$

If we estimate c_1 and d_1 on the assumption that $b_2 = 0$, we obtain

$$c_1 = -(0.8185)(-1.0329) = 0.8454$$

and

$$d_1 = -(0.4346)(-1.0329) = -0.4489$$

Our structural demand function would then be

$$Q = a'_1 - 1.0329P + 0.8454\,Y - 0.4489W + u$$

Transposing P and Q and dividing through by the coefficient of P, the structural equation becomes

$$P = a''_1 - 0.9682Q + 0.8185\,Y - 0.4346W + u'$$

The same variables fitted by least squares with P in the dependent position give the following result:

$$\hat{P} = a'''_1 - 1.0645Q + 0.8815\,Y - 0.5247W \qquad R^2 = 0.95$$
$$(0.1179) \quad (0.0620) \quad (0.0887)$$

The respective coefficients differ by about one standard error in each instance, or about 0.7 standard error of their differences *if* the regressions had been fitted to two random samples from the same universe. The similarities between the two equations can be rationalized on the same basis as for pork.[16]

---

[16] The structural equations for the beef model have been estimated by Joan Friedman, using the simultaneous equations method theoretically appropriate in the overidentified case. The equations, with standard errors of the respective coefficients, are

$$\text{Demand:} \quad P = a''_1 - 0.97Q + 0.89\,Y - 0.47W$$
$$(0.24) \quad (0.13) \quad (0.18)$$

$$\text{Supply:} \quad Q = a''_2 + 0.09P + 0.94Z$$
$$(0.06) \quad (0.11)$$

As expected, the coefficient of P in the supply function was nonsignificant. All other coefficients of the least squares counterpart equations differed from corresponding coefficients of the limited information equations by much less than one standard error of the latter coefficients.

In concluding this section, we should like to make one point which would suggest to experienced price analysts some of the difficulties to be expected in the measurement of simultaneous supply functions. Our ability to establish statistically significant coefficients in the subordinate or less influential members of a simultaneous equation model will be limited both by specification and data problems. For example, the reduced-form equation upon which depends our ability to estimate the simultaneous elasticity of supply will frequently take the following form:

$$(11.57) \qquad q = k_0 + k_1 z + k_2 y + v$$

where z is a combination of the predetermined variables underlying commodity production and y is the disposable income of consumers. The statistical significance of b_2, the elasticity of supply, depends on that of k_2—that is, we must show a statistically significant association between the production of a specific commodity and total consumer income *after* the influence of factors directly and obviously affecting commodity production has been eliminated. Since the influence of consumer income upon production operates through the retail price of the commodity and thence, via the marketing system, upon and through its farm price, data, disturbance, and aggregation problems at each of these levels may obscure the relationship between production and income.

The foregoing does not deny the possibility of establishing significant simultaneous supply elasticities for some farm products. It does suggest that the data requirements for the simultaneous equations approach are more exacting than has been commonly realized, and probably more exacting than many of our existing food and agricultural time series can support.

11.3 CAUSAL ORDERING, RECURSIVENESS, AND INTER-DEPENDENCY: A FRAMEWORK FOR CHOOSING METHODS OF ESTIMATION

The preceding section has pointed out a number of reasons why a least squares regression equation gives us good estimates of a consumer demand function in a multiple equation structure *if the structure as a whole possesses certain properties*. One justification advanced for treating consumption as an independent variable was the near-identity of current consumption and current production and the fact that current production was almost wholly determined by a combination of *past* values of economic variables (and current values of exogenous variables such as weather).

A simple time lag would be sufficient to produce identification in the model of (11.58) and (11.59). The original model is, in deviation form,

(11.58)   *Demand:* $p = b_1q + u$

(11.59)   *Supply:* $p = b_2q + v$

where p and q refer to the same time unit. When we introduce time lags we must be careful to designate the time unit to which each price or quantity applies, so we rewrite the model in which p and q are simultaneously determined as

(11.60)   *Demand:* $p_{(t)} = b_1q_{(t)} + u_{(t)}$

(11.61)   *Supply:* $p_{(t)} = b_2q_{(t)} + v_{(t)}$

Suppose that the current supply $q_{(t)}$ is actually determined by last year's price $p_{(t-1)}$. We rewrite the supply equation as

(11.62)   *Supply:* $q_{(t)} = \beta_2 p_{(t-1)} + w_{(t)}$

The following diagram may be helpful in visualizing the operation of the model consisting of (11.60) and (11.61):

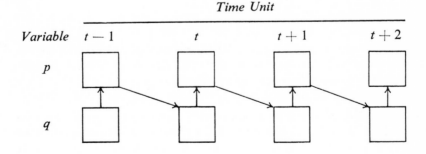

The supply equation is represented by the arrows slanting downward from $p_{(t-1)}$ to $q_{(t)}$, $p_{(t)}$ to $q_{(t+1)}$, and $p_{(t+1)}$ to $q_{(t+2)}$. The demand equation is represented by the vertical arrows leading from $q_{(t)}$ to $p_{(t)}$, $q_{(t+1)}$ to $p_{(t+1)}$, and $q_{(t+2)}$ to $p_{(t+2)}$.

By a slight extension of this diagram we can include every element in the model:

Time Unit

If $w_{(t)}$ is not correlated with $u_{(t)}$, the supply equation can be fitted by least squares with $q_{(t)}$ as the dependent variable, and the demand equation can be separately fitted by least squares with $p_{(t)}$ as the dependent variable.

In one sense our model still includes only two variables, price and quantity. But in a statistical sense it includes *three* variables since $p_{(t-1)}$ is a fixed number, fully determined in period $(t - 1)$ before the opening day of period (t). When used as an independent variable in estimating $q_{(t)}$, $p_{(t-1)}$ is logically equivalent to one of the controlled variables in a regression model based on experimental data. Causality moves forward in time, and the regression of $p_{(t-1)}$ on $q_{(t)}$ would have no explanatory value.

It will be useful to rearrange terms in (11.60) and (11.61) as follows:

$$\text{Supply:} \qquad -\beta_2 p_{(t-1)} + q_{(t)} = w_{(t)}$$

$$\text{Demand:} \qquad -b_1 q_{(t)} + p_{(t)} = u_{(t)}$$

We can also display the elements of these equations in the following form:

$$
\begin{array}{c}
\text{Supply:} \\
\text{Demand:}
\end{array}
\quad
\begin{array}{cccc}
p_{(t-1)} & q_{(t)} & p_{(t)} & \\
\end{array}
\begin{bmatrix}
-\beta_2 & 1 & \\
 & -b_1 & 1
\end{bmatrix}
=
\begin{array}{cc}
w_{(t)} & u_{(t)} \\
\end{array}
\begin{bmatrix}
1 & \\
 & 1
\end{bmatrix}
$$

We can reconstitute the equations simply by multiplying each variable or disturbance by the coefficient or coefficients in the column immediately below it.

If this pattern of coefficients represents the true economic (and statistical) structure of the model, it is clear that neither $p_{(t)}$ nor $u_{(t)}$ enter into the supply function at all. The estimation of the supply function coefficient β_2 is a "private matter" involving only $q_{(t)}$, $p_{(t-1)}$, and $w_{(t)}$.

The value of $q_{(t)}$, then, has also been fully determined by $p_{(t-1)}$ and $w_{(t)}$. We may now regard $q_{(t)}$ as a fixed number and a logically independent variable as we enter it into the demand function. The estimation of the demand function coefficient b_1 becomes a "private matter" involving only $q_{(t)}$, $p_{(t)}$, and $u_{(t)}$.

From the arrow diagrams of this model it is clear that the impacts of $p_{(t-1)}$ on $q_{(t)}$ and of $q_{(t)}$ on $p_{(t)}$ are linked together in a repetitive or recursive causal chain. This kind of model is frequently referred to as a "recursive model" to distinguish it from an "interdependent" or simultaneous model such as that formed by (11.60) and (11.61). The elements of that interdependent model may be displayed as

$$
\begin{array}{c}
\textit{Supply:} \\
\textit{Demand:}
\end{array}
\begin{array}{cc}
q_{(t)} & p_{(t)} \\
\begin{bmatrix} -b_2 & 1 \\ -b_1 & 1 \end{bmatrix}
\end{array}
=
\begin{array}{cc}
v_{(t)} & u_{(t)} \\
\begin{bmatrix} 1 & \\ & 1 \end{bmatrix}
\end{array}
$$

The arrays formed by the coefficients of the endogenous variables $q_{(t)}$ and $p_{(t)}$ are characteristic of recursive models and simultaneous models, respectively. In the recursive model this array or matrix is *triangular*. In a purely recursive model no coefficients of endogenous variables will appear above the major diagonal of this matrix if the equations are arranged in the order of their causal relationships in the model. To the extent that one or more coefficients of endogenous variables appear above the major diagonal we have a simultaneous or interdependent model.

A slightly larger model will help to illustrate the relationship of triangularity to causal ordering, namely the model of Figure 4.14, the supply and demand structure for potatoes. The variables in the model are

$X_1 =$ weather
$X_2 =$ disposable personal income
$X_3 =$ charge for marketing services
$X_4 =$ production
$X_5 =$ consumption (quantity offered for sale by retailers)
$X_6 =$ retail price
$X_7 =$ farm price (current year)
$X_8 = X_{7(t-1)} =$ farm price (previous year)

We regard four of these variables as exogenous (weather, disposable personal income, the charge for marketing services, and farm price in the previous year) and four as endogenous (production, consumption, retail price, and farm price in the current year).

These variables can be grouped into the following equations:

Production: $\qquad\qquad\qquad\qquad\qquad X_4 = f(X_8, X_1) + u_4$

Supply available to consumers: $\qquad\qquad X_5 = f(X_4) + u_5$

Consumer demand: $\qquad\qquad\qquad\quad X_6 = f(X_5, X_2) + u_6$

Relation between farm price and retail price: $\quad X_7 = f(X_6, X_3) + u_7$

Assuming that (1) the functions are linear, (2) the variables are expressed as deviations from their means, and (3) the disturbances u_4, u_5, u_6, and u_7 are not correlated with one another, we may write the model as follows:

$$
\begin{aligned}
x_4 - b_{48}x_8 - b_{41}x_1 &= u_4 \\
x_5 - b_{54}x_4 \qquad\quad &= u_5 \\
x_6 - b_{65}x_5 - b_{62}x_2 &= u_6 \\
x_7 - b_{76}x_6 - b_{73}x_3 &= u_7
\end{aligned}
$$

The elements may be arranged as

Exogenous variables				Endogenous variables				Disturbances			
$(x_8$	x_1	x_2	x_3	x_4	x_5	x_6	$x_7)$	u_4	u_5	u_6	u_7
$-b_{48}$	$-b_{41}$			1				1			
				$-b_{54}$	1				1		
		$-b_{62}$			$-b_{65}$	1				1	
			$-b_{73}$			$-b_{76}$	1				1

The coefficient matrix linking the endogenous variables to one another has no coefficients above the major diagonal; it is therefore triangular and the model is fully recursive. Although we have assumed no correlation among u_4, u_5, u_6, and u_7 it is well to remember (1) that they *could* be correlated in the population and (2) if we could actually measure the disturbances in particular samples as in our constructed example of Chapter 7 we would find that the correlations among them were nonzero and varied from sample to sample. In the remainder of this section we will ignore the disturbance terms and concentrate on the patterns of coefficients between variables.

It is clear that the current value of the four endogenous variables is determined in a certain logical sequence or *causal order* which is reflected

Causal Order

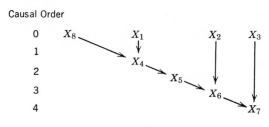

Figure 11.3.

in the triangularity of the coefficient matrix. We can diagram this causal ordering as in Figure 11.3.

We assign the four exogenous variables to Causal Order 0 since they are not determined or caused within the model. They are predetermined given numbers, ready for use in explaining the movements of the endogenous variables.

If any endogenous variable is a function only of exogenous variables we assign it to Causal Order 1. This is true of X_4, production, in the present model, which is determined by X_8, the previous year's farm price, and X_1, weather.

At this point the values of five variables—the four exogenous variables and X_4—are fully determined. No endogenous variable other than X_4 could be determined at Causal Order 1 because no other endogenous variables could be explained exclusively by exogenous variables. However, given X_4, we can now determine the value of X_5; we assign X_5 to Causal Order 2. No other endogenous variable can be determined at Causal Order 2 because the value of X_5 is a prerequisite for the estimation of X_6 and X_7.

The value of X_6 is determined at Causal Order 3; it is a function of X_5 and X_2. Finally, the value of X_7 is determined at Causal Order 4 as a function of X_6 and X_3; X_7 could not have been determined logically at any earlier stage.

If the error terms in the four equations are independent of (uncorrelated with) one another, each equation can be estimated optimally by least squares. If the error terms are not independent of one another, triangularity would justify the following procedure: Regress X_4 on X_1; then, regress X_5 on $\hat{X}_4$, where $\hat{X}_4$ is estimated from the first regression equation; next, regress X_6 upon X_2 and upon $\hat{X}_5$ as estimated from the second sequential regression; and, finally, regress X_7 upon X_3 and upon $\hat{X}_6$ as estimated from the third sequential regression.

Since $\hat{X}_4$, $\hat{X}_5$, and $\hat{X}_6$ are exact functions of the exogenous variables, they are independent of the error terms and are suitable regressors for the successive least squares equations. This sequential procedure based on causal ordering is logically very close to two-stage least squares which will be discussed later in this chapter.

The concepts of a "basic model" and a "derived model" also throw some light on the nature of interdependence in economic models. We may conceive of a complete model incorporating explicitly all the actions of each and every individual economic agent—thus a model pushing the disaggregation process over subjects and goods to its ultimate microlimit—and in which time is introduced in such a way that periods are sufficiently short to correspond to the actions of the subjects. Let us call this a "basic model." This type is always recursive. Each subject acts on the basis of information acquired in or before time $t - 1$, before the moment of his action at time t. His action as known to others, or, as it affects the economic environments of others, becomes part of the information which other subjects use in deciding on their own actions in time $t + 1$ or later.

A derived model, in contrast to a basic model, is an aggregated and gross approximation of reality. The availability of data often determines the unit of time selected as well as the degree of aggregation, introducing essentially arbitrary elements into the model. These elements may be responsible for the interdependent nature of many derived models.

Two examples may suffice to clarify this last point. First, many published time series are available only on a quarterly basis or even an annual basis. Time lags between the plans and the actions of economic subjects and between the actions and their effects on other variables in the system do not correspond to the temporal breakdown of the time series. In most instances, the basic lags are of a shorter duration than the minimum time span between successive observations in the statistical time series. If this is true, interdependency may appear in the derived model simply as a consequence of data limitations. The longer the unit of time in the derived model, the more "simultaneous" relationships will be found in it which in fact were not simultaneously determined since they took place at different points in time within the unit specified by the model.

For example, suppose the basic model of interaction between consumers and retail food stores is

$$\textit{Consumer demand:} \quad q_{(t)} = b_1 p_{(t)} + u_{(t)}$$

$$\textit{Retailers' supply:} \quad q_{(t)} = b_2 p_{(t-1)} + w_{(t)}$$

We assume that each week retailers offer consumers a definite supply $q_{(t)}$, and the average price for the week $p_{(t)}$ seeks the level necessary to move the quantity $q_{(t)}$ into consumption. Toward the end of week (t) retailers decide on the basis of $p_{(t)}$ how large a supply $q_{(t+1)}$ they will order from wholesalers and offer for sale to consumers in week $(t + 1)$. This quantity moves into consumption at the price $p_{(t+1)}$.

If this weekly response mechanism operated throughout the year, then from week 52 in year 0 to week 52 in year 1 there would have been 52 supply responses, each relating $q_{(t)}$ to $p_{(t-1)}$ according to the coefficient b_2 and 52 price adjustments along the consumer demand curve, each relating $p_{(t)}$ to $q_{(t)}$ according to the coefficient b_1. The annual or even quarterly observations on $p_{(t)}$ and $q_{(t)}$ would present us with a serious problem of interdependence and identification. However, using weekly data we could estimate b_1 and b_2, the structural coefficients of the basic behavioral model, quite readily.

A second kind of interdependency in the derived model when none existed in the basic model could follow from some types of aggregation procedures. If four variables are causally related so that A causes B which in turn is the cause of C which causes D, grouping together, respectively, A and C in variable I and B and D in variable II introduces interdependency between I and II where the original (basic) system was recursive.

Although the logical arguments for recursiveness are very strong as far as basic models are concerned, we are nevertheless often faced with the practical problem of constructing important economic models from annual or quarterly data. Whatever the cause of interdependency in these relatively gross time units, we must nevertheless take it into account in our estimation procedures and/or by drawing on other sources of information than the annual or quarterly time series.

In Section 11.4 we will deal with one of the several techniques which have been devised for estimating the structural coefficients of interdependent equations directly from the data. The straightforward logic and computational simplicity of the method of two-stage least squares makes it a useful introduction to the more complicated methods which are described in Chapter 12.

11.4 TWO-STAGE LEAST SQUARES AND THE ESTIMATION OF INTERDEPENDENT EQUATIONS

Given the same demand and supply model for pork as before, including random disturbances u and v,

(11.63)   *Demand:* $Q = a_1 + b_1 P + c_1 Y + u$

(11.64)   *Supply:* $Q = a_2 + b_2 P + c_2 Z + v$

we can demonstrate the method of two-stage least squares.

We assume that P and Q are jointly dependent endogenous variables and that Y and Z are exogenous variables. By hypothesis, the disturbances in the two structural equations are not correlated with Y and Z.

Consider the corresponding reduced-form equations, including disturbance terms which are combinations of the structural disturbances, u and v:

$$(11.65) \qquad P = A_1 + B_1 Y + C_1 Z + \frac{v - u}{b_1 - b_2}$$

$$(11.66) \qquad Q = A_2 + B_2 Y + C_2 Z + \frac{b_1 v - b_2 u}{b_1 - b_2}$$

If we fit (11.65) by least squares, we obtain a series of estimated values of P, namely $\hat{P}$, which are exact linear functions of Y and Z. If u and v are uncorrelated with Y and Z, exact linear combinations of u and v should be uncorrelated with exact linear combinations of Y and Z. The disturbance term in (11.65) is just such a function of u and v; it should therefore be uncorrelated with $\hat{P}$.

The method of least squares applied to (11.65) produces this result in the particular set of data which constitutes our sample. The hypotheses about zero correlations in the preceding two paragraphs relate to the parent population—hence to the *expected values* of correlation coefficients rather than to their values in individual samples. Just as the standard error of estimate in a single-equation least squares model is only an estimate of the standard error in the population, so the residual variance about $\hat{P} = A_1 + B_1 Y + C_1 Z$ is only an estimate of the variance of $[1/(b_1 - b_2)](v - u)$ in the population underlying our two-equation model.

The same reasoning applies in (11.66) to the least squares residuals $Q - \hat{Q}$. Let us call the two series of reduced-form residuals or disturbances D_1 and D_2. Knowing that $D_1 = (v - u)/(b_1 - b_2)$ and $D_2 = (b_1 v - b_2 u)/(b_1 - b_2)$, we can derive estimates of the structural disturbances u and v as follows:

From the equations defining D_1 and D_2 we write

$$(11.67) \qquad v - u = (b_1 - b_2)D_1$$

$$(11.68) \qquad b_1 v - b_2 u = (b_1 - b_2)D_2$$

We then multiply both sides of the first equation by $(-b_2)$ obtaining

$$(11.69) \qquad -b_2 v + b_2 u = -b_2(b_1 - b_2)D_1$$

Adding (11.69) and (11.68) we obtain

$$(b_1 - b_2)v = (b_1 - b_2)(D_2 - b_2 D_1)$$

therefore

$$v = D_2 - b_2 D_1$$

Then since $(v - u) = (b_1 - b_2)D_1$, we have $u = v - (b_1 - b_2)D_1$. For each observation on the variables P, Q, Y, and Z, D_1 and D_2 will be known numbers; b_1 and b_2 will also be known numbers, so numerical estimates of u and v can be calculated readily.

The first stage of two-stage least squares consists of fitting each reduced-form equation by least squares. In the pork example, we obtain the reduced-form equations previously cited:

(11.70) $\hat{P} = -0.0101 + 1.0813\,Y - 0.8320Z \qquad R^2 = 0.893$
$\qquad\qquad\quad (0.1339) \quad (0.1159)$

(11.71) $\hat{Q} = 0.0026 - 0.0018\,Y + 0.6839Z \qquad R^2 = 0.898$
$\qquad\qquad\quad (0.0673) \quad (0.0582)$

The second "stage" of two-stage least squares is equally simple. In the structural demand function we replace P by $\hat{P}$ and fit the resulting equation $Q = f(\hat{P}, Y)$ by least squares. In the structural supply function we replace P by $\hat{P}$ and fit the resulting equation $Q = f(\hat{P}, Z)$ by least squares.

There is a certain ambiguity in the second stage, for we could also transpose P to the left side of (11.63) and (11.64), obtaining

(11.72) $\qquad Demand:\quad P = -\dfrac{a_1}{b_1} + \dfrac{1}{b_1}Q - \dfrac{c_1}{b_1}Y + \dfrac{1}{b_1}u$

(11.73) $\qquad Supply:\quad P = -\dfrac{a_2}{b_2} + \dfrac{1}{b_2}Q - \dfrac{c_2}{b_1}Z + \dfrac{1}{b_2}v$

In each of these equations we could replace Q by $\hat{Q}$, and fit each of the equations $P = f(\hat{Q}, Y)$ and $P = f(\hat{Q}, Z)$ by least squares. Or we could take P as dependent in the demand function and Q as dependent in the supply function—or Q dependent in the demand function and P dependent in the supply function.

It is a simple matter to run all these alternatives on an electronic computer. The cases are the following.

Case I
   Demand: $Q = -0.0057 - 0.8221\hat{P} + 0.8854\,Y + u;$
$\qquad\qquad\quad (0.0033) \quad (0.0695) \qquad (0.1067)$
$\qquad\qquad\qquad\qquad\qquad\qquad\qquad R^2 = 0.8991; \quad \bar{S} = 0.0140$

   Supply: $Q = 0.0025 - 0.0022\hat{P} + 0.6820Z + v;$
$\qquad\qquad\quad (0.0033) \quad (0.0623) \quad (0.0829)$
$\qquad\qquad\qquad\qquad\qquad\qquad\qquad R^2 = 0.8977; \quad \bar{S} = 0.0141$

Case II
   Demand: $P = -0.0069 - 1.2164\hat{Q} + 1.0763\,Y - \dfrac{u'}{b'_1};$
$\qquad\qquad\quad (0.0065) \quad (0.1698) \qquad (0.1342)$
$\qquad\qquad\qquad\qquad\qquad\qquad\qquad R^2 = 0.8930; \quad \bar{S} = 0.0282$

Supply: $P = 0.0025 - 96.3080\hat{Q} + 64.9210Z - \dfrac{v'}{b'_2};$
         (0.0011) (39.7828) (27.2116)

$$R^2 = 0.6033; \quad \bar{S} = 0.0543$$

Case III

Demand: $P = -0.0069 - 1.2164\hat{Q} + 1.0763Y - \dfrac{u'}{b'_1};$
         (0.0065) (0.1698) (0.1342)

$$R^2 = 0.8930; \quad \bar{S} = 0.0282$$

Supply: $Q = -0.0025 - 0.0022\hat{P} + 0.6820Z + v;$
         (0.0033) (0.0623) (0.0829)

$$R^2 = 0.8977; \quad \bar{S} = 0.0141$$

Case IV

Demand: $Q = -0.0057 - 0.8221\hat{P} + 0.8854Y + u;$
         (0.0033) (0.0695) (0.1067)

$$R^2 = 0.8991; \quad \bar{S} = 0.0140$$

Supply: $P = 0.0025 - 96.3080\hat{Q} + 64.9210Z - \dfrac{v'}{b'_2};$
         (0.0011) (39.7828) (27.2116)

$$R^2 = 0.6033; \quad \bar{S} = 0.0543$$

If our objective is still to arrive at unique estimates of coefficients of reversible demand curves and supply curves, it is reasonable to divide through each of the equations which was fitted with P in the dependent position by the coefficient of $\hat{Q}$, obtaining equations with $\hat{Q}$ on the left-hand side. We know that the least squares net regression of Q on P does not exactly equal the reciprocal of the least squares net regression of P on Q. Although we are not yet sure of the properties of $\hat{Q}$ as an "independent" variable, we write the disturbances of equations fitted with P in the dependent position as $(-u'/b'_1)$ and $(-v'/b'_2)$ to allow for the possibility that $b'_1 \neq b_1$, $b'_2 \neq b_2$, $u' \neq u$, and $v' \neq v$.

For easy comparison, the two estimates of the demand curve are shown directly above one another:

Demand: $Q = -0.0057 - 0.8221\hat{P} + 0.8854Y + u$
        $\hat{Q} = -0.0057 - 0.8221P + 0.8848Y + u'$

Supply: $Q = 0.0025 - 0.0022\hat{P} + 0.6820Z + v$
        $\hat{Q} = 0.0026 - 0.0104P + 0.6741Z + v'$

Table 11.3 Two-Stage Least Squares: Comparison of Disturbances Computed in Alternative Manners (Pork Example)

Year	Disturbances in Demand Functions		Disturbances in Supply Functions	
	u	u'	v	v'
1923	0.013	0.013	0.009	0.009
1924	0.009	0.009	0.013	0.013
1925	0.020	0.020	−0.005	−0.005
1926	0.002	0.002	−0.007	−0.008
1927	0.010	0.010	0.001	0.001
1928	0.002	0.002	0.009	0.009
1929	−0.010	−0.010	0.000	0.000
1930	0.022	0.021	−0.013	−0.014
1931	0.003	0.002	0.013	0.012
1932	−0.023	−0.023	−0.017	−0.018
1933	0.015	0.015	−0.004	−0.004
1934	0.023	0.024	−0.031	−0.030
1935	−0.017	−0.017	0.005	0.005
1936	0.010	0.010	−0.010	−0.009
1937	−0.003	−0.003	−0.003	−0.003
1938	0.013	0.013	0.019	0.019
1939	−0.008	−0.007	0.000	0.000
1940	−0.014	−0.014	0.025	0.025
1941	−0.011	−0.011	−0.003	−0.003

The estimated structural disturbances u and u' are almost identical with each other and with those computed in Table 11.2; v and v' are also nearly identical with each other and with those computed in Table 11.2.

Table 11.3 presents the comparison of estimated structural disturbances, u and u', v and v'.

For the four cases outlined, the following presents the correlation matrices of the disturbances.

Case I
$$\begin{array}{c c} & \begin{array}{cc} u & v \end{array} \\ \begin{array}{c} u \\ v \end{array} & \begin{bmatrix} 1.0000 & \\ -0.2889 & 1.0000 \end{bmatrix} \end{array}$$

Case II
$$\begin{array}{c c} & \begin{array}{cc} u' & v' \end{array} \\ \begin{array}{c} u' \\ v' \end{array} & \begin{bmatrix} 1.0000 & \\ -0.2896 & 1.0000 \end{bmatrix} \end{array}$$

$$\begin{array}{cc} & u' \qquad\qquad v \end{array}$$

Case III
$$\begin{array}{c} u' \\ v \end{array} \begin{bmatrix} 1.0000 & \\ -0.2989 & 1.0000 \end{bmatrix}$$

$$\begin{array}{cc} & u \qquad\qquad v' \end{array}$$

Case IV
$$\begin{array}{c} u \\ v' \end{array} \begin{bmatrix} 1.0000 & \\ -0.2805 & 1.0000 \end{bmatrix}$$

The correlation matrix of P, Q, $\hat{P}$, $\hat{Q}$, Y, and Z is also of interest:

	P	Q	$\hat{P}$	$\hat{Q}$	Y	Z
P	1.0000					
Q	−0.7247	1.0000				
$\hat{P}$	0.9458	−0.6816	1.0000			
$\hat{Q}$	−0.6803	0.9475	−0.7209	1.0000		
Y	0.7414	−0.1248	0.7837	−0.1346	1.0000	
Z	−0.6772	0.9474	−0.7173	0.9999	−0.1294	1.0000

Interpretation of the Results. Some peculiarities of the present example follow:

1. Since Q is highly correlated with $Z(r_{QZ} = 0.9474; r_{QZ}{}^2 = 0.8976)$ and is almost negligibly correlated with $Y(r_{QY} = -0.1248; r_{QY}{}^2 = 0.0156)$, $\hat{Q} = f(Y, Z)$ proves to be very nearly an exact linear function of $Z(r_{\hat{Q}Z} = 0.9999)$; Y has almost no effect on $\hat{Q}$.

In the second-stage calculations, $\hat{Q}$ is virtually an alias for Z, except that the standard deviations are different, $s_{\hat{Q}} = 0.03948$ and $s_Z = 0.05772$. If we multiply the regression coefficient of P on Z in the reduced form by $(s_Z/s_{\hat{Q}}) = 1.46$ we obtain $-0.8320Z(1.46) = -1.2147\hat{Q}$, almost identical with the regression coefficient of P on $\hat{Q}$ in the second stage or structural demand function of Case II.

2. And there is very little intercorrelation between Y and Z $(r_{YZ} = -0.1294; r_{YZ}{}^2 = 0.0167)$ so the effects of Y and Z on P are essentially independent and additive.

3. It appears that the pork demand and supply model is almost purely recursive. In Case III form, the model can be displayed as

$$\begin{array}{ccccc} Z & Y & \hat{Q} & \hat{P} & a \end{array}$$
$$\begin{bmatrix} -0.6820 & & 1 & 0.0022 \\ & -1.0763 & 1.2164 & 1 \end{bmatrix} + \begin{bmatrix} 0.0025 \\ 0.0069 \end{bmatrix} = \begin{bmatrix} 0 \\ 0 \end{bmatrix}$$

The coefficient above the diagonal (0.0022) is negligibly small and statistically nonsignificant.

Since our example is so nearly recursive, two-stage least squares has not improved on or significantly changed the results of ordinary least squares. On the positive side, however, two-stage least squares has given us sound results for the demand function—results almost identical with, and therefore as good as, ordinary least squares.

4. When the second-stage supply function was fitted with $\hat{Q}$ and Z as independent variables we encountered an extreme instance of multicollinearity. It is clear that two-stage least squares is as vulnerable to high intercorrelation among the exogenous variables as is single-stage least squares. We shall see shortly that the second-stage estimation procedure is more vulnerable than the first, for the second stage used variables such as $\hat{Q}$ and $\hat{P}$, which are exact linear functions of the exogenous variables, as independent variables alongside of certain of the exogenous variables. Although extremes such as the $\hat{Q}$ and Z intercorrelation may be rare, the possibility cannot be ignored.

11.4.1 *Two-Stage Least Squares in the Overidentified Case*

Suppose we decide that the "true" model determining the demand for and supply of pork includes an additional variable W the per capita supply of beef, which we regard as a wholly predetermined variable along with Y and Z. The new variable, in terms of original units (pounds), logarithms, and first differences of logarithms, is shown in Table 11.4. The new variable appears in the structural demand function but not in the structural supply function. Hence our revised model is

(11.74)   *Demand:* $Q = a_1 + b_1 P + c_1 Y + d_1 W + u$

(11.75)   *Supply:* $Q = a_2 + b_2 P + c_2 Z + v$

We noted earlier that the method of reduced forms applied to this model gives two alternative estimates of the structural coefficients; elaborate computations are required (in the limited information maximum likelihood approach) to achieve a unique set of estimates which is in some sense "best."

To focus on the distinctive features resulting from the addition of W, we will decide in advance that the second-stage estimates will use $P = f(\hat{Q}, Y, W)$ in the demand function and $Q = f(\hat{P}, Z)$ in the supply function. This corresponds to Case III of the just-identified model.

Table 11.4   Beef Supply (Consumption) per Capita, United States, 1922–1941

		Beef Supply (Consumption) per Capita	
Year	Pounds	Logarithms,[a] Three Decimal Places	First differences of Logarithms, W
1922	59.1	1.772	–
1923	59.6	1.775	0.003
1924	59.5	1.775	0.000
1925	59.5	1.775	0.000
1926	60.3	1.780	0.005
1927	54.5	1.736	− 0.044
1928	48.7	1.688	− 0.048
1929	49.7	1.696	0.008
1930	48.9	1.689	− 0.007
1931	48.6	1.687	− 0.002
1932	46.7	1.669	− 0.018
1933	51.5	1.712	0.043
1934	55.9	1.747	0.035
1935	52.9	1.723	− 0.024
1936	58.1	1.764	0.041
1937	55.2	1.742	− 0.022
1938	54.4	1.736	− 0.006
1939	54.7	1.738	0.002
1940	54.9	1.740	0.002
1941	60.9	1.785	0.045

[a] To base 10.

The reduced-form equations now express P and Q, respectively, as functions of all three exogenous or predetermined variables:

$$P = f(Y, Z, W) \quad \text{and} \quad Q = f(Y, Z, W)$$

The fitted reduced-form equations follow:

$$\hat{P} = -0.0101 + 1.0375\,Y - 0.8471Z + 0.2368\,W;$$
$$\quad (0.0066) \quad (0.1439) \quad (0.1180) \quad (0.2706)$$
$$R^2 = 0.8986; \quad \bar{S} = 0.0283$$

$$\hat{Q} = 0.0025 + 0.0331\,Y + 0.6959Z - 0.1885\,W;$$
$$\quad (0.0032) \quad (0.0695) \quad (0.0570) \quad (0.1307)$$
$$R^2 = 0.9102; \quad \bar{S} = 0.0137$$

The second stage gives us the following estimates of the structural equations:

Demand: $\quad P = -0.0069 - 1.2169\hat{Q}_w + 1.0752\,Y + 0.0037W - \dfrac{u''}{b_1''};$

$\qquad\qquad$ (0.0065) (0.1692) $\qquad$ (0.1428) $\quad$ (0.2674)

$\qquad\qquad\qquad\qquad\qquad\qquad\qquad R^2 = 0.8989; \quad \bar{S} = 0.0283$

Supply: $\quad Q = 0.0025 - 0.0108\hat{P}_w + 0.6738Z + v'$

$\qquad\qquad$ (0.0033) (0.0617) $\qquad$ (0.0824)

$\qquad\qquad\qquad\qquad\qquad\qquad R^2 = 0.8979; \quad \bar{S} = 0.0141$

In this example, the resulting equations are very close to the three-variable demand function of Case II and the supply function of Case I, the same two functions that are paired as Case III.

As far as computations are concerned, two-stage least squares can be applied just as easily to overidentified as to just-identified models. From the standpoint of convenience, then, there is a good deal to say for two-stage least squares in the overidentified case.

In the underidentified case, the method of reduced forms enabled us to estimate one coefficient of the model,

$$\text{\emph{Demand:}} \quad Q = f(P, Y, u)$$

$$\text{\emph{Supply:}} \quad Q = f(P, v)$$

but not the others. If we try to apply two-stage least squares to this model using the pork data, we obtain:

Reduced forms

(1) $\hat{Q} = f(Y);$ $\quad \hat{Q} = 0.0015 - 0.1041\,Y;$ $\quad r^2 = 0.0156; \quad \bar{S} = 0.0425$

$\qquad\qquad\qquad$ (0.0098) (0.2008)

(2) $\hat{P} = f(Y);$ $\quad \hat{P} = -0.0088 + 1.2058\,Y;$ $\quad r^2 = 0.5498; \quad \bar{S} = 0.0561$

$\qquad\qquad\qquad$ (0.0130) (0.2646)

Choosing $P = f(\hat{Q}, Y, u)$ as our demand function and $Q = f(\hat{P}, v)$ as our supply function, our second-stage equations are as follows:

Demand: $\quad P = 0.0133 + 13.8174\hat{Q} + 0.2260\,Y - \dfrac{u'}{b'_1};$

$\qquad\qquad$ (0.0501) (30.1843) $\quad$ (3.1396)

$\qquad\qquad\qquad\qquad\qquad\qquad R^2 = 0.5556; \quad \bar{S} = 0.0574$

Supply: $\quad Q = 0.00074 - 0.0858\hat{P} + v; \quad r^2 = 0.0154; \quad \bar{S} = 0.0426$

$\qquad\qquad$ (0.00977) (0.1664)

Unfortunately, $\hat{Q}$ is an exact linear function of Y, so an attempt to fit the

foregoing demand function involves multicollinearity in the absolute sense.
For the correlation matrix of P, $\hat{Q}$ and Y is

$$
\begin{array}{ccccc}
 & & (1) & (2) & (3) \\
 & & P & \hat{Q} & Y \\
(1) & P & \begin{bmatrix} 1.0000 \\ r_{12} \\ r_{13} = r_{12} \end{bmatrix} & \begin{matrix} r_{12} \\ 1.0000 \\ 1.0000 \end{matrix} & \begin{matrix} r_{13} = r_{12} \\ 1.0000 \\ 1.0000 \end{matrix} \\
(2) & \hat{Q} & & & \\
(3) & Y & & &
\end{array}
$$

Since $\hat{Q}$ correlates perfectly with Y, the correlation coefficients of any third
variable (such as P) with $\hat{Q}$ and Y, respectively, will be identical. If P is
the dependent variable in a least squares multiple regression equation, the
regression coefficients and their standard errors will be calculated as ratios
with $1 - r_{\hat{Q}Y}^2$ in the denominators. Since $r_{\hat{Q}Y}^2 = 1$, this denominator is zero
so the coefficients and standard errors become infinite.

The values actually obtained for the foregoing correlation matrix are

$$
\begin{array}{cccc}
 & P & \hat{Q} & Y \\
P & \begin{bmatrix} 1.0000 \\ -0.7453 \\ 0.7414 \end{bmatrix} & \begin{matrix} -0.7453 \\ 1.0000 \\ -0.9962 \end{matrix} & \begin{matrix} 0.7414 \\ -0.9962 \\ 1.0000 \end{matrix} \\
\hat{Q} & & & \\
Y & & &
\end{array}
$$

Two points should be noted. First, the sign of the regression coefficient of $\hat{Q}$
on Y in the reduced form was negative, so we have perfect *negative* correlation
between $\hat{Q}$ and Y. Second, because of rounding errors, the correlation coefficient between $\hat{Q}$ and Y is computed as -0.9962 instead of -1.0000.
By carrying more decimal places, we could have caused the coefficient to
approach -1.0000 as closely as we liked.

As a further consequence of these small rounding errors, the correlation
coefficients obtained between P and $\hat{Q}$ and between P and Y are not identical
in absolute value but differ by a fraction of 1%, that is, -0.7453 as against
0.7414. Finally, if the rounding errors had been reduced, the standard errors
of the regression coefficients of P on $\hat{Q}$ and P on Y in the structural demand
function would have become even larger than the very large figures shown.

It should be clear that perfect negative correlation produces the same
effects as perfect positive correlation, for the determinant of the correlation
submatrix of $\hat{Q}$ and Y is

$$
1 - r_{\hat{Q}Y}^2 = \begin{vmatrix} 1 & -1 \\ -1 & 1 \end{vmatrix} = 1^2 - (-1)^2 = 1 - 1 = 0
$$

With rounding errors, the determinant is

$$1 - r_{\hat{Q}Y}{}^2 = \begin{vmatrix} 1.0000 & -0.9962 \\ -0.9962 & 1.0000 \end{vmatrix} = (1.0000)^2 - (-0.9962)^2$$
$$= 1.0000 - 0.9924 = 0.0076$$

The standard errors of the net regression coefficients may be calculated from the formulas

$$s_{b_P \hat{Q}.Y} = \left[\frac{1 - R^2_{P.\hat{Q}Y}}{(1 - r_{\hat{Q}Y}{}^2)(n - 3)} \right]^{\frac{1}{2}} \cdot \frac{s_P}{s_{\hat{Q}}}$$

and

$$s_{b_P Y.\hat{Q}} = \left[\frac{1 - R^2_{P.\hat{Q}Y}}{(1 - r_{\hat{Q}Y}{}^2)(n - 3)} \right]^{\frac{1}{2}} \cdot \frac{s_P}{s_Y}$$

therefore if $r_{\hat{Q}Y}{}^2$ is identically zero each of the standard errors becomes infinite.

It is less clear what is accomplished in the second-stage supply function. From the reduced-form equation, $\hat{P} = f(Y)$, P is an exact linear function of Y. If we now regress Q on $\hat{P}$, the regression estimates $\hat{Q}$ will also be an exact linear function of Y. From a common sense standpoint, a supply function which makes the current output of pork a linear function of consumer income (and nothing else) leaves much to be desired.

We may also consider the implications of two-stage least squares in the model

$$\text{Demand:} \quad P = f(Q, Y, W, u)$$

$$\text{Supply:} \quad Q = f(P, v)$$

The reduced-form equations are $\hat{Q} = f(Y, W)$ and $\hat{P} = f(Y, W)$.

What happens when we try to estimate the demand function as $P = f(\hat{Q}, Y, W)$? We again have strict multicollinearity, but in a less obvious form. The correlation matrix of the four variables is

		(1) P	(2) $\hat{Q}$	(3) Y	(4) W
(1)	P	1.0000	r_{12}	r_{13}	r_{14}
(2)	$\hat{Q}$	r_{12}	1.0000	r_{23}	r_{24}
(3)	Y	r_{13}	r_{23}	1.0000	r_{34}
(4)	W	r_{14}	r_{24}	r_{34}	1.0000

The reduced-form equation $\hat{Q} = f(Y, W)$ implies that $R^2_{2.34} = 1$, and that the determinant of the 3 by 3 correlation matrix involving r_{23}, r_{24}, and r_{34}

equals zero. For in order that $R^2_{2.34}$ may equal 1, the *numerator* of the ratio in

$$R^2_{2.34} = 1 - \frac{\begin{vmatrix} 1 & r_{23} & r_{24} \\ r_{23} & 1 & r_{34} \\ r_{24} & r_{34} & 1 \end{vmatrix}}{\begin{vmatrix} 1 & r_{34} \\ r_{34} & 1 \end{vmatrix}}$$

must equal zero. Hence as this numerator appears in the denominators of the formulas for regression coefficients and their standard errors when P is the dependent variable, standard errors become infinite, as in the three-variable instance.

A supply function in which $Q = f(\hat{P}) = f(Y, W)$ makes the estimates of production an exact linear function of Y and W, two variables which appear only in the structural demand function, does not appear very attractive.

11.5 FURTHER COMMENTS ON ESTIMATION IN MULTIPLE EQUATION MODELS

During the late 1950s and early 1960s, the journal literature on statistical estimation of simultaneous economic relations had expanded rapidly. It is not feasible for an introductory book such as this one to survey the many ramifications of this literature.

This chapter has tried to establish some perspective on the relative importance of simultaneity and the so-called identification problem in economic models. As in the earlier chapters, our perspective has been that of economists who are interested in appropriate statistical techniques as an aid to the measurement and clarification of economic relationships.

The spirit of our attempt is closely paralleled in a statement by L. R. Klein (1960):

"If econometric results are today more useful than in the past, this is only partly a result of the particular method of estimation but much more significantly a product of painstaking research of a more pedestrian nature. The building of institutional reality into *a priori* formulations of economic relationships and the refinement of basic data collection have contributed much more to the improvement of empirical econometric results than have more elaborate methods of statistical inference. I look towards improvements in precision of econometric judgments of the order of magnitude of 50 percent as a result of a better knowledge of the functioning of economic institutions, through the use of new measurements on variables, and through the use of more accurate data. In contrast, I would expect marginal improvements of 5 or 10 percent through the use of more powerful methods of statistical inference. All routes to improvement must be followed since any gains, no matter how small, are precious, yet different contributions should be kept in proper perspective. The adoption of more powerful methods of mathematical statistics is no panacea." [17]

In Chapters 10 and 11 our comparisons between different methods of estimation applied to the same data have showed more similarities than differences. In the area of demand and supply analysis, many instances could be found which, if we limited ourselves to official data, would be more favorable to simultaneous methods of estimation than the pork and beef examples we have presented. On the other hand, if an economic problem involving demand and supply relationships is really important either to a business firm or to a public agency, more direct and intensive methods of data collection, experimental design, surveys, and interviews can resolve many identification problems which seem bewildering or inconclusive on the basis of published data which are highly aggregated over firms and over time.

For example, if we refer to Figures 11.1 and 11.2, we may find situations in which a particular firm knows the coefficients of its own supply function quite accurately. It may have a near monopoly of a certain line of goods or services in a limited trade area. Even if one or two competitors are involved in addition to his own firm, the proprietor may know enough through long experience to specify the coefficients of the supply function that is relevant to his "identification problem."

Consider equation (11.76) which we used to express the identification problem:

$$(11.76) \qquad B_{pq} = \frac{b_1 s_v{}^2 - (b_1 + b_2)r_{uv}s_u s_v + b_2 s_u{}^2}{s_v{}^2 - 2r_{uv}s_u s_v + s_u{}^2}$$

If the supplier knew the values of b_2 and s_v in his own supply function, he could substitute their numerical values in the equation. He could estimate B_{pq} as the least squares regression coefficient of P on Q. When this numerical value also was substituted into (11.76), the equation would express the slope of the demand function, b_1, as a function of s_u and r_{uv}. On our assumptions, the supplier could specify the values of v in each time period; if he knew a quantifiable variable (weather, consumer income) that accounted for most of the shifts in consumer demand, he could correlate this variable with his

[17] L. R. Klein, "Single Equation vs. Equation System Methods of Estimation in Econometrics," *Econometrica* **28**, 4, p. 867 (October 1960).

own private time series on v and estimate r_{uv}. He could then express b_1 as a function only of s_u. From conversations with customers, or from family budget data, or from other types of investigation and introspection, he might set reasonable upper and lower bounds for s_u (which, in our example, is expressed in units of the price variable).

Although this procedure is inelegant, it may be quite practical, particularly if knowledge of the consumer demand function will contribute several thousand dollars a year to the supplier's net income and/or to his peace of mind.

Apart from two-stage least squares, it is difficult to discuss methods of estimating interdependent equations without drawing on more advanced mathematics than we have used thus far. Chapter 12, by J. K. Sengupta and B. C. Sanyal, provides a compact exposition of these methods, using matrix and calculus notations when required.

EXERCISES

1. Using the data given in the following table, plot a scatter diagram of the price and production values. From observation, do the data appear to represent

Sheep and Lamb numbers, Annual Lamb and Mutton Production, Yearly Average Price

Year	Sheep and Lambs on Farms January 1, Million	Commercial Production of Lamb and Mutton[a] Million lb	Price Slaughter Lambs, Iowa[b] Dollars/cwt.
1950	29.8	581	25.30
1951	30.6	508	31.40
1952	32.0	635	24.90
1953	31.9	715	20.30
1954	31.4	721	19.50
1955	31.6	744	18.80
1956	31.3	728	18.96
1957	30.8	694	19.90
1958	31.2	674	20.90
1959	32.6	724	18.70
1960	33.2	754	18.10
1961	33.0	818	16.40
1962	31.3	795	17.70
1963	29.8	757	18.50
1964	28.0	703	20.40

[a] Carcass weight of total commercial slaughter of sheep and lambs.
[b] Average annual price received by Iowa farmers.

Source: "Livestock and Meat Statistics," Statistical Bulletin No. 333, AMS, USDA.

a supply or demand curve? Using the technique presented in Section 11.1.1, compute estimates of both a demand and a supply curve from the data.

2. Discuss as carefully as possible the "identification problem."

3. Suppose we have a model of the following form:

(a) $Y_t = a_1 X_{1t} + a_2 X_{2t} + a_3 X_{1,t-1}$

(b) $Y_t = b_1 X_{1t} + b_2 X_{2t} + b_3 X_{2,t-1}$

(c) $Y_t = c_1 X_{1t} + c_2 X_{2t} + c_3 X_{3t}$

where X_3 is exogenous, Y_1, X_1, and X_2 are endogenous.

(i) Derive the reduced-form equations of this model.

(ii) Is the model under-identified, just identified, or over-identified?

(iii) Derive the consistent and reversible estimates of the structural relations between the endogenous variables.

4. Define carefully the concept of *recursiveness*. What are the main advantages derived from having a recursive model rather than a strictly interdependent or simultaneous structural model?

5. Suppose we have the following models (Model I):

(a) $Y_t = a_1 X_{1t} + a_2 X_{2t}$

(b) $Y_t = b_1 X_{1t} + b_2 X_{3t} + b_3 X_{4t}$

where Y, X_1 are endogenous variables

X_2, X_3, X_4 are exogenous variables

and Model II:

(a) $Y_t = a_1 X_{1t} + a_2 X_{2t} + a_3 X_{3t}$

(b) $X_{2t} = b_1 X_{3t}$

(c) $X_{1t} = c_1 X_{2t} + c_2 X_{3t}$

where Y, X_1, X_2 are endogenous variables

X_3 is an exogenous variable.

(i) From the discussion in this chapter, determine the proper way to estimate each of the two models.

(ii) Derive explicitly the estimators of the structural parameters of the models on the basis of your answer to part (i).

(iii) Set up a causal ordering diagram for Model II. What conclusions can you reach from this diagram?

REFERENCES

1. Fox, Karl A., "Structural Analysis and the Measurement of Demand for Farm Products," *Review of Economics and Statistics* 37, No. 1, pp. 57–66, 1954.
2. Fox, Karl A., J. K. Sengupta, and E. Thorbecke, *The Theory of Quantitative Economic Policy*, Amsterdam: North-Holland Publishing Co., and Chicago: Rand McNally and Co., pp. 51–72, 1966.
3. Girshick, M. A. and T. A. Haavelmo, "Statistical Analysis of the Demand for Food: Examples of Simultaneous Estimation of Structural Equations," *Econometrica* 15, pp. 79–111, April 1947.
4. Konijn, H. S., "Identification and Estimation in a Simultaneous Equation Model with Errors in the Variables," *Econometrica* 30, pp. 79–87, January 1962.

5. Koopmans, T. C., "Identification Problems in Economic Model Construction," in *Studies in Econometric Method*, W. Hood, T. C. Koopmans (eds.), New York: John Wiley and Sons, 1953.

6. Schultz, Henry, *Statistical Laws of Supply and Demand*, Chicago: The University of Chicago Press, 1928.

7. Simon, H., "Causal Ordering and Identifiability," in *Studies in Econometric Method*, W. Hood and T. C. Koopmans (eds.), New York: John Wiley and Sons, 1953.

8. Strotz, R. and H. Wold, "Recursive Versus Nonrecursive Systems: An Attempt at Synthesis," *Econometrica* **28**, pp. 417–427, April 1960.

CHAPTER 12

Alternative Methods of Estimation in Economic Models

J. K. SENGUPTA[1] AND B. C. SANYAL[2]

This chapter is written on a more technical level than the other chapters. Students who can understand Appendix B to Chapter 7, "Multiple Regression Analysis in Matrix Notation," will be able to follow most of this discussion. However, Chapters 13 and 14 are not directly dependent on Chapter 12, and some instructors will find it preferable to omit Chapter 12.

For students with strong backgrounds in mathematics and statistical theory, this chapter will serve as an introduction to the extensive and growing literature on methods of estimation in multiple equation economic models. We begin with a discussion of several variants of the least squares approach, including two-stage and three-stage least squares and the concept of k-class estimators. The second section deals with the method of maximum likelihood, including full information and limited information versions. The third section deals with a number of special situations involving simultaneous estimation. The chapter concludes with an introduction to Bayesian methods of estimation.

The methods of estimation actually applied to large-scale economic models so far have belonged to "classical" as distinct from "Bayesian" statistics. The classical estimation techniques that have been used belong to two well-known types, the method of least squares and the method of maximum likelihood. These estimation techniques may be applied to either single

---

[1] Professor of Economics and Statistics, Iowa State University (Ames).
[2] Post-doctoral research associate, Iowa State University (Ames).

equation or simultaneous equation models. In macroeconomic applications, simultaneous equation models have often been used on the grounds that (given the time units imposed by published data) many variables reflecting consumption and production, or government policies and the effects of those policies, are determined simultaneously. In microeconomic applications, there may be interdependence among variables relating to different firms in an industry or interdependence among variables in the factor and product markets confronting a single firm; these interdependencies would also seem to require simultaneous equation models.

The classical estimation techniques of least squares and maximum likelihood are essentially *parametric* in that they assume the parameters of the relationships to be unknown constants. These methods must be sharply differentiated from the so-called Bayesian methods, which postulate that the unknown parameters belong to a class of prior statistical distributions. There is a close relationship between the Bayesian approach to estimation and the statistical theory of decision functions initiated by Wald. In effect, Wald's approach views estimation techniques as a sequential process of arriving at good *decision rules* or rules for taking action under conditions of risk. According to this approach, the specification of a good decision rule is essentially dependent on the shape of the preference function of the decision maker which indicates his attitudes toward risks.

12.1   THE METHOD OF LEAST SQUARES

The application of Bayesian techniques of estimation to economic models is not yet well developed and there are special problems in adapting them to simultaneous models. Compared to the Bayesian techniques, the classical techniques of least squares and maximum likelihood have two great advantages in simplicity of calculation and specificity of results. The classical theories of least squares and maximum likelihood for single equation models have proved to be rather easily adaptable to simultaneous equation models. The theories underlying these techniques are helpful in indicating the specific situations in which they are likely to give good results, thus suggesting by implication the situations in which new techniques are needed.

The two classical methods of least squares and maximum likelihood when applied to single equation linear models have certain desirable properties such as consistency and efficiency, provided the errors in the model satisfy the usual conditions. But when applied to simultaneous equation models, these methods need slight modifications. First, the simultaneity of different equations means that some of the endogenous variables tend to play the role of explanatory variables in particular equations. And the restrictions and the information structure underlying different equations of the complete model are only implicitly specified, so that there is a need for distinction between the original model and the reduced form model, where the latter expresses the column vector of all endogenous variables as a function of only those explanatory variables which are exogenous or predetermined. These two aspects of simultaneity and implicit specification of the information structure of different equations require modification of the classical least squares and maximum likelihood techniques.[3]

The classical least squares technique is dependent on the Markov theorem, which assumes the additive errors of a single equation linear model to be mutually independently distributed. It also assumes that the explanatory variables (that is, independent variables) are statistically independent of the errors. To satisfy these conditions in a simultaneous equation model, there are at least three well-known possibilities. These will be discussed in turn.

12.1.1 *The Method of Indirect Least Squares*

The first step in this method is to express the original model in its reduced form either exactly (for just-identification in a linear model) or approximately (approximation is required for a nonlinear model). If the additive errors are mutually independent and not serially correlated, the second step is to apply ordinary least squares to each equation of the reduced form model to derive estimates of the parameters of the reduced form.

The parameters of the reduced form model are only functions of the parameters of the original model. It is well known, however, that for *just-identification*, there is a unique transformation relating the reduced form parameters to the parameters of the original model. Hence for *just-identification*, there is a unique way of obtaining the original parameters from the least squares estimates of the reduced form parameters.

For *overidentification*, there is more than one way of obtaining estimates of original parameters from the estimates of reduced form parameters and some further *a priori* conditions are needed. These conditions are, in effect, restrictions on the classical least squares technique. An alternative way to describe these restrictions is to say that the least squares method is applied to the reduced form model with the further condition that we get precisely that number of parameter estimates (from a larger number of possible parameter estimates) which defines a unique transformation to the original parameters. This may be said to define a method of "least least squares."

---

[3] By "information structure" we mean the set of restrictions imposed by all individual equations of a simultaneous equation model through their simultaneous relations and hence through their simultaneous explanatory implications. See T. C. Koopmans (ed.), *Statistical Inference in Dynamic Economic Models*, Cowles Commission for Research in Economics, Monograph No. 10, John Wiley and Sons, New York, 1950.

For example, if there are k $(k \geq 1)$ ways of obtaining estimates of the original parameters from the reduced form estimates, then for each of these ways there is an estimate of the least squares residuals. Finally, we accept that transformation which results in the smallest sum of squared residuals.[4]

If the additive errors in the original model are normally and independently distributed, the least squares and maximum likelihood methods define identical estimates. Since the properties of maximum likelihood estimates are preserved under suitable transformations, the indirect least squares estimates in this instance retain the desirable properties of maximum likelihood estimates such as consistency, and even efficiency under certain conditions.

12.1.2 *The Method of Two-Stage Least Squares*

This approach, as the name suggests, applies the method of least squares at two stages. Taking any given equation of a simultaneous model, we assume at least one coefficient of one endogenous variable to be unity. (This is called the normalization rule.) We divide both sides of that equation by the nonzero parameter value associated with the chosen endogenous variable. Then we replace all the other endogenous variables except the normalized one by their estimated values, which are nonstochastic. This replacement is done by regressing each of the endogenous variables in question upon all of the exogenous variables in the whole model, using the method of least squares. After such replacement, each equation of the simultaneous model specifies a single endogenous variable as a function of only exogenous variables, including (1) exogenous variables as such and/or (2) first-stage least squares estimates of the other endogenous variables in the equation. Note that these estimates are exact linear functions of the exogenous variables in the model.

Let the original simultaneous linear model be written as

$$(12.1) \qquad\qquad Ay + Gx = u$$

where A is an $M \cdot M$ and G an $M \cdot N$ matrix; y, x, and u are $M \cdot 1$, $N \cdot 1$, and $M \cdot 1$ vectors, respectively. The reduced form is

$$(12.2) \qquad\qquad y = H_1 x + v$$

where H_1 is $M \cdot N$ matrix denoting $(-A^{-1}G)$ and $v = A^{-1}u$. The complete model includes M endogenous variables, y, and N exogenous variables, x; there is a disturbance term, u, associated with each of the M equations.

---

[4] This implies selection of a rule for "normalizing" the variables in different equations since the original variables (and hence the residuals) may be expressed in different and essentially arbitrary units of measurement.

Any single structural equation belonging to the general system (12.1) may be expressed as

$$(12.3) \qquad\qquad y = Y\alpha + X_1\beta + u$$

where y is the column vector of T times series observations on the single dependent variable and α and β denote column vectors, respectively, of m and n parameters $(m + 1 \leq M, n < N)$ which are to be estimated. The dimensions $T \cdot m$ of matrix Y indicate that m other endogenous variables are present in the equation, and the dimensions $T \cdot n$ of matrix X_1 show that there are n predetermined variables in the equation.

Now we replace the matrix Y of endogenous variables occurring in the right-hand side of (12.3) by its least squares estimate $\hat{Y}$, where

$$(12.4) \qquad\qquad Y = \hat{Y} + \hat{V}$$

and $\hat{V}$ represents the estimates of true disturbances V in the first-stage least squares regressions. Then (12.3) may be rewritten as

$$(12.5) \qquad\qquad y = (Y - \hat{V})\alpha + X_1\beta + (u + \hat{V}\alpha)$$

This is the basis for the second stage of application of least squares, whereas (12.4) results from the first-stage application.

Equation (12.5) is in a form suitable for application of least squares since the disturbance term $(u + \hat{V}\alpha)$ satisfies the conditions of mutual independence and the term $(Y - \hat{V})$ is nonstochastic by construction.[5] Hence by applying least squares to (12.5) and solving the normal equations we get the two-stage least squares estimates:

$$(12.6) \qquad \begin{pmatrix} \hat{\alpha} \\ \hat{\beta} \end{pmatrix} = \begin{bmatrix} Y'Y - \hat{V}'\hat{V} & Y'X_1 \\ X'_1 Y & X'_1 X \end{bmatrix}^{-1} \begin{bmatrix} Y' - \hat{V}' \\ X'_1 \end{bmatrix} y$$

However, two points deserve special mention. First, the estimate $\hat{V}$ of the residuals in (12.4) obtained in the first-stage application of least squares is only an approximation to the unknown (true) disturbance V. This approximation will utilize all the information implied by the simultaneous interdependence of equations in the general model only if it is obtained from the reduced form equation (12.2) of the general model. If, however, this first-stage approximation is obtained without using the reduced form, it will essentially be an alternative approach (closely related to the method of instrumental variables).[6]

[5] Note that the exogenous variables are regarded as fixed numbers; they do not have probability distributions (that is, are not stochastic). The term $(Y - \hat{V})$ consists of exact linear functions of fixed numbers and these functions are also nonstochastic.

[6] Concerning instrumental variables, see L. R. Klein, *A Textbook of Econometrics*, Row Peterson, Evanston, Illinois, 1953.

Second, the method of replacement of stochastic Y by the estimated non-stochastic $\hat{Y}$ in (12.4) (that is, in the first-stage application of least squares) is not the only possible way and there is no particular reason why the least squares method of replacement should be applied. It appears that any other method of replacement ("purging" stochastic elements out of the matrix Y) would be feasible provided the usual conditions for identification were satisfied and the error term in the second-stage application of least squares satisfied the usual conditions required by the Markov theorem. (Incidentally, it may be mentioned that three-stage least squares capitalizes on a "method of replacement" which is somewhat different from that of two-stage least squares.)

If the additive errors in the two stages of application of least squares retain their mutual independence and are, moreover, normally distributed, these estimates turn out to be identical with the maximum likelihood estimates, provided the simultaneous model is a just-identifiable one. Otherwise, they retain at least the consistency property of maximum likelihood estimates.

12.1.3 *The k-Class Estimator*

This method generalizes the two-stage least squares technique by suggesting a more flexible method of replacement than that discussed in the preceding section. Technically, this estimator, denoted by

$$\begin{pmatrix} \hat{\alpha} \\ \hat{\beta} \end{pmatrix}$$

is

(12.7) $$\begin{pmatrix} \hat{\alpha} \\ \hat{\beta} \end{pmatrix} = \begin{bmatrix} Y'Y - k\hat{V}'\hat{V} & Y'X_1 \\ X'_1 Y & X'_1 X_1 \end{bmatrix}^{-1} \begin{bmatrix} Y' - k\hat{V}' \\ X'_1 \end{bmatrix} y$$

where k is an arbitrary scalar quantity. For $k = 1$ this is the usual two-stage least squares estimator given by (12.6).[7] It is more interesting to observe that the value of k could be optimally selected to obtain something like "least" least squares. The scalar k suggests that in the first stage of application of least squares one might even define a restricted least squares estimate in order to obtain unbiasedness and efficiency to any desired degree.

12.1.4 *Three-Stage Least Squares*

Three-stage least squares specifies a method of replacement of Y by $\hat{Y}$ in (12.4) different from that of two-stage least squares since it utilizes

---

[7] Note also that if $k = 0$, (12.7) gives us the ordinary single-stage least squares estimator.

the method of "generalized" least squares. Note that the purpose of replacing Y by $\hat{Y}$ is to "purge" stochastic elements out of the term Y in (12.4).

Instead of two-stage least squares we could follow an alternative approach. First we multiply (12.3) by a variable x_j, where j runs over all the exogenous and predetermined variables of the entire model:

(12.8)　　$x'_j y = x'_j Y\alpha + x'_j X_1\beta + x'_j u$　　　$j = 1, 2, \ldots, n, n + 1 \ldots K \leq N$

In matrix form this becomes

(12.9)　　　　　　　　$X'y = X'Y\alpha + X'X_1\beta + X'u$

where X is a T by K matrix formed from the x_j's defined in (12.8). (Incidentally, the condition $K \leq N$ is required for identification.)

We note from (12.9) that

$$E[X'y] = X'Y\alpha + X'X_1\beta$$

and

$$\text{Var}\,[X'u] = E[(X'u)(X'u)'] = E[X'uu'X] = (X'X)\sigma_u^2 I$$

where σ_u^2 = variance of u is a scalar constant, that is, the variance-covariance matrix $E(uu') = \sigma_u^2 I$, where I is the identity matrix of order K. Since $\text{Var}\,(X'u)$ is not identically equal to $(\sigma_u^2 I)$ because of the term $(X'X)$, we have an instance of "heteroscedasticity" and we have to apply the method of generalized least squares.

Since $(X'X\sigma_u^2 I)$ defines a nonsingular variance-covariance matrix, a transformation T must exist so that

(12.10)　　　　　　　　$T(X'X\sigma_u^2 I)T' = \sigma_u^2 I$ [8]

Hence multiplying both sides of (12.9) by this matrix T we get

(12.10a)　　　　　$TX'y = TX'Y\alpha + TX'X_1\beta + TX'u$

where

$$\text{Var}\,[TX'u] = E[TX'uu'XT'] = \sigma_u^2 I \qquad \text{by (12.10)}$$

Hence the usual least squares method is applicable to the model with transformed variables:

$$\tilde{y} = TX'y$$
$$\tilde{X} = [TX'Y \quad TX'X_1]$$
$$\tilde{u} = TX'u$$

---

[8] See Aitken, A. C., "On least squares and linear combinations of observations," *Proc. Roy. Soc. Edin.* **55**, p. 42 (1935).

In terms of the transformed variables, we have

(12.11) $$\tilde{y} = \tilde{X}\begin{pmatrix} \alpha \\ \beta \end{pmatrix} + \tilde{u} = TX'Y\alpha + TX'X_1\beta + \tilde{u}$$

The normal equations for estimating α and β then give

(12.12) $$\begin{pmatrix} \hat{\alpha} \\ \hat{\beta} \end{pmatrix} = (\tilde{X}'\tilde{X})^{-1}\tilde{X}'\tilde{y}$$

If this approach is applied simultaneously to each single equation of the simultaneous system, we have what is called the three-stage least squares approach.[9] Note that the three stages in this approach are defined by the following steps: (1) multiplication by X' in (12.9), (2) applying least squares to (12.11), and (3) simultaneous application of least squares to each single equation and then obtaining the estimates of the original parameters.

12.2 MAXIMUM LIKELIHOOD METHODS

The maximum likelihood method when applied to a single equation model defines estimating equations (also called likelihood equations) very similar to normal equations by maximizing the likelihood function of the jointly independent error variables of an additive model with respect to each parameter separately. Given a simultaneous model which is linear and just-identified, the reduced form version of the model provides a structure in which the maximum likelihood method can be applied to each equation separately. At the next step it is possible to derive unique estimates of the parameters of the original model. This is essentially the genesis of the full-information maximum likelihood method.

If the additive errors in each equation are not normally distributed, the maximum likelihood equations, unlike the least squares normal equations, tend to be nonlinear depending, of course, on the form of the error distribution assumed. The computational task may be quite heavy. Hence an alternative approach has been suggested which is sometimes called the "limited information" maximum likelihood method. The limited information maximum likelihood method essentially consists of maximizing the likelihood function of the joint distribution of the residuals, v, of the reduced form model (12.2) subject to restrictions on the parameters imposed by only a limited number of the equations belonging to the whole system. For example, if we consider the original model (12.1), its reduced form (12.2), and the particular equation (12.3) belonging to the general system, we maximize the likelihood

[9] See A. Zellner and H. Theil, "Three-Stage Least Squares: Simultaneous Estimation of Simultaneous Equations," *Econometrica* **30**, pp. 54–78 (1962).

function formed from the joint distribution of the residuals v of (12.2) subject to the restrictions imposed by the single structural equation (12.3); the maximization of the likelihood function is performed with respect to as many parameters as are contained in (12.3).

The full-information maximum likelihood method would form the likelihood function out of the jointly independently distributed residuals v of the reduced form model (12.2) as

$$(12.13) \quad L = p(v_1)p(v_2)\cdots p(v_M) = \frac{1}{(2\pi)^{M/2}}\cdots\frac{1}{|\phi|^{M/2}}\exp\left(-\tfrac{1}{2}\sum v'_i\phi^{-1}v_i\right)$$

assuming that the distribution of the residuals is normal with zero mean and variance-covariance matrix ϕ of order $M \cdot M$.[10]

Taking the logarithm of this expression, we set the first derivative of $\log L$ with respect to each parameter of the reduced form equal to zero to obtain the estimates of the reduced form parameters. If the model is just- or overidentified, we can then compute the original parameters from the reduced form parameters by the methods mentioned earlier.

In the limited information maximum likelihood approach we consider the particular structural equation (12.3) and the corresponding equation in the reduced form, which is written

$$(12.14) \qquad\qquad y = H_1 x + v$$

We partition x as (X_1, X_2) where X_1 is identical in both (12.14) and (12.3); similarly, (H_{11}, H_{12}) is the conforming partition of matrix H_1. Hence

$$(12.14a) \qquad\qquad y = H_{11}X_1 + H_{12}X_2 + v$$

Assuming that the distribution of v is jointly independently normal, the likelihood function is formed from the jointly independent residuals v. This function is maximized with respect to those parameters required, subject, however, to the conditions imposed by (12.3). For instance, we can write (12.3) in the form

$$(12.14b) \qquad\qquad Y_a\alpha_a + X_1\beta + u = 0$$

where Y_a is a $T \cdot (m + 1)$ matrix of observations on the included dependent variables, α_a is the $(m + 1)\cdot 1$ vector, and X_1, β, and u are defined as before. And, $Y_a = (y, Y)$ and $\alpha_a = \begin{pmatrix} \alpha_0 \\ \alpha \end{pmatrix}$, where the normalization $(\alpha_0 = -1)$ is ignored for the present.

[10] Good general treatments of the maximum likelihood principle may be found in (1) R. A. Fisher, *Contributions to Mathematical Statistics*, John Wiley and Sons, New York, 1950; (2) C. R. Rao, *Advanced Statistical Methods in Biometric Research*, John Wiley and Sons, New York, 1952.

Consistent estimators of α_a and β can be obtained if a consistent estimator of H_1 exists satisfying the condition $H_{12} \cdot \alpha_a = 0$. The unrestricted classical least squares estimators for (12.14a) minimize the generalized residual variance $|T^{-1}v'v|$. This leads us to minimize $|T^{-1}v'v|$ subject to the restriction $H_{12} \cdot \alpha_a = 0$, which is the same as minimizing $\frac{1}{2} \log |W|$ where $W = v'v$. We can write

(12.14c) $$z = \tfrac{1}{2} \log |W| - \mu' H_{12} \cdot \alpha_a$$

where μ is an $n \cdot 1$ vector of Lagrange multipliers. We have

(12.15) $$\frac{\partial z}{\partial H_1} = x' Y_a - x'x H_1 W^{-1} - \frac{\partial \mu'}{\partial H_1} H_{12} \cdot \alpha_a$$

(12.16) $$\frac{\partial z}{\partial H_{11}} = (X'_1 Y_a - X'_1 X_1 H_{11} - X'_1 X_2 H_{12})W^{-1} - 0$$

(12.17) $$\frac{\partial z}{\partial H_{12}} = (X'_2 Y_a - X'_2 X_1 H_{11} - X'_2 X_2 H_{12})W^{-1} - \mu \alpha'_a$$

and

(12.18) $$\frac{\partial z}{\partial \mu} = -H_{12}\alpha_a$$

(12.18a) $$\frac{\partial z}{\partial \alpha_a} = -H'_{12}\mu$$

From (12.15)–(12.18) we obtain

$$\hat{H}_{11} = (X'_1 X_1)^{-1} X'_1 Y_a - (X'_1 X_1)^{-1} X'_1 X_2 H_{12}$$

and

$$\hat{H}_{12} = (X'_2 M_1 X_2)^{-1} X'_2 M_1 Y_a - (X'_2 M_1 X_2)^{-1} \hat{\mu} \hat{\alpha}'_a \hat{W}$$

where

$$M_1 = I - X_1(X'_1 X_1)^{-1} X'_1$$

and

$$\hat{\mu} = (\hat{\alpha}'_a \hat{W} \alpha_a)^{-1} X'_2 M_1 Y_a \alpha_a$$

Replacing $\hat{\mu}$ in H_{12} with the foregoing expression we obtain

$$H_{12} = (X'_2 M_1 X_2)^{-1} X'_2 M_1 Y_a [I - (\hat{\alpha}'_a \hat{W} \alpha_a)^{-1} \hat{\alpha}_a \hat{\alpha}'_a \hat{W}]$$

And using the expression for $\hat{H}_{11}$ we may write $\hat{W}$ as

$$\hat{W} = Y'_a M_1 Y_a + \hat{H}'_{12} X'_2 M_1 X_2 \hat{H}_{12}$$
$$- \hat{H}'_{12} X'_2 M_1 Y_a - Y'_a M_1 X_2 \hat{H}_{12}$$

Again, inserting the value of $\hat{H}_{12}$, we get, after rearrangement,

$$\hat{W} = Y'_a M_1 Y_a - Y'_a M_1 X_2 (X'_2 M_1 X_2)^{-1} X'_2 M_1 Y_a + (\hat{\alpha}'_a \hat{W} \hat{\alpha}_a)^{-2} \hat{W} \hat{\alpha}_a$$
$$\times [\hat{\alpha}'_a Y'_a M_1 X_2 (X'_2 M_1 X_2)^{-1} X'_2 M_1 Y_a \hat{\alpha}_a] \hat{\alpha}'_a \hat{W}$$

It can be seen that the first two terms yield

$$W_{11} = Y'_a M_1 Y_a - Y'_a M_1 X_2 (X'_2 M_1 X_2)^{-1} X'_2 M_1 Y_a$$

which is T times the covariance matrix of the residuals from the least squares fit of Y_a on X_1 and X_2.
Thus

$$Y'_a M_1 X_2 (X'_2 M_1 X_2)^{-1} X'_2 M_1 Y_a = - W_{11} + Y'_a M_1 Y_a = W_{11}^{(1)} - W_{11}.$$

$W_{11}^{(1)}$ can be observed to be equal to T times the covariance matrix of the residuals from the least squares fit of Y on X_1 alone. Post-multiplying $\hat{W}$ by $\hat{\alpha}_a$ and inserting the result in the expression for $\hat{W}$ we set (12.18a) equal to zero and utilize the foregoing results to obtain

(12.19) $$(W_{11}^{(1)} - \lambda W_{11})\hat{\alpha}_a = 0$$

where

$$\lambda = [1 - (\hat{\alpha}'_a \hat{W} \hat{\alpha}_a)^{-1} \hat{\alpha}'_a Y'_a M_1 X_2 (X'_2 M_1 X_2)^{-1} X'_2 M_1 Y_a \hat{\alpha}_a]^{-1} \ {}^{11}$$

Equation (12.19) is a system of $(m + 1)$ homogeneous equations in $(m + 1)$ unknowns; for a nontrivial solution λ must be a root of the determinantal equation $|W_{11}^{(1)} - \lambda W_{11}| = 0$. To minimize $|\hat{W}|$ we take only the smallest root of λ. This value is inserted in (12.19), giving $\hat{\alpha}_a$ uniquely. Then $\hat{\beta}$ is determined as

$$\hat{\beta} = -\hat{H}_{11}\hat{\alpha}_a = -(X'_1 X_1)^{-1} X'_1 Y_a \hat{\alpha}_a$$

using the condition $\hat{H}_{12}\hat{\alpha}_a = 0$.

In this connection a few points may be useful. First, the maximum likelihood method generally preserves the properties of the estimators under suitable transformation; hence, although likelihood equations tend to be nonlinear, the method has some advantages because the consistency property is preserved. Even in situations where there is heteroscedasticity, the maximum likelihood method provides for an iterative procedure of obtaining estimates very similar to the procedure of generalized least squares already discussed. Second, however, the maximum likelihood estimates appear to be less stable than least squares estimates; this has been reported in several Monte Carlo

---

[11] For a detailed derivation see A. S. Goldberger, *Econometric Theory*, John Wiley and Sons, New York, 1964.

experiments.[12] Third, the likelihood equations are critically dependent on the correct specification of the form of the original model and the structural equations; hence, unlike the various least squares-like methods, the maximum likelihood estimates are quite vulnerable to slight deviations from the correct specification of the original model. Finally, the maximum likelihood estimates are susceptible to the presence of multicollinearity or intercorrelation among explanatory variables to a greater extent than the least squares estimates are (see Chapter 13).

12.2.1 *Restricted Maximum Likelihood*

There is one particular situation of great importance in economic models in which the maximum likelihood method is far less useful than the least squares method. This arises when the restrictions on the parameters to be estimated occur in the form of inequalities. For instance, it is required that for ordinary commodities the price elasticities of demand should be negative and the income elasticities of demand should be non-negative. Sometimes there are more precise bounds on these coefficients.

The likelihood method in this instance must achieve maximization under these additional restrictions on the parameters. In general, this leads to a complicated nonlinear programming problem if the restrictions on the parameters are not exact equalities but inequalities. The restricted least squares method in this situation requires only a quadratic programming procedure for which computational techniques are better known.

An alternative approach in this direction is called the method of "extraneous" estimates or *a priori* estimates (see Chapter 13).[13]

12.3   SPECIAL SITUATIONS INVOLVING SIMULTANEOUS ESTIMATION

In a single equation model the ordinary least squares method is most appropriate if the explanatory variables are all predetermined or exogenous. However, if the explanatory variables are subject to error quite apart from the equational error, the ordinary least squares method can be applied only

---

[12] See, for example (1) H. Wagner, "A Monte Carlo Study of Estimates of Simultaneous Linear Structural Equations," *Econometrica* **26**, pp. 117–133 (1958); (2) R. L. Bassmann, "An Experimental Investigation of Some Small Sample Properties of GCL Estimators of Structural Equations: Some Preliminary Results," General Electric Company, Hanford Laboratory, Richland, Washington, November 1958 (mimeo).

[13] Some of these methods are discussed in Chapters 3 and 4, *The Theory of Quantitative Economic Policy* by K. A. Fox, J. K. Sengupta, and E. Thorbecke, Rand McNally and North-Holland Publishing Company, 1966.

with certain modifications. For this situation, which is sometimes referred to as a model with errors in both types of variables (exogenous and endogenous), two methods are generally suggested, provided the appropriate conditions are satisfied.

The first method is very similar to two-stage least squares because it attempts to "purge" the explanatory variables subject to error on the right-hand side of the equation of their error components by replacing these variables with suitable estimates which may be derived from a separate least squares regressor or through "extraneous" methods. For a single equation model, one possibility is the method of group averages discussed by Wald.[14,15] In Wald's method, the observations for all variables which are subject to error are first grouped into as many subsets as there are parameters to be estimated. The subset averages for each variable replace the original observations, and a least squares equation is fitted. This first step yields an approximate estimate of the original parameters, which is then improved by successive iterations, utilizing the behavior of the estimated residuals of the fitted equation.

Specifically, the estimated residuals in an ordinary least squares situation should behave like mutually independent random variables with zero mean and finite standard deviation. If this behavior is not reproduced, as evidenced by significant values of the so-called Durbin-Watson statistic or the von Neumann ratio, we may separately incorporate this information to add a correction factor to the original estimate by the method of generalized least squares discussed earlier.

In a simultaneous equation model, this method should also be applicable to the reduced form of the original model if the explanatory variables in the reduced form equation contain errors which are independent of the additive error terms at the end of each equation. It should be noted that this method fails if the errors in the explanatory variables in the original model, and hence in the reduced form model, produce multicollinearity or a high degree of intercorrelation among the explanatory variables (see Chapter 13). In such instances, the method of extraneous information (that is, replacing the parameters of those explanatory variables by *a priori* estimates obtained extraneously) seems to be the best operational procedure. However, if this procedure is taken to define only a first approximation, the estimates could be successively improved by observing the behavior of the estimated residuals of the reduced form model with the parameter values equated to their first-stage approximation.

[14] A. Wald, "The Fitting of Straight Lines if Both Variables Are Subject to Error," *Annals of Mathematical Statistics* **11**, pp. 284–300 (1940).

[15] H. Theil and J. van Ijzeren, "On the Efficiency of Wald's Method of Fitting Straight Lines," *Review of International Statistical Institute* (1956).

The second method of attacking the problem in which both types of variables are subject to error is essentially related to the method of weighted least squares. It is apparent that if the explanatory variables in a single equation model or in any given equation of the reduced form of a simultaneous equation model contain errors for which the variance-covariance matrix is known or estimable, one may partition the original matrix of explanatory variables X into two parts ($X = \hat{X} + V$), where V specifies the errors for which the variance structure is known and $\hat{X}$, which is equal to $X - V$, defines an appropriate replacement for X so that $\hat{X}$ is free from the contamination of errors.

However, usually the error structure is not specifiable with such precision and hence an indirect step is required in using the method of weighted least squares. When applied to a linear model (that is, to the original equation if the model contains only one equation or to each equation of the reduced form version of the original simultaneous equation model), the essential step is to utilize the information contained in the joint distribution of the two types of errors—errors in the variables and errors in the equations. This process of utilization could be carried in an iterative fashion to different degrees of approximation.

For example, suppose the model is

$$Y = (\hat{X} + V)\beta + U = \hat{X}\beta + (V\beta + U)$$

where V and u are error terms and both types of errors are assumed to be additive. If the error term ($V\beta + U$) defines only the problem of heteroscedasticity, the method of generalized least squares would provide a good estimate for the β's. For example, if ($V\beta + U$) has a nonsingular variance-covariance matrix, then there exists a nonsingular matrix M such that the variance-covariance matrix $E[M(V\beta + U)(V\beta + U)'M']$ specifies a homoscedastic structure. In this instance, we have only to transform the original model as

(12.20) $MY = M\hat{X}\beta + N$ where $N = M(V\beta + U)$

and then apply least squares to this model to estimate the parameters β.

However, this method is critically dependent on the assumption that the errors V in the term $\hat{X} + V$ are additive like the equational error term U. If the errors V associated with X are multiplicative, for example, XV, whereas the equational error U is still additive, then (12.20) would not be the most appropriate except as a first approximation. If the errors U and V have autoregressive structures, that is, time lags, the first-stage approximation could be improved by successive first-order autoregressions of the estimated residuals at each further stage. (This is sometimes called the method of autoregressive least squares.)

One more point needs mentioning at this stage concerning multicollinearity (see also Chapter 13). If the problem of multicollinearity in a model is generated by errors in the variables, the problem might be reduced or eliminated through obtaining either more precise data or more sample observations so that the error structure associated with the explanatory variables could be more accurately specified.

A problem called specification bias arises from incorrect specification of a given model. This may be because any given linear model could be generated by a somewhat more general nonlinear model. An operational procedure to guard against this specification bias is to fit two or three versions of a given equation, some of which are nonlinear, for example, belonging to the polynomial class or log linear class. This approach can be readily applied to a single equation model. However, for a simultaneous equation model, any nonlinear specification except the log linear type generally tends to make the reduced form equations either unobtainable or only very approximately obtainable. Hence some method of recursive improvement of an approximate initial estimate must be incorporated.[16]

A simple two-equation example should make this point clear. Consider a two-equation Keynesian model with consumption C, investment I, and national income Y:

$$C = \alpha + \beta_1 Y + \beta_2 Y^2 + u$$

and

$$Y = I + C$$

where it is assumed that the error term is mutually independently distributed and the investment variable I is the only exogenous variable in the model. It is not ordinarily possible to derive the reduced form version of this model unless Y^2 is replaced by a nonstochastic estimate. Replacing Y^2 by $(EY)^2$ where E is expectation, an approximate version of the reduced form can be obtained:

$$C = \frac{\alpha}{1 - \beta_1} + \frac{\beta_1}{1 - \beta_1} I + \frac{\beta_2}{1 - \beta_1} (EY)^2 + \frac{u\beta_1}{1 - \beta_1}$$

(12.21)

$$Y = \frac{\alpha}{1 - \beta_1} + \frac{I}{1 - \beta_1} + \frac{\beta_2}{1 - \beta_1} (EY)^2 + \frac{u}{1 - \beta_1}$$

The estimates of the parameters of this reduced form are only approximate, however, and are critically dependent on the approximation of Y^2 by $(EY)^2$. The first estimates could be improved by iterative methods using better approximations of $(EY)^2$.

[16] H. O. Hartley, "The Modified Gauss–Newton Method for the Fitting of Nonlinear Regression Functions by Least Squares," *Technometrics* 3, 269–280 (1961).

At this point it may be worthwhile to make a few comments on the method of approximation used in maximum likelihood estimation techniques. Even in single equation models, an assumption of non-normal distribution for the equational errors in some instances make the usual likelihood equations non-linear, and the approximation method called the method of scoring is generally adopted. Let the set of likelihood equations be denoted by

(12.22) $$\frac{\partial \log L}{\partial \theta_j} = 0 \qquad j = 1, 2, \ldots, k$$

The jth efficient score is given by (12.22). The information matrix is given by

$$I_{jh}{}^0 = -\frac{\partial^2 \log L}{\partial \theta_j \, \partial \theta_h}\bigg|_{\substack{\theta_j = \theta_j{}^0 \\ \theta_h = \theta_h{}^0}}$$

where $\lambda_j{}^0$ is some initial estimate of θ_j. In matrix notation, the correction to the vector λ of estimates at each iteration is given by

$$I^0 \, \Delta\lambda = S^0$$

$$I^0(\lambda^1 - \lambda^0) = S^0 \qquad \text{or} \qquad \lambda^1 = \lambda^0 + (I^0)^{-1}S_0$$

where I^0 is the information matrix, S^0 is the vector of scores, λ^0 is the vector of initial estimates, and λ' is the vector of corrected estimates. In general,

$$\lambda^t = \lambda^{t-1} + (I^{t-1})^{-1}S^{t-1}$$

If this process converges, the vector of scores vanishes and the maximum likelihood equation (12.22) is satisfied. The sufficient condition for convergence is that I^t should be positive definite for all t. The condition that I, the true information matrix, be positive definite is sufficient for the identifiability of the parameters.[17,18]

For linear models with equational errors distributed in a non-normal fashion, the maximum likelihood method could be applied to the reduced form version, and estimates of reduced form parameters could be obtained by the foregoing method of scoring. This technique is applicable even to

[17] Let $\phi_{ij} = (-\partial^2 \log \phi)/(\partial \theta_i \, \partial \theta_j)$ and $E(\phi_{ij}) = I_{ij}$. The matrix $I = (I_{ij})$, $(i, j = 1, 2, \ldots, k)$ is called the information matrix, when ϕ is the probability density of the set of observations, and θ_i, θ_j are the parameters occurring in the likelihood function. A typical element of the information matrix is simply the expected value of the second partial derivative of the log-likelihood function except for signs.

[18] D. W. Jorgenson, "Multiple Regression Analysis of a Poisson Process," *Journal of the American Statistical Association* LVI, 235–245 (1961).

nonlinear models provided the reduced form version of the nonlinear model can be approximately obtained by the method illustrated in (12.21). There may be more than one method of approximation and, formally speaking, one could define the best by the criterion of "maximum maximum likelihood" quite analogously to the method we referred to as "least least squares."

However, there is one crucial difficulty in the maximum likelihood method of estimation. Apart from the somewhat erratic behavior of the maximum likelihood estimates in small sample situations, the method of scoring itself depends on the nonsingularity of the "information matrix."[19] Frequently the singularity results from a slightly incorrect specification of the original model. This leads to the question of the sensitivity of an estimate to (1) the assumption made concerning the distribution of residuals (for example, normal or otherwise) and (2) the estimation approach adopted (for example, parametric or nonparametric; least squares, maximum likelihood, or other methods). In other words, in a general situation we must be concerned not only with the unbiased quality and efficiency of an estimate, but with its sensitivity to assumptions of departure from normality and other specifications. This last aspect is sometimes referred to as the "robustness" of an estimate.

Research work on the relative degree of robustness of different types of estimators is still in progress. But some specific cases and situations have been clarified by means of estimation techniques which are known to be nonparametric.

12.4   THE BAYESIAN METHOD OF ESTIMATION

In the previous sections we have discussed estimation techniques which are essentially parametric in that they assume the parameters to be unknown constants. We now consider a technique of estimation which assumes some additional information about the parameters to be estimated.

The Bayesian method of estimation essentially depends on three basic postulates. First, the unknown parameters θ are assumed to belong to a class of prior statistical distributions either known or estimable. Second, any method of estimating the parameters θ by $\hat{\theta}$, say, where $\hat{\theta}$ is a function of sample observations, is considered a rule of guess resulting in a "disutility" or a "loss," which is dependent on a particular prior distribution of θ and the particular rule of guess; the function which specifies this "loss" or "disutility" is called the "loss function," with its expected value—the "risk" or the "risk function." In other words, if D denotes the particular method

---

[19] See Footnote 17.

of guessing θ by $\hat{\theta}$, then a very common form of the loss function $\lambda(D, \theta)$ is given by

$$\lambda(D, \theta) = (\hat{\theta} - \theta)^2$$

and two simple examples of the method of guessing (that is, method of estimating) may be

1. D_1: accept $\hat{\theta}$ as that value for which the expected value is $\theta(\hat{\theta} = k_1$ so that $E(k_1) = \theta$).
2. D_2: accept the rule of estimate defined by d_1 five times out of ten and for the remaining five times accept an *a priori* constant value of $\hat{\theta}$ ($\hat{\theta} = pk_1 + (1 - p)k_2$ where $p = 0.5$ and k_2 is an *a priori* constant value).

Third, the method defines a technique of selecting a best rule of guess or a best estimating procedure by defining alternative classes of estimates and evaluating them in terms of the expected value of the loss function. Ideally, the expected value of the loss function should be zero for the best estimate whenever it exists. Otherwise, estimates are sought in a class of estimates which is "uniformly better" than another class of estimates in the sense that the average loss or risk for any estimate in the former class is less than or equal to (but not greater than) that for any estimate in the latter class. (The estimates belonging to the former class may include the minimax estimators and even other estimators based on different forms of the loss function.) In most instances, if the prior distribution of θ is known to belong to well-known categories such as the normal distribution, and the loss function is represented as $(\hat{\theta} - \theta)^2$, the Bayesian estimate $\hat{\theta}$ can be easily derived by the usual methods and it will have the property of a uniformly better estimator compared to another class which may be suitably defined. For example, consider a single parametric case. We write the density function of x as

$$f(x|\theta)$$

to indicate that the parameter θ is also a random variable. We draw a random sample of size n from the density function $f(x|\theta)$. We want to estimate the θ that determined the density function from which the random sample was taken. Let $p(\theta)$ be the marginal density of θ and $\lambda(\hat{\theta}; \theta)$ be the loss function. Although θ is a random variable, we want to estimate a particular value of θ that determined the density $f(x|\theta)$ from which the particular random sample has been drawn since different values of θ yield different densities and from one of them the random sample is drawn. The risk can be defined as $E[\lambda(\hat{\theta}; \theta)] = F(d, \theta)$. Since θ is a random variable, we are interested in finding the function $d(x_1, x_2, \ldots, x_n)$, where $x_1, x_2, \ldots, x_n$ are sample observations which will minimize the risk expected for estimating θ by

$d(x_1, x_2, \ldots, x_n)$. Then d will be called the Bayes estimator of the parameter θ. The risk expected can be written as

$$(12.23) \quad R(d) = E[F(d, \theta)] = \int_{-\infty}^{\infty} F(d, \theta) p(\theta)\, d\theta$$

$$= \int_{-\infty}^{\infty} \left\{ \int_{-\infty}^{\infty} \cdots \int_{-\infty}^{\infty} \lambda[d(x_1, x_2, \ldots, x_n); \theta] \right.$$
$$\left. \times\, g(x_1, x_2, \ldots, x_n | \theta)\, dx_1 \cdots dx_n \right\} p(\theta)\, d\theta$$

where $g(x_1, x_2, \ldots, x_n | \theta)$ is the joint density of $x_1, x_2, \ldots, x_n$. Interchanging the order of integration of the x's and θ in (12.23) we obtain

$$(12.24) \quad R(d) = \int_{-\infty}^{\infty} \cdots \int_{-\infty}^{\infty} \left\{ \int_{-\infty}^{\infty} \lambda[d(x_1, x_2, \ldots, x_n); \theta] \right.$$
$$\left. \times\, g(x_1, x_2, \ldots, x_n | \theta) p(\theta)\, d\theta \right\}$$
$$\times\, dx_1, dx_2, \ldots, dx_n$$

We want to find $d(x_1, x_2, \ldots, x_n)$ which minimizes

$$(12.25) \quad \int_{-\infty}^{\infty} \lambda[d(x_1, x_2, \ldots, x_n); \theta] g(x_1, x_2, \ldots, x_n | \theta) p(\theta)\, d\theta$$

It may be noted that the quantity of $g(x_1, x_2, \ldots, x_n | \theta) p(\theta)$ in (12.25) is the joint distribution of $x_1, x_2, \ldots, x_n, \theta$. The marginal distribution of the x's, $K(x_1, x_2, \ldots, x_n)$, is obtained by integrating out θ from (12.25). The conditional distribution of θ given $x_1, x_2, \ldots, x_n$ is

$$(12.26) \quad H(\theta | x_1, x_2, \ldots, x_n) = \frac{g(x_1, x_2, \ldots, x_n | \theta) p(\theta)}{K(x_1, x_2, \ldots, x_n)}$$

where $H(\theta | x_1, x_2, \ldots, x_n)$ is called the *a posteriori* density. Hence (12.25) can be written

$$(12.27) \quad K(x_1, x_2, \ldots, x_n) \int_{-\infty}^{\infty} \lambda[d(x_1, x_2, \ldots, x_n); \theta] H(\theta | x_1, x_2, \ldots, x_n)\, d\theta$$

Thus a Bayes estimator is the value of $\hat{\theta}$ which will minimize for each possible sample $x_1, x_2, \ldots, x_n$ the quantity

$$(12.28) \quad q(\hat{\theta}; x_1, x_2, \ldots, x_n) = \int_{-\infty}^{\infty} \lambda(\hat{\theta}; \theta) H(\theta | x_1, x_2, \ldots, x_n)\, d\theta$$

The function q is called the *a posteriori* risk for estimating θ.

Example

Let $x_1, x_2, \ldots, x_n$ be a random sample from the normal density function with variance unity

$$f(x|\mu) = \frac{1}{\sqrt{2\pi}} e^{(-\frac{1}{2})(x-\mu)^2}$$

Then

$$g(x_1, x_2, \ldots, x_n|\mu) = \frac{1}{(2\pi)^{n/2}} \exp\left[-\tfrac{1}{2} \sum (x_i - \mu)^2\right]$$

Suppose μ is a random variable and the density of μ is

$$p(\mu) = \frac{1}{\sqrt{2\pi}} e^{-\mu^2/2} \qquad -\infty < \mu < \infty$$

Then the joint distribution of $x_1, x_2, \ldots, x_n, \mu = g(x_1, x_2, \ldots, x_n|\mu)p(\mu)$

$$= \frac{1}{(2\pi)^{(n+1)/2}} \exp\left[-\tfrac{1}{2}\{\sum x_i^2 + (n+1)\mu^2 - 2\mu n\bar{x}\}\right]$$

and

$$K(x_1, x_2, \ldots, x_n) = \frac{1}{(2\pi)^{(n+1)/2}} \exp\left(-\tfrac{1}{2}\sum x_i^2\right)$$

$$\times \int_{-\infty}^{\infty} \exp\left\{-\tfrac{1}{2}[(n+1)\mu^2 - 2\mu n\bar{x}]\right\} d\mu$$

$$= \frac{1}{(n+1)^{\frac{1}{2}}(2\pi)^{n/2}} \exp\left[-\tfrac{1}{2}\left(\sum x_i^2 - \frac{n^2\bar{x}^2}{n+1}\right)\right]$$

and

$$H(\mu|x_1, x_2, \ldots, x_n)$$

$$= \frac{(2\pi)^{-[(n+1)/2]} \exp\left\{-\tfrac{1}{2}[\sum x_i^2 + (n+1)\mu^2 - 2n\bar{x}\mu]\right\}}{(2\pi)^{-n/2}(n+1)^{-\frac{1}{2}} \exp\left[-\tfrac{1}{2}\left(\sum x_i^2 - \frac{n^2\bar{x}^2}{n+1}\right)\right]}$$

$$= \frac{(n+1)^{\frac{1}{2}}}{(2\pi)^{\frac{1}{2}}} \exp\left[-\tfrac{1}{2}(n+1)\left(\mu - \frac{n\bar{x}}{n+1}\right)^2\right]$$

Hence the conditional distribution of μ given $x_1, x_2, \ldots, x_n$ is normal with mean $\bar{x}n/(n+1)$ and variance $1/(n+1)$. Let the loss function be of the form

$$\lambda(\hat{\mu}; \mu) = (\hat{\mu} - \mu)^2$$

Then the Bayes estimator is the value of $\hat{\mu}$ as a function of the x's which minimizes $q(\hat{\mu}; x_1, x_2, \ldots, x_n)$

where

$$q(\hat{\mu}; x_1, x_2, \ldots, x_n) = \int_{-\infty}^{\infty} (\hat{\mu} - \mu)^2 H(\mu | x_1, x_2, \ldots, x_n) \, d\mu$$

$$= \hat{\mu}^2 - \frac{2n\hat{\mu}\bar{x}}{n+1} + \frac{1}{n+1} + \frac{\bar{x}^2 n^2}{(n+1)}$$

We solve the equation

$$\frac{\partial[q(\hat{\mu}; x_1, x_2, \ldots)]}{\partial \hat{\mu}} = 2\hat{\mu} - \frac{2n\bar{x}}{n+1} = 0$$

which gives $\hat{\mu} = \sum x_i/(n+1)$.

It may be mentioned here that the Bayes estimator corresponding to an arbitrary *a priori* probability distribution is consistent and asymptotically efficient and is also a best asymptotically normal (BAN) estimator under quite general conditions.

This method could be applied to estimate the parameters of the reduced form version of the simultaneous equation model, provided some prior distribution of the parameter could be reasonably postulated. The main difficulty in this approach, however, is how to choose an appropriate prior distribution so that the resulting estimates can be easily derived. Some interesting work along this line has been reported by Raiffa and Schlaifer[20] and others who have shown that it is sometimes possible to define a conjugate pair of distributions which facilitate the derivation of Bayes' type estimators. Another very remarkable breakthrough has been pioneered by Robbins who has proposed "an empirical Bayes' estimator" which could be derived in at least some specific situations and which has been shown to have very desirable statistical properties.[21] Successful applications of these Bayesian techniques have been made by Zellner and Tiao to autoregressive systems of linear equations with time-lagged variables.[22]

[20] H. Raiffa and R. Schlaifer, *Applied Statistical Decision Theory*, Division of Research, Harvard Business School, Boston, 1961.

[21] H. Robbins, "An Empirical Bayes' Approach to Statistics," *Proceedings of Third Berkeley Symposium on Statistics and Probability*, University of California Press, Berkeley, I, pp. 157–164 (1956).

[22] A. Zellner and G. C. Tiao, "Bayesian Analysis of the Regression Model with Auto-correlated Errors," *Journal of the American Statistical Association* **59** (September 1964).

CHAPTER 13

Multicollinearity and the Use of *A Priori* Information in Economic Models

This chapter will deal with two of the special problems mentioned in Chapter 10. First, the discussion of multicollinearity in single equation models will be extended to cases involving four or more variables. The discussion will then be broadened to include multiple equation models and the more "simultaneous" methods of estimation such as two-stage least squares. The second part of the chapter is concerned with the use of *a priori* information.

The use of *a priori* information, meaning in general any information not obtained directly from the experiment or sample at hand, has a long history in other disciplines as well as in economics. We will attempt to clarify the circumstances under which *a priori* information not only can but must be used as, for example, to break impasses created by multicollinearity in a particular time series sample. We will stress, however, that the *a priori* or "outside" information with which we supplement the information in our sample must be strongly supported by economic reasoning. Bad economics will not rescue us from ambiguous statistics; good economics may.

13.1 EFFECTS OF INTERCORRELATION IN THE FOUR-VARIABLE CASE

The problem of intercorrelation in the four-variable case is more complicated than in the three-variable case of Chapter 7 (Section 5) because there are now three intercorrelation coefficients instead of one. We have three independent variables X_2, X_3, and X_4, and we may have intercorrelation between X_2 and X_3, X_2 and X_4, and X_3 and X_4.

Following the approach used in the three-variable case, let us suppose that we have a large number of four-variable regression analyses on different sets of data. We select a number of these analyses in which the values of r_{12}, r_{13}, and r_{14} (the direct or simple correlation coefficients between the dependent and each independent variable) are about the same. Nevertheless, we find that the partial correlation and net regression coefficients are different in each instance. These differences are due to the varying degrees of intercorrelation, represented by combinations of values of r_{23}, r_{24}, and r_{34}.

A systematic exploration of the effects of intercorrelation in the four-variable case would involve a great deal of labor. One possibility would be to fix the values of r_{23} and r_{24} and to trace the effects of variations in r_{34} upon the different regression measures. Except for a change in notation, such a demonstration would apply equally well to changes in either of the other intercorrelation coefficients, r_{23} or r_{24}. Before doing this, however, we shall illustrate the complications of the four-variable case in terms of the basic formulas for correlation and regression coefficients.

13.1.1 *Basic Formulas*

It will be convenient at this point to introduce a determinant notation, which avoids excessive rewriting of the simple correlation coefficients. This notation can be extended to five or more variables, and also to the three-variable case previously considered.

In the three-variable case, the three-rowed determinant of correlation coefficients

$$(13.1) \qquad \triangle_3 = \begin{vmatrix} 1 & r_{12} & r_{13} \\ r_{12} & 1 & r_{23} \\ r_{13} & r_{23} & 1 \end{vmatrix}$$

can be made to yield nine different two-rowed determinants by deleting one column and one row of $\triangle_3$. Suppose we call the two-row determinant obtained by deleting the first column and the first row $\triangle_{3\,11}$ ($= 1 - r_{23}^2$); that obtained by deleting the first column and the second row $\triangle_{3\,12}$ ($= r_{12} - r_{13}r_{23}$); and so on. The complete set of two-row determinants, which we call the $\triangle_{3\,ij}$'s, follows:

$$(13.1a) \qquad \triangle_{3\,11} = 1 - r_{23}^2$$

$$(13.1b) \qquad \triangle_{3\,22} = 1 - r_{13}^2$$

(13.1c) $$\Delta_{33} = 1 - r_{12}^2$$

(13.1d) $$\Delta_{12} = r_{12} - r_{13}r_{23} = \Delta_{21}$$

(13.1e) $$\Delta_{13} = -(r_{13} - r_{12}r_{23}) = \Delta_{31}$$

(13.1f) $$\Delta_{23} = (r_{23} - r_{12}r_{13}) = \Delta_{32}$$

All of the formulas for correlation and regression measures given in Chapter 7, Section 5 for the three-variable case can be stated in terms of Δ and the Δ_{ij}'s, as follows:

(13.2) $$R_{1.23}^2 = 1 - \frac{\Delta}{\Delta_{11}}$$

(13.3) $$\beta_{12.3} = \frac{\Delta_{12}}{\Delta_{11}}$$

(13.4) $$\beta_{13.2} = \frac{-\Delta_{13}}{\Delta_{11}}$$

(13.5) $$r_{12.3} = \frac{\Delta_{12}}{\sqrt{\Delta_{11} \cdot \Delta_{22}}}$$

(13.6) $$r_{13.2} = \frac{\Delta_{13}}{\sqrt{\Delta_{11} \cdot \Delta_{33}}}$$

(13.7) $$S_{\beta_{12.3}} = \sqrt{\frac{\Delta}{\Delta_{11}(N - 3)}} = S_{\beta_{13.2}}$$

Once we have fixed the values of r_{12} and r_{13}, $\triangle_3$ and all but two of the $\triangle_{3\,ij}$'s are functions only of r_{23}; these two, $\triangle_{3\,22}$ and $\triangle_{3\,33}$, are constants. Each of the foregoing six formulas involves $\triangle_{3\,11}$, which changes with r_{23}, and another determinant which also changes with r_{23}. This means that we cannot vary r_{23} arbitrarily without consistently varying $\triangle_3$ and the $\triangle_{3\,ij}$'s.

In the four-variable case, the determinant of correlation coefficients is

(13.8)
$$\triangle_4 = \begin{vmatrix} 1 & r_{12} & r_{13} & r_{14} \\ r_{12} & 1 & r_{23} & r_{24} \\ r_{13} & r_{23} & 1 & r_{34} \\ r_{14} & r_{24} & r_{34} & 1 \end{vmatrix}$$

The determinant of the three intercorrelation coefficients is

(13.9)
$$\triangle_{4\,11} = \begin{vmatrix} 1 & r_{23} & r_{24} \\ r_{23} & 1 & r_{34} \\ r_{24} & r_{34} & 1 \end{vmatrix} = 1 + 2r_{23}r_{24}r_{34} - r_{23}^2 - r_{24}^2 - r_{34}^2$$

Each of the 15 other possible $\triangle_{4\,ij}$'s is now also a three-rowed determinant. The preceding formulas still apply, with an appropriate change in notation. For example,

$$\beta_{12.34} = \frac{\triangle_{4\,12}}{\triangle_{4\,11}} = \frac{\begin{vmatrix} r_{12} & r_{13} & r_{14} \\ r_{23} & 1 & r_{34} \\ r_{24} & r_{34} & 1 \end{vmatrix}}{\begin{vmatrix} 1 & r_{23} & r_{24} \\ r_{23} & 1 & r_{34} \\ r_{24} & r_{34} & 1 \end{vmatrix}}$$

All of the $\triangle_{4\,ij}$'s for which $i \neq j$ involve all three intercorrelation coefficients $\triangle_{4\,22}$, $\triangle_{4\,33}$, and $\triangle_{4\,44}$ each contains only one of these coefficients. But this last point is not very helpful since each formula (13.2) through (13.7) includes either $\triangle_4$ itself or a $\triangle_{4\,ij}$ for which $i \neq j$.

We noted in the three-variable case that the values assumed for r_{12} and r_{13} impose certain limits upon the values which might be assumed by r_{23}. Similarly, the values assumed for r_{12} and r_{14} impose restrictions on r_{24}, and those assumed for r_{13} and r_{14} impose restrictions on r_{34}. For example, if $r_{12} = r_{13} = r_{14} = 0.7$, each of the three intercorrelation coefficients may range from -0.02 to 1.0. However, the values of r_{23} and r_{24} also set limits to the permissible values of r_{34}. A consistent set of limits for the six simple r's can be derived from the fact that $\triangle_{22}$, $\triangle_{33}$, $\triangle_{44}$, and $\triangle_{11}$ must all lie between 0 and 1.

13.1.2 Discussion of Charts and Tables

Figures 13.1 through 13.6 and Tables 13.1 through 13.6 provide some insights into the effects of intercorrelation in the four-variable case. The first five cases assume that all three of the direct correlation coefficients r_{12}, r_{13}, and r_{14} are equal to 0.7. Two of the intercorrelation coefficients, r_{23} and r_{24}, are then set equal to 0.9, 0.7, 0.5, 0.3, and 0.1, respectively. In each instance, the third intercorrelation coefficient r_{34} is allowed to vary over its entire range of possible values given the values of the other five coefficients and the basic requirements $R^2_{1.234} \leq 1$ and $|r_{34}| \leq 1$.

Table 13.1 Data for Case in Which $r_{12} = r_{13} = r_{14} = 0.7$, $r_{23} = r_{24} = 0.9$, and $N = 20$

					t-ratio for		
r_{34}	$\beta_{12.34}$	$\beta_{13.24}$	$\beta_{14.23}$	$S_\beta{}^{a}$	$\beta_{12.34}$	$\beta_{13.24}$	$\beta_{14.23}$
0.6392[b]	-5.8586	3.6436	3.6436	3.0000	-1.9529	1.2145	1.2145
0.6500	-3.5000	2.3333	2.3333	2.2105	-1.5834	1.0556	1.0556
0.6900	-1.1000	1.0000	1.0000	1.3474	-0.8164	0.7422	0.7422
0.6941	-1.0000	0.9444	0.9444	1.3102	-0.7633	0.7208	0.7208
0.7000	-0.8750	0.8750	0.8750	1.2627	-0.6930	0.6930	0.6930
0.7500	-0.2692	0.5385	0.5385	1.0429	-0.2582	0.5163	0.5163
0.7720	-0.1290	0.4605	0.4605	1.0000	-0.1290	0.4605	0.4605
0.8000	0	0.3889	0.3889	0.9721	0	0.4000	0.4000
0.8500	0.1522	0.3044	0.3044	0.9825	0.1549	0.3098	0.3098
0.8645	0.1847	0.2862	0.2862	1.0000	0.1847	0.2862	0.2862
0.9000	0.2500	0.2500	0.2500	1.0827	0.2309	0.2309	0.2309
0.9500	0.3182	0.2121	0.2121	1.4044	0.2266	0.1510	0.1510
1.0000[c]	$-$	$-$	$-$	$-$	$-$	$-$	$-$

[a] Identical for each β.
[b] Lowest possible value of r_{34}.
[c] Highest possible value of r_{34}.

Table 13.2 Data for Case in Which $r_{12} = r_{13} = r_{14} = 0.7$, $r_{23} = r_{24} = 0.7$, and $N = 20$

r_{34}	$\beta_{12.34}$	$\beta_{13.24}$	$\beta_{14.23}$	$S_\beta{}^a$	t-ratio for $\beta_{12.34}$	$\beta_{13.24}$	$\beta_{14.23}$
0.1529[b]	−1.0000	1.2143	1.2143	0.6532	−1.5310	1.8590	1.8590
0.1900	−0.7000	1.0000	1.0000	0.5782	−1.2106	1.7294	1.7294
0.2000	−0.6364	0.9546	0.9546	0.5625	−1.1314	1.6971	1.6971
0.3000	−0.2188	0.6562	0.6562	0.4622	−0.4733	1.4199	1.4199
0.4000	0	0.5000	0.5000	0.4167	0	1.2000	1.2000
0.5000	0.1346	0.4038	0.4038	0.3982	0.3381	1.0142	1.0142
0.5765	0.2071	0.3521	0.3521	0.3973	0.5214	0.8862	0.8862
0.6000	0.2258	0.3387	0.3387	0.3992	0.5657	0.8485	0.8485
0.7000	0.2917	0.2917	0.2917	0.4210	0.6928	0.6928	0.6928
0.8000	0.3415	0.2561	0.2561	0.4772	0.7155	0.5367	0.5367
0.9000	0.3804	0.2283	0.2283	0.6309	0.6030	0.3618	0.3618
0.9592	0.3998	0.2145	0.2145	0.9520	0.4199	0.2253	0.2253
0.9632	0.4010	0.2136	0.2136	1.0000	0.4010	0.2136	0.2136
0.9800	0.4060	0.2100	0.2100	1.3440	0.3021	0.1562	0.1562
1.0000[c]	−	−	−	−	−	−	−

[a] Identical for each β. [b] Lowest possible value of r_{34}. [c] Highest possible value of r_{34}.

Table 13.3 Data for Case in Which $r_{12} = r_{13} = r_{14} = 0.7$, $r_{23} = r_{24} = 0.5$, and $N = 20$

r_{34}	$\beta_{12.34}$	$\beta_{13.24}$	$\beta_{14.23}$	$S_\beta{}^a$	t-ratio for $\beta_{12.34}$	$\beta_{13.24}$	$\beta_{14.23}$
−0.0196[b]	−0.0286	0.7286	0.7286	0.3572	−0.0800	2.0396	2.0396
0	0	0.7000	0.7000	0.3500	0	2.0000	2.0000
0.1000	0.1167	0.5833	0.5833	0.3224	0.3618	1.8091	1.8091
0.2000	0.2000	0.5000	0.5000	0.3062	0.6532	1.6330	1.6330
0.2500	0.2333	0.4667	0.4667	0.3012	0.7746	1.5492	1.5492
0.3000	0.2625	0.4375	0.4375	0.2981	0.8806	1.4676	1.4676
0.4000	0.3111	0.3889	0.3889	0.2970	1.0474	1.3093	1.3093
0.5000	0.3500	0.3500	0.3500	0.3031	1.1547	1.1547	1.1547
0.6000	0.3818	0.3182	0.3182	0.3182	1.2000	1.0000	1.0000
0.7000	0.4083	0.2917	0.2917	0.3472	1.1762	0.8402	0.8402
0.8000	0.4308	0.2692	0.2692	0.4038	1.0667	0.6667	0.6667
0.9000	0.4500	0.2500	0.2500	0.5449	0.8259	0.4588	0.4588
0.9500	0.4586	0.2414	0.2414	0.7538	0.6084	0.3202	0.3202
0.9800	0.4635	0.2365	0.2365	1.1763	0.3940	0.2010	0.2010
1.0000[c]	−	−	−	−	−	−	−

[a] Identical for each β. [b] Lowest possible value of r_{34}. [c] Highest possible value of r_{34}.

Table 13.4 Data for Case in Which $r_{12} = r_{13} = r_{14} = 0.7$, $r_{23} = r_{24} = 0.1$, and $N = 20$

r_{34}	$\beta_{12.34}$	$\beta_{13.24}$	$\beta_{14.23}$	S_β[a]	t-ratio for $\beta_{12.34}$	$\beta_{13.24}$	$\beta_{14.23}$
0.5765[b]	0.6191	0.4048	0.4048	0.3079	2.0105	1.3145	1.3145
0.6000	0.6202	0.3987	0.3987	0.3133	1.9799	1.2728	1.2728
0.7000	0.6250	0.3750	0.3750	0.3455	1.0891	1.0854	1.0854
0.8000	0.6292	0.3539	0.3539	0.4054	1.5522	0.8731	0.8731
0.9000	0.6330	0.3351	0.3351	0.5507	1.1494	0.6085	0.6085
0.9500	0.6347	0.3264	0.3264	0.7641	0.8307	0.4272	0.4272
1.0000[c]	–	–	–	–	–	–	–

[a] Identical for each β.
[b] Lowest possible value of r_{34}.
[c] Highest possible value of r_{34}.

Table 13.5 Data for Case in Which $r_{12} = r_{13} = r_{14} = 0.5$, $r_{23} = r_{24} = 0.5$, and $N = 20$

r_{34}	$\beta_{12.34}$	$\beta_{13.24}$	$\beta_{14.23}$	S_β[a]	t-ratio for $\beta_{12.34}$	$\beta_{13.24}$	$\beta_{14.32}$
−0.3333[b]	−1.0000	1.4999	1.4999	0.5303	−1.8856	2.8285	2.8285
−0.3000	−0.7500	1.2500	1.2500	0.4586	−1.6353	2.7255	2.7255
−0.2500	−0.5000	1.0000	1.0000	0.3873	−1.2910	2.5820	2.5820
−0.2000	−0.3333	0.8333	0.8333	0.3402	−0.9798	2.4495	2.4495
−0.1000	−0.1250	0.6250	0.6250	0.2827	−0.4422	2.2111	2.2111
0	0	0.5000	0.5000	0.2500	0	2.0000	2.0000
0.1000	0.0833	0.4167	0.4167	0.2303	0.3618	1.8091	1.8091
0.2000	0.1429	0.3571	0.3571	0.2187	0.6532	1.6329	1.6329
0.3000	0.1875	0.3125	0.3125	0.2129	0.8806	1.4676	1.4676
0.4000	0.2222	0.2778	0.2778	0.2122	1.0474	1.3093	1.3093
0.5000	0.2500	0.2500	0.2500	0.2165	1.1547	1.1547	1.1547
0.6000	0.2727	0.2273	0.2273	0.2273	1.2000	1.0000	1.0000
0.7000	0.2917	0.2083	0.2083	0.2480	1.1762	0.8401	0.8401
0.8000	0.3077	0.1923	0.1923	0.2885	1.0667	0.6667	0.6667
0.9000	0.3214	0.1786	0.1786	0.3892	0.8259	0.4588	0.4588
1.0000[c]	–	–	–	–	–	–	–

[a] Identical for each β.
[b] Lowest possible value of r_{34}.
[c] Highest possible value of r_{34}.

Table 13.6 Data for Case in Which $r_{12} = r_{13} = r_{14} = 0.5$, $r_{23} = r_{24} = 0$, and $N = 20$

r_{34}	$\beta_{12.34}$	$\beta_{13.24}$	$\beta_{14.23}$	$S_\beta{}^a$	*t*-ratio for $\beta_{12.34}$	$\beta_{13.24}$	$\beta_{14.23}$
-0.3333 [b]	0.5000	0.7500	0.7500	0.2652	1.8856	2.8284	2.8284
-0.3000	0.5000	0.7143	0.7143	0.2574	1.9429	2.7756	2.7756
-0.2500	0.5000	0.6667	0.6667	0.2472	2.0226	2.6968	2.6968
-0.2000	0.5000	0.6250	0.6250	0.2387	2.0949	2.6186	2.6186
-0.1000	0.5000	0.5556	0.5556	0.2255	2.2172	2.4636	2.4636
0	0.5000	0.5000	0.5000	0.2165	2.3094	2.3094	2.3094
0.1000	0.5000	0.4546	0.4546	0.2109	2.3708	2.1553	2.1553
0.2000	0.5000	0.4167	0.4167	0.2083	2.4000	2.0000	2.0000
0.3000	0.5000	0.3846	0.3846	0.2088	2.3950	1.8423	1.8423
0.4000	0.5000	0.3571	0.3571	0.2125	2.3525	1.6803	1.6803
0.5000	0.5000	0.3333	0.3333	0.2205	2.2678	1.5118	1.5118
0.6000	0.5000	0.3125	0.3125	0.2344	2.1333	1.3333	1.3333
0.7000	0.5000	0.2941	0.2941	0.2582	1.9363	1.1390	1.1390
0.8000	0.5000	0.2778	0.2778	0.3027	1.6518	0.9177	0.9177
0.9000	0.5000	0.2632	0.2632	0.4109	1.2170	0.6405	0.6405
1.0000 [c]	–	–	–	–	–	–	–

[a] Identical for each β.
[b] Lowest possible value of r_{34}.
[c] Highest possible value of r_{34}.

The fact that we have set all three of the direct coefficients equal to one another, and two of the intercorrelation coefficients equal to each other, produces several symmetries in the results. One is that $\beta_{13.24}$ and $\beta_{14.23}$ are equal in each instance. Another is that at the point where r_{34} is equal to r_{23} and r_{24}, all three beta coefficients are equal.

Figure 13.1 reflects a very high degree of intercorrelation. One symptom of this is the fact that $\boxed{4}_{11}$, the determinant of intercorrelation coefficients, takes on very small values, 0.036 or less, over its entire range. In Figure 13.6, in contrast, the value of $\boxed{4}_{11}$ reaches a peak of 1.0 when all three intercorrelation coefficients are zero and exceeds 0.5 over a considerable range of values of r_{34}. Figure 13.1 approaches the extreme of multicollinearity to which Ragnar Frisch gave so much attention in the 1930s.[1] The values of the

[1] Ragnar Frisch, *Statistical Confluence Analysis by Means of Complete Regression Systems* (Oslo: Klara Civiltryckeri), 192 pp., 1934.

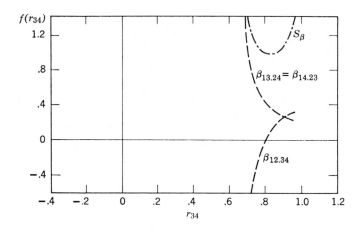

Figure 13.1 Effects of intercorrelation—four-variable case: $r_{12} = r_{13} = r_{14} = 0.7$; $r_{23} = r_{24} = 0.9$; $N = 20$. (From U.S. Department of Agriculture)

beta coefficients are very unstable and are smaller than their standard errors in all but a small portion of the range of permissible values of r_{34}. And the range of permissible values of r_{34} is limited.

Figure 13.2, in which r_{23} and r_{24} equal 0.7, shows a greater stability of the beta coefficients with respect to given changes in r_{34} than does Figure 13.1. The standard error of the beta coefficients is also more stable than in the

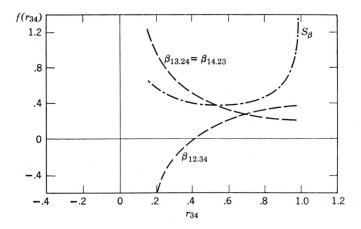

Figure 13.2 Effects of intercorrelation—four-variable case: $r_{12} = r_{13} = r_{14} = 0.7$; $r_{23} = r_{24} = 0.7$; $N = 20$. (From U.S. Department of Agriculture)

preceding chart. The beta coefficients exceed their standard errors over a considerably wider range of values, although they do not reach twice the level of their standard errors anywhere in the permissible range. In both of these figures the behavior of $\beta_{12.34}$ corresponds to that of the weaker coefficient in some of the three-variable charts. When the level of r_{34} drops significantly below the levels of r_{23} and r_{24}, $\beta_{12.34}$ changes sign from positive to negative. Visually, it appears that $\beta_{13.24}$ ($= \beta_{14.23}$) is a reflection of $\beta_{12.34}$ about the particular level at which all three intercorrelation coefficients, and hence all three beta coefficients, are equal. The value of the betas at this

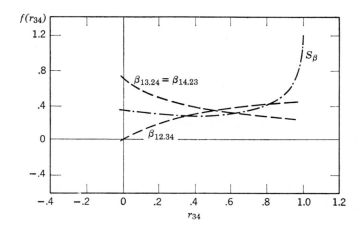

Figure 13.3 Effects of intercorrelation—four-variable case: $r_{12} = r_{13} = r_{14} = 0.7$; $r_{23} = r_{24} = 0.5$; $N = 20$. (From U.S. Department of Agriculture)

point of equality increases from one case to the next as the paired intercorrelation coefficients (r_{23} and r_{24}) decrease.

Figure 13.3 shows still greater stability in the values of the beta coefficients and their standard errors. The beta coefficients exceed their standard errors over a large part of the permissible range and for certain limited values of r_{34}, near zero, they exceed two standard errors.

Figure 13.4 shows a still greater contraction of the range of permissible values of r_{34}. The values of the beta coefficients are quite stable within this limited range, but the standard errors of these coefficients is changing rapidly within it. The t-ratio, β/S_β, for $\beta_{12.34}$ exceeds 2.0 toward the lower end of the permissible range of r_{34}; t-ratios for the other beta coefficients do not exceed 1.3 at any value of r_{34}.

It is evident from the foregoing results that to have each of the three direct correlation coefficients equal to 0.7 already constitutes a high degree of inter-correlation if one hopes to achieve significant regression coefficients in a four-variable equation involving only 20 or so observations.

In Figure 13.5, the direct correlation coefficients are reduced to 0.5 and two of the intercorrelation coefficients are also set equal to 0.5. This chart may be compared with Figure 13.2, in which all five of these coefficients were set equal to 0.7. The beta coefficients and their standard errors in Figure 13.5 are considerably more stable and cover a wider range of permiss-

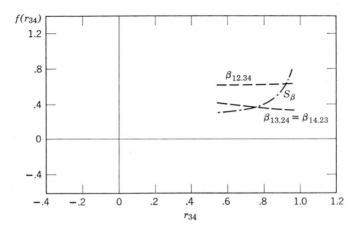

Figure 13.4 Effects of intercorrelation—four-variable case: $r_{12} = r_{13} = r_{14} = 0.7$; $r_{23} = r_{24} = 0.1$; $N = 20$. (From U.S. Department of Agriculture)

ible values than in Figure 13.2. The coefficients exceed their standard errors over most of the permissible range, and the t-ratios for $\beta_{13.24}$ and $\beta_{14.23}$ exceed 2.0 over a sizable range, reaching a maximum of 2.83 when r_{34} reaches its lowest value.

In Figure 13.6, the three direct correlation coefficients are again set equal to 0.5 and two of the intercorrelation coefficients are set at zero. The range of permissible values of r_{34} is about the same as in Figure 13.5, but the degree of stability of the beta coefficients and their standard errors is con-siderably greater. The coefficient $\beta_{12.34}$ is independent of r_{34}. The t-ratios are greater than one over almost the full range of permissible values and exceed two over considerable portions of this range.

If larger numbers of observations are available, the t-ratios associated

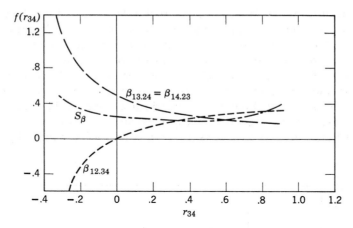

Figure 13.5 Effects of intercorrelation—four-variable case: $r_{12} = r_{13} = r_{14} = 0.5$; $r_{23} = r_{24} = 0.5$; $N = 20$. (From U.S. Department of Agriculture)

with any given set of correlation coefficients will increase in proportion to the square root of the number of degrees of freedom. And some sets of values of the direct correlation coefficients will lead to much higher *t*-ratios for at least one or two regression coefficients than any of those shown in these tables. The tables display neither the best for which we may hope nor the worst which we may encounter.

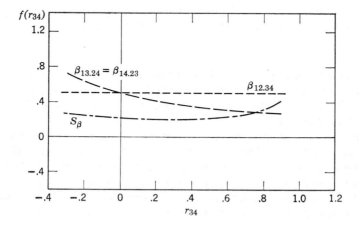

Figure 13.6 Effects of intercorrelation—four variable case: $r_{12} = r_{13} = r_{14} = 0.5$; $r_{23} = r_{24} = 0$; $N = 20$. (From U.S. Department of Agriculture)

13.2 THE ZERO INTERCORRELATION CASE IN DETERMINANTAL NOTATION

We have noted that the situation which is most favorable to accurate estimates of the separate effects of two or more independent variables upon a dependent variable is that in which all intercorrelations among the independent variables are zero. This can be artificially assured in controlled experiments.

The following determinants (13.10 through 13.13) will suggest by induction the nature of the "no intercorrelation" situation. We note that the determinantal notation of the preceding section is perfectly general; it suffices equally well for the two-, three-, four-, and five-variable determinants shown and for all higher orders.

For two variables we have the correlation matrix

$$(13.10) \quad \begin{array}{c} \\ X_1 \\ X_2 \end{array} \begin{array}{cc} X_1 & X_2 \\ \begin{bmatrix} 1 & r_{12} \\ r_{12} & 1 \end{bmatrix} \end{array}; \quad r^2 = 1 - \frac{\triangle{2}}{\triangle{2}_{11}} = 1 - \frac{1 - r_{12}{}^2}{1} = r_{12}{}^2$$

For three variables with $r_{23} = 0$ we obtain

$$(13.11) \quad \begin{array}{c} \\ X_1 \\ X_2 \\ X_3 \end{array} \begin{array}{ccc} X_1 & X_2 & X_3 \\ \begin{bmatrix} 1 & r_{12} & r_{13} \\ r_{12} & 1 & 0 \\ r_{13} & 0 & 1 \end{bmatrix} \end{array};$$

$$R_{1.23}^2 = 1 - \frac{\triangle{3}}{\triangle{3}_{11}} = 1 - \frac{1 - r_{12}{}^2 - r_{13}{}^2}{1} = r_{12}{}^2 + r_{13}{}^2$$

The four-variable correlation matrix with r_{23}, r_{24}, and $r_{34} = 0$ is

$$(13.12) \quad \begin{array}{c} \\ X_1 \\ X_2 \\ X_3 \\ X_4 \end{array} \begin{array}{cccc} X_1 & X_2 & X_3 & X_4 \\ \begin{bmatrix} 1 & r_{12} & r_{13} & r_{14} \\ r_{12} & 1 & 0 & 0 \\ r_{13} & 0 & 1 & 0 \\ r_{14} & 0 & 0 & 1 \end{bmatrix} \end{array};$$

$$R_{1.234}^2 = 1 - \frac{\triangle{4}}{\triangle{4}_{11}} = 1 - \frac{1 - r_{12}{}^2 - r_{13}{}^2 - r_{14}{}^2}{1} = r_{12}{}^2 + r_{13}{}^2 + r_{14}{}^2$$

We can evaluate $\underline{/4\backslash}$ through the process of multiplying each element in the first column by its cofactor, namely the determinant formed by the elements of the second, third, and fourth columns *excluding* the row in which the particular first column element is located. If the subscripts of the specified element in column 1 sum to an even number, its cofactor is given a positive sign; if the subscripts of the column 1 element sum to an odd number, its cofactor is given a negative sign. Thus from (13.12) we obtain

$$\underline{/4\backslash} = 1 \begin{vmatrix} 1 & 0 & 0 \\ 0 & 1 & 0 \\ 0 & 0 & 1 \end{vmatrix} - r_{12} \begin{vmatrix} r_{12} & r_{13} & r_{14} \\ 0 & 1 & 0 \\ 0 & 0 & 1 \end{vmatrix}$$

$$+ r_{13} \begin{vmatrix} r_{12} & r_{13} & r_{14} \\ 1 & 0 & 0 \\ 0 & 0 & 1 \end{vmatrix} - r_{14} \begin{vmatrix} r_{12} & r_{13} & r_{14} \\ 1 & 0 & 0 \\ 0 & 1 & 0 \end{vmatrix}$$

$$= 1(1) - r_{12}(r_{12}) + r_{13}(-r_{13}) - r_{14}(r_{14}) = 1 - r_{12}{}^2 - r_{13}{}^2 - r_{14}{}^2$$

as indicated above.

The five-variable correlation matrix with r_{23}, r_{24}, r_{25}, r_{34}, r_{35}, and $r_{45} = 0$ should suffice to conclude the demonstration:

(13.13)
$$\begin{bmatrix} 1 & r_{12} & r_{13} & r_{14} & r_{15} \\ r_{12} & 1 & 0 & 0 & 0 \\ r_{13} & 0 & 1 & 0 & 0 \\ r_{14} & 0 & 0 & 1 & 0 \\ r_{15} & 0 & 0 & 0 & 1 \end{bmatrix};$$

$$R^2_{1.2345} = 1 - \frac{\underline{/5\backslash}}{\underline{/5\backslash}_{11}} = 1 - \frac{1 - r_{12}{}^2 - r_{13}{}^2 - r_{14}{}^2 - r_{15}{}^2}{1}$$

$$= r_{12}{}^2 + r_{13}{}^2 + r_{14}{}^2 + r_{15}{}^2$$

In the zero intercorrelation case, the value of the determinant of intercorrelation coefficients among the independent variables is always one. We recall that $r_{11}{}^2$, $r_{22}{}^2$, $r_{33}{}^2$, $r_{44}{}^2$, and $r_{55}{}^2$ are the *variances* of the corresponding normalized variables, x_i/s_i—$i = 1, 2, 3, 4, 5$. The structure of the correlation matrices (13.11), (13.12), and (13.13) indicates that the effects of (say) X_2 on X_1 are measured in a direction perpendicular or orthogonal to the effects of X_3, X_4, and X_5. If intercorrelation is zero the entire variance of each independent variable is *separately* available to contribute to the explanation of the dependent variable X_1, and there is no ambiguity as to whether part of the apparent contribution of X_2 is really attributable to X_3, X_4, or X_5. The effect of each independent variable is *additive* to the others; there are no cross product or intercorrelation terms. Thus in the five-variable case, $R^2_{1.2345} = r_{12}{}^2 + r_{13}{}^2 + r_{14}{}^2 + r_{15}{}^2$.

Even with zero intercorrelation, the addition of more and more independent variables in a regression equation presents more and more of a challenge to the "resolving power" of the regression technique. If there are $m - 1$ independent variables, the *average* proportion of variance explained by each is $(R^2_{1.23\cdots m})/(m - 1)$. The unexplained variance (per degree of freedom) is $(1 - R^2_{1.2\cdots 3m})/(n - m)$. If $n = 20$ observations, $m = 10$ variables, and $R^2_{1.23\cdots m} = 0.90$, the *average* variance explained by each of the nine independent variables is 0.10. The normalized variance of deviations about the regression equation is

$$\frac{1 - R^2_{1.23\cdots m}}{20 - 10} \quad \text{is} \quad \frac{0.10}{20 - 10} = 0.01$$

Hence the *average* F-ratio for testing the significance of the contribution of an independent variable would be $F = 0.10/0.01 = 10$. With one degree of freedom for the numerator and ten degrees for the denominator, a value of $F = 10.04$ would occur in one random sample out of 100 in which the population F-ratio was unity. At the 5% level for one and ten degrees of freedom, $F = 4.96$.

If, as frequently happens, two or three independent variables explain 70 or 80% of the variance, the remaining seven or six variables in our example can explain only 0.10/6 or 0.20/7 of the total variance, or an average of 0.017 to 0.029 per variable. With a residual error variance of $0.10/(20 - 10) = 0.01$ as before, this means average F-ratios of 1.7 to 2.9 which are not statistically significant at anything near the 5% level.

Intercorrelation rapidly reduces the value of the determinant of correlation coefficients among the independent variables, which we may call $\triangle_{m\,11}$ when there are $m - 1$ independent variables. The numerator of the formula for $R^2_{1.23\cdots m}$ fills up with terms such as $r_{12}r_{23}r_{34}\cdots r_{m-1,m}$ in addition to $r_{12}{}^2, r_{13}{}^2, \ldots, r_{1m}{}^2$. As we have seen in connection with some of the examples in Chapter 11, if the value of $\triangle_{m\,11}$ approaches zero, the standard errors of the regression coefficients approach infinity and the contributions of the individual independent variables cannot be distinguished from one another.

If $\triangle_{m\,11}$ equals zero, the correlation matrix of the independent variables is said to be *singular*. Phrases such as "near-singularity" or "almost singular" are not numerically defined, but their use in any particular context denotes that $\boxed{m}_{11}$ is approaching zero closely enough to make the standard errors of regression coefficients unacceptably large. For an extremely close approach of $\boxed{m}_{11}$ to zero even the arithmetic of the analysis may break down into a meaningless juggling of rounding errors.

The experiments with two-stage least squares reported in Chapter 11 offer cases in point. In the correlation matrix involving P, $\hat{Q}$, and Y (where $\hat{Q} = a + bY$), the true intercorrelation matrix is

$$\boxed{3}_{11} = \begin{vmatrix} 1.0000 & -1.0000 \\ -1.0000 & 1.0000 \end{vmatrix} = 1 - 1 = 0$$

With rounding errors,

$$\boxed{3}_{11(e)} = \begin{vmatrix} 1.0000 & -0.9962 \\ -0.9962 & 1.0000 \end{vmatrix} = 1.0000 - 0.9924 = 0.0076$$

The square root of this expression, 0.0872, multiplied by $N - 3$, formed the denominator of the formula for $s_{\beta_{12.3}}$ ($= s_{\beta_{13.2}}$). The determinant of the true correlation matrix involving $\hat{Q}$, Y, and W (where $\hat{Q} = a + bY + cW$) must also be exactly equal to zero—that is, $\boxed{4}_{11} = 0$. With rounding errors, we would find that $\boxed{4}_{11(e)} \neq 0$. Hence $s_{\beta_{12.34(e)}}$, like $s_{\beta_{12.3(e)}}$, would not become infinite as it would if the true (zero) value of $\boxed{4}_{11}$ were entered into its denominator.

Thus when better information is lacking, the computer is quite capable of turning out regression coefficients and standard errors derived strictly from rounding errors. The coefficients are, of course, completely worthless.

13.3 RELATION OF CORRELATION FORMULAS IN DETERMINANTAL NOTATION TO THE INVERSE CORRELATION MATRIX

It is difficult to discuss estimation problems and multicollinearity in the general instance (any number of variables) without using the concept of an inverse matrix. An inverse correlation matrix can be described readily on the basis of the determinantal notation we have been using.

13.3.1 Relation of Correlation Formulas in Determinantal Notation to the Inverse Correlation Matrix

The elements of the inverse of a matrix of simple correlation coefficients may, in the three-variable case, be written as follows:

$$R_{(3)}^{-1} = \begin{bmatrix} \dfrac{\triangle_{3\,11}}{\triangle_3} & -\dfrac{\triangle_{3\,12}}{\triangle_3} & \dfrac{\triangle_{3\,13}}{\triangle_3} \\[2em] -\dfrac{\triangle_{3\,21}}{\triangle_3} & \dfrac{\triangle_{3\,22}}{\triangle_3} & -\dfrac{\triangle_{3\,23}}{\triangle_3} \\[2em] \dfrac{\triangle_{3\,31}}{\triangle_3} & -\dfrac{\triangle_{3\,32}}{\triangle_3} & \dfrac{\triangle_{3\,33}}{\triangle_3} \end{bmatrix}$$

The array of elements in the inverse was referred to as "the P_{ij} table" by Waugh in his 1935 article on regression computations.[2] In this notation, $P_{11} = \triangle_{3\,11}/\triangle_3$, $P_{12} = -\triangle_{3\,12}/\triangle_3$, and so on. We will write $R_{(3)}^{-1}$ out as

$$R_{(3)}^{-1} = \begin{bmatrix} P_{11} & P_{12} & P_{13} \\ P_{21} & P_{22} & P_{23} \\ P_{31} & P_{32} & P_{33} \end{bmatrix}$$

Like the original correlation matrix itself, the inverse correlation matrix is symmetric, so that $P_{21} = P_{12}$, $P_{31} = P_{13}$, and $P_{32} = P_{23}$.

To calculate $\beta_{12.3}$ from the inverse or P_{ij} table, we divide $-P_{12}$ by P_{11}. This is equivalent to (13.14):

$$(13.14) \qquad \beta_{12.3} = \frac{-P_{12}}{P_{11}} = \frac{\triangle_{3\,12}}{\triangle_3} \cdot \frac{\triangle_3}{\triangle_{3\,11}} = \frac{\triangle_{3\,12}}{\triangle_{3\,11}}$$

All the other formulas in the text can be derived in the same fashion from the P_{ij} table. For example,

$$(13.15) \qquad R_{1.23}^2 = 1 - \frac{1}{P_{11}} = 1 - \frac{\triangle_3}{\triangle_{3\,11}}$$

[2] F. V. Waugh, "A Simplified Method of Determining Multiple Regression Constants," *American Statistical Association Journal* **30**, pp. 694–700 (1935).

$$(13.15a) \quad \beta_{13.2} = \frac{-P_{13}}{P_{11}} = \frac{-\underset{13}{\triangle_3}}{\triangle_3} \cdot \frac{\triangle_3}{\underset{11}{\triangle_3}} = \frac{-\underset{13}{\triangle_3}}{\underset{11}{\triangle_3}}$$

$$(13.16) \quad r_{12.3} = \frac{-P_{12}}{\sqrt{P_{11}} \cdot \sqrt{P_{22}}} = \frac{\dfrac{\underset{12}{\triangle_3}}{\triangle_3}}{\left(\dfrac{\underset{11}{\triangle_3} \cdot \underset{22}{\triangle_3}}{\triangle_3}\right)^{\!\!1/2}} = \frac{\underset{12}{\triangle_3}}{\left(\underset{11}{\triangle_3} \cdot \underset{22}{\triangle_3}\right)^{\!1/2}}$$

and so on.

The text formulas in determinantal notation can be generalized for any number of variables. The same is true of the corresponding formulas in the P_{ij} notation. Thus,

$$(13.17) \quad \beta_{12.34} = \frac{-P_{12}}{P_{11}} = \frac{-\underset{12}{\triangle_4}}{\triangle_4} \cdot \frac{\triangle_4}{\underset{11}{\triangle_4}} = \frac{\underset{12}{\triangle_4}}{\underset{11}{\triangle_4}}$$

where P_{11} and P_{12} are the first and second elements in the first row of a four-row determinant,

$$R_{(4)}^{-1} = \left| \frac{\underset{ij}{\triangle_4}}{\triangle_4} \right| \quad i, j = 1, \ldots, 4$$

We may note in passing that the inverse correlation matrix permits us to calculate the regression constants not only for $X_1 = f(X_2, X_3)$ but also for $X_2 = f(X_1, X_3)$ and for $X_3 = f(X_1, X_2)$. Thus,

$$\beta_{21.3} = \frac{-P_{21}}{P_{22}} = \frac{\underset{21}{\triangle_3}}{\triangle_3} \cdot \frac{\triangle_3}{\underset{22}{\triangle_3}} = \frac{\underset{21}{\triangle_3}}{\underset{22}{\triangle_3}}$$

and

$$\beta_{31.2} = \frac{-P_{31}}{P_{33}} = \frac{-\underset{31}{\triangle_3}}{\triangle_3} \cdot \frac{\triangle_3}{\underset{33}{\triangle_3}} = \frac{-\underset{31}{\triangle_3}}{\underset{33}{\triangle_3}}$$

When the inverse correlation matrix is multiplied (according to the rules for matrix operations) by the original correlation matrix, the resulting product is the "identity matrix"

$$I_{(3)} = \begin{bmatrix} 1 & 0 & 0 \\ 0 & 1 & 0 \\ 0 & 0 & 1 \end{bmatrix} = R_{(3)}^{-1} R_{(3)}$$

We may check this relation as follows:

$$I_{(3)} = \begin{bmatrix} \dfrac{\Delta_{3\,11}}{\Delta_3} & -\dfrac{\Delta_{3\,12}}{\Delta_3} & \dfrac{\Delta_{3\,13}}{\Delta_3} \\[2ex] -\dfrac{\Delta_{3\,21}}{\Delta_3} & \dfrac{\Delta_{3\,22}}{\Delta_3} & -\dfrac{\Delta_{3\,22}}{\Delta_3} \\[2ex] \dfrac{\Delta_{3\,31}}{\Delta_3} & -\dfrac{\Delta_{3\,32}}{\Delta_3} & \dfrac{\Delta_{3\,33}}{\Delta_3} \end{bmatrix} \begin{bmatrix} 1 & r_{12} & r_{13} \\ r_{21} & 1 & r_{23} \\ r_{31} & r_{32} & 1 \end{bmatrix}$$

The element in row 1, column 1 of $I_{(3)}$ should be equal to the sum of the three elements in row 1 of $R_{(3)}^{-1}$ each multiplied by the corresponding element in column 1 of R, the original correlation matrix, or

$$i_{11} = 1 = \frac{\left(\Delta_{3\,11}\right)1}{\Delta_3} + \frac{\left(-\Delta_{3\,12}\right)r_{21}}{\Delta_3} + \frac{\left(\Delta_{3\,13}\right)r_{31}}{\Delta_3}$$

Expanding the Δ's into the original correlation coefficients from which they are built up, we have $\left(\text{after multiplying both sides of the equation by } \Delta_3\right)$,

$$\Delta_3 = 1 - r_{12}{}^2 - r_{13}{}^2 - r_{23}{}^2 + 2r_{12}r_{13}r_{23}$$
$$= (1 - r_{23}{}^2) \cdot 1 - (r_{12} - r_{13}r_{23})r_{12} + (r_{12}r_{23} - r_{13})r_{13}$$
$$= 1 - r_{23}{}^2 - r_{12}{}^2 + r_{12}r_{13}r_{23} - r_{13}{}^2 + r_{12}r_{13}r_{23}$$

The two sides of the equation are identical, so $i_{11} = 1$.

If we write out the elements of $I_{(3)}$ as

$$I_{(3)} = \begin{bmatrix} i_{11} & i_{12} & i_{13} \\ i_{21} & i_{22} & i_{23} \\ i_{31} & i_{32} & i_{33} \end{bmatrix}$$

the values of the other eight elements should satisfy the following relations:

$$i_{21} = 0 = \frac{\left(-\Delta_{21}\right)1}{\Delta} + \frac{\left(\Delta_{22}\right)r_{21}}{\Delta} + \frac{\left(-\Delta_{23}\right)r_{31}}{\Delta}$$

$$i_{31} = 0 = \frac{\left(\Delta_{31}\right)1}{\Delta} + \frac{\left(-\Delta_{32}\right)r_{21}}{\Delta} + \frac{\left(\Delta_{33}\right)r_{31}}{\Delta}$$

$$i_{12} = 0 = \frac{\left(\Delta_{11}\right)r_{12}}{\Delta} + \frac{\left(-\Delta_{12}\right)1}{\Delta} + \frac{\left(\Delta_{13}\right)r_{33}}{\Delta}$$

$$i_{22} = 1 = \frac{\left(-\Delta_{21}\right)r_{12}}{\Delta} + \frac{\left(\Delta_{22}\right)1}{\Delta} + \frac{\left(-\Delta_{23}\right)r_{32}}{\Delta}$$

$$i_{32} = 0 = \frac{\left(\Delta_{31}\right)r_{12}}{\Delta} + \frac{\left(-\Delta_{32}\right)}{\Delta} + \frac{\left(\Delta_{33}\right)r_{32}}{\Delta}$$

$$i_{13} = 0 = \frac{\left(\Delta_{11}\right)r_{13}}{\Delta} + \frac{\left(-\Delta_{12}\right)r_{23}}{\Delta} + \frac{\left(\Delta_{13}\right)1}{\Delta} = i_{31}$$

$$i_{23} = 0 = \frac{\left(-\Delta_{21}\right)r_{13}}{\Delta} + \frac{\left(\Delta_{22}\right)r_{23}}{\Delta} + \frac{\left(-\Delta_{23}\right)1}{\Delta} = i_{32}$$

$$i_{33} = 1 = \frac{\left(\Delta_{31}\right)r_{13}}{\Delta} + \frac{\left(-\Delta_{32}\right)r_{23}}{\Delta} + \frac{\left(\Delta_{33}\right)}{\Delta}$$

The reader should verify the foregoing identities for himself, using the definitions of the Δ's given at the beginning of this chapter.

13.4 MULTICOLLINEARITY IN MULTIPLE EQUATION MODELS AND IN MORE "SIMULTANEOUS" METHODS OF ESTIMATION: TWO-STAGE LEAST SQUARES AND LIMITED INFORMATION MAXIMUM LIKELIHOOD

In a major theoretical study of the problem of multicollinearity in multiple equation models, Klein and Nakamura (1962)[3] noted that multicollinearity involves not only statistical and theoretical problems but also problems on the mundane level of arithmetic.

13.4.1 Problems of Arithmetical Accuracy in Computing Structural Coefficients in Multiple Equation Models

Klein and Nakamura note that the formula for a least squares regression equation may be written in matrix notation as

$$a = M^{-1}m_y$$

where

$$a = \begin{pmatrix} a_1 \\ a_2 \\ \vdots \\ a_n \end{pmatrix}$$

and

$$m_y = \begin{pmatrix} m_{1y} \\ m_{2y} \\ \vdots \\ m_{ny} \end{pmatrix}$$

Each element in the vector a is a least squares regression coefficient, and each element in the vector m_y is a sum of cross products of y and x_i where these variables are expressed as deviations from their means; y is the dependent variable and x_i is one of the n independent variables. The complete definition of m_{iy} is

$$m_{iy} = \frac{1}{T} \sum_{t=1}^{T} (x_{it} - \bar{x}_i)(y_t - \bar{y})$$

where t is time.

Finally, M^{-1} is the inverse of the matrix of cross product or "product moments" M involving the n independent variables x_i, x_j $(i, j = 1, 2, \ldots, n)$.

[3] L. R. Klein and Mitsugu Nakamura, "Singularity in the Equation Systems of Econometrics: Some Aspects of the Problem of Multicollinearity," *International Economic Review* **3**, No. 3, pp. 274–299 (September 1962).

This is simply a generalization of the determinantal notation used in preceding pages. Like m_{iy} the elements m_{ij} $(i, j = 1, 2, 3, \ldots, n)$ of M are in units of the original variables. The matrix M approaches zero under the same conditions which cause the corresponding matrix of intercorrelation coefficients among independent variables to approach zero. Each element of the n by n inverse matrix M^{-1} contains the value of one determinant in its numerator and the value of the determinant of M in its denominator. Hence as the value of M approaches zero, small errors in it may cause quite appreciable errors in the numerical value of elements in the inverse M^{-1} and hence in the calculation of the regression coefficients, the a_i.

As for the computing problem, Klein and Nakamura observe that if the determinant of M for two independent variables differs from zero by a very small number (say 0.000001) the elements of the inverse M^{-1} can still be evaluated numerically with sufficient accuracy by carrying enough digits at each stage of the computations. The computations, of course, involve only multiplications, divisions, additions, and subtractions of pairs of the basic product moment elements of M, which for the two independent variables are m_{11}, m_{12} $(= m_{21})$, and m_{22}:

$$|M| = \begin{vmatrix} m_{11} & m_{12} \\ m_{12} & m_{22} \end{vmatrix} = m_{11}m_{22} - m_{12}{}^2$$

Note that the inverse matrix M^{-1} for two independent variables is simply

$$M^{-1} = \frac{1}{(m_{11}m_{22} - m_{12}{}^2)} \begin{bmatrix} m_{22} & -m_{12} \\ -m_{12} & m_{11} \end{bmatrix}$$

or

$$M^{-1} = \begin{bmatrix} \dfrac{m_{22}}{|M|} & \dfrac{-m_{12}}{|M|} \\[2ex] \dfrac{-m_{12}}{|M|} & \dfrac{m_{11}}{|M|} \end{bmatrix}$$

where $|M|$ is the numerical value of the determinant of M, namely $(m_{11}m_{22} - m_{12}{}^2)$. And the matrix equation $a = M^{-1}m_y$ becomes simply

$$\begin{bmatrix} a_1 \\ a_2 \end{bmatrix} = \begin{bmatrix} \dfrac{m_{22}}{|M|} & \dfrac{-m_{12}}{|M|} \\[2ex] \dfrac{-m_{12}}{|M|} & \dfrac{m_{11}}{|M|} \end{bmatrix} \begin{bmatrix} m_{1y} \\ m_{2y} \end{bmatrix}$$

whence

$$a_1 = m_{1y}\left(\frac{m_{22}}{|M|}\right) - m_{2y}\left(\frac{m_{12}}{|M|}\right)$$

$$a_2 = -m_{1y}\left(\frac{m_{12}}{|M|}\right) + m_{2y}\left(\frac{m_{11}}{|M|}\right)$$

or

$$a_1 = \frac{\sum x_1 y \cdot \sum x_2{}^2 - \sum x_2 y \cdot \sum x_1 x_2}{\sum x_1{}^2 \cdot \sum x_2{}^2 - (\sum x_1 x_2)^2}$$

and

$$a_2 = \frac{-\sum x_1 y \cdot \sum x_1 x_2 + \sum x_2 y \cdot \sum x_1{}^2}{\sum x_1{}^2 \cdot \sum x_2{}^2 - (\sum x_1 x_2)^2}$$

In normalized units and the notation of the preceding section, where $X_1 = f(X_2, X_3)$,

$$a_1 = \beta_{12.3} = \frac{r_{12} - r_{13} r_{23}}{1 - r_{23}{}^2}$$

and

$$a_2 = \beta_{13.2} = \frac{r_{13} - r_{12} r_{23}}{1 - r_{23}{}^2}$$

However, Klein and Nakamura go on to say that an accurate evaluation of the elements of M^{-1} is considerably more difficult to obtain if the matrix M is of size 5 times 5 or higher. A clerk working with a desk calculator of the conventional sort may find substantial difficulty in getting accurate figures with matrices (determinants) of this size. Further, "the problem is not solved if we point to the existence of powerful electronic computers, for the types of intercorrelation that we often encounter in economic time series have been found to give computing trouble with matrices no larger than 20 times 20. At the size of 30 times 30, difficulties have been found that prove to be almost insuperable with the most powerful machines.

"In most estimates of single regression equations, it is unlikely that the number of explanatory variables will exceed 15, and it is quite possible that the most advanced computing machines will be able to provide accurate estimates of any single equation calculated by standard least squares methods. However, the initial step in many equation systems methods of estimation is the estimation of properties of a large set of regression equations. These equations are likely to include more than 20 explanatory variables, and the computing problem, as it arises when multicollinearity is present, might be formidable. This has been our sad experience."

After an extensive analysis of the logical and statistical problems associated with multicollinearity, Klein and Nakamura return to the computational problem in a final paragraph:

"Finally, extreme care and precaution with accuracy of computation is not a fruitless and vain search for superfluous digits beyond the number significant in the original input. In spite of the fact that we have only two or three digits of significance in our original input variables and want only two- or three-digit coefficients as an end result, we may have to carry out intermediate calculations to a very large number of places. The intermediate stages of equations systems methods of estimation are quite intricate, and if we do not carry out all our results to many places and use the most accurate arithmetic procedures, we may find that our giant machines are spewing out masses of meaningless figures."

The basis for the foregoing comments will be intuitively clear if we consider that the operations involved in inverting an n by n correlation matrix include the evaluation of one determinant of order n by n and several other determinants of order $n - 1$ by $n - 1$. If our original matrix of intercorrelation coefficients includes only two variables, with the correlation coefficients recorded to four decimal places, we will multiply these coefficients together in pairs in the process of evaluating M; the exact numerical products will have eight decimal places. If M is of order 3 by 3, we will require the products of many sets of three correlation coefficients, each product involving 12 decimal places if we retain absolute arithmetical accuracy. If M were of order 20 times 20, absolute computational accuracy would require us to work with large sets of 80 digit numbers.

If all intercorrelations among independent variables are zero, there is no problem; the determinant which figures in the denominators of all elements of M^{-1} would in that case have a value of 1.00 regardless of the number of independent or exogenous variables. Very high intercorrelation among several or many independent variables requires us to multiply together chains of correlation coefficients that are slightly below unity and subtract them from the products of other multiplicative chains involving the same correlation coefficients in different sequences. It is this situation which makes multicollinearity serious even at the computational level.

13.4.2 *Effects of Multicollinearity in Two-Stage Least Squares Estimation*

Suppose we consider the estimation of one equation in a multiple equation model by means of two-stage least squares, say

$$(13.18) \qquad y_0 = \beta_1 y_1 + \beta_2 y_2 + \gamma_1 x_1 + \gamma_2 x_2 + \gamma_3 x_3 + u$$

where y_0, y_1, and y_2 are the endogenous variables and x_1, x_2, and x_3 the exogenous variables appearing in this particular structural equation. There are additional exogenous variables, say x_4, x_5, x_6, and x_7, in other equations of the model.

In the first stage of the estimation procedure we fit by least squares

$$(13.19) \qquad \hat{y}_1 = f_1(x_1, x_2, x_3; x_4, x_5, x_6, x_7)$$

$$(13.20) \qquad \hat{y}_2 = f_2(x_1, x_2, x_3; x_4, x_5, x_6, x_7)$$

In the second stage, we fit

(13.21) $y_0 = \beta_1 \hat{y}_1 + \beta_2 \hat{y}_2 + \gamma_1 x_1 + \gamma_2 x_2 + \gamma_3 x_3 + u$

Let us denote x_1, x_2, and x_3 by x^* and x_4, x_5, x_6, and x_7 by x^{**}. Then $\hat{y}_1$ is an exact linear function of (x^*, x^{**}), and $\hat{y}_2$ is also an exact linear function of (x^*, x^{**}). We may rewrite the second-stage equation as

(13.22) $y_0 = \beta_1 \left[\sum_{i=1}^{3} \lambda_{1i} x_i^* + \sum_{j=4}^{7} \lambda_{1j} x_j^{**} \right]$

$$+ \beta_2 \left[\sum_{i=1}^{3} \lambda_{2i} x^* + \sum_{j=4}^{7} \lambda_{2j} x^{**} \right] + \sum_{i=1}^{3} \gamma_i x_i^* + u$$

If it happens that the x_j^{**} have little correlation with y_1 and y_2, $\hat{y}_1$ and $\hat{y}_2$ will be nearly exact functions of the x_i^*. The correlation matrix of the five series which are treated as independent variables in the second-stage fitting of (13.22) is

$$M_r = \begin{array}{c} \\ \hat{y}_1 \\ \hat{y}_2 \\ x_1 \\ x_2 \\ x_3 \end{array} \begin{array}{ccccc} \hat{y}_1 & \hat{y}_2 & x_1 & x_2 & x_3 \\ \begin{bmatrix} 1 & r_{\hat{y}_1 \hat{y}_2} & r_{\hat{y}_1 x_1} & r_{\hat{y}_1 x_2} & r_{\hat{y}_1 x_3} \\ r_{\hat{y}_1 \hat{y}_2} & 1 & r_{\hat{y}_2 x_1} & r_{\hat{y}_2 x_2} & r_{\hat{y}_2 x_3} \\ r_{\hat{y}_1 x_1} & r_{\hat{y}_2 x_1} & 1 & r_{x_1 x_2} & r_{x_1 x_3} \\ r_{\hat{y}_1 x_2} & r_{\hat{y}_2 x_2} & r_{x_2 x_1} & 1 & r_{x_2 x_3} \\ r_{\hat{y}_1 x_3} & r_{\hat{y}_2 x_3} & r_{x_3 x_1} & r_{x_3 x_2} & 1 \end{bmatrix} \end{array}$$

If $R^2_{\hat{y}_2 . x_1 x_2 x_3}$ approaches one, the determinant of the 4 by 4 matrix of correlation coefficients among $\hat{y}_2$, x_1, x_2, and x_3 approaches zero. This in itself means serious multicollinearity, and it is compounded by the fact that $R^2_{\hat{y}_1 . x_1 x_2 x_3}$ also approaches one. This is a larger scale example of the situation we found in the supply function for pork in Chapter 11, when $\hat{Q}$ proved to be almost perfectly correlated with Z in the explanation of P. For although Y had a chance to influence $\hat{Q}$ in the first-stage fitting of $\hat{Q} = f(Z, Y)$, the correlation between $\hat{Q}$ and Y in the sample was extremely low.

Another possibility for multicollinearity is that x^* and x^{**} are highly correlated with each other, so that $\hat{y}_1$ given x^* is very nearly the same as $\hat{y}_1$ given (x^*, x^{**}). So once again in the fitting of (13.22) we will have near-multicollinearity between $\hat{y}_1$ and a combination of x_1, x_2, and x_3.

In brief, if the coefficients of (13.22) are to be estimated without excessively large standard errors, the endogenous variables y_1 and y_2 must not be wholly or almost wholly explained by x^*. There must be exogenous variables *in the system but not in the equation being estimated*, namely some of the x^{**} that are closely related to the endogenous variables y_1 and y_2 in that equation.

13.4.3 *Multicollinearity in Estimation by the Limited Information Maximum Likelihood and Full Information Maximum Likelihood Methods*

Since we are not attempting to present the theory and mathematics of these methods of estimation, we shall comment only briefly on the Klein and Nakamura findings with respect to them. They pointed to some particular examples in which limited information estimates "exploded" after apparently minor revisions in data or specifications and the corresponding least squares estimates did not, and commented as follows:

"Results like these have been found in numerous calculations. We notice that two-stage-least-squares estimates 'explode' in this way less frequently than do limited information estimates. We were originally led to conjecture that two-stage-least-squares estimates were more sensitive to multicollinearity than are ordinary least-squares estimates and that limited information estimates are more sensitive to multicollinearity than are two-stage-least-squares estimates."

The authors then define a "difference matrix"

$$(13.23) \qquad B = M_{yx}M_{xx}^{-1}M_{xy} - M_{yx^*}M_{x^*x^*}^{-1}M_{x^*y}$$

which appears in both the two-stage least squares and the limited information computations. The matrix M_{xx}^{-1} is the inverse of the matrix of product moments of *all exogenous or predetermined variables in the equation system*— the subscript xx stands in our earlier notation for $(x^* + x^{**})(x^* + x^{**})$. The largest matrix that would have to be inverted in ordinary least squares would be of order $(y + x^*)$—the number of variables appearing in a single equation. This matrix will rarely exceed 10 by 10, whereas M_{xx}^{-1} may well be as large as 30 by 30.

Hence with respect to the matrix B (via M_{xx}^{-1}) the two-stage least squares and limited information maximum likelihood methods of estimation are equally vulnerable to multicollinearity, and both are more vulnerable than ordinary least squares. But the limited information method also involves a determinantal equation $|B - \lambda W| = 0$, which is solved for its smallest root λ_0. The properties of this equation open up additional possibilities of singularity and "explosiveness" which are not found in two-stage least squares.

Klein and Nakamura conclude: "In summary, we may say that it is more plausible to expect that we will encounter singularity [determinants with values of zero] by the limited information method than by the two-stage least-squares method, because singularity of the former implies that of the latter ($|B| = 0$), while the converse is not necessarily true since there may be cases in which limited information estimates happen to be indeterminate or explosive with nonsingular B."

Although few serious applications have been made of the full information maximum likelihood method, it is a logical extension of the limited information maximum likelihood method and is, on certain assumptions, theoretically superior to the latter in infinite samples. Klein and Nakamura comment that calculations by the full information method involve matrices of higher order than do any of the other methods discussed, so that numerical precision in the face of multicollinearity is more difficult to obtain.

The measures suggested by Klein and Nakamura for getting on with the economist's business of estimating economic relationships involve a selective use of personal judgment. Instead of using all the x^* and x^{**} variables in our estimation procedures for every equation, we could withdraw enough variables (for example, in the first stage of two-stage least squares) to reduce multicollinearity to manageable proportions. Although different investigators might make different selections of variables, this approach seems somewhat more promising than including all of the exogenous variables despite the known presence of extremely high intercorrelations.

It should not be assumed that *every* multiple equation model involving economic time series will be plagued by multicollinearity. But many will be and we feel justified in placing great emphasis upon this problem.

It is sometimes possible to cut through the impasses produced by multicollinearity through the judicious use of *a priori* or extraneous information. A concrete example of a rather elaborate use of extraneous information for this purpose is given in the next section.

13.5   EXTRANEOUS OR *A PRIORI* INFORMATION AS ONE ANSWER TO MULTICOLLINEARITY: AN EXAMPLE

A first-hand encounter with multicollinearity may serve to illustrate its reality and also to introduce the possibility of using information from sources other than the particular sample at hand to supply realistic values for coefficients which cannot be estimated from the sample because of multicollinearity.

13.5.1 *The Agricultural Submodel of the Brookings–SSRC Model of the United States Economy*

The Brookings–SSRC model was described briefly in Chapter 10. The original version of its agricultural submodel was completed by Karl A. Fox in 1963. The individual equations of the submodel were fitted by least squares to quarterly data for the 14-year period 1947–1960. The submodel consists of 15 equations. It may be divided into one block of eight equations focusing on the determination of farm product prices and a second block of seven equations directed toward the estimation of net farm income. Altogether the submodel contains 15 endogenous and 30 exogenous or predetermined variables.

Two of the equations express the domestic consumer demand for foods of livestock and crop origin, respectively; each equation includes eight variables. The high degree of multicollinearity among the explanatory variables in both consumption functions makes it impossible to estimate certain coefficients from time series. The correlation matrix of the four most highly intercorrelated variables (all four appear in both equations) is

$$
\begin{array}{cccc}
& t & P_{nf} & \left(\dfrac{Y - T + T_r}{PN}\right) & P_c
\end{array}
$$

$$
\begin{array}{c}
t \\[4pt]
P_{nf} \\[4pt]
\left(\dfrac{Y - T + T_r}{PN}\right) \\[6pt]
P_c
\end{array}
\begin{bmatrix}
1.0000 & 0.9926 & 0.9785 & 0.9330 \\
0.9926 & 1.0000 & 0.9749 & 0.9406 \\
0.9785 & 0.9749 & 1.0000 & 0.9003 \\
0.9330 & 0.9406 & 0.9003 & 1.0000
\end{bmatrix}
$$

The value of the determinant is approximately 0.00009, a very near approach to singularity. (Recall that the determinant of a matrix with zero intercorrelation would have a value of 1.) If we assign *a priori* coefficients to three of these variables we can estimate the coefficient of the fourth variable by statistical means. The intercorrelations of the other three explanatory variables in each equation among themselves and with the trend-dominated four are not unduly high. The trend-dominated, highly intercorrelated four are time t, retail prices of foods of crop origin P_c, retail prices of nonfoods P_{nf}, and real disposable income per capita $[(Y - T + T_r)/PN]$.

The least squares estimates of the two consumer demand functions for food, *each containing four a priori coefficients*, follow.

Food Livestock Products:

(13.24) $\quad P_l = \quad 634.3751 - 0.2083t + 24.3988d_1 + 0.4504(P_l^*)_{-1}$
$\qquad\qquad$ (121.9413) $\quad$ (0.1869) $\quad$ (5.9470) $\qquad$ (0.1033)

$$
+ \left[-11.3177q_l + 0.1222P_c + 1.2718P_{nf} \right.
$$

$$
\left. + 0.2360\left(\frac{Y - T + T_r}{PN}\right) \right] + u_l
$$

$$
R^2 = 0.7226; \quad \bar{S} = \$15.3026; \quad \delta = 1.9788
$$

Standard deviations of dependent variable:

Original (P_l): $31.0537
Adjusted (P_l^*): $28.2530
Percentage of original
   variance explained by
   equation: $R_{ps}^2 = 1 - \dfrac{(15.3026)^2}{(31.0537)^2} = 0.7572$

Food Crop Products:

(13.25) $q_c = 27.3305 + 0.016163t + 0.3533d_1 + 0.7600(q_c^*)_{-1}$
          (10.1136)   (0.010021)   (0.3519)   (0.0878)

$$+ \left[-0.15952\left(\frac{C_1}{N}\right) - 0.06776P_c + 0.07527P_{nf} \right.$$

$$\left. + 0.01397\left(\frac{Y - T + T_r}{PN}\right) \right] + u_c$$

$R^2 = 0.6340; \quad \bar{S} = 0.9161; \quad \delta = 1.8627$

Standard deviations of dependent variable:

Original: 0.9862 index points
Adjusted q_c^*:   1.4726 index points
Percentage of original
   variance explained by
   equation: $R_{ps}^2 = 1 - \dfrac{(0.9161)^2}{(0.9862)^2} = 0.1371$

The first equation expresses a retail price index for food livestock products as a function of the following variables: a time trend t, a "dummy" variable d_1 intended to reflect the abnormal accumulation of consumer assets during 1947–1948, and a sharp increase in livestock prices during the first year or so of hostilities in Korea; an adjusted value of the retail price of livestock food products in the preceding quarter (the adjustment will be described shortly); real disposable income per capita; the index of per capita consumption of food livestock products; a retail price index for foods of crop origin; and the implicit price deflator for consumer expenditures on nonfood products and services.

During most of the 1947–1960 period, Department of Agriculture made little direct effort to support prices of livestock products. Therefore, it is appropriate to regard the retail price of food livestock products as a dependent variable and the supply of food livestock products purchased by consumers (hence offered for sale by retailers) in a given quarter as a predetermined variable. Time lags and inertia in the production of livestock products justify this treatment in quarterly data.

In contrast, (13.25) takes per capita consumption of foods of crop origin as the dependent variable and the corresponding retail price as a predetermined variable. The rationalization for this is that prices of many crops had been supported at the farm level; and some perishable crops such as vegetables had been in abundant supply and harvesting costs had provided a floor under their farm prices during most of the 1947–1960 period.[4] In other respects (13.25) is identical in form with (13.24). In each equation, the four coefficients in square brackets are based on information from sources other than the time series sample.

There is a long tradition of statistical demand analysis for farm products and foods in the United States based on time series data. There have also been a number of major studies of food purchases by households at particular points in time.

In a 1961 publication, George E. Brandow reviewed all of the better-known demand analyses for food products in the United States and, following a suggestion by Frisch (1959), synthesized from them a complete matrix of elasticities and cross-elasticities of consumer demand for 24 foods and food groups. Constraints implied in the pure theory of consumer demand were used in forcing a consistent set of demand elasticities (price and income) for the 24 food items.

Table 13.7 reproduces Brandow's consumer demand matrix in its entirety. Most of the own-price elasticities (the elements in the major diagonal) are based on time series analyses; so are some of the larger cross-elasticities, particularly within the meat, poultry, and fish group. The smaller cross-elasticities have been supplied by Brandow on a reproducible, but inevitably somewhat arbitrary, basis.

The nature of the conditions imposed from consumption theory may be illustrated in terms of Row 1 (beef). Column (1) indicates that a 1% increase in the retail price of beef would reduce beef consumption by 0.95000%. One percent increases in the prices of the other 23 foods would tend to increase beef consumption; the sum of these 23 cross-elasticities is 0.32490. Column (25) indicates that a 1% increase in the prices of all foods, including beef, would reduce beef consumption by 0.62510% (the algebraic sum of the own-elasticity of −0.95000 and the 23 cross-elasticities). Column (26) implies that

---

[4] In terms of Figure 11.3, farm price X_7 is determined by harvesting costs or by government action; retail price X_6 is equal to the sum of X_7 and X_3 (marketing charges); and consumption X_5 is determined by X_6 and X_2 (disposable personal income). To the extent that government price supports are involved, the free market causal ordering is reversed by the deliberate use of a policy instrument. When some quantities of a perishable crop are left unharvested because price has fallen to the level of harvesting cost, an inequality needed for maintenance of the normal causal ordering is replaced by an equality —a "boundary condition" becomes effective—and the effect on causal ordering is the same as in the government price support instance.

an increase of 1% in prices of all consumer goods and services other than foods would increase food consumption by 0.15510%. Column (27) indicates an elasticity of 0.47000 for beef consumption with respect to income.[5] The algebraic sum of Columns (25), (26), and (27) is zero, implying that a 1% increase in the prices of all commodities and in money income would leave the consumption of beef unchanged.

The figure at the intersection of Row 25 and Column (25) implies that a 1% increase in the prices of all foods would decrease the consumption of all foods by 0.34137%. This figure, -0.34137, is a weighted average of the first 24 figures in Column (25) using percentages of total food expenditures as weights. For a fuller statement, the reader is referred to Brandow (1961, pp. 15–18) and Frisch (1959).

13.5.2 *Adapting Extraneous Information to the Form Required by the Submodel*

Since Brandow's results seemed reasonable and were in close accord with our own demand analyses, we aggregated his matrix into three commodity groups—food livestock products, food crops, and nonfoods. In concept, these exhaust personal consumption expenditures or (if we lump personal savings with nonfoods) disposable personal income. The coefficients in Table 13.7 are elasticities, so the three aggregates can be expressed as equations in the logarithms of all variables:

(13.26)

$$
\begin{bmatrix} \log q_l \\ \log q_c \\ \log q_{nf} \end{bmatrix} = \begin{bmatrix} -0.479227 & 0.046226 & 0.107438 \\ 0.078203 & -0.304264 & 0.056090 \\ -0.098000 & -0.100700 & -1.025560 \end{bmatrix} \begin{matrix} \log P_l & \log P_c & \log P_{nf} \end{matrix} + \begin{bmatrix} 0.325568 \\ 0.169971 \\ 1.224260 \end{bmatrix} \log Y
$$

Each row satisfies the "homogeneity condition" except for rounding errors, that is, a 1% increase in the price of all commodities and in money income would leave the consumption of each individual commodity unchanged.[6]

The three equations are displayed in the manner of Chapter 11, so that the equations in their customary form can be "reconstituted" simply by multiplying the variable at the top of the column by each of the coefficients in the column below. Thus the first equation is

$$\log q_l = -0.479227 \log P_l + 0.046226 \log P_c + 0.107438 \log P_{nf}$$
$$+ 0.325568 \log Y$$

[5] Empirical evidence on cross-elasticities of demand for individual foods with respect to nonfood prices is limited. Brandow sets each of these cross-elasticities equal to 0.33 times the corresponding income elasticity.

[6] See also Chapter 14.

Table 13.7 Price and Income Elasticities of Demand at Retail: Percentage Change in Quantities Demanded Resulting from 1% Changes in Prices or Income, 1955–1957 (after Brandow)

Quantities Demanded of	Retail Prices of								
	(1) Beef	(2) Veal	(3) Pork	(4) Lamb and Mutton	(5) Chicken	(6) Turkey	(7) Fish	(8) Butter	(9) Shortening
1. Beef	−0.95000	0.05680	0.10019	0.03971	0.07496	0.00804	0.00380	0.00159	0.00050
2. Veal	0.37844	−1.60000	0.18527	0.07279	0.13808	0.01351	0.00321	0.00159	0.00050
3. Pork	0.13367	0.03672	−0.75000	0.03462	0.06603	0.00733	0.00463	0.00159	0.00050
4. Lamb and mutton	0.62008	0.17035	0.41480	−2.35000	0.21533	0.02073	0.00281	0.00159	0.00050
5. Chicken	0.23399	0.06428	0.15653	0.04268	−1.16027	0.12493	0.00436	0.00159	0.00050
6. Turkey	0.09758	0.02681	0.06528	0.01780	0.50000	−1.40426	0.00369	0.00159	0.00050
7. Fish	0.02091	0.00311	0.01618	0.00133	0.00678	0.00169	−0.65000	0.00159	0.00050
8. Butter	0.01554	0.00276	0.00874	0.00130	0.00412	0.00130	0.00276	−0.85000	0.07000
9. Shortening	0.01554	0.00276	0.00874	0.00130	0.00412	0.00130	0.00276	0.11044	−0.80000
10. Margarine	0.01554	0.00276	0.00874	0.00130	0.00412	0.00130	0.00276	0.40244	0.15000
11. Other edible oils	0.01554	0.00276	0.00874	0.00130	0.00412	0.00130	0.00276	0.12375	0.16215
12. Lard, direct[b]	0.01554	0.00276	0.00874	0.00130	0.00412	0.00130	0.00276	0.01000	0.28000
13. Eggs	0.01756	0.00312	0.00989	0.00148	0.00466	0.00148	0.00312	0.00128	0.00040
14. Fluid milk and cream	0.00825	0.00146	0.00464	0.00069	0.00219	0.00069	0.00146	0.00077	0.00024
15. Evaporated milk[c]	0.02014	0.00358	0.01134	0.00169	0.00535	0.00169	0.00358	0.00254	0.00080
16. Cheese	0.02044	0.00363	0.01151	0.00172	0.00543	0.00172	0.00363	0.00212	0.00066
17. Ice cream	0.01703	0.00302	0.00958	0.00143	0.00452	0.00143	0.00302	0.00176	0.00055
18. Fruit[d]	0.01369	0.00243	0.00771	0.00115	0.00364	0.00116	0.00243	0.00169	0.00053
19. Vegetables	0.02023	0.00360	0.01140	0.00170	0.00538	0.00170	0.00360	0.00279	0.00087
20. Cereals, baking products[d]	0.03021	0.00537	0.01701	0.00254	0.00802	0.00254	0.00537	0.00362	0.00114
21. Sugar and syrups[d]	0.01220	0.00217	0.00687	0.00103	0.00324	0.00103	0.00217	0.00089	0.00028
22. Beverages[d]	0	0	0	0	0	0	0	0	0
23. Potatoes, sweet potatoes	0.01885	0.00335	0.01062	0.00158	0.00501	0.00158	0.00335	0.00137	0.00043
24. Dry beans, peas, nuts[d]	0.01820	0.00323	0.01025	0.00153	0.00483	0.00153	0.00325	0.00133	0.00042
25. All foods	−0.07040	−0.01260	−0.03891	−0.00601	−0.01847	−0.00590	−0.01242	−0.00724	−0.00207
26. Nonfoods	−0.01565	−0.00169	−0.01682	−0.00053	−0.00639	−0.00120	−0.00345	−0.00298	−0.00264
27. All goods and services	−0.02834	−0.00422	−0.02194	−0.00180	−0.00919	−0.00229	−0.00553	−0.00396	−0.00251

480

Table 13.7 (continued)

				Retail Prices of				
	(10)	(11)	(12)	(13)	(14)	(15)	(16)	(17)	(18)
Quantities Demanded of	Margarine	Other Oils	Lard, Direct	Eggs	Fluid Milk and Cream	Evaporated Milk	Cheese	Ice Cream	Fruit
1. Beef	0.00013	0.00036	0.00005	0.00342	0.00012	0.00039	0.00257	0.00281	0.00771
2. Veal	0.00013	0.00036	0.00005	0.00342	0.00012	0.00039	0.00257	0.00281	0.00771
3. Pork	0.00013	0.00036	0.00005	0.00342	0.00012	0.00039	0.00257	0.00281	0.00771
4. Lamb and mutton	0.00013	0.00036	0.00005	0.00342	0.00012	0.00039	0.00257	0.00281	0.00771
5. Chicken	0.00013	0.00036	0.00005	0.00342	0.00012	0.00039	0.00257	0.00281	0.00771
6. Turkey	0.00013	0.00036	0.00005	0.00342	0.00012	0.00039	0.00257	0.00281	0.00771
7. Fish	0.00013	0.00036	0.00005	0.00342	0.00012	0.00039	0.00257	0.00281	0.00771
8. Butter	0.16057	0.10000	0.00343	0.00223	0.00365	0.00035	0.00224	0.00266	0.00905
9. Shortening	0.09442	0.20673	0.15171	0.00223	0.00365	0.00035	0.00224	0.00266	0.00905
10. Margarine	−0.80000	0.10072	0.06974	0.00223	0.00365	0.00035	0.00224	0.00266	0.00905
11. Other edible oils	0.04973	−0.46225	0.00825	0.00223	0.00365	0.00035	0.00224	0.00266	0.00905
12. Lard, direct[b]	0.08000	0.01940	−0.40000	0.00223	0.00365	0.00035	0.00224	0.00266	0.00905
13. Eggs	0.00011	0.00029	0.00004	−0.30000	0.00413	0.00039	0.00254	0.00300	0.01024
14. Fluid milk and cream[c]	0.00006	0.00018	0.00002	0.00167	−0.28500	0.01207	0.00173	0.00197	0.00654
15. Evaporated milk[c]	0.00021	0.00058	0.00008	0.00436	0.20000	−0.30000	0.00267	0.00337	0.01056
16. Cheese	0.00018	0.00048	0.00006	0.00437	0.00481	0.00045	−0.70000	0.00328	0.00879
17. Ice cream	0.00015	0.00040	0.00005	0.00359	0.00400	0.00038	0.00246	−0.55000	0.00821
18. Fruit[d]	0.00014	0.00039	0.00005	0.00357	0.00322	0.00030	0.00198	0.00234	−0.60000
19. Vegetables[d]	0.00023	0.00064	0.00008	0.00504	0.00476	0.00045	0.00293	0.00346	0.01086
20. Cereals, baking products[d]	0.00031	0.00083	0.00011	0.00623	0.00710	0.00067	0.00437	0.00517	0.01762
21. Sugar and syrups[d]	0.00007	0.00020	0.00003	0.00237	0.00287	0.00027	0.00176	0.00209	0.00712
22. Beverages[d]	0	0	0	0	0.05	0	0	0	0
23. Potatoes, sweet potatoes	0.00012	0.00032	0.00004	0.00287	0.00443	0.00042	0.00272	0.00323	0.01099
24. Dry beans, peas, nuts[d]	0.00011	0.00030	0.00004	0.00277	0.00428	0.00040	0.00263	0.00312	0.01062
25. All foods	−0.00040	−0.00128	−0.00002	−0.01145	−0.02827	−0.00044	−0.00896	−0.01130	−0.03958
26. Nonfoods	−0.00193	−0.00378	−0.00176	−0.01123	−0.02774	−0.00211	−0.00218	−0.00427	−0.01200
27. All goods and services	−0.00158	−0.00320	−0.00136	−0.01128	−0.02786	−0.00172	−0.00375	−0.00590	−0.01839

continued

481

Table 13.7 *(continued)*

| | | | | Retail Prices of | | | | | |
Quantities Demanded of	(19) Vegetables	(20) Cereals, Baking Products	(21) Sugar and Syrups	(22) Beverages	(23) Potatoes, Sweet Potatoes	(24) Dry Beans Peas, Nuts	(25) All Foods	(26) Nonfoods	(27) Income[a]
1. Beef	0.00886	0.00999	0.00250	-0.00196	0.00124	0.00112	-0.62510	0.15510	0.47000
2. Veal	0.00886	0.00999	0.00250	-0.00196	0.00124	0.00112	-0.76730	0.19038	0.57692
3. Pork	0.00886	0.00999	0.00250	-0.00196	0.00124	0.00112	-0.42560	0.10560	0.32000
4. Lamb and mutton	0.00886	0.00999	0.00250	-0.00196	0.00124	0.00112	-0.86450	0.21450	0.65000
5. Chicken	0.00886	0.00999	0.00250	-0.00196	0.00124	0.00112	-0.49210	0.12210	0.37000
6. Turkey	0.00886	0.00999	0.00250	-0.00196	0.00124	0.00112	-0.65170	0.16170	0.49000
7. Fish	0.00886	0.00999	0.00250	-0.00196	0.00124	0.00112	-0.55860	0.13860	0.42000
8. Butter	0.00901	0.00630	0.00275	0.00103	0.00061	0.00070	-0.43890	0.10890	0.33000
9. Shortening	0.00901	0.00630	0.00275	0.00103	0.00061	0.00070	-0.15960	0.03960	0.12000
10. Margarine	0.00901	0.00630	0.00275	0.00103	0.00061	0.00070	0	0	0
11. Other edible oils	0.00901	0.00630	0.00275	0.00103	0.00061	0.00070	-0.04127	0.01024	0.03103
12. Lard, direct[b]	0.00901	0.00630	0.00275	0.00103	0.00061	0.00070	0.06650	-0.01650	-0.05000
13. Eggs	0.01019	0.00713	0.00380	0.00072	0.00082	0.00081	-0.21280	0.05280	0.16000
14. Fluid milk and cream	0.00376	0.00173	0.00203	0.01923	0.00037	0.00045	-0.21280	0.05280	0.16000

482

15. Evaporated milk[c]	0.00961	0.00709	0.00556	0.00237	0.00152	0.00131	0	0	0
16. Cheese	0.01124	0.01301	0.00329	-0.00227	0.00167	0.00128	-0.59850	0.14850	0.45000
17. Ice cream	0.00902	0.00957	0.00304	-0.00124	0.00130	0.00123	-0.46550	0.11550	0.35000
18. Fruit[d]	0.00795	0.01015	0.00276	-0.00175	0.00130	0.00117	-0.53200	0.13200	0.40000
19. Vegetables	-0.30000	0.01092	0.00549	0.00082	0.00187	0.00167	-0.19950	0.04950	0.15000
20. Cereals, baking products[d]	0.01753	-0.15000	0.00746	0.00237	0.00235	0.00206	0	0	0
21. Sugar and syrups[d]	0.00708	0.00495	-0.30000	0.00052	0.00069	0.00070	-0.23940	0.05940	0.18000
22. Beverages[d]	0	0	0	-0.35590	0	0	-0.30590	0.07590	0.23000
23. Potatoes, sweet potatoes	0.01094	0.00765	0.00408	0.00155	-0.20270	0.00080	-0.10640	0.02640	0.08000
24. Dry beans, peas, nuts[d]	0.01056	0.00739	0.00394	0.00113	0.00077	-0.25223	-0.15960	0.03960	0.12000
25. All foods	-0.02259	-0.00467	-0.01830	-0.01388	-0.00298	-0.00323	-0.34137	0.08470	0.25667
26. Nonfoods	-0.02358	-0.02227	-0.01595	-0.00923	-0.00521	-0.00431	-0.19870	-1.02556	1.22426
27. All goods and services	-0.02335	-0.01819	-0.01649	-0.01031	-0.00469	-0.00392	-0.23177	-0.76823	1.00000

[a] The food income elasticities satisfy the homogeneity condition but may be too high. See Brandow, especially p. 24.

[b] Does not include lard contained shortening and margarine.

[c] Includes condensed milk.

[d] These food groups are described in *Consumption of Food in the United States, 1909–52*, USDA Agr. Handbook No. 62 (September 1953).

Source: George E. Brandow, *Interrelations Among Demands for Farm Products and Implications for Control of Market Supply, Pa. Agr. Exp. Sta. Bul. 680*, Table 1, p. 17 (1961).

For reasons already noted, it was necessary to choose retail price rather than consumption as the dependent variable in the food livestock products equation. This was done by transposing $\log P_l$ to the dependent position in the first row (equation) of (13.26) and substituting the resulting right-hand member into the second and third rows (equations), respectively:

$$(13.27) \qquad \begin{matrix} (\log q_l & \log P_c & \log P_{nf}) & (\log Y) \end{matrix}$$

$$\begin{bmatrix} \log P_l \\ \log q_c \\ \log q_{nf} \end{bmatrix} = \begin{bmatrix} -2.086694 & 0.096460 & 0.224190 \\ -0.163186 & -0.296721 & 0.073622 \\ 0.204496 & -0.110153 & -1.047531 \end{bmatrix} + \begin{bmatrix} 0.679361 \\ 0.223099 \\ 1.157683 \end{bmatrix}$$

The elasticity coefficients in rows 1 and 2 were then multiplied by ratios of the 1947–1960 mean values of the appropriate variables to convert the equations into arithmetic form. Row 3 was discarded at this point, as the variable q_{nf} is deeply imbedded in the nonagricultural sectors of the SSRC model and it would not have been useful to the total project to add an equation explaining q_{nf} to the agricultural submodel. The arithmetic forms of the first and second rows (equations) are as follows:

$$(13.28) \quad P_l = -11.317682q_l + 0.122229P_c + 1.271780P_{nf} + 0.236049y$$

$$(13.29) \quad q_c = -0.159516q_l - 0.067764P_c + 0.075271P_{nf} + 0.013971y$$

A simplified notation has been used here for convenience, P_l and P_c standing for prices of livestock and crop foods, respectively, q_l and q_c for the corresponding per capita consumption indices, and P_{nf} and q_{nf} for price and per capita consumption of nonfoods. Per capita income y is expressed in real terms. It is assumed to be an exogenous variable with respect to the agricultural submodel, so that there is no need to allow for interactions between y and the other predetermined variables in (13.28) and (13.29).

13.5.3 *Combining a priori Information with Coefficients Estimated Directly from the Time Series Sample*

In the livestock consumption equation, the coefficients of (13.28) were imposed in the following fashion [using the notation of (13.26) and (13.27)]:

$$P_l^* = P_l - \left[-11.3177q_l + 0.1222P_c + 1.2718P_{nf} + 0.2360\left(\frac{Y - T + T_r}{PN}\right) \right]$$

The adjusted variable P_l^* was regressed on its own value for the previous quarter $(P_l^*)_{-1}$, on time t, and on the dummy "inflationary period" variable d_1, yielding the following equation:

$$P_l^* = 634.3751 - 0.2083t + 24.3988d_1 + 0.4504(P_l)_{-1} + u_1$$
$$\qquad\quad (121.9413) \quad (0.1869) \qquad (5.9470)$$
$$R^2 = 0.7226; \quad \bar{S} = 15.3026; \quad \delta = 1.9788$$

The expression in brackets (containing the four *a priori* coefficients) was then added to each side of the last equation to obtain the form presented in (13.24).

The crop food consumption equation was handled in the same way, using an adjusted variable

$$q_c^* = q_c - \left[-0.15952q_l - 0.06776P_c + 0.07527P_{nf} + 0.01397\left(\frac{Y - T + T_r}{PN}\right) \right]$$

The adjusted variable q_c^* was regressed on its own value for the preceding quarter, $(q_c)_{-1}^*$, on time t, and on the dummy variable d_1, yielding:

$$q_c^* = 27.3305 + 0.016163t + 0.3533d_1 + 0.7600(q_c^*)_{-1} + u_c$$
$$\qquad\quad (10.1136) \quad (0.010021) \quad (0.3519) \qquad (0.0878)$$
$$R^2 = 0.6340; \quad \bar{S} = 0.9161; \quad \delta = 1.8627$$

The expression in brackets was then added to each side of the foregoing equation to obtain (13.25).

In summary Brandow's matrix provides us with *a priori* coefficients for three of the four trend-dominated variables and for one other (q_l). Hence the combination of *a priori* and statistical information is sufficient to give us useful estimates of the net effects of all seven explanatory variables upon retail prices of food livestock products and per capita consumption of food crops.

The elasticity coefficients in matrix (13.13) look reasonable in relation to some earlier results by Karl A. Fox. The own-price elasticity of -0.48 for food livestock products may be compared with the author's estimates of -0.52 to -0.56 during 1922–1941.[7] The own-price elasticity of -0.34 for all food compares with the author's 1922–1941 estimates of -0.34 to -0.37.[8]

13.6 FURTHER COMMENTS ON THE USE OF *A PRIORI* OR EXTRANEOUS INFORMATION

We will not attempt a general discussion of the use of *a priori* or extraneous information. The journal literature on such topics as "mixed estimation" and

[7] See Karl A. Fox, *Econometric Analysis for Public Policy*, Ames: Iowa State University Press, p. 116 (1958).

[8] See Karl A. Fox, "Structural Analysis and the Measurement of Demand for Farm Products," *Review of Economics and Statistics*, p. 65 (February 1954).

"incomplete prior information" was expanding rapidly in the early 1960s. However, there is a rather long history of the use of *a priori* information in connection with regression analysis. A few points will be mentioned briefly.

13.6.1 *The Sample versus the Rest of the World*

In the regression model based on designed experiments, intercorrelations can be set at zero and a clear *unidirectional causal dependence* specified between the independent variables and the dependent variable. The observations on each independent variable are spread out over a wide range to reduce the standard errors of the regression coefficients. Having built a nearly optimal design into the experiment, it seems reasonable for the scientist to consider the results of this one experiment in isolation from all the rest of human knowledge. He calculates his standard errors, makes his significance tests, and presumably stands or falls on his probability statements without drawing upon prior experience or outside information of any kind.

But should he? Yates (1951), who has made important methodological contributions to the analysis of experimental data, had this to say:

"The emphasis on tests of significance, and the consideration of the results of each experiment in isolation, have had the unfortunate consequence that scientific workers have often regarded the execution of a test of significance on an experiment as the ultimate objective. Results are significant or not and that is the end of it.

"Research workers, therefore, have to accustom themselves to the fact that in many branches of research the really critical experiment is rare, and that it is frequently necessary to combine the results of numbers of experiments dealing with the same issue in order to form a satisfactory picture of the true situation."[9]

Williams himself comments (page 4) that: "The tendency to base the interpretation of data entirely on the results of significance tests has its dangers. Many workers apply significance tests excessively, sometimes at the expense of sound judgment and a careful overall assessment of the work. A sound interpretation will take into account not only such individual tests as are made but also prior knowledge and experience and the general consistency of the effects that show up."

[9] F. Yates, "The Influence of *Statistical Methods for Research Workers* on the Development of the Science of Statistics," *Journal of the American Statistical Association,* **46,** pp. 19–34. Quoted in E. J. Williams, *Regression Analysis* (New York: John Wiley and Sons), p. 5, 1959.

If scientists whose materials permit them to use controlled experiments still find it advisable to cumulate or compare the results of many experiments (when available) rather than to base an important decision on the results of a single experiment, it seems even more reasonable for economists to combine other information with the results of an analysis based on a limited number of nonexperimental observations. The appropriate stance might be: "Do not trust an observation unless it is confirmed by a good theory." And do not trust a multiple regression analysis of economic time series unless the results accord with prior or outside information.

We are confronted with an area of permissiveness which is more likely to be reduced by advances in economic knowledge than by advances in statistical technique. At one extreme, we might elect to stand or fall on the results of purely statistical estimates based on a set of time series observations—despite multicollinearity, latent variables, errors of measurement, and aggregation problems, not to mention changes in technology and in consumer preferences. At the other extreme, we might ignore statistical estimation entirely and impose all coefficients in a model on the basis of (1) restrictions supplied by economic theory, accounting identities, and technical coefficients and (2) judgments based on all kinds of information, collated intuitively rather than rigorously.

As economists, we would be most unwise to cast aside the wealth of theory and empirical observation that has been painstakingly built up by brilliant and dedicated scholars and to base our scientific conclusions exclusively on statistical analyses of particular time series samples. So we must use "prior information" to some extent to supplement our statistical estimation procedures.

But note that if we impose our economics on our statistics, we are inviting the judgments of economists on the cogency of our economic reasoning and the validity of any facts or relationships we adduce from empirical economic studies. "*A priori* information" is of varying qualities. If we use purely arbitrary coefficients to get around a statistical impasse we deserve criticism from both economists and statisticians. Bad economics will not rescue us from ambiguous statistics; good economics may.

13.6.2 *Some Examples of the Use of* a priori *Information in Regression Analysis*

Like Monsieur Jourdain, who was surprised to learn that he had been speaking prose all his life, we may be surprised to realize the extent to which "prior information" is used in setting up almost any regression analysis.

What Variables Shall Be Included in a Demand Function? In Chapter 11, we referred to a demand function of the type

$$(13.30) \qquad p_1 = a_1 + b_{11}q_1 + c_1 y + u_1$$

where p_1 = price of (say) pork, q_1 = per capita consumption of pork, and y = disposable personal income per capita.

Implicitly, (13.30) has assigned a regression coefficient of zero to all other conceivable variables, including prices or quantities of other commodities. If we had included terms such as $b_{12}q_2$ and $b_{13}q_3$ in our initial statement of (13.30), we might then have proceeded to say "*but* we assume on the basis of other information that b_{12} and b_{13} are either zero or negligibly small." And we might find after fitting (13.30) to some time series observations that y had shown little variation other than a linear upward trend. We could not tell from the time series whether the true model might not be

$$(13.31) \qquad p_1 = a_1 + b_{11}q_1 + d_1 t + u$$

where t = "time" in years. But if we accept (13.31) as the true model we are assigning an *a priori* value of zero to the coefficient of y, namely $c_1 = 0$.

If decisions as to the inclusion or exclusion of variables are regarded as the *a priori* assignment of zero values to certain regression coefficients, it is clear that any regression analysis is a nucleus surrounded by *a priori* information.

Nonzero Restrictions on the Values of Regression Coefficients. In the gasoline consumption example of Chapter 6, the constant term in the regression equation

$$(13.32) \qquad \text{Gasoline used} = a + b \text{ (miles traveled)} + z$$

was not significantly different from zero. With or without that information, we would probably have been justified on *a priori* grounds in setting a equal to zero. Let us use X_1 for gasoline used and X_2 for mileage traveled. If we stipulate that $a = 0$, we simply calculate b as

$$(13.33) \qquad b' = \frac{\sum X_1 X_2}{\sum X_2{}^2}$$

The formulas with an unrestricted a value would be

$$(13.34) \qquad b = \frac{\sum X_1 X_2 - n\bar{X}_1\bar{X}_2}{\sum X_2{}^2 - n(\bar{X}_2)^2}$$

and

$$(13.35) \qquad a = \bar{X}_1 - b\bar{X}_2$$

The formula for b' is derived by the method of Chapter 4, Appendix A substituting "0" for a in deriving the normal equations.[10] It is clear from the demonstration in footnote 10 that we could also impose the restriction that a be equal to some nonzero constant.[11]

Wold (1953) and Stone (1945), among others, have imposed consumption income regression coefficients obtained from family budget studies at a particular point in time upon analyses in which the regressions of consumption on price were to be estimated from time series. Wold chose this procedure because of high intercorrelation between prices and income in his time series data. He refers to this technique as "regression analysis with *side conditions on the parameters*, or briefly *conditional regression analysis*."[12]

The implications of this technique can be shown in terms of the normal equations.[13] If X_1 is consumption, X_2 is price, and X_3 is income, all in the

[10] Specifically, we are to fit by least squares the equation

$$X_1 = a + b'X_2 + z$$

subject to the restriction that $a = 0$.

We minimize the sum of squares $\sum z^2 = \sum (X_1 - a - b'X_2)^2$, but since $a = 0$, this reduces to $\sum z^2 = \sum (X_1 - b'X_2)^2$. We choose the value of b' to minimize $\sum z^2$:

$$\frac{\partial \sum z^2}{\partial b'} = 0 = -2X_2 \sum (X_1 - b'X_2)$$

or $\qquad \sum X_1 X_2 - b' \sum X_2{}^2 = 0 \qquad$ and $\qquad b' = \dfrac{\sum X_1 X_2}{\sum X_2{}^2}$

[11] Suppose we wish to fit the regression $X_1 = a + b'X_2 + z$ subject to the restriction that $a = 2$. We minimize $\sum z^2 = \sum (X_1 - 2 - b'X_2)^2$; since $a = 2$ is predetermined and the X_1 and X_2 observations are known numbers, the only variable in the equation is b'. Then,

$$\frac{\partial \sum z^2}{\partial b'} = 0 = -2X_2 \cdot \sum (X_1 - 2 - b'X_2) \qquad \text{or} \qquad \sum X_1 X_2 - 2 \sum X_2 - b' \sum X_2{}^2 = 0;$$

$$b' = \frac{\sum X_1 X_2 - 2(n\overline{X}_2)}{\sum X_2{}^2} = \frac{\sum [(X_1 - 2)X_2]}{\sum X_2{}^2}$$

If the X_2's are positive numbers, it is clear that b' *given* $a = 2$ will be smaller than the value of b' *given* $a = 0$, as in footnote 10.

[12] Herman Wold, *Demand Analysis* (New York: John Wiley and Sons), p. 47, 1953.

[13] Suppose we fit the equation $X_1 = a + b'_{12}X_2 + b_{13}X_3 + z$, subject to the constraint that $b_{13} = 0.6$ and (for simplicity) $a = 0$. We may rewrite the equation as

$$X_1 = b'_{12}X_2 + 0.6X_3 + z$$

We minimize

$$\sum z^2 = \sum (X_1 - b'_{12}X_2 - 0.6X_3)^2 \text{ with respect to } b_{12}$$

obtaining

$$\frac{\partial \sum z^2}{\partial b'_{12}} = 0 = -2X_2 \sum (X_1 - b'_{12}X_2 - 0.6X_3)$$

or $\qquad b'_{12} \sum X_2{}^2 - \sum X_1 X_2 + 0.6 \sum X_2 X_3 = 0$

Then $\qquad b'_{12} = \dfrac{\sum X_1 X_2 - 0.6 \sum X_2 X_3}{\sum X_2{}^2} = \dfrac{\sum (X_1 - 0.6X_3)X_2}{\sum X_2{}^2}$

form of time series observations, and we wish to stipulate that the regression coefficient of X_1 on X_3 be (say) 0.6, we can simply regress $(X_1 - 0.6X_3)$ upon X_2 by least squares. This is the intuitively obvious procedure and is borne out by the demonstration in footnote 13.

Some *a priori* conditions on regression coefficients turn out to be self-policing, although this should never be assumed without proof. For example, the regression coefficients of a complete set of components, each regressed on their sum, will add up to 1. For if we consider a total $(x_1 + x_2)$ and its components x_1 and x_2, then

$$b_{1T} = \frac{\sum x_1(x_1 + x_2)}{\sum (x_1 + x_2)^2} \quad \text{and} \quad b_{2T} = \frac{\sum x_2(x_1 + x_2)}{\sum (x_1 + x_2)^2}$$

We obtain

$$b_{1T} + b_{2T} = \frac{\sum (x_1^2 + x_1 x_2 + x_1 x_2 + x_2^2)}{\sum (x_1^2 + 2x_1 x_2 + x_2^2)} = \frac{1}{1} = 1$$

Hence a considerable variety of *a priori* restrictions can be imposed upon either single equation or multiple equation models by building the restrictions into the structures of the models so that estimates of other coefficients and minimization of sums of squared residuals are secured, subject to the restrictions. Once an investigator recognizes these possibilities he must also recognize that the quality of the statistically estimated coefficients is directly dependent upon the validity and accuracy of the restrictions.

13.6.3 *The Sensitivity of Statistically Estimated Coefficients to Alternative Values of Coefficients Based on Extraneous Information*

In the early 1960s techniques were being proposed whereby *a priori* coefficients would be imposed not as exact values but as values subject to sampling error. For example, if a coefficient estimated from family budget data was 0.6 with a standard error of 0.03, restrictions could be imposed in such a way that the coefficient must lie between 0.54 and 0.66. This would be roughly equivalent to accepting values of the coefficient anywhere within a 95% confidence interval.

We could also take into account our uncertainty as to the exact value of an *a priori* coefficient by introducing a number of values over a reasonable range and observing the effects on the statistically estimated coefficients. For example, in footnotes 10 and 11 we found the following results:

A Priori Value of a	Statistically Estimated Value of b'
0	$\dfrac{\sum (X_1 - 0)X_2}{\sum X_2^2}$
2	$\dfrac{\sum (X_1 - 2)X_2}{\sum X_2^2}$

The difference between the two values of b' is $-2 \sum X_2 / \sum X_2^2$. Since $\sum X_2 = n\bar{X}_2$ and $\sum X_2^2$ in the sample are known numbers, $-\sum X_2 / \sum X_2^2$ is a constant, and b' is a linear function of the assigned values of a:

$$b'_{(a)} = b'_{(a=0)} - \left(\frac{\sum X_2}{\sum X_2^2} \right) a$$

In the gasoline use and mileage traveled example, the mileages x_2 were positive numbers on the order of 200 and the gasoline consumption figures X_1 (in gallons) were positive numbers on the order of 14. If $a = 0$, the regression line rises about 14 gallons per 200 miles; if $a = 2$ (gallons), the regression lines rise only 12 gallons per 200 miles.

In footnote 13 the effects of alternative imposed values of the consumption-income regression coefficient b_{13} upon the statistically estimated values of b_{12} can be shown as follows (note that we also imposed the restriction that $a = 0$):

A Priori Value of b_{13}	Statistically Estimated Value of b'_{12}
0.5	$\dfrac{\sum (X_1 - 0.5X_3)X_2}{\sum X_2^2}$
0.6	$\dfrac{\sum (X_1 - 0.6X_3)X_2}{\sum X_2^2}$
0.7	$\dfrac{\sum (X_1 - 0.7X_3)X_2}{\sum X_2^2}$

The difference between the values of b'_{12} for $b_{13} = 0.7$ and $b_{13} = 0.6$ is $-0.1 \sum X_2 X_3 / \sum X_2^2$. Here again, since $\sum X_2 X_3$ and $\sum X_2^2$ in the sample are known numbers, b'_{12} is a linear function of b_{13}. (The expression $\sum X_2 X_3 / \sum X_2^2$ would be the simple regression of income on price if the constant term of that regression were set at zero.)

13.6.4 *Using* a priori *Information about Levels of Measurement Error in Variables*

A priori information on absolute or relative levels of measurement error in variables is also helpful. The following examples are based on experiments by the author.[14]

The literature on simultaneous equations estimating methods has generally assumed that all observed variables are measured without error. On this assumption, the unexplained residuals from each reduced-form equation

---

[14] See Karl A. Fox, *op. cit.*, pp. 64–66 (1954).

consist only of random disturbances or shocks which affect the endogenous or "dependent" variable. The standard assumption in least squares regression analysis is similar except for terminology. The independent variables are assumed to be measured without error, and the unexplained residuals are considered to be a random component of the dependent variable.

In the 1920s and 1930s some analysts experimented with weighted regressions in an effort to arrive at what are now called structural relations. For example, consumer demand curves are generally thought of as reversible or exact functions, such that the net effect on price of a unit change in consumption should be precisely the reciprocal of the effect on consumption of a unit change in price. But consider the following least squares equations relating to the demand for food:

(13.36)
$$p_f = -0.004 - 2.00q_f + 0.91y; \quad R^2 = 0.86$$
$$ (0.49) \quad\; (0.08)$$

(13.37)
$$q_f = -0.000 - 0.25p_f + 0.25y; \quad R^2 = 0.66$$
$$ (0.06) \quad\; (0.05)$$

where p_f and q_f are indices, respectively, of retail food prices and per capita food consumption; y is per capita disposable income. All variables are expressed as first differences of logarithms for the period 1922–1941. The first equation implies that a 1% drop in price would be associated with a 0.50% increase in food consumption; the second implies a consumption increase of only 0.25%.

If it is assumed that there are no disturbances because of omitted variables, any unexplained variance in (13.36) and (13.37) must be attributed to errors in the data. A "correct" adjustment for such errors would produce perfect correlation among p_f, q_f, and y regardless of the direction in which residuals were minimized. In the present instance, one adjustment yields the equations

(13.38)
$$p_f = a_1 - 2.97q_f + 0.95y; \quad R^2 = 1.00$$

(13.39)
$$q_f = a_2 - 0.34p_f + 0.32y; \quad R^2 = 1.00$$

Another, equally plausible, adjustment yields the equations

(13.40)
$$p_f = a_{12} - 2.70q_f + 0.92y; \quad R^2 = 1.00$$

(13.41)
$$q_f = a_{22} - 0.37p_f + 0.34y; \quad R^2 = 1.00$$

In each of these pairs, demand elasticity is the exact reciprocal of price flexibility. The two adjustments reflect different assumptions concerning the relative levels of error in the three variables.

However, if the true model is believed to include random disturbances in the dependent or endogenous variable, an adjustment for errors in variables should not be sufficient to produce perfect correlation between their corrected values. The ideal adjustment would involve subtracting from the observed variance of each variable an estimate of the variance due to (random) measurement error. If the values of each variable were estimated from probability samples, the error variances could be estimated from standard error formulas.

In some other instances, rough judgments as to the levels of measurement error in a series might be formed on the basis of first-hand information as to the method by which it was constructed.

For example, a least squares equation for eggs, based on first differences of logarithms during 1922–1941, gave the following results:

$$(13.42) \qquad p_e = -0.010 - 1.83q_e + 1.24y; \quad R^2 = 0.80$$
$$(0.48) \quad\;\; (0.15)$$

where p_e is retail price and q_e per capita production of eggs, and y is per capita disposable income. Because of the extremely limited year-to-year variability of q_e, an allowance for relatively small absolute errors in the series accounted for 15% of its observed variance; p_e and y fluctuated much more sharply, and the error levels estimated for them accounted for less than 2% of their observed variances. The equation adjusted for these error allowances is

$$(13.43) \qquad p_e = -0.010 - 2.34q_e + 1.34y; \quad R^2 = 0.87$$
$$(0.44) \quad\;\; (0.13)$$

The adjustments leave 13% of the variation in retail egg prices to be explained by other factors or "disturbances."

This type of adjustment is consistent with the assumption of the simultaneous equations approach that variables can be classified into endogenous and predetermined categories, with the later distributed independently of the disturbances. The weighted regression adjustment which forces perfect correlation implicitly denies the validity or usefulness of this classification.

EXERCISES

1. Summarize briefly the primary problems of multicollinearity involved in extending the regression model to four or more variables. Does this extension change the general results of the answer to Exercise 7 of Chapter 7?

2. Verify the identities ($i_{i,j}$, $i, j = 1, 2, 3$) given on p. 467.

3. There are three views of the role of econometrics:

(a) Statistical techniques should be used *only* to test economic theory which is based on abstract reasoning and nonrigorous observation of the world.

(b) We apply statistical techniques to raw data (in many forms) in order to generate theories about the behavior of the world.

(c) We employ statistical techniques in order to see how the world has behaved in the past, and with this information in hand, forecast what will happen in the future.

From the discussion in this chapter, answer the following questions:

(i) Are these three views mutually exclusive, that is, if one is true, then the others are false? If so, which one is correct, and why?

(ii) Should good econometrics include some combination of all three, and if so, which of the views should be given the greatest weight? Why?

(iii) Where does the use of *a priori* information fall in these positions?

REFERENCES

1. Brandow, G. E., "Interrelations Among Demands for Farm Products and Implications for Control of Market Supplies, University Park: *Pennsylvania State University Agricultural Experiment Station Bulletin* 680 (an interregional publication), 1961.

2. Fox, Karl A., "Structural Analysis and the Measurement of Demand for Farm Products," *Review of Economics and Statistics*, February 1954.

3. Fox, Karl A., "A Submodel of the Agricultural Sector," in *The Brookings Quarterly Econometric Model of the United States*, J. S. Duesenberry, Gary Fromm, L. R. Klein, and Edwin Kuh (eds.), Chicago: Rand McNally and Co., and Amsterdam: North-Holland Publishing Co., 1965.

4. Fox, Karl A., *Econometric Analysis for Public Policy*, Ames: Iowa State University Press, 1958.

5. Fox, Karl A. and J. F. Cooney, *Effects of Intercorrelation Upon Multiple Correlation and Regression Measures*, Washington: Dept. of Agriculture, *Agricultural Marketing Service Bulletin*, April 1954, reissued October 1959.

6. Frisch, Ragnar, *Statistical Confluence Analysis by Means of Complete Regression Systems*, Oslo: Klara Civiltryckeri, 1934.

7. Klein, L. R. and Mitsugu Nakamura, "Singularity in the Equation Systems of Econometrics: Some Aspects of the Problem of Multicollinearity," *International Economic Review* 3, No. 3, pp. 274–299, September 1962.

8. Waugh, F. V., "A Simplified Method of Determining Multiple Regression Constants," *Journal of the American Statistical Association* 30, pp. 694–700, 1935.

9. Wold, Herman, *Demand Analysis*, New York: John Wiley and Sons, p. 47, 1953.

CHAPTER 14

The Measurement of Economic Aggregates

Most of the basic concepts of economic theory reviewed in Chapter 2 apply to individual consumers and producers. The downward slope of market demand curves is rationalized on the basis of the downward slopes of the demand curves of individuals. The apparent horizontal or rising market supply curves in different industries are explained on the basis of the horizontal or rising marginal cost curves of individual firms. The individual consumers and firms are viewed as decision makers with definite objectives and tangible criteria for judging their success in attaining them.

National economic policy is designed to influence national economic aggregates. But the impacts of such policies must be felt and responded to by the individual decision-making units. Hence to anticipate the effects of proposed macroeconomic policies (tax reductions, accelerated government expenditures, changes in social security provisions, and many others) we must have a clear understanding of the manner in which these policies impinge on the individual, how they enter into his decision-making framework, and the responses which would be (1) rational from the standpoint of maximizing real income or profit and (2) probable considering imperfections of knowledge and other factors which cause individuals to make nonoptimal responses.

Purely empirical relationships between economic aggregates, such as an observation that one series has turned down earlier than another in three of the last four business recessions, have a very limited scientific appeal. If we can demonstrate that one series enters in a specific way into the decisions of the firms whose activities are reflected in the other series, we have knowledge of a structural nature. The crucial test of this structural knowledge would be its capacity to explain why the typical lead-lag relationship was reversed in one of the four recessions.

If we are to avoid a naive empiricism in dealing with economic aggregates we must first do some rather careful bridge-building between the *microvariables* and *microrelationships* associated with individual consumers or firms and the *macrovariables* and *macrorelationships* associated with large aggregates of consumers or firms at a national or regional level. In our bridge-building we shall make extensive use of the concept of "perfect aggregation" proposed and analyzed by Theil (1954).

We shall start out with some problems of aggregating microvariables relating to consumers.

14.1 THE MEASUREMENT OF PRICE, QUANTITY, AND INCOME AGGREGATES RELATING TO CONSUMERS

In Figures 2.1–2.4, we presented some basic elements of the theory of consumer demand. Although our diagrams related only to two commodities, the basic concepts can readily be generalized to any number of goods and services.

First, we specify that the sense of well-being or level of utility attained by a consumer is a function of the quantities of goods and services he is able to acquire and consume. This concept is expressed in (14.1):

$$(14.1) \qquad u = f(q_1, q_2, \ldots, q_n)$$

If the prices of all commodities remain constant and the money income of the consumer rises, he is able to purchase larger quantities of some or all commodities. It is always possible in principle to convert an increase in money income into a uniform percentage increase in the quantities purchased of all commodities. The level of utility u will certainly increase as the consumer purchases additional units of this composite commodity made up of fixed proportions of each of the n goods.

We noted also that a change in the relative prices of two commodities leads to a movement along an indifference curve so that purchases of the commodity which has become relatively cheaper are increased and purchases of the commodity which has become relatively dearer are reduced. A reduction in the price of one commodity while the prices of all other commodities remain constant will lead to a movement along an indifference surface and will also increase real income, thereby moving the consumer to a somewhat higher indifference surface. (When we deal with more than two commodities, we speak of an indifference *surface* rather than an indifference curve. The change in terminology is no more than a courteous nod to the geometry of the three commodity or n-commodity situation; it in no way changes the basic economic idea.)

There is no known way to measure the indifference map or surface of a consumer. However, the consumer's purchases of goods and services, and the prices he pays for them, are certainly measurable in concept. If we have the active cooperation of the consumer, as in consumer expenditure studies, these prices and quantities are also measurable in fact. The consumer's income is also measurable.

In principle, therefore, we could express the behavior of a particular consumer or household by means of the set of (14.2):

$$q_1 = a_1 + b_{11}p_1 + b_{12}p_2 + \cdots + b_{1n}p_n + c_1 y$$
$$q_2 = a_2 + b_{21}p_1 + b_{22}p_2 + \cdots + b_{2n}p_n + c_2 y$$
$$\vdots$$
$$q_n = a_n + b_{n1}p_1 + b_{n2}p_2 + \cdots + b_{nn}p_n + c_n y$$

(14.2)

The first of these n equations simply indicates that the quantity purchased of commodity 1 will be influenced by the prices of each of the n commodities and by the household's money income. Similarly, the quantity purchased of each of the $n - 1$ other commodities will be influenced by the n prices and by household income. In the spirit of Figures 2.1–2.4, we specify in (14.3) that total expenditures for the n commodities are equal to total income:

$$(14.3) \qquad \sum_{i=1}^{n} q_i p_i = y$$

We may think of y as *total consumption expenditures*, so that all of the n commodities are objects of expenditure. Alternatively, we could think of y as disposable personal income and define the nth "commodity" as *personal saving*—either convention would cause (14.3) to hold.

Let us suppose now that we have a similar set of n equations for each of the k households in a relatively isolated town. We assume further that consumers do all of their purchasing from local stores and service establishments. Finally, let us assume that the various proprietors pool their information and that each of them keeps a complete record of quantities purchased and prices paid by each household in the community in such a way that purchases made by a particular household at each of the stores can be identified with that household.

Let us simplify the problem slightly by assuming that no commodity is sold by more than one store in the community, so that there is only one price charged for a given commodity to all households. In concept, the merchant selling commodity 1 could raise its price p_1 by one unit. If the various consumer demand relations indicated for each consumer held exactly (and if all merchants colluded to hold the prices of other commodities constant and employers colluded to hold constant the income of each household) he could calculate the coefficient b_{11} for each household in the community. For the hth household,

(14.4) $$b_{11.h} = \frac{\Delta q_{1.h}}{\Delta p_1}$$

By pooling information with other proprietors, he would in principle be able to compute for each household the other $n - 1$ coefficients involving p_1, namely those showing the effects of changes in p_1 upon the purchases of q_2 through q_n:

(14.5)
$$b_{21.h} = \frac{\Delta q_{2.h}}{\Delta p_1}; \quad b_{31.h} = \frac{\Delta q_{3.h}}{\Delta p_1}; \ldots$$

$$\vdots$$

$$b_{n1.h} = \frac{\Delta q_{n.h}}{\Delta p_1} \quad (h = 1, 2, 3, \ldots, k)$$

By successive manipulations of each of the other $n - 1$ prices, one price at a time, and by a separate manipulation of money income, each of the other coefficients in the demand equations for each household could in principle be computed. In brief, we have described a set of operations by means of which the coefficients of the microequations for each household could (in theory) be determined.

We are, of course, abstracting from a great many realistic problems, some of which will be mentioned later. If the invasions of privacy implied in these operations make us uncomfortable, we may proceed at once to a related experiment which makes no attempt whatsoever to identify the purchases of individual consumers.

This experiment requires that all retail stores and service establishments in the community pool their information concerning the total quantities of each commodity sold to all residents of the community combined. By varying the price of one commodity at a time, the pooled information should in principle permit the calculation of aggregative coefficients B_{ij} which measure the effect of a unit change in the price of commodity i upon purchases of each of the n commodities, that is, aggregate purchases by the k households in the community. To measure the aggregative coefficient C_i our experiment may require that all employers collude to increase the money incomes of every household in the community by the same percentage.

We may write a pseudoutility function for all households as a function of total quantities purchased of each of the n commodities, as in (14.6):

(14.6) $$U = f(Q_1, Q_2, \ldots, Q_n)$$

recognizing that we cannot really add up the utilities of the different consumers.

This reservation does not apply to the corresponding demand functions. We may write the aggregative community demand equations as

(14.7)
$$
\begin{aligned}
Q_1 &= A_1 + B_{11}P_1 + B_{12}P_2 + \cdots + B_{1n}P_n + C_1Y \\
Q_2 &= A_2 + B_{21}P_1 + B_{22}P_2 + \cdots + B_{2n}P_n + C_2Y \\
&\vdots \\
Q_n &= A_n + B_{n1}P_1 + B_{n2}P_2 + \cdots + B_{nn}P_n + C_nY
\end{aligned}
$$

In (14.8), we impose the condition that the value of total purchases of the n commodities must be equal to the total income of all households:

(14.8)
$$
\sum_{i=1}^{n} Q_iP_i = Y
$$

We have assumed that the demand equations for each household were exact, and that the various prices, quantities, and household incomes were recorded without error. Each quantity in (14.7), such as Q_1, is a simple and exact summation of the purchases of each household $q_{1.k}$. The total consumer expenditure or income Y is a simple and presumably exact summation of the y's for each of the k households. For the moment, we may eliminate prices from the realm of controversy by assuming that the price of each commodity is the same for every consumer, so that P_1, for example, is exactly equal to p_1 for every household. Thus we eliminate for the present any problem of aggregation or averaging involving prices.

Each B_{ij} is a simple sum of the corresponding coefficients, the small b_{ij}'s in the demand functions for individual households. Since (14.2) and (14.7) are in arithmetic form, C_1 will be a simple arithmetic mean of the c_1's only if the income of each household has been changed by the same number of dollars in the process of calculating C_1.

For complete clarity, we may write that

(14.9)
$$
B_{11} = \frac{\Delta q_{1.1}}{\Delta p_1} + \frac{\Delta q_{1.2}}{\Delta p_1} + \frac{\Delta q_{1.3}}{\Delta p_1} + \cdots + \frac{\Delta q_{1.k}}{\Delta p_1} = \frac{\Delta Q_1}{\Delta P_1}
$$

(14.10)
$$
B_{21} = \frac{\Delta q_{2.1}}{\Delta p_1} + \frac{\Delta q_{2.2}}{\Delta p_1} + \frac{\Delta q_{2.3}}{\Delta p_1} + \cdots + \frac{\Delta q_{2.k}}{\Delta p_1} = \frac{\Delta Q_2}{\Delta P_1}
$$
$$\vdots$$

(14.11)
$$
B_{nn} = \frac{\Delta q_{n.1}}{\Delta p_n} + \frac{\Delta q_{n.2}}{\Delta p_n} + \frac{\Delta q_{n.3}}{\Delta p_n} + \cdots + \frac{\Delta q_{n.k}}{\Delta p_n} = \frac{\Delta Q_n}{\Delta P_n}
$$

(14.12)
$$
C_1 = \frac{1}{k}\left[\frac{\Delta q_{1.1}}{\Delta y} + \frac{\Delta q_{1.2}}{\Delta y} + \frac{\Delta q_{1.3}}{\Delta y} + \cdots + \frac{\Delta q_{1.k}}{\Delta y}\right] = \frac{\Delta Q_1}{\Delta Y}
$$
$$\vdots$$

(14.13)
$$
C_n = \frac{1}{k}\left[\frac{\Delta q_{n.1}}{\Delta y} + \frac{\Delta q_{n.2}}{\Delta y} + \frac{\Delta q_{n.3}}{\Delta y} + \cdots + \frac{\Delta q_{n.k}}{\Delta y}\right] = \frac{\Delta Q_n}{\Delta Y}
$$

where there are n commodities, n^2 aggregative quantity-price coefficients B_{ij}, and n aggregative income coefficients C_i; all aggregations are performed over k households.

These equations may be regarded, if we wish, as linear approximations to nonlinear functions, applicable within a moderate range of some initial set of values of the prices, quantities, and incomes. Such uses of linear approximations are very common in economic analysis.

Equations (14.2) reflect the behavior of an individual consumer allocating his total income among various objects of expenditure in the presence of a specified array of prices. Given the attitudes and preferences of the consumer which are reflected in the demand equations (14.2), the set of q_i's which he selects will presumably make him feel better off than if he had acquired some other set.

We will use the words *consumer* and *household* interchangeably when talking about observed or observable behavior in the allocation of income among goods and services. Even within a household we cannot add up the indifference levels or utility levels attained by the individual members. The household's demand functions simply describe *how* it will allocate its expenditures among different commodities under different combinations of retail prices and levels of its own money income. They are positive or existential rather than normative relationships.

If we knew the coefficients of (14.2) for a given household (we assume the equations to be exact functions), we should be able to predict the values of the q_i's it would select given any specified set of values of the p_i's and y. If there were 1000 households in the community of our example, knowledge of the incomes received and prices paid by each of the 1000 households would permit an exact prediction of the commodity purchases of each of them. The sum of these "perfect predictions" for each household would constitute a "perfect prediction" of the total purchases Q_i of the 1000 households.

Evidently, exact knowledge of the microrelations and values of the price and income microvariables enables us to make a perfect prediction of the macrovariables Q_i. But can we make perfect predictions of the macrovariables Q_i if our knowledge is limited to the values of the *macrorelations* and the macrovariables, P_i and Y, in (14.7)? If we can make perfect predictions of the Q_i's from (14.7), we may say that these equations represent a *perfect aggregation* of the microrelations for the thousand households.

Theil (pp. 16–17, 1954) expresses the concept essentially as follows:

It is clear that the effects of a change in an independent macrovariable Y on a dependent macrovariable, say Q_1, can be measured in two ways. First, we can measure it *directly* by means of the macroequation

$$(14.14) \qquad Q_1 = A_1 + B_{11}P_1 + \cdots + B_{1n}P_n + C_1 Y$$

from which we have

(14.15) $$\Delta Q_1 = C_1 \Delta Y$$

Second, we can measure it directly by means of the microequations

(14.16) $$q_{1.h} + a_{1.h} + b_{11.h}p_1 + \cdots + b_{1n.h}p_n + c_{1.h}y_h$$
$$(h = 1, 2, 3, \ldots, 1000)$$

from which we have

(14.17) $$\Delta Q_1 = \sum_{h=1}^{1000} \Delta q_{1.h} = \sum_{h=1}^{1000} c_{1.h} \Delta y_h$$

where

$$\sum_{h=1}^{1000} \Delta y_h = \Delta Y$$

In (14.12) we showed that the coefficients $c_{1.h} = \Delta q_{1.h}/\Delta y_h$ were defined in such a way that if $\Delta y_h = (1/1000)(\Delta Y)$ for each of the $k = 1000$ households,

(14.18) $$C_1 = \frac{\Delta Q_1}{\Delta Y} \quad \text{and} \quad \Delta Q_1 = C_1 \Delta Y$$

In this instance the estimates of ΔQ_1 are identical whether we use the macro-relation directly, $\Delta Q_1 = C_1 \Delta Y$, or whether we divide ΔY among the households, enter $\Delta y = 1/k \Delta Y$ in each of the microequations, and add up the resulting estimates of $\Delta q_{1.h}$ for each of the 1000 households. We shall find, however, that in general the direct and the indirect methods will *not* give identical estimates or predictions of ΔQ_1. There are *contradictions* between the conclusions (estimates) drawn from the macrotheory and those from the microtheory.

14.1.1 The Concept of "Perfect Aggregation" over Consumers: Consumption, Income, and the Marginal Propensity to Consume

For the moment, let us consider the aggregation problem in terms of one commodity and two coefficients. We will lighten our expository burden even further by limiting our aggregates to only two households. Specifically, we consider the two microrelations

(14.19) $$q_{1.1} = a_{1.1} + c_{1.1}y_1$$

(14.20) $$q_{1.2} = a_{1.2} + c_{1.2}y_2$$

for households 1 and 2, respectively. The corresponding macrorelation is

(14.21) $\quad Q_1 = A_1 + C_1 Y \quad$ where $\quad Q_1 = (q_{1.1} + q_{1.2}) \quad$ and $\quad Y = (y_1 + y_2)$

If we simply add up the microrelations for the two households we obtain

$$(14.22) \qquad (q_{1.1} + q_{1.2}) = (a_{1.1} + a_{1.2}) + (c_{1.1}y_1 + c_{1.2}y_2)$$

Simple addition evidently gives us the correct or definitional value of Q_1. But y_1 and y_2 enter the aggregate in a multiplicative relationship with $c_{1.1}$ and $c_{1.2}$, respectively. Whereas $Y = (y_1 + y_2)$ is a simple sum or aggregate of y_1 and y_2, the term $(c_{1.1}y_1 + c_{1.2}y_2)$ is a *weighted* aggregate.

An exact estimate of ΔQ_1 by means of the two microrelations is given by

$$(14.23) \qquad \Delta Q_1 = c_{1.1}\Delta y_1 + c_{1.2}\Delta y_2$$

But our macrorelation (14.21) allows us only the single coefficient C_1 to transmit the effects of *both* Δy_1 and Δy_2. Furthermore, our macrorelation permits us only the single income variable Y.

If (14.21) is to give us the same exact estimate of ΔQ_1 as we obtain through the two microrelations, the following equality must hold for all possible pairs of values of y_1 and y_2:

$$(14.24) \qquad C_1 Y = c_{1.1}y_1 + c_{1.2}y_2$$

or

$$(14.25) \qquad Y = \frac{1}{C_1}(c_{1.1}y_1 + c_{1.2}y_2)$$

or

$$(14.26) \qquad Y = \left(\frac{c_{1.1}}{C_1}y_1 + \frac{c_{1.2}}{C_1}y_2\right)$$

This equality would also have to hold, of course, for *changes* in y_1 and y_2:

$$(14.27) \qquad \Delta Y = \left(\frac{c_{1.1}}{C_1}\Delta y_1 + \frac{c_{1.2}}{C_1}\Delta y_2\right)$$

For the moment, let us choose an arbitrary but plausible value for C_1,

$$(14.28) \qquad C_1 = \frac{(c_{1.1} + c_{1.2})}{2} = \bar{c}_1$$

and consider the implications for ΔY, Δy_1, and Δy_2. The "weights" in (14.27) may now be written,

$$\frac{c_{1.1}}{\bar{c}_1} + \frac{c_{1.2}}{\bar{c}_1} = 2$$

the arithmetic mean of the two weights is 1. When we define ΔY as the simple sum of Δy_1 and Δy_2, we are implicitly assigning *equal weights*, 1 and 1, to the income changes of the two households.

Unless $c_{1.1}/\bar{c}_1 = c_{1.2}/\bar{c}_1 = 1$, and $c_{1.1} = c_{1.2} = \bar{c}_1$, it is not possible that $(\Delta y_1 + \Delta y_2) = [(c_{1.1}/\bar{c}_1)\,\Delta y_1 + (c_{1.2}/\bar{c}_1)\,\Delta y_2]$ except in the special instance where $\Delta y_1 = \Delta y_2$. We cannot tolerate the latter restriction because in general Δy_1 and Δy_2 will be unequal. The alternative special condition, that $c_{1.1} = c_{1.2}$, is a question of fact; in general we must expect that $c_{1.1}$ and $c_{1.2}$ will be unequal.

The only way in which we can validate (14.27) or (14.26) for all possible sets of values of the variables Δy_1 and Δy_2 and the fixed behavioral coefficients $c_{1.1}$ and $c_{1.2}$ is to turn (14.26) into the *definition* of a specially weighted aggregative income variable Y^*:

(14.29) $$Y^* = \left(\frac{c_{1.1}}{C_1}\,y_1 + \frac{c_{1.2}}{C_1}\,y_2\right)$$

or letting

$$C_1 = \bar{c}_1 = \tfrac{1}{2}(c_{1.1} + c_{1.2})$$

(14.30) $$Y^* = \frac{1}{\bar{c}_1}\sum_{h=1}^{2} c_{1.h}y_h$$

Substituting these values of C_1 and Y^* in (14.21) and letting $A_1 = (a_{1.1} + a_{1.2})$, we have

(14.31) $$Q_1 = A_1 + \bar{c}_1 Y^*$$

or

$$(q_{1.1} + q_{1.2}) = (a_{1.1} + a_{1.2}) + \bar{c}_1\left(\frac{1}{\bar{c}_1}\right)(c_{1.1}y_1 + c_{1.2}y_2)$$

which is identically equal to (14.22) obtained by simple addition of the two microrelations.

On the surface, this result seems rather odd. We are perfectly comfortable with a definition of the aggregate income of the two households as $Y = y_1 + y_2$; in concept, this is the way our national income measures are built up. But we are reluctant to admit this strange *weighted* income variable Y^* as a legitimate economic aggregate.

We may clarify the difference between Y and Y^* by writing Y^* in the form

(14.32) $$Y^* = \frac{1}{\bar{c}_1}\sum_{h=1}^{2} c_{1.h}y_h$$

The coefficient $c_{1.h}$ for a particular commodity and a particular household is the household's *marginal propensity to consume* that commodity. It measures the number of units by which the household's consumption of q_1 will increase when its income y rises by one unit. The marginal propensity to consume a given commodity will vary from one household to another. The ratio $c_{1.h}/\bar{c}_1$ is the ratio of the marginal propensity to consume of household h to the simple arithmetical mean of the marginal propensities of the two households. The simple average of these ratios for the two households is 1.

The same effect would be given us by (14.21) if and only if the incomes of both households were precisely the same. In this special instance, Y^* would be exactly equal to Y.

We are using the two households of our example to represent the millions of households that are involved in the real aggregates of macroeconomics. In some actual situations, we might find that the larger marginal propensities to consume were concentrated among households with below-average incomes. In this instance, Y^* would be smaller than Y. If the commodity in question were an expensive luxury, we might find that the marginal propensity to consume it among most of the lower-income households was zero and that the above-average marginal propensities to consume were found among the households with above-average incomes. In this case, Y^* would be larger than Y.

In any of the foregoing instances, Y^* would be of the same general order of magnitude as Y. For the United States as a whole, the personal consumption expenditures component of the gross national product would correspond to Y. The numerical value of Y^* as determined in relation to a commodity of almost universal consumption might well prove to be within 10 or 15% of Y.

At this point we are faced with a minor dilemma. In order to obtain the aggregative variable Y^* we must know the $c_{1.h}$'s for each individual household. But if we knew each of these microcoefficients (and presumably each of the coefficients $a_{1.h}$), we could simply calculate the value of $q_{1.h}$ for each household and add them up to obtain a perfect prediction of Q_1. We could simply ignore the unorthodox Y^* method of aggregating the incomes of individual households in order to arrive at a macrorelation which would *also* permit a perfect prediction of Q_1.

In practice, the usual situation is that we have estimates of the values of the simple aggregative variables Q_1 and Y over a number of time periods. We do not have information about the individual $c_{1.h}$'s and y_h's so we cannot use the $c_{1.h}$'s as a basis for calculating $C_1 = \bar{c}_1$. In general, we try to obtain estimates of A_1 and C_1 by simply relating the regression or other statistical estimators.

Hence it may be that our hard-won knowledge of the concept of perfect aggregation will have little operational value in dealing with most practical situations. But before deciding this, let us carry the concept of perfect aggregation a step or two further.

14.1.2 *"Perfect Aggregation" over Consumers: Responses of Consumption to Price Changes*

Again our demonstration will be in terms of only two households.

We now consider a microrelation which expresses the consumption of a commodity as a linear function of its own price:

(14.33) $$q_{1.1} = a_{1.1} + b_{1.1}p_{1.1}$$

(14.34) $$q_{1.2} = a_{1.2} + b_{1.2}p_{1.2}$$

As in the previous example, we wish to consider whether it is possible to derive a single macrorelation,

(14.35) $$Q_1 = A_1 + B_1 P_1{}^*$$

which will enable us to make a perfect prediction of Q from any specified value of P^*. The standard for perfect prediction is set by:

(14.36) $$Q_1 = (q_{1.1} + q_{1.2}) = (a_{1.1} + a_{1.2}) + (b_{1.1}p_{1.1} + b_{1.2}p_{1.2})$$

or

$$Q_1 = \sum_{h=1}^{2} a_{1.h} + \sum_{h=1}^{2} b_{1.h}p_{1.h}$$

The algebra involved in deriving (14.35) is precisely the same as for (14.34). Equation (14.35) will give us perfect predictions of Q_1 if the following conditions are met:

$$A_1 = \sum_{h=1}^{2} a_{1.h}; \quad B_1 = \bar{b}_1 = \tfrac{1}{2} \sum_{h=1}^{2} b_{1.h}$$

and

$$P_1{}^* = \frac{1}{\bar{b}_1} \sum_{h=1}^{2} b_{1.h}p_{1.h} = \left(\frac{b_{1.1}}{\bar{b}_1} p_{1.1} + \frac{b_{1.2}}{\bar{b}_1} p_{1.2} \right)$$

Substituting these values in (14.35), we find that (14.35) will give a perfect prediction of Q_1:

(14.37) $$Q_1 = A_1 + \bar{b}_1 P_1{}^*$$

or

$$(q_{1.1} + q_{1.2}) = (a_{1.1} + a_{1.2}) + \bar{b}_1 \left(\frac{1}{\bar{b}_1} \right)(b_{1.1}p_{1.1} + b_{1.2}p_{1.2})$$

which is identically equal to (14.36) obtained by simple addition of the two microrelations.

The definitions of B_1 and $P_1{}^*$ are somewhat unconventional since $P_1{}^*$ is a "total price" rather than the customary *average price*; B_1 is the simple arithmetic mean of the slopes of the microrelations. We can transform $P_1{}^*$ to a more conventional form by defining $P'_1 = P_1{}^*/2$ and $B'_1 = 2B_1 = \sum_{h=1}^{2} b_{1.h}$. Then (14.35) can be rewritten as

(14.38) $$Q_1 = A_1 + B'_1 P'_1$$

where

$$P'_1 = \frac{1}{2} \sum_{h=1}^{2} b_{1.h} p_{1.h} = \frac{1}{2} \sum_{h=1}^{2} \left(\frac{b_{1.h}}{\bar{b}_1}\right) p_{1.h}$$

In the foregoing demonstration we have extended the subscript of p_1 to $p_{1.h}$ to allow for the possibility that different consumers, presumably in different neighborhoods, will be paying different prices for the same commodity.

In general, P'_1 should be within a few percent of a simple arithmetic mean of the prices paid by the different households, $\bar{p}_1 = \frac{1}{2}(p_{1.1} + p_{1.2})$, or, if there are many households as in real economic aggregates, $\bar{p}_1 = 1/k \sum_{h=1}^{k} p_{1.h}$, where k represents the number of households in the nation or area with which we are concerned. However, in P'_1 the prices paid by households whose consumption responses to price are larger (in absolute value, since all the $b_{1.h}$'s are negative) than the simple arithmetic mean ($\bar{b}_1$) of these coefficients will be more heavily weighted than those of households with below-average consumption responses to price for this commodity.

From a practical standpoint, aggregation of prices seems likely to cause us much less trouble than aggregation of incomes. For we know there are great variations among households with respect to income even in a single community. Prices paid by different households for precisely the same commodity will show much less variation, particularly in advanced economies in which most retailers charge the same price to all persons who enter their establishments. We may find large variations over space in the prices charged for personal services and at least moderate price variations associated with transportation costs from surplus to deficit regions with respect to a given commodity. And there is no compelling reason for believing that those consumers who are paying higher-than-average prices for a commodity have anything other than average responses of consumption to changes in its price. Our greatest difficulties with relationships involving prices arise when we consider aggregating over commodities.

14.1.3 *"Perfect Aggregation" over Commodities with Respect to an Individual Consumer*

Aggregation over commodities gives rise to the conventional problems of index number construction. However, we may obtain more economic insight into the design and interpretation of index numbers if we first approach the question of aggregation over commodities in terms of an individual consumer.

Aggregation and Index Number Formulas When Consumption of Each Commodity Is a Function Only of Its Own Price.[1] The consumer whose demand functions are presented in (14.2) is interested in n commodities. As the equations are written, his consumption of each of these commodities is subject to influence by his income and by the prices of every one of the n commodities. However, to open the present discussion we will make some drastic simplifications. We shall assume that the quantity purchased by our consumer of the ith commodity depends exclusively on its own price p_i and on no other prices. And we disregard any possible influences of income upon the consumption of any commodity. We now consider the problem of aggregating the demand equations for m commodities—m is smaller than n. Specifically, we are dealing with the following microrelations:

$$\begin{aligned}
q_1 &= a_1 + b_{11}p_1 \\
q_2 &= a_2 && + b_{22}p_2 \\
(14.39) \quad q_3 &= a_3 &&&& + b_{33}p_3 \\
&\;\;\vdots \\
q_m &= a_m &&&&&& + b_{mm}p_m
\end{aligned}$$

This aggregation problem is serious. Quantities of the different commodities are measured in different units. For example, q_1 might be beefsteak measured in pounds and q_2 might be electrical energy measured in terms of kilowatt hours.

The consumer's utility or sense of well-being is a function of the q_i:

$$(14.40) \qquad u = f(q_1, q_2, \ldots, q_m)$$

The utility function does not include the prices of the commodities.

However, we have noted in Chapter 2 that an optimal allocation of the consumer's income between two commodities requires that the marginal rate of substitution of commodity 1 for commodity 2 be numerically equal to the ratio of the price of commodity 2 to the price of commodity 1:

$$(14.41) \qquad \frac{\Delta q_1}{\Delta q_2} = -\frac{p_2}{p_1} \quad \text{and} \quad \Delta q_1 p_1 = -\Delta q_2 p_2$$

In (14.41) Δq_1 and Δq_2 are associated with a small movement along a *specified indifference curve*. If Δq_1 is positive, Δq_2 is negative, and the loss in utility associated with the decrease in q_2 is exactly offset by the increase in

[1] This corresponds to the case of *additive preferences* in the theory of consumer demand.

utility resulting from the increase in q_1. Although we cannot measure utility directly or even the marginal utility of a single commodity, we know that if the consumer has made an optimal allocation of his income the ratio of the marginal utilities to him of any two commodities is equal to the ratio of their prices. We may represent this in (14.42) as

$$(14.42) \qquad \frac{\dfrac{\Delta u}{\Delta q_2}}{\dfrac{\Delta u}{\Delta q_1}} = -\frac{p_2}{p_1} \quad \text{and} \quad \frac{\Delta q_1}{\Delta q_2} = -\frac{p_2}{p_1}$$

as in (14.41).

Since the Δu's in numerator and denominator are equal for movements along a given indifference curve, we can divide both numerator and denominator of the left-hand term by Δu and reproduce (14.41) exactly.[2]

Equations (14.43), (14.44), and (14.45) represent successive manipulations of the second form of (14.42), namely $\Delta q_1 p_1 = -\Delta q_2 p_2$. The manipulation in (14.43) simply multiplies each side of the equation by 1. However, it permits us to rearrange terms as in (14.44):

$$(14.43) \qquad \Delta q_1 p_1 \left(\frac{q_1}{q_1}\right) = -\Delta q_2 p_2 \left(\frac{q_2}{q_2}\right)$$

or

$$(14.44) \qquad \frac{\Delta q_1}{q_1} (p_1 q_1) = -\frac{\Delta q_2}{q_2} (p_2 q_2)$$

The form of (14.44) has the advantage that Δq_1 and q_1 itself are in the same units, say pounds. When we divide Δq_1 by q_1 the units in numerator and denominator cancel out and we have simply a pure number. The same is true of Δq_2 divided by q_2. The other member in the left-hand side of the equation is $p_1 q_1$, the number of dollars spent on commodity 1. Similarly, the corresponding term on the right side of the equation $p_2 q_2$ is the number of dollars spent on commodity 2. The total number of dollars spent for the two commodities by our consumer can be written as

$$E = p_1 q_1 + p_2 q_2 = \sum_{i=1}^{2} p_i q_i$$

Without loss of generality and with some gain in concreteness, we can continue our discussion of commodity aggregation and index numbers in terms

[2] Δu, Δq_1, and Δq_2 are infinitesimally small quantities. The ratio $\Delta u / \Delta q_2$ may be taken to mean that a small loss of utility, $\Delta u(2)$, is threatened by a small reduction, Δq_2, in q_2. To precisely offset this loss of Δu and remain on the same indifference curve as before, we increase Δq_1 just enough so that the corresponding small gain in utility, $\Delta u(1)$, exactly equals $\Delta u(2)$.

of only two commodities. We proceed to divide both sides of (14.44) by $\sum_{i=1}^{2} p_i q_i$, obtaining

(14.45)
$$\frac{\Delta q_1}{q_1} \left(\frac{p_1 q_1}{\sum\limits_{i=1}^{2} p_i q_i} \right) = -\frac{\Delta q_2}{q_2} \left(\frac{p_2 q_2}{\sum\limits_{i=1}^{2} p_i q_i} \right)$$

We may interpret (14.45) as follows: The gain in utility associated with a very small *percentage* increase in consumption of commodity 1, weighted by the proportion of total expenditures allocated to commodity 1, is equal in absolute value to the loss in utility associated with that *percentage* reduction in consumption of commodity 2 (weighted by the proportion of total expenditures allocated to commodity 2), which is necessary to keep the consumer on the same indifference curve or level he was on before the small increase in q_1.

We may define *expenditure weights* for the two commodities as follows:

(14.46)
$$w_1 = \frac{p_1 q_1}{(p_1 q_1 + p_2 q_2)}; \quad w_2 = \frac{p_2 q_2}{(p_1 q_1 + p_2 q_2)}$$

Then

(14.47)
$$w_1 + w_2 = \frac{p_1 q_1 + p_2 q_2}{p_1 q_1 + p_2 q_2} = 1$$

If we say that a 1% increase in q_1 brings with it the same increase in utility as a 2% increase in q_2 when these percentage changes are weighted by w_1 and w_2, respectively, it seems only a short step to say that a 2% increase in q_1, weighted by w_1, is twice as important as a 2% increase in q_2, weighted by w_2. Consumption theory does not permit us to say just how much inaccuracy is involved in such a statement or how large the percentage changes in the q_i's can be before such comparisons and interpretations become seriously misleading. We can say with some assurance, however, that (14.45) supplies us with a reasonable basis for *aggregating percentage changes in consumption* of the two commodities.

We proceed to define a *quantity relative* for the ith commodity as q_i/q_{io}, and a *price relative* for the ith commodity as p_i/p_{io}. The subscript o serves to define q_{io} as a fixed number, representing the level of q_i at a particular point in time, and p_{io} as a fixed number representing the level of p_i at that same point in time. It is clear that these relatives are pure numbers. For example, q_i/q_{io} in a particular instance might mean 11 lb/10 lb = 1.1, and p_i/p_{io} might mean 48¢/lb/60¢/lb = 0.8. Since in (14.47) the sum of the weights w_i for the two commodities is equal to 1, a weighted average of the two quantity relatives if each q_i differs from its reference value q_{io} by less than 10% (or 0.1) will be a pure number somewhere between 0.9 and 1.1.

We can now complete our demonstration of "perfect aggregation" over commodities for a single consumer. We start from

(14.48) $$q_1 = a_1 + b_{11}p_1$$

(14.49) $$q_2 = a_2 + b_{22}p_2$$

or

(14.50) $$q_i = a_i + b_{ii}p_i \qquad (i = 1, 2)$$

At first glance, the corresponding "macrorelation" would appear to be (14.51):

(14.51) $$q_T = a_T + b_T p_T$$

where the T subscript implies that the relationship involves "totals" for a number of commodities, in this case, two. But we cannot add up the q_i's directly because they are expressed in different units. Instead, we shall have to base our aggregation procedure upon the price and quantity relatives. We proceed to divide both sides of (14.50) by q_{io}:

(14.52) $$\frac{q_i}{q_{io}} = \frac{a_i}{q_{io}} + \frac{b_{ii}p_i}{q_{io}}$$

and perform further manipulations on the term involving p_i as follows:

(14.53) $$\frac{b_{ii}p_i}{q_{io}} = \frac{b_{ii}p_i}{q_{io}} \frac{p_{io}}{p_{io}} = \left(b_{ii}\frac{p_{io}}{q_{io}}\right)\frac{p_i}{p_{io}}$$

Simultaneously multiplying and dividing the term $b_{ii}p_i/q_{io}$ by the same number p_{io} does not, of course, change its value. Rearranging terms, we obtain the price relative p_i/p_{io} multiplied by an expression in b_{ii}. Let us represent this expression by β_{ii}. As indicated in (14.54),

(14.54) $$\beta_{ii} = b_{ii}\frac{p_{io}}{q_{io}} = \frac{\Delta q_i}{\Delta p_i}\frac{p_{io}}{q_{io}} = \frac{\Delta q_i/q_{io}}{\Delta p_i/p_{io}} \qquad (i = 1, 2)$$

Hence β_{ii} turns out to be nothing else than the price-elasticity of demand for commodity i at the index number base or reference point (q_{io}, p_{io}).

By a slight change in notation, we can redefine the weights in (14.46) in terms of base or reference point values for each of the prices and quantities:

(14.55) $$w_{io} = \frac{p_{io}q_{io}}{\sum\limits_{i=1}^{2} p_{io}q_{io}}$$

We now define two new variables, $q'_i = w_{io}(q_i/q_{io})$ and $p'_i = w_{io}(p_i/p_{io})$. We may note, for example, that q'_1 is identical in units and essentially identical in form with the left-hand side of (14.45). If the quantity relatives are only moderately different from 1, a change of say 0.01 in q'_1 should involve essentially the same change in utility as does that shift in q'_2 associated with a change in Δq_2, which is just sufficient to offset the change in utility resulting from

$$\Delta q_i = \frac{q_i - q_{io}}{q_{io}} = \frac{q_i}{q_{io}} - 1 = 0.01$$

It seems permissible, therefore, to perform a simple aggregation of the q'_i's for the two commodities and obtain a consumption aggregate. Our typical microrelation is now

(14.56) $$q'_i = w_{io} \frac{a_i}{q_{io}} + \beta_{ii} p'_i$$

Each of the microrelations will give us a "perfect prediction" of q'_i for one commodity. Therefore, a perfect prediction of aggregate consumption of the two commodities can be obtained by simply adding up the two microrelations as indicated in (14.57):

(14.57) $$\sum_{i=1}^{2} q'_i = \sum_{i=1}^{2} w_{io} \frac{a_i}{q_{io}} + \sum_{i=1}^{2} \beta_{ii} p'_i$$

or

$$(q'_1 + q'_2) = \left(w_{10} \frac{a_1}{q_{10}} + w_{20} \frac{a_2}{q_{20}} \right) + (\beta_{11} p'_1 + \beta_{22} p'_2)$$

We now consider whether it is possible to achieve a similarly perfect prediction of $\sum_{i=1}^{2} q'_i$ by means of a single "macrorelation," "macro" in this connection implying nothing more than aggregation over commodities for a single consumer. We may write such a macrorelation as

(14.58) $$q'_T = a'_T + \beta p_T^*$$

We can test the validity and implication of aggregation for each term of this equation as follows:

(14.59) $$q'_T = \sum_{i=1}^{2} q'_i = \sum_{i=1}^{2} w_{io} \frac{q_i}{q_{io}} = \sum_{i=1}^{2} \frac{p_{io} q_{io}}{\sum_{i=1}^{2} p_{io} q_{io}} \frac{q_i}{q_{io}}$$

$$= \frac{1}{\sum_{i=1}^{2} p_{io} q_{io}} \sum_{i=1}^{2} \frac{(p_{io} q_{io}) q_i}{q_{io}} = \frac{\sum_{i=1}^{2} p_{io} q_i}{\sum_{i=1}^{2} p_{io} q_{io}} = \frac{(p_{10} q_1 + p_{20} q_2)}{(p_{10} q_{10} + p_{20} q_{20})}$$

The right-hand term in the sequence just presented proves to be a standard formula for the construction of quantity indices, namely the *Laspeyres* formula.

Equation (14.60) presents the expression for a'_T in expanded form. The only point worth noting here is that, inasmuch as a_i was expressed in the original quantity units of commodity i, a'_T turns out to be a pure number; the price and quantity units in both numerator and denominator cancel out:

$$(14.60) \qquad a'_T = \frac{1}{\sum\limits_{i=1}^{2} p_{io}q_{io}} \sum\limits_{i=1}^{2} \frac{(p_{io}q_{io})a_i}{q_{io}} = \frac{\sum\limits_{i=1}^{2} p_{io}a_i}{\sum\limits_{i=1}^{2} p_{io}q_{io}}$$

Finally, we must consider the implications of βp^*_T. We shall define $\bar{\beta}$ as the simple arithmetic mean of the β_{ii}'s included in (14.57): $\beta = \bar{\beta} = \frac{1}{2}\sum_{i=1}^{2}\beta_{ii}$. Then we may rewrite βp_T^* as follows:

$$(14.61) \qquad \beta p_T^* = \sum\limits_{i=1}^{2} \beta_{ii}p'_i = \sum\limits_{i=1}^{2} \beta_{ii}w_{io}\frac{p_i}{p_{io}} = \beta \sum\limits_{i=1}^{2} \left(\frac{\beta_{ii}}{\beta}\right) w_{io} \left(\frac{p_i}{p_{io}}\right)$$

For purposes of comparison, consider the price variable obtained by simple aggregation:

$$(14.62) \qquad p'_T = \sum\limits_{i=1}^{2} p'_i = \sum\limits_{i=1}^{2} w_{io}\frac{p_i}{p_{io}} = \frac{\sum\limits_{i=1}^{2} p_i q_{io}}{\sum\limits_{i=1}^{2} p_{io}q_{io}}$$

The extreme right-hand expression is the well-known Laspeyres formula for an index number of commodity prices.

It is clear that p^*_T does not in general equal p'_T. For if we compare the two expressions we see a striking difference. In the present context, p^*_T represents a "perfect aggregation" which permits us to make a perfect prediction of q'_T by means of a single macrorelation; p'_T does not have this property.

The simple aggregative variable p'_T applies standard Laspeyres formula weights to each of the commodity price relatives. In the "perfect aggregation" p^*_T the price relative for each commodity is weighted not only by the standard Laspeyres formula weight but also by *the ratio of the price elasticity of demand for the given commodity to the simple arithmetic mean of the price elasticities for the two commodities.* Both of the β_{ii}'s and, consequently, $\bar{\beta}$, are negative, reflecting the negative slopes of the commodity demand curves.

Price relatives for commodities with above-average elasticities of demand will receive higher weights than in the Laspeyres formula, and price relatives for commodities which have less than average price elasticities of demand will receive smaller weights than in the Laspeyres formula:

$$(14.63) \qquad \sum\limits_{i=1}^{2} \left(\frac{\beta_{ii}}{\beta}\right) w_{io}\left(\frac{p_i}{p_{io}}\right) \neq \sum\limits_{i=1}^{2} w_{io}\left(\frac{p_i}{p_{io}}\right)$$

These results can be generalized for any number of commodities m simply by letting the subscript i range from 1 to m.

Aggregation and Index Number Formulas When Consumption of Each Commodity Is a Function of the Prices of Other Commodities as Well as Its Own Price. The preceding demonstration has made a very special assumption that the consumption of a given commodity is influenced only by its own price and not at all by the prices of other commodities. But in principle the consumption of each commodity is influenced by the prices of all other commodities, as indicated in (14.2).

We can best examine this more general situation in terms of a system which includes only two commodities and ignores the effects of income. We shall regard the two equations which follow as two microrelations which we wish to aggregate "perfectly" into a single macrorelation:

$$(14.64) \qquad \begin{aligned} q_1 &= a_1 + b_{11}p_1 + b_{12}p_2 \\ q_2 &= a_2 + b_{21}p_1 + b_{22}p_2 \end{aligned}$$

Let

$$q'_1 = \left(\frac{w_{10}}{q_{10}}\right)q_1 \quad \text{and} \quad q'_2 = \left(\frac{w_{20}}{q_{20}}\right)q_2$$

Also let

$$p'_1 = \left(\frac{w_{10}}{p_{10}}\right)p_1 \quad \text{and} \quad p'_2 = \left(\frac{w_{20}}{p_{20}}\right)p_2$$

This is the same device we used in (14.56)–(14.63).

In the first equation we obtain

$$(14.65) \qquad \left(\frac{w_{10}}{q_{10}}\right)q_1 = \left(\frac{w_{10}}{q_{10}}\right)a_1 + \left(\frac{w_{10}}{q_{10}}\right)b_{11}p_1 + \left(\frac{w_{10}}{q_{10}}\right)b_{12}p_2$$

As in (14.53) we may convert the term in p_1 into

$$(14.66) \qquad \left(\frac{w_{10}}{q_{10}}\right)b_{11}p_1\left(\frac{p_{10}}{p_{10}}\right) = \left(b_{11}\frac{p_{10}}{q_{10}}\right)w_{10}\left(\frac{p_1}{p_{10}}\right) = \beta_{11}p'_1$$

where β_{11} is the elasticity of demand for commodity 1 with respect to changes in its own price.

The term in p_2 requires a different manipulation than this if we are to transform p_2 into p'_2. We can accomplish this in the following way:

$$(14.67) \quad \left(\frac{w_{10}}{q_{10}}\right)b_{12}p_2\left(\frac{p_{20}}{p_{20}}\right)\left(\frac{w_{20}}{w_{20}}\right) = \left(b_{12}\frac{p_{20}}{q_{10}}\right)w_{20}\left(\frac{p_2}{p_{20}}\right)\left(\frac{w_{10}}{w_{20}}\right) = \beta_{12}p'_2\left(\frac{w_{10}}{w_{20}}\right)$$

where β_{12} is the elasticity of demand for commodity 1 with respect to changes in the price of commodity 2.

So, letting $a'_1 = (w_{10}/q_{10})a_1$, we can rewrite (14.65) as:

$$(14.68) \qquad q'_1 = a'_1 + \beta_{11}p'_1 + \left(\frac{w_{10}}{w_{20}}\right)\beta_{12}p'_2$$

The original equation for q_2 is multiplied through by (w_{20}/q_{20}) and transformed into

$$(14.69) \qquad q'_2 = a'_2 + \beta_{21}p'_1\left(\frac{w_{20}}{w_{10}}\right) + \beta_{22}p'_2$$

Once again, we consider the problem of "perfect aggregation" in the sense of perfect prediction of $q'_T = (q'_1 + q'_2)$ by means of a single macrorelation,

$$(14.70) \qquad q'_T = a'_T + \beta_T p^*_T$$

Simple aggregation of the two microrelations gives us

$$(14.71) \qquad (q'_1 + q'_2) = (a'_1 + a'_2) + \left[\beta_{11} + \beta_{21}\left(\frac{w_{20}}{w_{10}}\right)\right]p'_1$$
$$+ \left[\beta_{22} + \beta_{12}\left(\frac{w_{10}}{w_{20}}\right)\right]p'_2$$

Hence $q'_T = (q'_1 + q'_2)$ and $a'_T = (a'_1 + a'_2)$; simple aggregation is appropriate. But for $\beta_T p^*_T$ the aggregation is more complex:

$$(14.72) \qquad \beta_T p^*_T = \left[\beta_{11} + \beta_{21}\left(\frac{w_{20}}{w_{10}}\right)\right]p'_1 + \left[\beta_{22} + \beta_{12}\left(\frac{w_{10}}{w_{20}}\right)\right]p'_2$$

The terms in brackets are pure numbers, as are p'_1, p'_2, and β_T, so p^*_T must also be a pure number.

Simple aggregation of p'_1 and p'_2 results in

$$(14.73) \qquad p'_T = p'_1 + p'_2$$

which (for two commodities) is the conventional Laspeyres formula for an index number of prices.

We may simplify the notation in (14.72) by letting B_1 and B_2 stand for the coefficients of p'_1 and p'_2, respectively. Then let $\beta_T = \bar{B} = (B_1 + B_2)/2$.

Equation (14.72) becomes

$$(14.74) \qquad \bar{B}p^*_T = \bar{B}\left[\frac{B_1}{\bar{B}}p'_1 + \frac{B_2}{\bar{B}}p'_2\right]$$

and

$$p^*_T = \frac{B_1}{\bar{B}}p'_1 + \frac{B_2}{\bar{B}}p'_2$$

It follows that p^*_T will not equal p'_T except in the very special case in which $B_1 = B_2 = \bar{B}$.

The preceding exposition can be generalized to any number of commodities with appropriate changes in notation. For m commodities, we have

$$B_1 = \beta_{11}\left(\frac{w_{10}}{w_{10}}\right) + \beta_{21}\left(\frac{w_{20}}{w_{10}}\right) + \beta_{31}\left(\frac{w_{30}}{w_{10}}\right) + \cdots + \beta_{m1}\left(\frac{w_{mo}}{w_{10}}\right)$$

$$B_2 = \beta_{12}\left(\frac{w_{10}}{w_{20}}\right) + \beta_{22}\left(\frac{w_{20}}{w_{20}}\right) + \beta_{32}\left(\frac{w_{30}}{w_{20}}\right) + \cdots + \beta_{m2}\left(\frac{w_{mo}}{w_{20}}\right)$$

(14.75)
$$B_3 = \beta_{13}\left(\frac{w_{10}}{w_{30}}\right) + \beta_{32}\left(\frac{w_{20}}{w_{30}}\right) + \beta_{33}\left(\frac{w_{30}}{w_{30}}\right) + \cdots + \beta_{m3}\left(\frac{w_{mo}}{w_{30}}\right)$$

$$\vdots$$

$$B_m = \beta_{1m}\left(\frac{w_{10}}{w_{mo}}\right) + \beta_{2m}\left(\frac{w_{20}}{w_{mo}}\right) + \beta_{3m}\left(\frac{w_{30}}{w_{mo}}\right) + \cdots + \beta_{mm}\left(\frac{w_{mo}}{w_{mo}}\right)$$

Then $\bar{B} = (1/m)\sum_{i=1}^{m} B_i$, and

(14.76)
$$\bar{B}p^*_T = \bar{B}\sum_{i=1}^{m}\left(\frac{B_i}{\bar{B}}\right)p'_i$$

therefore

$$p^*_T = \sum_{i=1}^{m}\left(\frac{B_i}{\bar{B}}\right)p'_i$$

We may note in passing that B_1 is a weighted sum of the price effects of p'_1 on all the q'_i's. There is no conventional term for B_1 in the literature of economics. It is essentially the *price elasticity of demand for the composite or aggregative commodity q'_T with respect to the weighted price relative p'_1 of commodity 1*. The composite variable q'_T is a Laspeyres index measuring the change in the individual's or household's consumption of all m commodities, and p'_1 is a component of the corresponding Laspeyres index of the prices of all m commodities. A similar interpretation could be given to each of the B_i's, for $i = 1, 2, 3, \ldots, m$.

In the two-commodity case of (14.74), the price relative p'_i for each commodity i is weighted by the ratio of the elasticity of demand for q'_T with respect to p'_i (namely B_i) to the arithmetic mean of the corresponding elasticities for both commodities. The situation is similar to that of (14.61) except that in (14.74) the total effect of a change in p'_1 upon q'_T is propagated partly through one microrelation ($\beta_{11}p'_1$) and partly through the other $[\beta_{21}(w_{20}/w_{10})p'_1]$. If $w_{10} = w_{20} = 0.5$, we may write

$$\bar{B} = \frac{\beta_{11} + \beta_{21}\left(\dfrac{0.5}{0.5}\right) + \beta_{22} + \beta_{12}\left(\dfrac{0.5}{0.5}\right)}{2}$$

or

$$\bar{B} = \frac{\beta_{11} + \beta_{22}}{2} + \frac{\beta_{21} + \beta_{12}}{2}$$

The own-price elasticities β_{11} and β_{22} are always negative; the cross-elasticities β_{21} and β_{12} will usually be positive, and will average smaller in absolute value than β_{11} and β_{22}. Empirical studies of consumer demand usually suggest that the average β_{ij} is considerably smaller in absolute value than the average β_{ii}. Some further comments on the relationships among the β_{ij}'s and β_{ii}'s for an individual consumer are made in the following section.

If we consider (14.75) for only two commodities, we may write

(14.77)
$$B_1 = \frac{1}{w_{10}} [\beta_{11}w_{10} + \beta_{21}w_{20}]$$

$$B_2 = \frac{1}{w_{20}} [\beta_{12}w_{10} + \beta_{22}w_{20}]$$

or

(14.78)
$$w_{10}B_1 = [\beta_{11}w_{10} + \beta_{21}w_{20}]$$

$$w_{20}B_2 = [\beta_{12}w_{10} + \beta_{22}w_{20}]$$

The right-hand term in each of (14.78) is a weighted average of the own-price and cross-price elasticities; the weights w_{10} and w_{20} are repeated for each of the two commodities, and $w_{10} + w_{20} = 1$. The coefficients β_{11} and β_{21} transmit a 1% change in the price of commodity 1 into changes of $\beta_{11}\%$ and $\beta_{21}\%$ in the consumer's purchases, q_1 and q_2, of commodities 1 and 2, respectively; these percentages are *weighted* by the importance of the respective commodities in terms of the consumer's base period expenditures, as

$$w_{10} = \frac{p_{10}q_{10}}{p_{10}q_{10} + p_{20}q_{20}}$$

and

$$w_{20} = \frac{p_{20}q_{20}}{p_{10}q_{10} + p_{20}q_{20}}$$

The coefficient B_1 is the percentage change in the Laspeyres index $q'_T = (q'_1 + q'_2)$ occasioned by a 1% change in the price of commodity 1; each commodity may be regarded as a path into q'_T, and B_1 gathers up the effects of p'_1 upon q'_T via both of the commodity paths. If we want to add up the effects on q'_T of 1% increases in *both* p'_1 and p'_2, we must weight B_1 by the importance (w_{10}) of commodity 1 and B_2 by the importance (w_{20}) of commodity 2 in base period expenditures:

$$B_w = w_{10}B_1 + w_{20}B_2$$

We may generalize these points also. In (14.75) it will also be noted that each term in the square brackets defining B_1 has the same denominator w_{10}. Hence we may rewrite B_1 as

(14.79) $$B_1 = \frac{1}{w_{10}} [\beta_{11}w_{10} + \beta_{21}w_{20} + \cdots + \beta_{m1}w_{mo}]$$

or

$$B_1 = \frac{1}{w_{10}} \sum_{i=1}^{m} \beta_{i1}w_{io}$$

Similarly

$$B_2 = \frac{1}{w_{20}} \sum_{i=1}^{m} \beta_{i2}w_{io}$$

$$\vdots$$

$$B_m = \frac{1}{w_{mo}} \sum_{i=1}^{m} \beta_{im}w_{io}$$

Using a double summation notation, we can consolidate all of the B_j's into the single equation:

(14.80) $$\sum_{j=1}^{m} B_j = \sum_{j=1}^{m} \sum_{i=1}^{m} \beta_{ij}\left(\frac{w_{io}}{w_{jo}}\right)$$

We can also multiply each equation j in (14.79) by the weight w_{jo}, and obtain an expression equivalent to (14.78) for all m commodities:

(14.81) $$\sum_{j=1}^{m} w_{jo}B_j = \sum_{j=1}^{m} \sum_{i=1}^{m} \beta_{ij}w_{io}$$

Some Relationships among Price and Income Elasticities of Demand on the Part of an Individual Consumer. Some limitations on the sizes of the β_{ii}'s and β_{ij}'s are provided by the theory of consumer demand.

We may convert all the price and quantity variables in (14.2) into logarithms, giving us (14.82):

(14.82)
$$\log q_1 = \alpha_1 + \beta_{11} \log p_1 + \beta_{12} \log p_2 + \cdots + \beta_{1n} \log p_n + \gamma_1 \log y$$
$$\log q_2 = \alpha_2 + \beta_{21} \log p_1 + \beta_{22} \log p_2 + \cdots + \beta_{2n} \log p_n + \gamma_2 \log y$$
$$\vdots$$
$$\log q_n = \alpha_n + \beta_{n1} \log p_1 + \beta_{n2} \log p_2 + \cdots + \beta_{nn} \log p_n + \gamma_n \log y$$

In these equations, each β_{ii} and β_{ij} is a *price elasticity of demand* and each small γ is an *income elasticity of demand*. A change of one unit in the logarithm of p_1 will lead to a change of β_{11} units in the logarithm of q_1.

Logarithmic relationships are essentially percentage relationships if prices and quantities vary only moderately (not more than say 10 or 15%) from their average values. Hence we can say approximately that a 1% change in p_1 will lead to a change of $\beta_{11}\%$ in q_1. These are the same β_{ii}'s and β_{ij}'s we have used in (14.54)–(14.81).

It is an axiom of consumption theory that *an equal percentage change in all prices and in money income* will not cause any changes in the quantities of the various commodities purchased. Hence for moderate variations of prices and money income from their initial values, we may write (14.83):

(14.83)
$$\begin{aligned} \beta_{11} + \beta_{12} + \cdots + \beta_{1n} + \gamma_1 &= 0 \\ \beta_{21} + \beta_{22} + \cdots + \beta_{2n} + \gamma_2 &= 0 \\ &\vdots \\ \beta_{n1} + \beta_{n2} + \cdots + \beta_{nn} + \gamma_n &= 0 \end{aligned}$$

For some base period set of values of the p_i's and q_i's, we may calculate the proportion of total income which is spent on each commodity. By definition, the consumer's total expenditures $\sum_{i=1}^{n} p_{io}q_{io}$ are equal to his income y_o.

(14.84)
$$w_{10} = \frac{p_{10}q_{10}}{\sum_{i=1}^{n} p_{io}q_{io}} = \frac{p_{10}q_{10}}{y_o}; \quad w_{20} = \frac{p_{20}q_{20}}{y_o}; \ldots$$

$$w_{no} = \frac{p_{no}q_{no}}{y_o}. \quad w_{10} + w_{20} + \cdots + w_{no} = \frac{\sum_{i=1}^{n} p_{io}q_{io}}{y_o} = \frac{y_o}{y_o} = 1$$

If money income y rises by 1% and *prices* remain constant, each q_i in (14.82) will rise by $\gamma_i\%$. We can express this in terms of quantity relatives q_i/q_{io}, and an income relative y/y_o:

(14.85)
$$\frac{q_i}{q_{io}} = \gamma_i\left(\frac{y}{y_o}\right)$$

If we weight each commodity by its relative importance in base period expenditures, we obtain

(14.86)
$$w_{io}\left(\frac{q_i}{q_{io}}\right) = w_{io}\gamma_i\left(\frac{y}{y_o}\right)$$

or

$$\frac{p_{io}q_{io}}{y_o}\left(\frac{q_i}{q_{io}}\right) = \frac{p_{io}q_{io}}{y_o}\gamma_i\left(\frac{y}{y_o}\right)$$

Then,

(14.87)
$$\frac{p_{io}q_i}{y_o} = w_{io}\gamma_i\left(\frac{\sum_{i=1}^{n} p_{io}q_i}{y_o}\right)$$

for the total money expenditure after the 1% rise in money income is $\sum_{i=1}^{n} p_{io}q_i = y$. If we sum both sides of (14.87) we have

$$(14.88) \qquad \sum_{i=1}^{n} \left(\frac{p_{io}q_i}{y_o} \right) = \frac{\sum_{i=1}^{n} p_{io}q_i}{y_o} = \sum_{i=1}^{n} w_{io}\gamma_i \left(\frac{\sum_{i=1}^{n} p_{io}q_i}{y_o} \right)$$

Dividing both sides of the equation by

$$\left(\frac{\sum_{i=1}^{n} p_{io}q_i}{y_o} \right)$$

yields

$$(14.89) \qquad 1 = \sum_{i=1}^{n} w_{io}\gamma_i$$

or

$$\sum_{i=1}^{n} w_{io}\gamma_i = 1$$

Equation (14.89) states that the weighted average income elasticity of demand for all commodities purchased by a given consumer is 1. This is, perhaps, intuitively obvious once we have defined total income y as equal to total expenditures.

Equation (14.89) also has implications for the β_{ii}'s and β_{ij}'s. To make these implications apparent, we multiply each equation i in (14.83) by the corresponding expenditure weight w_{io} and transpose the term $w_{io}\gamma_i$ to the right-hand side:

$$
(14.90) \qquad
\begin{aligned}
w_{10}[\beta_{11} + \beta_{12} + \beta_{13} + \cdots + \beta_{1n}] &= -w_{10}\gamma_1 \\
w_{20}[\beta_{21} + \beta_{22} + \beta_{23} + \cdots + \beta_{2n}] &= -w_{20}\gamma_2 \\
&\vdots \\
w_{no}[\beta_{n1} + \beta_{n2} + \beta_{n3} + \cdots + \beta_{nn}] &= -w_{no}\gamma_n
\end{aligned}
$$

Summing the n equations, we obtain

$$(14.91) \qquad \sum_{i=1}^{n} \sum_{j=1}^{n} w_{io}\beta_{ij} = -\sum_{i=1}^{n} w_{io}\gamma_i = -1$$

That is, the weighted average price elasticity of demand for all commodities, on the part of an individual consumer, is -1. This has to be true if all money income y is expended. For with total money expenditure constant, a 1% increase in the price of every commodity must be accompanied *on the average* by a 1% decrease in the quantities of commodities purchased.

We may separate out the own-price elasticities β_{ii} and the cross elasticities β_{ij} as follows:

(14.92)
$$w_{10}\beta_{11} + w_{10}[\beta_{12} + \beta_{13} + \cdots + \beta_{1n}] = -w_{10}\gamma_1$$
$$w_{20}\beta_{22} + w_{20}[\beta_{21} + \beta_{23} + \cdots + \beta_{2n}] = -w_{20}\gamma_2$$
$$\vdots$$
$$w_{no}\beta_{nn} + w_{no}[\beta_{n1} + \beta_{n2} + \cdots + \beta_{n,n-1}] = -w_{no}\gamma_n$$

In the first equation, dividing through by w_{10}, we have

$$[\beta_{12} + \beta_{13} + \cdots + \beta_{1n}] = -\beta_{11} - \gamma_1$$

Except for an "inferior good," γ_1 will be positive; β_{11} will be negative in all instances. The β_{ij}'s will be predominantly positive. If the *price* of commodity 2 rises, it becomes more expensive relative to commodity 1. Therefore the consumer will *increase* his consumption of commodity 1.

If the β_{ij}'s are predominantly positive, the β_{ii}'s must average greater in absolute value than -1. We may rewrite (14.91) as

(14.93)
$$\sum_{i=1}^{n} w_{io}\beta_{ii} + \sum_{i=1}^{n} w_{io} \sum_{j \neq i}^{n} \beta_{ij} = -1$$

Since

$$\sum_{i=1}^{n} w_{io} \sum_{j \neq i}^{n} \beta_{ij} > 0$$

$$\sum_{i=1}^{n} w_{io}\beta_{ii} = -1 - \sum_{i=1}^{n} w_{io} \sum_{j \neq i}^{n} \beta_{ij} < -1$$

The facts that (1) income elasticities of demand must average out at 1, (2) own-price elasticities of demand must average less than -1 in algebraic terms or more than 1 *in absolute value*, and (3) own-price and cross-price elasticities together must have a weighted average of -1 should give us some quantitative perspective on these otherwise abstract relationships.

The foregoing relationships have been recommended by Ragnar Frisch (1959) as a guide in constructing large-scale economic models, and they have been used by George Brandow (1961) in specifying all the numerical coefficients in a consumer-demand system involving 25 commodity groups. Brandow's matrix is reproduced as Table 13.5. Examination of this table should contribute to the reader's grasp of the problem of "perfect aggregation" over commodities.

We have already demonstrated the nature of perfect aggregation over consumers. In forming aggregates over both commodities and consumers for use in a macrorelation, appropriate weights could *in principle* be applied at both stages to achieve perfect aggregation.

Aggregation of Commodities into Logical Subgroups with Respect to an Individual Consumer. The term "economic aggregate" is relative. For example, we may speak of the totality of goods and services purchased by a consumer as an aggregate. This is the scope desired for a complete *consumer price index* or "cost of living" index. But we may also be interested in aggregate purchases of smaller groups of commodities, such as food or clothing, and in the price indices which can properly be associated with these subaggregates.

In subdividing a consumer price index, it seems logical to classify commodities according to their relevance to a certain class of wants. For example, in the national product accounts of the United States, total personal consumption expenditures are subdivided into 12 major categories, as follows: (1) food and tobacco; (2) clothing, accessories, and jewelry; (3) personal care; (4) housing; (5) household operation; (6) medical care and death expenses; (7) personal business; (8) transportation; (9) recreation; (10) private education and research; (11) religious and welfare activities; and (12) foreign travel and remittances.[3] Some of these major categories are further subdivided, so that separate estimates are published (in the source noted in footnote 3) for approximately 90 categories of consumer goods and services.

Let us assume for the moment that we can subdivide a set of four consumer goods into logical categories with two commodities in each. The complete array of equations in the format used in (14.75) follows:

(14.94)

$$q'_1 = a'_1 + \beta_{11}\left(\frac{w_{10}}{w_{10}}\right)p'_1 + \beta_{12}\left(\frac{w_{10}}{w_{20}}\right)p'_2 + \beta_{13}\left(\frac{w_{10}}{w_{30}}\right)p'_3 + \beta_{14}\left(\frac{w_{10}}{w_{40}}\right)p'_4$$

$$q'_2 = a'_2 + \beta_{21}\left(\frac{w_{20}}{w_{10}}\right)p'_1 + \beta_{22}\left(\frac{w_{20}}{w_{20}}\right)p'_2 + \beta_{23}\left(\frac{w_{20}}{w_{30}}\right)p'_3 + \beta_{24}\left(\frac{w_{20}}{w_{40}}\right)p'_4$$

$$q'_3 = a'_3 + \beta_{31}\left(\frac{w_{30}}{w_{10}}\right)p'_1 + \beta_{32}\left(\frac{w_{30}}{w_{20}}\right)p'_2 + \beta_{33}\left(\frac{w_{30}}{w_{30}}\right)p'_3 + \beta_{34}\left(\frac{w_{30}}{w_{40}}\right)p'_4$$

$$q'_4 = a'_4 + \beta_{41}\left(\frac{w_{40}}{w_{10}}\right)p'_1 + \beta_{42}\left(\frac{w_{40}}{w_{20}}\right)p'_2 + \beta_{43}\left(\frac{w_{40}}{w_{30}}\right)p'_3 + \beta_{44}\left(\frac{w_{40}}{w_{40}}\right)p'_4$$

Let us suppose that there is a significant amount of competition (substitutability) between commodities 1 and 2 and between commodities 3 and 4. Let us assume further that changes in the prices of commodities 3 and 4 have no effect on the consumer's purchases of commodities 1 and 2; and that the

[3] See U.S. Department of Commerce's *Survey of Current Business*, Table 14, p. 16 (July 1964).

prices of commodities 1 and 2 have no effect on the consumer's purchases of commodities 3 and 4. This situation is indicated in the following:

$$q'_1 = a'_1 + \beta_{11}\left(\frac{w_{10}}{w_{10}}\right)p'_1 + \beta_{12}\left(\frac{w_{10}}{w_{20}}\right)p'_2 + 0.p'_3 + 0.p'_4$$

$$q'_2 = a'_2 + \beta_{21}\left(\frac{w_{20}}{w_{10}}\right)p'_1 + \beta_{22}\left(\frac{w_{20}}{w_{20}}\right)p'_2 + 0.p'_3 + 0.p'_4$$

(14.95)

$$q'_3 = a'_3 + 0.p'_1 + 0.p'_2 + \beta_{33}\left(\frac{w_{30}}{w_{30}}\right)p'_3 + \beta_{34}\left(\frac{w_{30}}{w_{40}}\right)p'_4$$

$$q'_4 = a'_4 + 0.p'_1 + 0.p'_2 + \beta_{43}\left(\frac{w_{40}}{w_{30}}\right)p'_3 + \beta_{44}\left(\frac{w_{40}}{w_{40}}\right)p'_4$$

The first two equations in set (14.95) are identical with (14.68) and (14.69). If we aggregate these two equations, as in (14.96),

(14.96)　$(q'_1 + q'_2) = (a'_1 + a'_2) + \left[\frac{1}{w_{10}}(\beta_{11}w_{10} + \beta_{21}w_{20})p'_1\right.$

$$\left. + \frac{1}{w_{20}}(\beta_{12}w_{10} + \beta_{22}w_{20})p'_2\right]$$

we arrive at the same "perfect aggregation" for the corresponding price index of these two commodities as in (14.74):

(14.74)　$\bar{B}p^*{}_T = \bar{B}\left[\frac{B_1}{\bar{B}}p'_1 + \frac{B_2}{\bar{B}}p'_2\right]$　where　$\bar{B} = \dfrac{B_1 + B_2}{2}$

and

$$p^*{}_T = \left[\frac{B_1}{\bar{B}}p'_1 + \frac{B_2}{\bar{B}}p'_2\right]$$

We can follow the same procedure for commodities 3 and 4, arriving at a "perfect aggregation" of p'_3 and p'_4 which will enable us to make perfect predictions of the quantity aggregate $(q'_3 + q'_4)$ from a single macrorelation. The simple sum of the two microrelations is

(14.97)　$(q'_3 + q'_4) = (a'_3 + a'_4) + \left[\frac{1}{w_{30}}(\beta_{33}w_{30} + \beta_{43}w_{40})p'_3\right.$

$$\left. + \frac{1}{w_{40}}(\beta_{34}w_{30} + \beta_{44}w_{40})p'_4\right]$$

and a corresponding macrorelation in $\bar{B}$ and $p^*{}_T$ can readily be defined.

Let us simplify the notation by redefining the coefficients of p'_i in (14.96) and (14.97) as B_i for $i = 1, 2, 3$, and 4. This change in notation gives us (14.98) and (14.99):

(14.98) $(q'_1 + q'_2) = (a'_1 + a'_2) + B_1 p'_1 + B_2 p'_2$

(14.99) $(q'_3 + q'_4) = (a'_3 + a'_4) + B_3 p'_3 + B_4 p'_4$

We further call the subgroup consisting of commodities 1 and 2 group r, and the subgroup formed by commodities 3 and 4 group s:

(14.100) $$q'_r = a'_r + \bar{B}_r p^*_r$$

and

(14.101) $$q'_s = a'_s + \bar{B}_s p^*_s$$

where

$$p^*_r = \left(\frac{B_1}{\bar{B}_r} p'_1 + \frac{B_2}{\bar{B}_r} p'_2 \right)$$

and

$$p^*_s = \left(\frac{B_3}{\bar{B}_s} p'_3 + \frac{B_4}{\bar{B}_s} p'_4 \right)$$

and

$$\bar{B}_r = \frac{B_1 + B_2}{2}, \quad \bar{B}_s = \frac{B_3 + B_4}{2}$$

We can make a perfect prediction of q'_r on the basis of the single-price variable p^*_r and we can make a perfect prediction of q'_s as a function of the single aggregative price p^*_s (from (14.100) and (14.101)).

It is clear that we can add up (14.100) and (14.101) to obtain

(14.102) $q'_T = q'_r + q'_s = (a'_r + a'_s) + \bar{B}_r p^*_r + \bar{B}_s p^*_s$

Let us consider a final step in the aggregation of prices. We now require a p^*_T such that the single macrorelation

(14.103) $$q'_T = a'_T + B_T p^*_T$$

will give us a perfect prediction of q'_T.

Let

$$B_T = \bar{B}_T = \frac{\bar{B}_r + \bar{B}_s}{2}$$

Then

(14.104) $$\bar{B}_T p^*_T = \bar{B}_T \left(\frac{\bar{B}_r}{\bar{B}_T} p^*_r + \frac{\bar{B}_s}{\bar{B}_T} p^*_s \right)$$

and

$$p^*_T = \left(\frac{\bar{B}_r}{\bar{B}_T} p^*_r + \frac{\bar{B}_s}{\bar{B}_T} p^*_s \right)$$

since q'_r is affected only by $p*_r$ and q'_s is affected only by $p*_s$, this final stage of aggregation is precisely the same as that of (14.58).

14.2 AGGREGATION PROBLEMS AS THEY AFFECT THE ESTIMA-TION OF STRUCTURAL RELATIONSHIPS FROM ECONOMIC TIME SERIES

Our treatment of aggregation in this section will not be as elaborate as that in the preceding one, since the most novel and difficult *economic* aspects have been presented there. We will first present a common sense statement written by the author during 1951–1952 and then consider the implications of Theil's "perfect aggregation" concept when the macrorelations are to be estimated from time series.

14.2.1 *Aggregation over Consumers in Statistical Demand Functions Estimated from Time Series*

Suppose we have for a given commodity the demand functions of every spending unit i in the economy, which we assume to have the following form:

$$(14.105) \qquad q_{i(t)} = a_i + b_i p_{i(t)} + c_i y_{i(t)} + z_{i(t)}$$

where q is consumption, p is price, and y is disposable income; t is time.

Market demand is obtained by aggregating over spending units:

$$(14.106) \qquad Q_{(t)} = \sum_1^m q_{i(t)} = \sum_1^m a_i + \sum_1^m b_i p_{i(t)} + \sum_1^m c_i y_{i(t)} + \sum_1^m z_{i(t)}$$

where m is the total number of spending units in the economy. Equation (14.106) is a "true" aggregate, on our assumptions. It may also be written on a per spending unit basis as

$$(14.107) \qquad \bar{q}_{(t)} = A + B_t \bar{p}_{(t)} + C_t \bar{y}_{(t)} + \bar{z}_{(t)}$$

in which

$$(14.108) \qquad A = \frac{1}{m} \sum_{i=1}^m a_i$$

$$(14.109) \qquad B_t = \frac{\sum_{i=1}^m b_i p_{i(t)}}{\sum_{i=1}^m p_{i(t)}}$$

$$(14.110) \qquad C_t = \frac{\sum_{i=1}^m c_i y_{i(t)}}{\sum_{i=1}^m y_{i(t)}}$$

The coefficients B_t and C_t are weighted arithmetic means of the individual b_i and c_i; the weights are the individual $p_{i(t)}$ and $y_{i(t)}$, respectively. These coefficients are constant (independent of t) under the following conditions: (1) the distributions of $p_{i(t)}$ and $y_{i(t)}$ do not change over the time period considered, or (2) all prices change in fixed proportion λ_p and all incomes change in fixed proportion λ_y, or (3) the correlations between b_i and $p_{i(t)}$ and c_i and $y_{i(t)}$, respectively are, zero at all time points t. For these instances

$$(14.111) \qquad \bar{q}_{(t)} = A + B\bar{p}_{(t)} + C\bar{y}_{(t)} + \bar{z}_{(t)}$$

For case (3) the parameters B and C are simple averages of the individual b_i and c_i. Case (1) or (2) or (3) is more or less presupposed (assuming, of course, that the individual demand functions are linear) when a linear aggregative demand function is fitted statistically to United States average prices and per capita (or per spending unit) consumption and income data over a period of years.

Similar considerations apply to aggregate demand or supply functions for other groups—farmers, processors, or distributors. We must always bear in mind the possibility that the coefficients of the functions are conditioned by the particular average levels and distributions assumed by the "independent" variables during the period analyzed.

After briefly discussing problems of aggregating commodities, aggregating firms at different levels in the marketing system, aggregating transactions from different time periods, and aggregating different marketing or producing areas, our conclusions follow.

Enough has been said to indicate some of the aggregation problems which are always with us in the statistical analysis of demand based on time series of market data. If all the elements of an aggregate can be depended upon to change by the same arithmetic or logarithmic amounts, the regression coefficient we obtain in arithmetic or logarithmic formulations, respectively, has "structural" significance. If the coefficients of demand curves for all elements in the aggregate are identical, the regression coefficient will also have structural significance. But if the coefficients differ widely between the various elements, the regression coefficient obtained for the aggregate will depend in part upon the relative variability of the different elements of the aggregate during the period for which the equation is fitted. An aggregative analysis for "all food" might be seriously misleading for policy purposes, whereas an analysis for "all beef" might be relatively impervious to such variations in the grade composition of the beef supply as may reasonably be expected.

If the elements of an aggregate are sufficiently heterogeneous, we are faced with another version of the problem of "prediction-with-changing-structure."

In this instance, the structural coefficients are those pertaining to relatively homogeneous subdivisions of the aggregate as a whole.[4]

We might pause here to consider the realism of some of the alternative assumptions necessary to establish our macrorelation,

$$\bar{q}_{(t)} = A + B\bar{p}_{(t)} + C\bar{y}_{(t)} + \bar{z}_{(t)}$$

as a "true aggregate."

In the United States prices of most consumer *goods* are linked together by rather well-integrated national markets. Where there are regional price differentials based on transportation from surplus to deficit areas or simply from one national manufacturer to many consuming areas, these differentials tend to persist for considerable periods. Hence prices for many *goods* tend to change by equal or nearly equal amounts in all areas.

And prices paid by different consumers in the same city for standard commodities are likely to be about the same. Families with incomes of $20,000 a year frequent the same supermarkets as families with lower incomes. Different lines of clothing or automobiles appealing to different income groups should be regarded, initially at least, as different commodities.

Consumer services may have widely different prices in different labor market areas, and these prices over time may move differently in chronically or temporarily depressed areas than in areas of labor shortage.

With respect to *goods* once again, the input-output structure of the economy implies that increases in prices of basic raw materials and semifinished manufactures will tend to be passed up through later stages of manufacture and distribution. These effects will *tend* to produce some similarities of price movements among groups of commodities. However, it appears likely that aggregation over commodities is much more likely to give us trouble with nonuniform *price* changes than will aggregation over consumers.

There are wide *income* differences among consumers at any given place and time; these differences are probably correlated with differences in marginal propensities to consume various goods and services. But do nonuniform changes in income over time introduce major new aggregation problems?

During the 1930s in the United States it is possible that a sizeable part of the variation in total disposable income was associated with persons moving from jobs to no jobs and vice versa. Also, as we emerged from the depression into the World War II period of hyperemployment it may be that persons who had been unemployed in 1939 showed much larger *percentage* increases in consumption expenditures than persons who had been working full-time in 1939. Changes in income distribution can no doubt cause serious aggrega-

[4] Karl A. Fox, *Econometric Analysis for Public Policy* (Ames: Iowa State University Press), pp. 59–64, 1958.

tion problems under circumstances as extreme as those from 1929 to 1948.

In more stable periods, as from 1949 to 1965, it may be questioned whether changes in income distributions have caused serious aggregation problems in *national* aggregates. But this is a matter for empirical investigation. Hourly wage rates appear to have moved upward more or less together during 1949–1965; premiums for additional years of education also seem to be quite persistent.

In periods such as the 1950s and early 1960s, then, the new aggregation problems involved in the statistical estimation of macrorelations from time series, *over and above those discussed in the timeless and exact-function context of the earlier sections of this chapter*, deserve serious consideration, but it seems unlikely that they will produce *additional* errors or biases of more than 5 or 10%.

And if it is appropriate to estimate our macrorelations in terms of year-to-year changes (arithmetic or logarithmic first differences) we may be able to reduce the effects of long-term shifts in income distributions to relatively minor importance.

14.2.2 *Aggregation over Commodities: Regression Coefficients between Price and Quantity Index Numbers and other Aggregates*

A good many of the macrovariables used in economic models are either official index numbers, or can be interpreted as index numbers, of prices and quantities. Brandow's matrix of demand elasticities for foods provides an opportunity for readers to make numerical calculations, if they wish, and see what effects different time-patterns of the independent *microvariables* would have upon the dependent *microvariables*, the 24 different foods or food groups.

Let us assume that all variables *other than* the amounts of two foods available for consumption, q_i, remain constant. Our problem is to interpret the time series regression coefficient of an index of retail prices of the two foods upon an index of per capita consumption of the two foods.

We may write the microrelations in simplified form as

$$(14.112) \qquad \begin{aligned} P_{1(t)} &= b_{11}q_{1(t)} + b_{12}q_{2(t)} \\ P_{2(t)} &= b_{21}q_{1(t)} + b_{22}q_{2(t)} \end{aligned}$$

where t denotes a particular year or quarter ($t = 1, 2, 3, \ldots, n$). For the present at least we ignore constant terms (intercepts) and random disturbances.

Assume that p_i and q_i are price and quantity *relatives* and are combined into Laspeyres indices, P and Q, using the same set of expenditure weights in each index, $w_1 + w_2 = 1$. Thus $P = (w_1 p_1 + w_2 p_2)$ and $Q = (w_1 q_1 + w_2 q_2)$. We propose to take time series observations on P and Q and estimate a least squares regression coefficient β. The formula for β is

$$(14.113) \qquad \beta = \frac{\sum\limits_{t=1}^{n} PQ}{\sum\limits_{t=1}^{n} Q^2}$$

For each time t the appropriate elements in the numerator of (14.113) are

$$(14.114) \qquad P_{(t)} Q_{(t)} = (w_1 p_1 + w_2 p_2)(w_1 q_1 + w_2 q_2)$$

But from (14.112), we know that

$$(14.115) \qquad p_1 = b_{11} q_1 + b_{12} q_2$$

and

$$(14.116) \qquad p_2 = b_{21} q_1 + b_{22} q_2$$

If we wish to use our regression coefficient β to make "structural" predictions of $P_{(t+1)}$ from stipulated values of $Q_{(t+1)}$, it is logically desirable to make the regression coefficient depend only on values of the q_i.

We therefore substitute the values of p_1 and p_2 from (14.115) and (14.116) into (14.114) obtaining

$$(14.117) \quad P_{(t)} Q_{(t)} = [(w_1 b_{11} q_1 + w_1 b_{12} q_2) + (w_2 b_{21} q_1 + w_2 b_{22} q_2)] \\ \times (w_1 q_1 + w_2 q_2)$$

The complete product contains eight terms:

$$(14.118) \qquad P_{(t)} Q_{(t)} = \left\{ \begin{array}{l} w_1^2 b_{11} q_1^2 + w_1^2 b_{12} q_1 q_2 \\ + w_1 w_2 b_{21} q_1^2 + w_1 w_2 b_{22} q_1 q_2 \\ + w_1 w_2 b_{11} q_1 q_2 + w_1 w_2 b_{12} q_2^2 \\ + w_2^2 b_{21} q_1 q_2 + w_2^2 b_{22} q_2^2 \end{array} \right.$$

which may be grouped as

$$(14.119) \quad P_{(t)} Q_{(t)} = \begin{array}{l} b_{11}(w_1^2 q_1^2 + w_1 w_2 q_1 q_2) + b_{12}(w_1^2 q_1 q_2 + w_1 w_2 q_2^2) \\ + b_{21}(w_1 w_2 q_1^2 + w_2^2 q_1 q_2) + b_{22}(w_1 w_2 q_1 q_2 + w_2^2 q_2^2) \end{array}$$

The denominator at each time t is simply

$$(14.120) \qquad Q_{(t)}^2 = (w_1^2 q_1^2 + w_2^2 q_2^2 + 2 w_1 w_2 q_1 q_2)$$

If we sum these terms for all time periods we obtain

(14.121)

$$\beta = \frac{\sum\limits_{t=1}^{n} P_{(t)} Q_{(t)}}{\sum\limits_{t=1}^{n} Q_{(t)}^2}$$

$$= \frac{\left[\begin{array}{l} b_{11}(w_1^2 \sum q_1^2 + w_1 w_2 \sum q_1 q_2) + b_{12}(w_1^2 \sum q_1 q_2 + w_1 w_2 \sum q_2^2) \\ + b_{21}(w_1 w_2 \sum q_1^2 + w_2^2 \sum q_1 q_2) + b_{22}(w_1 w_2 \sum q_1 q_2 + w_2^2 \sum q_2^2) \end{array} \right]}{w_1^2 \sum q_1^2 + w_2^2 \sum q_2^2 + 2 w_1 w_2 \sum q_1 q_2}$$

where all summations run over the n time units, $t = 1, 2, 3, \ldots, n$.

The denominator is evidently a matrix of variances and covariances of the q_i with the variances weighted by w_i^2 and the covariances weighted by $w_i w_j$.[5] In the numerator, each structural coefficient b_{ii} and b_{ij} is complexly weighted by combinations of variances and covariances of the q_i with terms in w_i^2 and $w_i w_j$. If the covariances were all zero and the cross-flexibilities of price were zero or small, it is clear that the regression coefficient β in different time periods would depend upon the relative variances of the different q_i. If $\sum q_1 q_2 = 0$, (14.121) becomes

(14.122)

$$\beta = \frac{\left(\begin{array}{l} b_{11} w_1^2 \sum q_1^2 + b_{12} w_1 w_2 \sum q_2^2 \\ + b_{21} w_1 w_2 \sum q_1^2 + b_{22} w_2^2 \sum q_2^2 \end{array} \right)}{w_1^2 \sum q_1^2 + w_2^2 \sum q_2^2}$$

or

(14.123) $$\beta = \frac{(b_{11} w_1^2 + b_{21} w_1 w_2) \sum q_1^2 + (b_{12} w_1 w_2 + b_{22} w_2^2) \sum q_2^2}{w_1^2 \sum q_1^2 + w_2^2 \sum q_2^2}$$

If in addition $b_{21} = b_{12} = 0$, we would have

(14.124) $$\beta = \frac{b_{11} w_1^2 \sum q_1^2 + b_{22} w_2^2 \sum q_2^2}{w_1^2 \sum q_1^2 + w_2^2 \sum q_2^2}$$

Some numerical examples may be helpful. First, let us assume that q_1 and q_2 are percent changes from the preceding quarter—and that the index number weights w_1 and w_2 each equal 0.5. Then the change in the Laspeyres consumption index will be

(14.125) $$\Delta Q = 0.5 q_1 + 0.5 q_2 = 0.5(q_1 + q_2)$$

and the change in the Laspeyres price index will be

(14.126) $$\Delta P = 0.5 p_1 + 0.5 p_2 = 0.5(p_1 + p_2)$$

---

[5] If we divide through both numerator and denominator by n, we obtain the *variances* of q_1 and q_2, respectively, as $\sum q_1^2/n$ and $\sum q_2^2/n$, and the *covariance* of q_1 and q_2 as $\sum q_1 q_2/n$. The covariance can also be written as $r_{q_1 q_2} s_{q_1} s_{q_2}$.

But the p's and q's are connected in the real economy by the coefficient matrix B of (14.115) and (14.116):

(14.127)
$$\begin{bmatrix} p_1 \\ p_2 \end{bmatrix} = \begin{bmatrix} b_{11} & b_{12} \\ b_{21} & b_{22} \end{bmatrix} \begin{bmatrix} q_1 \\ q_2 \end{bmatrix}$$

or in the arrangement used earlier in this chapter,

$$\begin{matrix} & (q_1 \quad q_2) \\ \begin{bmatrix} p_1 \\ p_2 \end{bmatrix} = & \begin{bmatrix} b_{11} & b_{12} \\ b_{21} & b_{22} \end{bmatrix} \end{matrix}$$

where the q_i at the top of each column is multiplied by each of the coefficients in the column below to reconstitute (14.115) and (14.116) or to predict the values of p_1 and p_2 corresponding to specified values of q_1 and q_2.

If the coefficient matrix is $B = \begin{bmatrix} -2 & 0 \\ 0 & -4 \end{bmatrix}$, the microrelations give us

$p_1 = -2q_1 + 0q_2$ and $p_2 = 0q_1 - 4q_2$. Adding (since they are equally weighted), we have $(p_1 + p_2) = -2q_1 - 4q_2$ or

(14.128)
$$\Delta P = -q_1 - 2q_2$$

and

(20.129)
$$\Delta Q = 0.5(q_1 + q_2)$$

The ratio $\Delta P / \Delta Q$ is a "true" structural coefficient relating the two index numbers, since it includes all the information in the two microrelations.

If q_2 is zero, $\Delta P / \Delta Q = -q_1/0.5q_1 = -2$; if q_1 is zero, $\Delta P / \Delta Q = -2q_2/0.5q_2 = -4$; and if $q_1 = q_2$, $\Delta P / \Delta Q = -3q_1/0.5(2q_1) = -3$. Similar results would occur in the regression coefficient β if the *variances* of q_1 and q_2 took on specified relative values. Assuming zero covariance between q_1 and q_2, the regression coefficient of $P_{(t)}$ on $Q_{(t)}$ could range from -2 to -4 depending on which quantity showed the larger variance.

If the two commodities (groups) are substitutes to some extent, the elements of the main diagonal of B will be nonzero. Thus if

$$B = \begin{bmatrix} -2.0 & -0.3 \\ -0.6 & -4.0 \end{bmatrix}$$

we have

(14.130)
$$\begin{matrix} & (q_1 \quad q_2) \\ \begin{bmatrix} p_1 \\ p_2 \end{bmatrix} = & \begin{bmatrix} -2.0 & -0.3 \\ -0.6 & -4.0 \end{bmatrix} \end{matrix}$$

or

$$p_1 = -2.0q_1 - 0.3q_2 \quad \text{and} \quad p_2 = -0.6q_1 - 4.0q_2$$

Adding (since the weights are still equal) we obtain $(p_1 + p_2) = -2.6q_1 - 4.3q_2$.

In the new situation, a 1% increase in q_1 not only depresses p_1 by 2%, but also depresses p_2 by 0.6%. Similarly, a 1% increase in q_2 depresses p_2 by 4% and p_1 by 0.3%. If q_2 is zero, $\Delta P/\Delta Q = -2.6$; if q_1 is zero $\Delta P/\Delta Q = -4.3$; and if $q_1 = q_2$, $\Delta P/\Delta Q = -3.45$. The price flexibility of an aggregate of competing (substitute) commodities is larger in absolute value than the weighted average of the own-price flexibilities of the individual commodities. Since elasticities of demand are the reciprocals of price flexibilities, this means that the elasticity of demand for a group of competing commodities is less in absolute value than the weighted average of the own-elasticities of the individual commodities. Thus if $q_1 = q_2$, $\eta = \Delta Q/\Delta P = -0.333$ if there is no price substitution (off-diagonal coefficients of B are zero) and $\eta = \Delta Q/\Delta P = -0.290$ when the off-diagonal coefficients are -0.3 and -0.6.

If we know the detailed structure of relations among commodities or other elements within sets of aggregative variables, we are in a position to interpret changes that appear in regression coefficients between the aggregative variables. For example, suppose we found that the price-flexibility of the index of all food prices with respect to the index of per capita consumption of all foods, had apparently changed from (say) -4.0 before World War II to -3.0 afterward as evidenced by time series regressions of $P_{(t)}$ on $Q_{(t)}$. The change *might* be attributable to a change in the relative variability of supplies of livestock and crop foods between the two periods and not to a change in the elasticity of consumer demand for food. The elasticity is best defined in terms of a matrix such as Brandow's; if the available supply of every food increased by 1%, the elasticity of demand for all food might prove to be the same in both periods.

The foregoing interpretation of a time series regression coefficient between index numbers was derived by Karl A. Fox in 1951 to throw light on relationships between regression analyses for particular commodities and regression analyses between aggregates of these commodities.

In one sense we have avoided the aggregation problem in our demonstration, for we have felt free to use the microrelations directly. Instead of estimating $P_{(t+1)}$ as a function of $Q_{(t+1)}$ we have estimated p_1 and p_2 separately as functions of q_1 and q_2 and then added up p_1 and p_2 to obtain $P_{(t+1)}$ and q_1 and q_2 to obtain $Q_{(t+1)}$ after the fact.

If we insist on a perfect aggregation so that

$$(14.131) \qquad\qquad P_{(t+1)} = \bar{B}Q^*_{(t+1)}$$

we must convert our results into Theil's pattern. We have been treating p_1, p_2, p_3, and p_4 as *unweighted* price relatives. Now define $p'_1 = w_1 p_1$, $p'_2 = w_2 p_2$, $q'_1 = w_1 q_1$, and $q'_2 = w_2 q_2$, w_1 and w_2 being expenditure weights for Laspeyres index numbers, $w_1 = p_{10}q_{10}/(p_{10}q_{10} + p_{20}q_{20})$, $w_2 = p_{20}q_{20}/(p_{10}q_{10} + p_{20}q_{20})$; $w_1 + w_2 = 1$.

Starting from (14.115) and (14.116), we multiply the first equation by w_1 and the second by w_2:

(14.132) $$w_1 p_1 = w_1 b_{11} q_1 + w_1 b_{12} q_2$$

(14.133) $$w_2 p_2 = w_2 b_{21} q_1 + w_2 b_{22} q_2$$

or

(14.134) $$w_1 p_1 = b_{11} w_1 q_1 + b_{12} w_2 q_2 \left(\frac{w_1}{w_2}\right)$$

(14.135) $$w_2 p_2 = b_{21} w_1 q_1 \left(\frac{w_2}{w_1}\right) + b_{22} w_2 q_2$$

or by definition of p'_1, p'_2, q'_1, and q'_2,

(14.136) $$p'_1 = b_{11} q'_1 + b_{12}\left(\frac{w_1}{w_2}\right) q'_2$$

(14.137) $$p'_2 = b_{21}\left(\frac{w_2}{w_1}\right) q'_1 + b_{22} q'_2$$

Adding the two microrelations we obtain

(14.138) $$(p'_1 + p'_2) = \left[b_{11} + b_{21}\left(\frac{w_2}{w_1}\right)\right] q'_1 + \left[b_{12}\left(\frac{w_1}{w_2}\right) + b_{22}\right] q'_2$$

or letting $B_1 = [b_{11} + b_{21}(w_2/w_1)]$ and $B_2 = [b_{12}(w_1/w_2) + b_{22}]$, we have $P' = (p'_1 + p'_2) = B_1 q'_1 + B_2 q'_2$

Let $\bar{B} = (B_1 + B_2)/2$.
Then

$$P' = \bar{B}\left[\frac{B_1}{\bar{B}} q'_1 + \frac{B_2}{\bar{B}} q'_2\right] \quad \text{and} \quad Q'^* = \frac{B_1}{\bar{B}} q'_1 + \frac{B_2}{\bar{B}} q'_2$$

The single macrorelation

(14.139) $$P'_{(t+1)} = \bar{B} Q'^*_{(t+1)}$$

will give us perfect predictions of $P'_{(t+1)}$ from any stated value of $Q'^*_{(t+1)}$ assuming that the two microrelations used separately would permit us to make perfect predictions of p'_1 and p'_2.

The essence of Theil's approach to perfect aggregation should by this time be clear: *All the information concerning the individual microrelations is locked into the special weights of the independent macrovariable.* If we have enough information to form the special aggregate Q^* we also have enough information to use the microrelations directly, as in the case of Brandow's 24 by 24 matrix and the associated expenditure weights.

Each of the 24 columns j of Brandow's matrix, with the elements appropriately weighted by ratios such as (w_i/w_j), provides us with a term such as B_1—in the Brandow instance, a sum of the 24 elements $b_{ij}(w_i/w_j)$, where $i, j = 1, 2, 3, \ldots, 24$. Thus (using Q' in the dependent and P' in the independent position, as does Brandow, we may write

(14.140) $$Q' = \bar{B}P'*$$

where

$$\bar{B} = \frac{1}{24}[B_1 + B_2 + B_3 + \cdots + B_{24}]$$

and

$$P'* = \frac{1}{\bar{B}}[B_1 p'_1 + B_2 p'_2 + B_3 p'_3 + \cdots + B_{24} p'_{24}]$$

Each B_i may be interpreted as the elasticity of demand for all food with respect to changes in the price of the ith food.

The potency of $P'*$ as a macroestimator stems from the fact that it incorporates 576 microcoefficients and a weighting pattern which would almost certainly not occur to statisticians who were preoccupied with constructing the regular Laspeyres price index, $P' = (p'_1 + p'_2 + p'_3 + \cdots + p'_{24})$.

14.2.3 *Theil's Approach to Analysis of the Correspondence of Statistical Macrorelations to Microrelations, Both Estimated from Time Series*[6]

Suppose we wish to estimate the marginal propensity to consume a certain commodity, using time series observations on the macrovariables Q (consumption) and Y (income) where $Q = \sum_{i=1}^n q_i$ and $Y = \sum_{i=1}^n y_i$; q_i and y_i are the consumption and income of the ith consumer, and there are n consumers in the economy.

The microrelations are

(14.141) $$q_{i(t)} = a_i + c_i y_{i(t)} + u_{i(t)} \qquad (i = 1, 2, 3, \ldots, n)$$

and the macrorelation is

(14.142) $$Q_{(t)} = A + C Y_{(t)} + U_{(t)}$$

The incomes of different consumers will have somewhat different time paths during the period for which the macrorelation is to be estimated. We may express these individual time path differences by computing the least squares regression of each consumer's income upon the total income of all consumers:

(14.143) $$y_{i(t)} = \alpha_i + \beta_i Y_{(t)} + z_{i(t)}$$

[6] This exposition closely parallels that of R. G. D. Allen, *Mathematical Economics* (Second edition) (London: Macmillan), pp. 699–700, 1959.

Since $\sum_{i=1}^{n} y_{i(t)} = Y_{(t)}$, the following relations must hold:

$$\sum_{i=1}^{n} \alpha_i = 0; \quad \sum_{i=1}^{n} \beta_i = 1; \quad \text{and} \quad \sum_{i=1}^{n} z_i = 0$$

for the least squares regression of Y on itself is

(14.144) $$Y = 0 + 1 \cdot Y$$

this particular kind of restriction is self-policing, as we noted earlier in this chapter.

We may sum the n microrelations like (14.141) and substitute into each of them the expression $[\alpha_i + \beta_i Y_{(t)} + z_{i(t)}]$ for $y_{i(t)}$, obtaining

$$Q = \sum_i a_i + \sum_i c_i(\alpha_i + \beta_i Y + z_i) + \sum_i u_i$$

(14.145) $$Q = \sum_i a_i + \sum_i c_i\alpha_i + \sum_i c_i\beta_i Y + \sum_i c_i z_i + \sum_i u_i$$

$$Q = \left(\sum_i a_i + \sum_i c_i\alpha_i\right) + \left(\sum_i c_i\beta_i\right) Y + \sum_i c_i z_i + \sum_i u_i$$

which is of the form required for the macrorelation,

(14.146) $$Q_{(t)} = A' + C' Y_{(t)} + U'_{(t)}$$

Hence $A' = \sum_i a_i + \sum_i c_i\alpha_i$ and $C' = \sum_i c_i\beta_i$, where $\sum_i \alpha_i = 0$ and $\sum_i \beta_i = 1$.

Equation (14.146) is the statistical macrorelation. The residuals $U'_{(t)}$ and $z_{i(t)}$ have zero means over the period for which (14.146) and (14.143) are fitted.

The slope of the macrorelation C' turns out to be a *weighted* average of the slopes c_i of the microrelations. Each weight β_i depends on the time path of y_i, the income of the ith consumer, relative to the time path of the aggregate income Y during the specified time period. For,

$$\beta_i = \frac{\sum_{t=1}^{T} [y_{i(t)} - \bar{y}_i][Y_{(t)} - \bar{Y}]}{\sum_{t=1}^{T} [Y_{(t)} - \bar{Y}]^2}$$

and the $y_{i(t)}$ and $Y_{(t)}$ will be different in different time periods.

The macrointercept A' turns out to be a function not only of the microintercepts a_i but also of the microintercepts α_i [which depend on the time paths of $y_{i(t)}$ and $Y_{(t)}$] *weighted by* the microslopes or marginal propensities to consume, c_i. Neither A' nor C' give us the simple sum and simple average we might expect in a straightforward aggregation of the microrelations

(14.141) $$q_{i(t)} = a_i + c_i y_{i(t)} + u_{i(t)}$$

Allen expresses the biases in A' and C' as follows:

(14.147) $$A' = \sum_i a_i + n \operatorname{cov}(c_i \alpha_i)$$

and

(14.148) $$C' = \bar{c} + n \operatorname{cov}(c_i \beta_i)$$

where "cov" stands for "covariance of," and $\bar{c} = (1/n) \sum_i c_i$. We may also write these expressions as

(14.149) $$A' = \sum a_i + n r_{c_i \alpha_i} s_{c_i} s_{\alpha_i}$$

and

(14.150) $$C' = \bar{c} + n r_{c_i \beta_i} s_{c_i} s_{\beta_i}$$

The covariance terms represent the aggregation bias. If the incomes of all consumers followed identical time paths ($\alpha_i = \bar{\alpha}$ and $\beta_i = \bar{\beta}$ for all consumers), the covariances would be zero since $s_{\alpha_i} = 0$, $s_{\beta_i} = 0$, and $r_{c_i \alpha_i} = r_{c_i \beta_i} = 0$. Or if all consumers had identical marginal propensities to consume, $s_{c_i} = 0$ and $r_{c_i \alpha_i} = r_{c_i \beta_i} = 0$, and the covariances would be zero. But in general the covariances would not be zero, and they would vary from one time period to another.

If we include more variables and coefficients in our models, we find that the time series estimate of each coefficient in the macrorelation depends not only on the *corresponding* microcoefficients (as C_1 upon $c_{1.i}$) but on all the microcoefficients, corresponding and noncorresponding alike (as B_1 on $b_{1.i}$, $b_{2.i}, \ldots, b_{m.i}$, and $c_{1.i}$). And each coefficient is influenced by the time paths of all the independent microvariables.

Hence only the "perfect aggregation" approach of the preceding section will, in principle, avoid all contradictions between the microrelations and the macrorelation. The weighting system varies from one coefficient to another; there are as many different weighting systems as there are macrocoefficients in the macrorelation. This is not an excessive price to pay in models which may be used as partial bases for major policy decisions—*if* information about the microrelations exists or can be developed.

EXERCISES

1. Suppose we had a situation involving one commodity and three households, that is, the consumption microrelations are:

$$q_{1.1} = a_{1.1} + b_{1.1} p_{1.1} + c_{1.1} y_1$$
$$q_{1.2} = a_{1.2} + b_{1.2} p_{1.2} + c_{1.2} y_2$$
$$q_{1.3} = a_{1.3} + b_{1.3} p_{1.3} + c_{1.3} y_3$$

The corresponding macrorelation is

$$Q = A_1 + B_1 P_1 + C_1 Y$$

Derive all of the possible conditions which make the macrorelation a "perfect aggregate" (in the sense of Theil) of the microrelations.

2. Derive the relationship between the *Laspeyres* index number formula and the perfect aggregation in the instance in which we are deriving the aggregate consumption of n commodities by a single consumer where his consumption of each commodity q_i is a function of its own price p_i.

REFERENCES

1. Allen, R. G. D., *Mathematical Economics*, Second edition, London: The Macmillan Co., 1959.
2. Fox, Karl A., *Econometric Analysis for Public Policy*, Ames: Iowa State University Press, pp. 58–65, 1958.
3. Theil, H., *Linear Aggregation of Economic Relations*, Amsterdam: North-Holland Publishing Co., 1954.
4. Theil, H., *Economic Forecasts and Policy*, Second revised edition, Amsterdam: North-Holland Publishing Co., 1961.

APPENDIX I

Glossary of Symbols

The Greek and Roman letters used most frequently as symbols in this text and the most important of the other symbols are as follows:

X, Y (Roman)	= variables as observed.
x, y (Roman)	= variables in terms of departures from their means.
M_x, $\bar{X}$ (Roman)	= arithmetic mean of X.
σ (Greek small sigma)	= standard deviation in the population.
$\sum$ (Greek capital sigma)	= sum of the items specified.
n, N (Roman)	= number of observations in a sample.
b (Roman)	= coefficient of regression in a sample.
$f(\ )$ (Roman)	= function of the variable in the parentheses.
s, S (Roman)	= standard deviation in a sample.
$\bar{S}$ (Roman)	= standard error of estimate.
r (Roman)	= simple coefficient of correlation.
r^2, R^2 (Roman)	= coefficient of determination in univariate and multivariate case, respectively.
R (Roman)	= multiple correlation coefficient.
β (Greek)	= population coefficient of regression.
z (Roman)	= residual, or difference between observed and estimated values of a dependent variable.
I (Roman)	= identity matrix.
E (Roman)	= expectation of a variable.
μ (Greek)	= population mean.
ρ (Greek rho)	= population coefficient of correlation.
η (Greek small eta)	= coefficient of elasticity of demand.
π (Greek small pi)	= arbitrary symbol.
Δ (Greek capital delta)	= small increment in a variable.
δ (Greek small delta)	= von Neumann ratio.

List of Important Equations

For convenience in referring to the more important equations in the text, most of the equations expressing basic concepts and formulas are repeated here in numerical order. Equations containing coefficients specific to a particular example are omitted.

(2.1) $\quad \text{GNP} = C + I + G + (\Delta H_a - \Delta H_d) + (E - M)$

$$= \text{TG output} - \Delta H_d - M - \sum_{i=1}^{n} \sum_{j=1}^{n} X_{ij}$$

(2.2) $\quad \text{GNI} = D + T_b + W + i + R + \pi$

$$= \text{TG outlay} - \Delta H_d - M - \sum_{i=1}^{n} \sum_{j=1}^{n} X_{ij}$$

(2.3) $$\text{GNI} = \text{GNP}$$

(2.5) $$\Delta X_i = \alpha_{ij}(\Delta F_j)$$

(4.2) $$\bar{S} = \left(\frac{\sum_{i=1}^{n} z_i^2}{n-2} \right)^{1/2}$$

(4.4) $$\bar{r}^2 = 1 - (1 - r^2)\left(\frac{n-1}{n-2}\right)$$

(4.5) $$b = \frac{\sum_{i=1}^{n} q_i p_i}{\sum_{i=1}^{n} p_i^2}$$

(4.6) $$r^2 = \frac{\left(\sum_{i=1}^{n} q_i p_i\right)^2}{\sum_{i=1}^{n} q_i^2 \cdot \sum_{i=1}^{n} p_i^2}$$

(4.16) $$\bar{R}^2 = 1 - (1 - R^2)\left(\frac{n-1}{n-3}\right)$$

The equation of a second-degree parabola may be written as:

$$Q = a + bP + cP^2$$

The three constants a, b, and c may be calculated from any given set of observations as follows:

(4.17) $$b = \frac{\sum pq \cdot \sum u^2 - \sum uq \sum pu}{\sum p^2 \sum u^2 - (\sum pu)^2}$$

(4.18) $$c = \frac{\sum uq \cdot \sum p^2 - \sum pq \sum pu}{\sum p^2 \sum u^2 - (\sum pu)^2}$$

(4.19) $$a = \bar{Q} - b\bar{P} - c\bar{U}$$

where $q = Q - \bar{Q}$, $p = P - \bar{P}$, $u = U - \bar{U}$, $(U = P^2)$

(A.1, Chapter 4) $$Y = a + bX + z$$

(A.4b, Chapter 4) $$na \sum X + b(\sum X)^2 = \sum Y \cdot \sum X$$

(A.5b, Chapter 4) $$na \sum X + nb \sum X^2 = n \sum YX$$

(A.6) $$b = \frac{\sum Y \cdot \sum X - n \sum YX}{(\sum X)^2 - n \sum X^2}$$

(A.4c, Chapter 4) $$na \sum X^2 + b \sum X \cdot \sum X^2 = \sum Y \cdot \sum X^2$$

(A.5c, Chapter 4) $$a(\sum X)^2 + b \sum X \cdot \sum X^2 = \sum YX \cdot \sum X$$

(A.7, Chapter 4) $$a = \frac{\sum Y \cdot \sum X^2 - \sum YX \cdot \sum X}{n \sum X^2 - (\sum X)^2}$$

(A.7d, Chapter 4) $$a = \bar{Y} - b\bar{X}$$

(A.11, Chapter 4) $$Y = a + b_1 X_1 + b_2 X_2 + z$$

[With x_1 used for $X_1 - \bar{X}_1$, x_2 for $X_2 - \bar{X}_2$, (A.11) becomes $y = a + b_1 x_1 + b_2 x_2$. These symbols are used in (A.13a), (A.14a), (A.15), and (A.16)].

(A.12, Chapter 4) $$a = \bar{Y} - b_1\bar{X}_1 - b_2\bar{X}_2$$

(A.13a, Chapter 4) $$b_1 \sum x_1{}^2 + b_2 \sum x_1 x_2 = \sum yx_1$$

(A.14a, Chapter 4) $$b_1 \sum x_1 x_2 + b_2 \sum x_2{}^2 = \sum yx_2$$

(A.15, Chapter 4) $$b_1 = \frac{\sum yx_1 \cdot \sum x_2{}^2 - \sum yx_2 \cdot \sum x_1 x_2}{\sum x_1{}^2 \cdot \sum x_2{}^2 - (\sum x_1 x_2)^2}$$

(A.16, Chapter 4) $$b_2 = \frac{\sum yx_2 \cdot \sum x_1{}^2 - \sum yx_1 \cdot \sum x_1 x_2}{\sum x_1{}^2 \cdot \sum x_2{}^2 - (\sum x_1 x_2)^2}$$

$$(5.5) \qquad P_{L(t)} = \frac{p_{1t}q_{10}}{(p_{10}q_{10} + p_{20}q_{20})} + \frac{p_{2t}q_{20}}{(p_{10}q_{10} + p_{20}q_{20})} = \frac{\sum p_t q_0}{\sum p_0 q_0}$$

$$(5.10) \qquad P_{P(t)} = \frac{p_{1t}q_{1t}}{(p_{10}q_{1t} + p_{20}q_{2t})} + \frac{p_{2t}q_{2t}}{(p_{10}q_{1t} + p_{20}q_{2t})} = \frac{\sum p_t q_t}{\sum p_0 q_t}$$

$$(5.12) \qquad Q_{L(t)} = \frac{q_{1t}p_{10} + q_{2t}p_{20}}{(p_{10}q_{10} + p_{20}q_{20})} = \frac{\sum q_t p_0}{\sum q_0 p_0}$$

$$(5.14) \qquad Q_{P(t)} = \frac{q_{1t}p_{1t} + q_{2t}p_{2t}}{(q_{10}p_{1t} + q_{20}p_{2t})} = \frac{\sum q_t p_t}{\sum q_0 p_t}$$

$$(5.15) \qquad \frac{V_t}{V_0} = \frac{p_{1t}q_{1t} + p_{2t}q_{2t}}{p_{10}q_{10} + p_{20}q_{20}}$$

$$(5.16) \qquad P_{L(t)}Q_{L(t)} = \frac{(p_{1t}q_{10} + p_{2t}q_{20})(q_{1t}p_{10} + q_{2t}p_{20})}{(p_{10}q_{10} + p_{20}q_{20})^2}$$

$$(5.17) \qquad P_{P(t)}Q_{P(t)} = \frac{(p_{1t}q_{1t} + p_{2t}q_{2t})^2}{(p_{10}q_{1t} + p_{20}q_{2t})(q_{10}p_{1t} + q_{20}p_{2t})}$$

$$(5.18) \qquad P_{P(t)}Q_{L(t)} = \frac{(p_{1t}q_{1t} + p_{2t}q_{2t})}{(p_{10}q_{10} + p_{20}q_{20})} = \frac{V_t}{V_0}$$

$$(5.19) \qquad P_{L(t)}Q_{P(t)} = \frac{(q_{1t}p_{1t} + q_{2t}p_{2t})}{(p_{10}q_{10} + p_{20}q_{20})} = \frac{V_t}{V_0}$$

$$(6.7) \qquad s_{\hat{Y}} = \sqrt{s_{Y'}^2 + (s_b w)^2}$$

$$(6.8) \qquad s_{Y'}^2 = \bar{S}_{Y.W}^2 + s_{Y.W}^2 + (s_b w)^2$$

$$(\text{A.1, Chapter 6}) \qquad s_{\bar{X}_1} = \frac{s_1}{\sqrt{n}}$$

$$(\text{A.2, Chapter 6}) \qquad s_{(\bar{X}_1 | \bar{X}_2)} = \frac{\bar{S}_{1.2}}{\sqrt{n}}$$

$$(\text{A.2a, Chapter 6}) \qquad s_{(\bar{X}_1 | \bar{X}_2, \bar{X}_2{}^2)} = \frac{\bar{S}_{1.(2,2^2)}}{\sqrt{n}}$$

$$(\text{A.2b, Chapter 6}) \qquad s_{[\bar{X}_1 | \bar{X}_2, (\bar{X}_2{}^2), \ldots, (\bar{X}_2{}^{k-1})]} = \frac{\bar{S}_{1.2, 2^2, \ldots, 2^{k-1}}}{\sqrt{n}}$$

$$(\text{A.3, Chapter 6}) \qquad s_{b_{12}} = \frac{\bar{S}_{1.2}}{s_2 \sqrt{n}}$$

$$(\text{A.4, Chapter 6}) \qquad s_{(\hat{X}_1 | X_2)}^2 = \bar{S}_{1.2}^2 \left(\frac{1}{n} + \frac{x_2^2}{s_2^2 \cdot n} \right) = \frac{\bar{S}_{1.2}^2}{n} + \left(\frac{\bar{S}_{1.2}^2}{n s_2^2} \right) x_2^2$$

(A.4b, Chapter 6) $\qquad s_{(\hat{x}_1 | x_2)} = \sqrt{s_{\bar{x}_1}{}^2 + (s_{b_{12}} x_2)^2}$

(A.4c, Chapter 6) $\qquad s_{b_0} = \sqrt{s_{\bar{x}_1 | \bar{x}_2}{}^2 + (s_{b_{12}} \bar{X}_2)^2}$

(A.5, Chapter 6) $\qquad s^2_{(x_1 | x_2)} = S^2_{1.2}\left[1 + \dfrac{1}{n} + (s_{b_{12}} x_2)^2\right]$

(A.11a, Chapter 6) $\qquad z' = X'_1 - b' X'_{023}$

(A.12, Chapter 6) $\quad z'z = (X'_1 - b' X'_{023})(X_1 - X_{023} b)$
$$= X'_1 X_1 - 2 X'_1 X_{023} b + b' X'_{023} X_{023} b$$

(A.16, Chapter 6) $\qquad X'_{023} X_{023} b = X'_1 X_{023}$

(A.17a, Chapter 6) $\qquad b = (X'_{023} X_{023})^{-1} X'_1 X_{023}$

(A.18a, Chapter 6) $\qquad V(b) = \bar{S}^2_{1.023}(X'_{023} X_{023})^{-1}$

(A.31, Chapter 6) $\quad s_{\hat{x}_1}{}^2 = s_{\bar{x}_1}{}^2 + (s_{b_{12}} x_2)^2 + (s_{b_{13}} x_3)^2 + 2 s_{b_{12}} s_{b_{13}} x_2 x_3$

(7.11) $\qquad b_{12} = r_{12}\left(\dfrac{S_1}{S_2}\right)$

(7.28) $\qquad b_{1,2e} = b_{12}\left[\dfrac{1}{1 + (\sum z_2{}^2 / \sum x_2{}^2)}\right]$

(7.29) $\quad \triangle{3} = \begin{vmatrix} 1 & r_{12} & r_{13} \\ r_{12} & 1 & r_{23} \\ r_{13} & r_{23} & 1 \end{vmatrix} = 1 + 2 r_{12} r_{13} r_{23} - r_{12}{}^2 - r_{13}{}^2 - r_{23}{}^2$

(7.30) $\qquad R^2_{1.23} = \dfrac{r_{12}{}^2 + r_{13}{}^2 - 2 r_{12} r_{13} r_{23}}{1 - r_{23}{}^2}$

(7.31) $\qquad \beta_{12.3} = \dfrac{r_{12} - r_{13} r_{23}}{1 - r_{23}{}^2}$

(7.32) $\qquad b_{12.3} = \beta_{12.3} \cdot \dfrac{S_1}{S_2}$

(7.33) $\qquad \beta_{13.2} = \dfrac{r_{13} - r_{12} r_{23}}{1 - r_{23}{}^2}$

(7.34) $\qquad b_{13.2} = \beta_{13.2} \cdot \dfrac{S_1}{S_3}$

(7.35) $\qquad r_{12.3} = \dfrac{r_{12} - r_{13} r_{23}}{[(1 - r_{23}{}^2)(1 - r_{13}{}^2)]^{\frac{1}{2}}}$

(7.36) $\qquad r_{13.2} = \dfrac{r_{13} - r_{12} r_{23}}{[(1 - r_{23}{}^2)(1 - r_{12}{}^2)]^{\frac{1}{2}}}$

$$(7.37) \quad S_{\beta_{12.3}} = S_{\beta_{13.2}} = \left[\frac{1 + 2r_{12}r_{13}r_{23} - r_{12}{}^2 - r_{13}{}^2 - r_{23}{}^2}{(N-3)(1 - r_{23}{}^2)} \right]^{1/2}$$

$$= \left[\frac{1 - R_{1.23}^2}{(1 - r_{23}{}^2)(N-3)} \right]^{1/2}$$

$$(7.38) \qquad S_{b_{12.3}} = S_{\beta_{12.3}} \cdot \frac{S_1}{S_2}$$

$$(7.39) \qquad S_{b_{13.2}} = S_{\beta_{13.2}} \cdot \frac{S_1}{S_3}$$

(B.4, Chapter 7) $\qquad ns^2 = y'y - 2y'Xb + b'X'Xb$

(B.5, Chapter 7) $\qquad X'y = X'Xb$

(B.6, Chapter 7) $\qquad b = (X'X)^{-1}X'y$

(B.9, Chapter 7) $\qquad \beta = (X'X)^{-1}X'y - (X'X)^{-1}X'z$

(B.10, Chapter 7) $\qquad \beta = b - (X'X)^{-1}X'z$

(B.11, Chapter 7) $\qquad E[(b - \beta)(b - \beta)'] = \sigma^2(X'X)^{-1}$

(B.12, Chapter 7) $\quad V(\hat{y}) = \bar{S}_{y.12,\ldots,m}^2 \left[\frac{1}{n} + \sum_{j=1}^{m} \sum_{k=1}^{m} c_{jk}(x_j - \bar{x}_j)(x_k - \bar{x}_k) \right]$

(B.13, Chapter 7) $\qquad V(\hat{y}) = \frac{1}{n}(\bar{S}_{y.12,\ldots,m}^2)$

(B.14, Chapter 7) $\quad V(y) = \bar{S}_{y.12,\ldots,m}^2 \left[1 + \frac{1}{n} + \sum_{j=1}^{m} \sum_{k=1}^{m} c_{jk}(x_j - \bar{x}_j)(x_k - \bar{x}_k) \right]$

$$(8.1) \qquad t_b = \frac{\sum xy}{\bar{S}_{yx}\sqrt{\sum x^2}}$$

$$(8.2) \qquad F = \frac{(\sum xy)^2}{\bar{S}_{yx}{}^2(\sum x^2)}$$

(A.3, Chapter 9) $\quad y_t = \alpha_0 x_t + \alpha_1 x_{t-1} + \alpha_2 x_{t-2} + \alpha_3 x_{t-3} + \cdots + \alpha_n x_{t-n}$

(A.4, Chapter 9) $\quad \sum_{j=0}^{n} \alpha_0 \lambda^j = \alpha_0(1 + \lambda + \lambda^2 + \lambda^3 + \lambda^4 + \cdots + \lambda^n)$

(A.7, Chapter 9) $\quad y_t = \alpha_0 x_t + \alpha_0 \lambda x_{t-1} + \alpha_0 \lambda^2 x_{t-2} + \cdots$

(A.12, Chapter 9) $\quad \Delta y_t = \alpha_0 x_{t+1} - \gamma y_t, \qquad \gamma = 1 - \lambda$

(A.14, Chapter 9) $\qquad \alpha_L = \frac{\alpha_0}{1 - \lambda}$

$$(11.1) \qquad P = a_1 + b_1 Q + u$$

$$(11.2) \qquad P = a_2 + b_2 Q + v$$

(11.3) $$p = b_1 q + u$$

(11.4) $$p = b_2 q + v$$

(11.6) $$B_{pq} = \frac{b_1 s_v{}^2 - (b_1 + b_2) r_{uv} s_u s_v + b_2 s_u{}^2}{s_v{}^2 - 2 r_{uv} s_u s_v + s_u{}^2}$$

(11.17) $$Q = a_1 + b_1 P + c_1 Y$$

(11.18) $$Q = a_2 + b_2 P + c_2 Z$$

(11.19) $$Q = \left(\frac{-a_1 b_2 + a_2 b_1}{b_1 - b_2} \right) - \left(\frac{b_2 c_1}{b_1 - b_2} \right) Y + \left(\frac{b_1 c_2}{b_1 - b_2} \right) Z$$

(11.20) $$P = \left(\frac{a_2 - a_1}{b_1 - b_2} \right) - \left(\frac{c_1}{b_1 - b_2} \right) Y + \left(\frac{c_2}{b_1 - b_2} \right) Z$$

(11.21) $$P = A_1 + B_1 Y + C_1 Z$$

(11.22) $$Q = A_2 + B_2 Y + C_2 Z$$

(11.23) $$-a_1 b_2 + a_2 b_1 = A_2 (b_1 - b_2)$$

(11.24) $$-a_1 + a_2 = A_1 (b_1 - b_2)$$

(11.25) $$a_2 = A_2 - b_2 A_1$$

(11.28a) $$Y = \alpha + \beta X + u$$

(11.29) $$b = \frac{\beta \sum x^2 + \sum xu}{\sum x^2}$$

(11.37) $$p = \beta q + u$$

(11.38) $$q = \gamma z + v$$

(11.39) $$b = \frac{\sum pq}{\sum q^2} = \beta + \frac{\sum qu}{\sum q^2}$$

(11.42) $$E(b) = \beta + b_{uv} \left(\frac{\sigma_v{}^2}{\sigma_q{}^2} \right)$$

(11.45) $$p_1 = cy + bq_1 + u$$

(11.46) $$y = \gamma p_1 + \delta z + v$$

(11.47) $$p_1 = \left(\frac{b}{1 - \gamma c} \right) q_1 + \left(\frac{c\delta}{1 - \gamma c} \right) z + \frac{u + cv}{1 - \gamma c}$$

(11.48)[1] $$y = \left(\frac{\gamma b}{1 - \gamma c} \right) q_1 + \left(\frac{\delta}{1 - \gamma c} \right) z + \frac{\gamma u + v}{1 - \gamma c}$$

[1] [(11.47) and (11.48) represent the reduced form of the model represented by (11.45) and (11.46)].

(11.53)
$$Q = a_1 + b_1 P + c_1 Y + d_1 W + u$$

(11.54)
$$Q = a_2 + b_2 P + c_2 Z + v$$

(11.55)
$$P = \left(\frac{a_2 - a_1}{b_1 - b_2}\right) - \left(\frac{c_1}{b_1 - b_2}\right)Y + \left(\frac{c_2}{b_1 - b_2}\right)Z$$
$$- \left(\frac{d_1}{b_1 - b_2}\right)W + \frac{v - u}{b_1 - b_2}$$

(11.56)[2]
$$Q = \left(\frac{a_2 b_1 - a_1 b_2}{b_1 - b_2}\right) - \left(\frac{c_1 b_2}{b_1 - b_2}\right)Y + \left(\frac{c_2 b_1}{b_1 - b_2}\right)Z$$
$$- \left(\frac{d_1 b_2}{b_1 - b_2}\right)W + \left(\frac{b_1 v - b_2 u}{b_1 - b_2}\right)$$

(13.8)
$$\triangle_4 = \begin{vmatrix} 1 & r_{12} & r_{13} & r_{14} \\ r_{12} & 1 & r_{23} & r_{24} \\ r_{13} & r_{23} & 1 & r_{34} \\ r_{14} & r_{24} & r_{34} & 1 \end{vmatrix}$$

(13.9)
$$\triangle_{4_{11}} = \begin{vmatrix} 1 & r_{23} & r_{24} \\ r_{23} & 1 & r_{34} \\ r_{24} & r_{34} & 1 \end{vmatrix} = 1 + 2 r_{23} r_{24} r_{34} - r_{23}{}^2 - r_{24}{}^2 - r_{34}{}^2$$

(13.12)
$$R^2_{1.234} = 1 - \frac{\triangle_4}{\triangle_{4_{11}}}$$

(13.13)
$$R^2_{1.2345} = 1 - \frac{\triangle_5}{\triangle_{5_{11}}}$$

(13.14)
$$\beta_{12.3} = \frac{\triangle_{3_{12}}}{\triangle_{3_{11}}}$$

(13.15a)
$$\beta_{13.2} = - \frac{\triangle_{3_{13}}}{\triangle_{3_{11}}}$$

[2] [(11.55) and (11.56) represent the reduced form of the model represented by (11.53) and (11.54)].

$$(13.16) \qquad r_{12.3} = \frac{\triangle\!3_{12}}{\left(\triangle\!3_{11} \cdot \triangle\!3_{22}\right)^{1/2}}$$

$$(13.17) \qquad \beta_{12.34} = \frac{\triangle\!4_{12}}{\triangle\!4_{11}}$$

$$(13.18) \qquad y_0 = \beta_1 y_1 + \beta_2 y_2 + \gamma_1 x_1 + \gamma_2 x_2 + \gamma_3 x_3 + u$$

$$(13.19) \qquad \hat{y}_1 = f_1(x_1, x_2, x_3; x_4, x_5, x_6, x_7)$$

$$(13.20) \qquad \hat{y}_2 = f_2(x_1, x_2, x_3; x_4, x_5, x_6, x_7)$$

$$(13.21) \qquad y_0 = \beta_1 \hat{y}_1 + \beta_2 \hat{y}_2 + \gamma_1 x_1 + \gamma_2 x_2 + \gamma_3 x_3 + u$$

$$(13.22) \quad y_0 = \beta_1\left[\sum_{i=1}^{3} \lambda_{1i}x_i{}^* + \sum_{j=4}^{7} \lambda_{1j}x_j{}^{**}\right]$$
$$+ \beta_2\left[\sum_{i=1}^{3} \lambda_{2i}x{}^* + \sum_{j=4}^{7} \lambda_{2j}x{}^{**}\right] + \sum_{i=1}^{3} \gamma_i x_i{}^* + u$$

$$(14.2) \qquad \begin{aligned} q_1 &= a_1 + b_{11}p_1 + b_{12}p_2 + \cdots + b_{1n}p_n + c_1 y \\ &\vdots \\ q_n &= a_n + b_{n1}p_1 + b_{n2}p_2 + \cdots + b_{nn}p_n + c_n y \end{aligned}$$

$$(14.3) \qquad \sum_{i=1}^{n} q_i p_i = y$$

$$(14.4) \qquad b_{11.h} = \frac{\Delta q_{1.h}}{\Delta p_1}$$

$$(14.5) \qquad \begin{aligned} b_{21.h} &= \frac{\Delta q_{2.h}}{\Delta p_1} \\ &\vdots \\ b_{n1.h} &= \frac{\Delta q_{n.h}}{\Delta p_1} \qquad (h = 1, 2, 3, \ldots, k) \end{aligned}$$

$$(14.8) \qquad \sum_{i=1}^{n} Q_i P_i = Y$$

$$(14.9) \qquad B_{11} = \frac{\Delta Q_1}{\Delta P_1}$$

$$(14.12) \qquad C_1 = \frac{\Delta Q_1}{\Delta Y}$$

$$(14.14) \qquad Q_1 = A_1 + B_{11}P_1 + \cdots + B_{1n}P_n + C_1 Y$$

$$(14.19) \qquad q_{1.1} = a_{1.1} + c_{1.1}y_1$$

(14.20) $$q_{1.2} = a_{1.2} + c_{1.2}y_2$$

(14.21) $$Q_1 = A_1 + C_1 Y$$

(14.23) $$\Delta Q_1 = c_{1.1}\Delta y_1 + c_{1.2}\Delta y_2$$

(14.26) $$Y = \left(\frac{c_{.1}}{C_1}y_1 + \frac{c_{1.2}}{C_1}y_2\right)$$

(14.41) $$\frac{\Delta q_1}{\Delta q_2} = -\frac{p_2}{p_1}$$

(14.50) $$q_i = a_i + b_{ii}p_i \qquad (i = 1, 2)$$

(14.54) $$\beta_{ii} = b_{ii}\frac{p_{io}}{q_{io}} = \frac{\Delta q_i/q_{io}}{\Delta p_i/p_{io}} \qquad (i = 1, 2)$$

(14.58) $$q'_T = a'_T + \beta p^*_T$$

(14.60) $$a'_T = \frac{\sum\limits_{i=1}^{2} p_{io}a_i}{\sum\limits_{i=1}^{2} p_{io}q_{io}}$$

(14.61) $$\beta p^*_T = \bar{\beta} \sum_{i=1}^{2} \left(\frac{\beta_{ii}}{\bar{\beta}}\right)w_{io}\left(\frac{p_i}{p_{io}}\right)$$

(14.75)
$$B_1 = \beta_{11}\left(\frac{w_{10}}{w_{10}}\right) + \beta_{21}\left(\frac{w_{20}}{w_{10}}\right) + \cdots + \beta_{m1}\left(\frac{w_{mo}}{w_{10}}\right)$$
$$\vdots$$
$$B_m = \beta_{1m}\left(\frac{w_{10}}{w_{mo}}\right) + \beta_{2m}\left(\frac{w_{20}}{w_{mo}}\right) + \cdots + \beta_{mm}\left(\frac{w_{mo}}{w_{mo}}\right)$$

(14.76) $$p^*_T = \sum_{i=1}^{m} \left(\frac{B_i}{\bar{B}}\right)p'_i$$

(14.79)
$$B_1 = \frac{1}{w_{10}} \sum_{i=1}^{m} \beta_{i1}w_{io}$$
$$\vdots$$
$$B_m = \frac{1}{w_{mo}} \sum_{i=1}^{m} \beta_{im}w_{io}$$

(14.80) $$\sum_{j=1}^{m} B_j = \sum_{j=1}^{m}\sum_{i=1}^{m} \beta_{ij}\left(\frac{w_{io}}{w_{jo}}\right)$$

(14.81) $$\sum_{j=1}^{m} w_{jo}B_j = \sum_{j=1}^{m}\sum_{i=1}^{m} \beta_{ij}w_{io}$$

(14.106) $$Q_{(t)} = \sum_{1}^{m} q_{it} = \sum_{1}^{m} a_i + \sum_{1}^{m} b_i p_{i(t)} + \sum_{1}^{m} c_i y_{i(t)} + \sum_{1}^{m} z_{i(t)}$$

(14.107) $$\bar{q}_{(t)} = A + B_t \bar{p}_{(t)} + C_t \bar{y}_{(t)} + \bar{z}_{(t)}$$

(14.121) $$\beta = \frac{\sum\limits_{t=1}^{n} P_{(t)} Q_{(t)}}{\sum\limits_{t=1}^{n} Q_{(t)}^2}$$

$$= \frac{[b_{11}(w_1^2 \sum q_1^2 + w_1 w_2 \sum q_1 q_2) + b_{12}(w_1^2 \sum q_1 q_2 + w_1 w_2 \sum q_2^2) + b_{21}(w_1 w_2 \sum q_1^2 + w_2^2 \sum q_1 q_2) + b_{22}(w_1 w_2 \sum q_1 q_2 + w_2^2 \sum q_2^2)]}{w_1^2 \sum q_1^2 + w_2^2 \sum q_2^2 + 2 w_1 w_2 \sum q_1 q_2}$$

(14.139) $$P'_{(t+1)} = \bar{B} Q'^*_{(t+1)}$$

where

$$P' = \bar{B}\left[\frac{B_1}{\bar{B}} q'_1 + \frac{B_2}{\bar{B}} q'_2\right], \qquad Q'^* = \frac{B_1}{\bar{B}} q'_1 + \frac{B_2}{\bar{B}} q'_2$$

and

$$\bar{B} = \frac{B_1 + B_2}{2}$$

(14.141) $$q_{i(t)} = a_i + c_i y_{i(t)} + u_{i(t)} \qquad (i = 1, 2, 3, \ldots, n)$$

(14.143) $$y_{i(t)} = \alpha_i + \beta_i Y_{(t)} + z_{i(t)}$$

(14.146) $$Q_{(t)} = A' + C' Y_{(t)} + U'_{(t)}$$

where

$$A' = \sum_i a_i + \sum_i c_i \alpha_i, \qquad C' = \sum_i c_i \beta_i, \qquad \sum_i \alpha_i = 0 \quad \text{and} \quad \sum_i \beta_i = 1$$

(14.149) $$A' = \sum_i a_i + n r_{c_i \alpha_i} s_{c_i} s_{\alpha_i}$$

(14.150) $$C' = \bar{c} + n r_{c_i \beta_i} s_{c_i} s_{\beta_i}$$

APPENDIX II

Tables

Table 1 Four-Place Logarithms

	0	1	2	3	4	5	6	7	8	9
10	0000	0043	0086	0128	0170	0212	0253	0294	0334	0374
11	0414	0453	0492	0531	0569	0607	0645	0682	0719	0755
12	0792	0828	0864	0899	0934	0969	1004	1038	1072	1106
13	1139	1173	1206	1239	1271	1303	1335	1367	1399	1430
14	1461	1492	1523	1553	1584	1614	1644	1673	1703	1732
15	1761	1790	1818	1847	1875	1903	1931	1959	1987	2014
16	2041	2068	2095	2122	2148	2175	2201	2227	2253	2279
17	2304	2330	2355	2380	2405	2430	2455	2480	2504	2529
18	2553	2577	2601	2625	2648	2672	2695	2718	2742	2765
19	2788	2810	2833	2856	2878	2900	2923	2945	2967	2989
20	3010	3032	3054	3075	3096	3118	3139	3160	3181	3201
21	3222	3243	3263	3284	3304	3324	3345	3365	3385	3404
22	3424	3444	3464	3483	3502	3522	3541	3560	3579	3598
23	3617	3636	3655	3674	3692	3711	3729	3747	3766	3784
24	3802	3820	3838	3856	3874	3892	3909	3927	3945	3962
25	3979	3997	4014	4031	4048	4065	4082	4099	4116	4133
26	4150	4166	4183	4200	4216	4232	4249	4265	4281	4298
27	4314	4330	4346	4362	4378	4393	4409	4425	4440	4456
28	4472	4487	4502	4518	4533	4548	4564	4579	4594	4609
29	4624	4639	4654	4669	4683	4698	4713	4728	4742	4757
30	4771	4786	4800	4814	4829	4843	4857	4871	4886	4900
31	4914	4928	4942	4955	4969	4983	4997	5011	5024	5038
32	5051	5065	5079	5092	5105	5119	5132	5145	5159	5172
33	5185	5198	5211	5224	5237	5250	5263	5276	5289	5302
34	5315	5328	5340	5353	5366	5378	5391	5403	5416	5428
35	5441	5453	5465	5478	5490	5502	5514	5527	5539	5551
36	5563	5575	5587	5599	5611	5623	5635	5647	5658	5670
37	5682	5694	5705	5717	5729	5740	5752	5763	5775	5786
38	5798	5809	5821	5832	5843	5855	5866	5877	5888	5899
39	5911	5922	5933	5944	5955	5966	5977	5988	5999	6010
40	6021	6031	6042	6053	6064	6075	6085	6096	6107	6117
41	6128	6138	6149	6160	6170	6180	6191	6201	6212	6222
42	6232	6243	6253	6263	6274	6284	6294	6304	6314	6325
43	6335	6345	6355	6365	6375	6385	6395	6405	6415	6425
44	6435	6444	6454	6464	6474	6484	6493	6503	6513	6522
45	6532	6542	6551	6561	6571	6580	6590	6599	6609	6618
46	6628	6637	6646	6656	6665	6675	6684	6693	6702	6712
47	6721	6730	6739	6749	6758	6767	6776	6785	6794	6803
48	6812	6821	6830	6839	6848	6857	6866	6875	6884	6893
49	6902	6911	6920	6928	6937	6946	6955	6964	6972	6981
50	6990	6998	7007	7016	7024	7033	7042	7050	7059	7067
51	7076	7084	7093	7101	7110	7118	7126	7135	7143	7152
52	7160	7168	7177	7185	7193	7202	7210	7218	7226	7235
53	7243	7251	7259	7267	7275	7284	7292	7300	7308	7316
54	7324	7332	7340	7348	7356	7364	7372	7380	7388	7396

549

Table 1 Four-Place Logarithms (*continued*)

	0	1	2	3	4	5	6	7	8	9
55	7404	7412	7419	7427	7435	7443	7451	7459	7466	7474
56	7482	7490	7497	7505	7513	7520	7528	7536	7543	7551
57	7559	7566	7574	7582	7589	7597	7604	7612	7619	7627
58	7634	7642	7649	7657	7664	7672	7679	7686	7694	7701
59	7709	7716	7723	7731	7738	7745	7752	7760	7767	7774
60	7782	7789	7796	7803	7810	7818	7825	7832	7839	7846
61	7853	7860	7868	7875	7882	7889	7896	7903	7910	7917
62	7924	7931	7938	7945	7952	7959	7966	7973	7980	7987
63	7993	8000	8007	8014	8021	8028	8035	8041	8048	8055
64	8062	8069	8075	8082	8089	8096	8102	8109	8116	8122
65	8129	8136	8142	8149	8156	8162	8169	8176	8182	8189
66	8195	8202	8209	8215	8222	8228	8235	8241	8248	8254
67	8261	8267	8274	8280	8287	8293	8299	8306	8312	8319
68	8325	8331	8338	8344	8351	8357	8363	8370	8376	8382
69	8388	8395	8401	8407	8414	8420	8426	8432	8439	8445
70	8451	8457	8463	8470	8476	8482	8488	8494	8500	8506
71	8513	8519	8525	8531	8537	8543	8549	8555	8561	8567
72	8573	8579	8585	8591	8597	8603	8609	8615	8621	8627
73	8633	8639	8645	8651	8657	8663	8669	8675	8681	8686
74	8692	8698	8704	8710	8716	8722	8727	8733	8739	8745
75	8751	8756	8762	8768	8774	8779	8785	8791	8797	8802
76	8808	8814	8820	8825	8831	8837	8842	8848	8854	8859
77	8865	8871	8876	8882	8887	8893	8899	8904	8910	8915
78	8921	8927	8932	8938	8943	8949	8954	8960	8965	8971
79	8976	8982	8987	8993	8998	9004	9009	9015	9020	9025
80	9031	9036	9042	9047	9053	9058	9063	9069	9074	9079
81	9085	9090	9096	9101	9106	9112	9117	9122	9128	9133
82	9138	9143	9149	9154	9159	9165	9170	9175	9180	9186
83	9191	9196	9201	9206	9212	9217	9222	9227	9232	9238
84	9243	9248	9253	9258	9263	9269	9274	9279	9284	9289
85	9294	9299	9304	9309	9315	9320	9325	9330	9335	9340
86	9345	9350	9355	9360	9365	9370	9375	9380	9385	9390
87	9395	9400	9405	9410	9415	9420	9425	9430	9435	9440
88	9445	9450	9455	9460	9465	9469	9474	9479	9484	9489
89	9494	9499	9504	9509	9513	9518	9523	9528	9533	9538
90	9542	9547	9552	9557	9562	9566	9571	9576	9581	9586
91	9590	9595	9600	9605	9609	9614	9619	9624	9628	9633
92	9638	9643	9647	9652	9657	9661	9666	9671	9675	9680
93	9685	9689	9694	9699	9703	9708	9713	9717	9722	9727
94	9731	9736	9741	9745	9750	9754	9759	9763	9768	9773
95	9777	9782	9786	9791	9795	9800	9805	9809	9814	9818
96	9823	9827	9832	9836	9841	9845	9850	9854	9859	9863
97	9868	9872	9877	9881	9886	9890	9894	9899	9903	9908
98	9912	9917	9921	9926	9930	9934	9939	9943	9948	9952
99	9956	9961	9965	9969	9974	9978	9983	9987	9991	9996

Table 2   Four-Place Antilogarithms

Log.	0	1	2	3	4	5	6	7	8	9
.00	1000	1002	1005	1007	1009	1012	1014	1016	1019	1021
.01	1023	1026	1028	1030	1033	1035	1038	1040	1042	1045
.02	1047	1050	1052	1054	1057	1059	1062	1064	1067	1069
.03	1072	1074	1076	1079	1081	1084	1086	1089	1091	1094
.04	1096	1099	1102	1104	1107	1109	1112	1114	1117	1119
.05	1122	1125	1127	1130	1132	1135	1138	1140	1143	1146
.06	1148	1151	1153	1156	1159	1161	1164	1167	1169	1172
.07	1175	1178	1180	1183	1186	1189	1191	1194	1197	1199
.08	1202	1205	1208	1211	1213	1216	1219	1222	1225	1227
.09	1230	1233	1236	1239	1242	1245	1247	1250	1253	1256
.10	1259	1262	1265	1268	1271	1274	1276	1279	1282	1285
.11	1288	1291	1294	1297	1300	1303	1306	1309	1312	1315
.12	1318	1321	1324	1327	1330	1334	1337	1340	1343	1346
.13	1349	1352	1355	1358	1361	1365	1368	1371	1374	1377
.14	1380	1384	1387	1390	1393	1396	1400	1403	1406	1409
.15	1413	1416	1419	1422	1426	1429	1432	1435	1439	1442
.16	1445	1449	1452	1455	1459	1462	1466	1469	1472	1476
.17	1479	1483	1486	1489	1493	1496	1500	1503	1507	1510
.18	1514	1517	1521	1524	1528	1531	1535	1538	1542	1545
.19	1549	1552	1556	1560	1563	1567	1570	1574	1578	1581
.20	1585	1589	1592	1596	1600	1603	1607	1611	1614	1618
.21	1622	1626	1629	1633	1637	1641	1644	1648	1652	1656
.22	1660	1663	1667	1671	1675	1679	1683	1687	1690	1694
.23	1698	1702	1706	1710	1714	1718	1722	1726	1730	1734
.24	1738	1742	1746	1750	1754	1758	1762	1766	1770	1774
.25	1778	1782	1786	1791	1795	1799	1803	1807	1811	1816
.26	1820	1824	1828	1832	1837	1841	1845	1849	1854	1858
.27	1862	1866	1871	1875	1879	1884	1888	1892	1897	1901
.28	1905	1910	1914	1919	1923	1928	1932	1936	1941	1945
.29	1950	1954	1959	1963	1968	1972	1977	1982	1986	1991
.30	1995	2000	2004	2009	2014	2018	2023	2028	2032	2037
.31	2042	2046	2051	2056	2061	2065	2070	2075	2080	2084
.32	2089	2094	2099	2104	2109	2113	2118	2123	2128	2133
.33	2138	2143	2148	2153	2158	2163	2168	2173	2178	2183
.34	2188	2193	2198	2203	2208	2213	2218	2223	2228	2234
.35	2239	2244	2249	2254	2259	2265	2270	2275	2280	2286
.36	2291	2296	2301	2307	2312	2317	2323	2328	2333	2339
.37	2344	2350	2355	2360	2366	2371	2377	2382	2388	2393
.38	2399	2404	2410	2415	2421	2427	2432	2438	2443	2449
.39	2455	2460	2466	2472	2477	2483	2489	2495	2500	2506
.40	2512	2518	2523	2529	2535	2541	2547	2553	2559	2564
.41	2570	2576	2582	2588	2594	2600	2606	2612	2618	2624
.42	2630	2636	2642	2649	2655	2661	2667	2673	2679	2685
.43	2692	2698	2704	2710	2716	2723	2729	2735	2742	2748
.44	2754	2761	2767	2773	2780	2786	2793	2799	2805	2812
.45	2818	2825	2831	2838	2844	2851	2858	2864	2871	2877
.46	2884	2891	2897	2904	2911	2917	2924	2931	2938	2944
.47	2951	2958	2965	2972	2979	2985	2992	2999	3006	3013
.48	3020	3027	3034	3041	3048	3055	3062	3069	3076	3083
.49	3090	3097	3105	3112	3119	3126	3133	3141	3148	3155
	0	1	2	3	4	5	6	7	8	9

Table 2 Four-Place Antilogarithms (*continued*)

Log.	0	1	2	3	4	5	6	7	8	9
.50	3162	3170	3177	3184	3192	3199	3206	3214	3221	3228
.51	3236	3243	3251	3258	3266	3273	3281	3289	3296	3304
.52	3311	3319	3327	3334	3342	3350	3357	3365	3373	3381
.53	3388	3396	3404	3412	3420	3428	3436	3443	3451	3459
.54	3467	3475	3483	3491	3499	3508	3516	3524	3532	3540
.55	3548	3556	3565	3573	3581	3589	3597	3606	3614	3622
.56	3631	3639	3648	3656	3664	3673	3681	3690	3698	3707
.57	3715	3724	3733	3741	3750	3758	3767	3776	3784	3793
.58	3802	3811	3819	3828	3837	3846	3855	3864	3873	3882
.59	3890	3899	3908	3917	3926	3936	3945	3954	3963	3972
.60	3981	3990	3999	4009	4018	4027	4036	4046	4055	4064
.61	4074	4083	4093	4102	4111	4121	4130	4140	4150	4159
.62	4169	4178	4188	4198	4207	4217	4227	4236	4246	4256
.63	4266	4276	4285	4295	4305	4315	4325	4335	4345	4355
.64	4365	4375	4385	4395	4406	4416	4426	4436	4446	4457
.65	4467	4477	4487	4498	4508	4519	4529	4539	4550	4560
.66	4571	4581	4592	4603	4613	4624	4634	4645	4656	4667
.67	4677	4688	4699	4710	4721	4732	4742	4753	4764	4775
.68	4786	4797	4808	4819	4831	4842	4853	4864	4875	4887
.69	4898	4909	4920	4932	4943	4955	4966	4977	4989	5000
.70	5012	5023	5035	5047	5058	5070	5082	5093	5105	5117
.71	5129	5140	5152	5164	5176	5188	5200	5212	5224	5236
.72	5248	5260	5272	5284	5297	5309	5321	5333	5346	5358
.73	5370	5383	5395	5408	5420	5433	5445	5458	5470	5483
.74	5495	5508	5521	5534	5546	5559	5572	5585	5598	5610
.75	5623	5636	5649	5662	5675	5689	5702	5715	5728	5741
.76	5754	5768	5781	5794	5808	5821	5834	5848	5861	5875
.77	5888	5902	5916	5929	5943	5957	5970	5984	5998	6012
.78	6026	6039	6053	6067	6081	6095	6109	6124	6138	6152
.79	6166	6180	6194	6209	6223	6237	6252	6266	6281	6295
.80	6310	6324	6339	6353	6368	6383	6397	6412	6427	6442
.81	6457	6471	6486	6501	6516	6531	6546	6561	6577	6592
.82	6607	6622	6637	6653	6668	6683	6699	6714	6730	6745
.83	6761	6776	6792	6808	6823	6839	6855	6871	6887	6902
.84	6918	6934	6950	6966	6982	6998	7015	7031	7047	7063
.85	7079	7096	7112	7129	7145	7161	7178	7194	7211	7228
.86	7244	7261	7278	7295	7311	7328	7345	7362	7379	7396
.87	7413	7430	7447	7464	7482	7499	7516	7534	7551	7568
.88	7586	7603	7621	7638	7656	7674	7691	7709	7727	7745
.89	7762	7780	7798	7816	7834	7852	7870	7889	7907	7925
.90	7943	7962	7980	7998	8017	8035	8054	8072	8091	8110
.91	8128	8147	8166	8185	8204	8222	8241	8260	8279	8299
.92	8318	8337	8356	8375	8395	8414	8433	8453	8472	8492
.93	8511	8531	8551	8570	8590	8610	8630	8650	8670	8690
.94	8710	8730	8750	8770	8790	8810	8831	8851	8872	8892
.95	8913	8933	8954	8974	8995	9016	9036	9057	9078	9099
.96	9120	9141	9162	9183	9204	9226	9247	9268	9290	9311
.97	9333	9354	9376	9397	9419	9441	9462	9484	9506	9528
.98	9550	9572	9594	9616	9638	9661	9683	9705	9727	9750
.99	9772	9795	9817	9840	9863	9886	9908	9931	9954	9977
	0	1	2	3	4	5	6	7	8	9

Table 3 Areas Under the Normal Curve

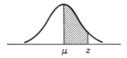

z	.00	.01	.02	.03	.04	.05	.06	.07	.08	.09
0.0	.0000	.0040	.0080	.0120	.0160	.0199	.0239	.0279	.0319	.0359
0.1	.0398	.0438	.0478	.0517	.0557	.0596	.0636	.0675	.0714	.0753
0.2	.0793	.0832	.0871	.0910	.0948	.0987	.1026	.1064	.1103	.1141
0.3	.1179	.1217	.1255	.1293	.1331	.1368	.1406	.1443	.1480	.1517
0.4	.1554	.1591	.1628	.1664	.1700	.1736	.1772	.1808	.1844	.1879
0.5	.1915	.1950	.1985	.2019	.2054	.2088	.2123	.2157	.2190	.2224
0.6	.2257	.2291	.2324	.2357	.2389	.2422	.2454	.2486	.2518	.2549
0.7	.2580	.2612	.2642	.2673	.2704	.2734	.2764	.2794	.2823	.2852
0.8	.2881	.2910	.2939	.2967	.2995	.3023	.3051	.3078	.3106	.3133
0.9	.3159	.3186	.3212	.3238	.3264	.3289	.3315	.3340	.3365	.3389
1.0	.3413	.3438	.3461	.3485	.3508	.3531	.3554	.3577	.3599	.3621
1.1	.3643	.3665	.3686	.3708	.3729	.3749	.3770	.3790	.3810	.3830
1.2	.3849	.3869	.3888	.3907	.3925	.3944	.3962	.3980	.3997	.4015
1.3	.4032	.4049	.4066	.4082	.4099	.4115	.4131	.4147	.4162	.4177
1.4	.4192	.4207	.4222	.4236	.4251	.4265	.4279	.4292	.4306	.4319
1.5	.4332	.4345	.4357	.4370	.4382	.4394	.4406	.4418	.4429	.4441
1.6	.4452	.4463	.4474	.4484	.4495	.4505	.4515	.4525	.4535	.4545
1.7	.4554	.4564	.4573	.4582	.4591	.4599	.4608	.4616	.4625	.4633
1.8	.4641	.4649	.4656	.4664	.4671	.4678	.4686	.4693	.4699	.4706
1.9	.4713	.4719	.4726	.4732	.4738	.4744	.4750	.4756	.4761	.4767
2.0	.4772	.4778	.4783	.4788	.4793	.4798	.4803	.4808	.4812	.4817
2.1	.4821	.4826	.4830	.4834	.4838	.4842	.4846	.4850	.4854	.4857
2.2	.4861	.4864	.4868	.4871	.4875	.4878	.4881	.4884	.4887	.4890
2.3	.4893	.4896	.4898	.4901	.4904	.4906	.4909	.4911	.4913	.4916
2.4	.4918	.4920	.4922	.4925	.4927	.4929	.4931	.4932	.4934	.4936
2.5	.4938	.4940	.4941	.4943	.4945	.4946	.4948	.4949	.4951	.4952
2.6	.4953	.4955	.4956	.4957	.4959	.4960	.4961	.4962	.4963	.4964
2.7	.4965	.4966	.4967	.4968	.4969	.4970	.4971	.4972	.4973	.4974
2.8	.4974	.4975	.4976	.4977	.4977	.4978	.4979	.4979	.4980	.4981
2.9	.4981	.4982	.4982	.4983	.4984	.4984	.4985	.4985	.4986	.4986
3.0	.49865	.4987	.4987	.4988	.4988	.4989	.4989	.4989	.4990	.4990
4.0	.4999683									

Illustration: For $z = 1.93$, shaded area is .4732 out of total area of 1.
Source: John Neter and William Wasserman, Fundamental Statistics for Business and Economics, Second Edition, Allyn and Bacon, Inc., Boston, 1961, with the permission of the publisher.

Table 4 Student's t Distribution

The first column lists the number of degrees of freedom (ν). The headings of the other columns give probabilities (P) for t to exceed numerically the entry value.

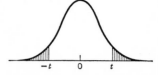

P \ ν	0.50	0.25	0.10	0.05	0.025	0.01	0.005
1	1.00000	2.4142	6.3138	12.706	25.452	63.657	127.32
2	0.81650	1.6036	2.9200	4.3027	6.2053	9.9248	14.089
3	0.76489	1.4226	2.3534	3.1825	4.1765	5.8409	7.4533
4	0.74070	1.3444	2.1318	2.7764	3.4954	4.6041	5.5976
5	0.72669	1.3009	2.0150	2.5706	3.1634	4.0321	4.7733
6	0.71756	1.2733	1.9432	2.4469	2.9687	3.7074	4.3168
7	0.71114	1.2543	1.8946	2.3646	2.8412	3.4995	4.0293
8	0.70639	1.2403	1.8595	2.3060	2.7515	3.3554	3.8325
9	0.70272	1.2297	1.8331	2.2622	2.6850	3.2498	3.6897
10	0.69981	1.2213	1.8125	2.2281	2.6338	3.1693	3.5814
11	0.69745	1.2145	1.7959	2.2010	2.5931	3.1058	3.4966
12	0.69548	1.2089	1.7823	2.1788	2.5600	3.0545	3.4284
13	0.69384	1.2041	1.7709	2.1604	2.5326	3.0123	3.3725
14	0.69242	1.2001	1.7613	2.1448	2.5096	2.9768	3.3257
15	0.69120	1.1967	1.7530	2.1315	2.4899	2.9467	3.2860
16	0.69013	1.1937	1.7459	2.1199	2.4729	2.9208	3.2520
17	0.68919	1.1910	1.7396	2.1098	2.4581	2.8982	3.2225
18	0.68837	1.1887	1.7341	2.1009	2.4450	2.8784	3.1966
19	0.68763	1.1866	1.7291	2.0930	2.4334	2.8609	3.1737
20	0.68696	1.1848	1.7247	2.0860	2.4231	2.8453	3.1534
21	0.68635	1.1831	1.7207	2.0796	2.4138	2.8314	3.1352
22	0.68580	1.1816	1.7171	2.0739	2.4055	2.8188	3.1188
23	0.68531	1.1802	1.7139	2.0687	2.3979	2.8073	3.1040
24	0.68485	1.1789	1.7109	2.0639	2.3910	2.7969	3.0905
25	0.68443	1.1777	1.7081	2.0595	2.3846	2.7874	3.0782
26	0.68405	1.1766	1.7056	2.0555	2.3788	2.7787	3.0669
27	0.68370	1.1757	1.7033	2.0518	2.3734	2.7707	3.0565
28	0.68335	1.1748	1.7011	2.0484	2.3685	2.7633	3.0469
29	0.68304	1.1739	1.6991	2.0452	2.3638	2.7564	3.0380
30	0.68276	1.1731	1.6973	2.0423	2.3596	2.7500	3.0298
40	0.68066	1.1673	1.6839	2.0211	2.3289	2.7045	2.9712
60	0.67862	1.1616	1.6707	2.0003	2.2991	2.6603	2.9146
120	0.67656	1.1559	1.6577	1.9799	2.2699	2.6174	2.8599
∞	0.67449	1.1503	1.6449	1.9600	2.2414	2.5758	2.8070

Table 5　F Distribution*

5% (Roman Type) and 1% (Bold-Face Type) Points for Distribution of F

Degrees of freedom for numerator (v_1)

Degrees of freedom for denominator (v_2)	1	2	3	4	5	6	7	8	9	10	11	12	14	16	20	24	30	40	50	75	100	200	500	∞
1	161 / **4052**	200 / **4999**	216 / **5403**	225 / **5625**	230 / **5764**	234 / **5859**	237 / **5928**	239 / **5981**	241 / **6022**	242 / **6056**	243 / **6082**	244 / **6106**	245 / **6142**	246 / **6169**	248 / **6208**	249 / **6234**	250 / **6258**	251 / **6286**	252 / **6302**	253 / **6323**	253 / **6334**	254 / **6352**	254 / **6361**	254 / **6366**
2	18.51 / **98.49**	19.00 / **99.01**	19.16 / **99.17**	19.25 / **99.25**	19.30 / **99.30**	19.33 / **99.33**	19.36 / **99.34**	19.37 / **99.36**	19.38 / **99.38**	19.39 / **99.40**	19.40 / **99.41**	19.41 / **99.42**	19.42 / **99.43**	19.43 / **99.44**	19.44 / **99.45**	19.45 / **99.46**	19.46 / **99.47**	19.47 / **99.48**	19.47 / **99.48**	19.48 / **99.49**	19.49 / **99.49**	19.49 / **99.49**	19.50 / **99.50**	19.50 / **99.50**
3	10.13 / **34.12**	9.55 / **30.81**	9.28 / **29.46**	9.12 / **28.71**	9.01 / **28.24**	8.94 / **27.91**	8.88 / **27.67**	8.84 / **27.49**	8.81 / **27.34**	8.78 / **27.23**	8.76 / **27.13**	8.74 / **27.05**	8.71 / **26.92**	8.69 / **26.83**	8.66 / **26.69**	8.64 / **26.60**	8.62 / **26.50**	8.60 / **26.41**	8.58 / **26.30**	8.57 / **26.27**	8.56 / **26.23**	8.54 / **26.18**	8.54 / **26.14**	8.53 / **26.12**
4	7.71 / **21.20**	6.94 / **18.00**	6.59 / **16.69**	6.39 / **15.98**	6.26 / **15.52**	6.16 / **15.21**	6.09 / **14.98**	6.04 / **14.80**	6.00 / **14.66**	5.96 / **14.54**	5.93 / **14.45**	5.91 / **14.37**	5.87 / **14.24**	5.84 / **14.15**	5.80 / **14.02**	5.77 / **13.93**	5.74 / **13.83**	5.71 / **13.74**	5.70 / **13.69**	5.68 / **13.61**	5.66 / **13.57**	5.65 / **13.52**	5.64 / **13.48**	5.63 / **13.46**
5	6.61 / **16.26**	5.79 / **13.27**	5.41 / **12.06**	5.19 / **11.39**	5.05 / **10.97**	4.95 / **10.67**	4.88 / **10.45**	4.82 / **10.27**	4.78 / **10.15**	4.74 / **10.05**	4.70 / **9.96**	4.68 / **9.89**	4.64 / **9.77**	4.60 / **9.68**	4.56 / **9.55**	4.53 / **9.47**	4.50 / **9.38**	4.46 / **9.29**	4.44 / **9.24**	4.42 / **9.17**	4.40 / **9.13**	4.38 / **9.07**	4.37 / **9.04**	4.36 / **9.02**
6	5.99 / **13.74**	5.14 / **10.92**	4.76 / **9.78**	4.53 / **9.15**	4.39 / **8.75**	4.28 / **8.47**	4.21 / **8.26**	4.15 / **8.10**	4.10 / **7.98**	4.06 / **7.87**	4.03 / **7.79**	4.00 / **7.72**	3.96 / **7.60**	3.92 / **7.52**	3.87 / **7.39**	3.84 / **7.31**	3.81 / **7.23**	3.77 / **7.14**	3.75 / **7.09**	3.72 / **7.02**	3.71 / **6.99**	3.69 / **6.94**	3.68 / **6.90**	3.67 / **6.88**
7	5.59 / **12.25**	4.74 / **9.55**	4.35 / **8.45**	4.12 / **7.85**	3.97 / **7.46**	3.87 / **7.19**	3.79 / **7.00**	3.73 / **6.84**	3.68 / **6.71**	3.63 / **6.62**	3.60 / **6.54**	3.57 / **6.47**	3.52 / **6.35**	3.49 / **6.27**	3.44 / **6.15**	3.41 / **6.07**	3.38 / **5.98**	3.34 / **5.90**	3.32 / **5.85**	3.29 / **5.78**	3.28 / **5.75**	3.25 / **5.70**	3.24 / **5.67**	3.23 / **5.65**
8	5.32 / **11.26**	4.46 / **8.65**	4.07 / **7.59**	3.84 / **7.01**	3.69 / **6.63**	3.58 / **6.37**	3.50 / **6.19**	3.44 / **6.03**	3.39 / **5.91**	3.34 / **5.82**	3.31 / **5.74**	3.28 / **5.67**	3.23 / **5.56**	3.20 / **5.48**	3.15 / **5.36**	3.12 / **5.28**	3.08 / **5.20**	3.05 / **5.11**	3.03 / **5.06**	3.00 / **5.00**	2.98 / **4.96**	2.96 / **4.91**	2.94 / **4.88**	2.93 / **4.86**
9	5.12 / **10.56**	4.26 / **8.02**	3.86 / **6.99**	3.63 / **6.42**	3.48 / **6.06**	3.37 / **5.80**	3.29 / **5.62**	3.23 / **5.47**	3.18 / **5.35**	3.13 / **5.26**	3.10 / **5.18**	3.07 / **5.11**	3.02 / **5.00**	2.98 / **4.92**	2.93 / **4.80**	2.90 / **4.73**	2.86 / **4.64**	2.82 / **4.56**	2.80 / **4.51**	2.77 / **4.45**	2.76 / **4.41**	2.73 / **4.36**	2.72 / **4.33**	2.71 / **4.31**

* Reprinted, by permission, from Snedecor, *Statistical Methods*, Collegiate Press, Iowa State College, Amer.

n																								
10	2.54/3.91	2.55/3.93	2.56/3.96	2.59/4.01	2.61/4.05	2.64/4.12	2.67/4.17	2.70/4.25	2.74/4.33	2.77/4.41	2.82/4.52	2.86/4.60	2.91/4.71	2.94/4.78	2.97/4.85	3.02/4.95	3.07/5.06	3.14/5.21	3.22/5.39	3.33/5.64	3.48/5.99	3.71/6.55	4.10/7.56	4.96/10.04
11	2.40/3.60	2.41/3.62	2.42/3.66	2.45/3.70	2.47/3.74	2.50/3.80	2.53/3.86	2.57/3.94	2.61/4.02	2.65/4.10	2.70/4.21	2.74/4.29	2.79/4.40	2.82/4.46	2.86/4.54	2.90/4.63	2.95/4.74	3.01/4.88	3.09/5.07	3.20/5.32	3.36/5.67	3.59/6.22	3.98/7.20	4.84/9.65
12	2.30/3.36	2.31/3.38	2.32/3.41	2.35/3.46	2.36/3.49	2.40/3.56	2.42/3.61	2.46/3.70	2.50/3.78	2.54/3.86	2.60/3.98	2.64/4.05	2.69/4.16	2.72/4.22	2.76/4.30	2.80/4.39	2.85/4.50	2.92/4.65	3.00/4.82	3.11/5.06	3.26/5.41	3.49/5.95	3.88/6.93	4.75/9.33
13	2.21/3.16	2.22/3.18	2.24/3.21	2.26/3.27	2.28/3.30	2.32/3.37	2.34/3.42	2.38/3.51	2.42/3.59	2.46/3.67	2.51/3.78	2.55/3.85	2.60/3.96	2.63/4.02	2.67/4.10	2.72/4.19	2.77/4.30	2.84/4.44	2.92/4.62	3.02/4.86	3.18/5.20	3.41/5.74	3.80/6.70	4.67/9.07
14	2.13/3.00	2.14/3.02	2.16/3.05	2.19/3.11	2.21/3.14	2.24/3.21	2.27/3.26	2.31/3.34	2.35/3.43	2.39/3.51	2.44/3.62	2.48/3.70	2.53/3.80	2.56/3.86	2.60/3.94	2.65/4.03	2.70/4.14	2.77/4.28	2.85/4.46	2.96/4.69	3.11/5.03	3.34/5.56	3.74/6.51	4.60/8.86
15	2.07/2.87	2.08/2.89	2.10/2.92	2.12/2.97	2.15/3.00	2.18/3.07	2.21/3.12	2.25/3.20	2.29/3.29	2.33/3.36	2.39/3.48	2.43/3.56	2.48/3.67	2.51/3.73	2.55/3.80	2.59/3.89	2.64/4.00	2.70/4.14	2.79/4.32	2.90/4.56	3.06/4.89	3.29/5.42	3.68/6.36	4.54/8.68
16	2.01/2.75	2.02/2.77	2.04/2.80	2.07/2.86	2.09/2.89	2.13/2.96	2.16/3.01	2.20/3.10	2.24/3.18	2.28/3.26	2.33/3.37	2.37/3.45	2.42/3.55	2.45/3.61	2.49/3.69	2.54/3.78	2.59/3.89	2.66/4.03	2.74/4.20	2.85/4.44	3.01/4.77	3.24/5.29	3.63/6.23	4.49/8.53
17	1.96/2.65	1.97/2.67	1.99/2.70	2.02/2.76	2.04/2.79	2.08/2.86	2.11/2.92	2.15/3.00	2.19/3.08	2.23/3.16	2.29/3.27	2.33/3.35	2.38/3.45	2.41/3.52	2.45/3.59	2.50/3.68	2.55/3.79	2.62/3.93	2.70/4.10	2.81/4.34	2.96/4.67	3.20/5.18	3.59/6.11	4.45/8.40
18	1.92/2.57	1.93/2.59	1.95/2.62	1.98/2.68	2.00/2.71	2.04/2.78	2.07/2.83	2.11/2.91	2.15/3.00	2.19/3.07	2.25/3.19	2.29/3.27	2.34/3.37	2.37/3.44	2.41/3.51	2.46/3.60	2.51/3.71	2.58/3.85	2.66/4.01	2.77/4.26	2.93/4.58	3.16/5.09	3.55/6.01	4.41/8.28
19	1.88/2.49	1.90/2.51	1.91/2.54	1.94/2.60	1.96/2.63	2.00/2.70	2.02/2.76	2.07/2.84	2.11/2.92	2.15/3.00	2.21/3.12	2.26/3.19	2.31/3.30	2.34/3.36	2.38/3.43	2.43/3.52	2.48/3.63	2.55/3.77	2.63/3.94	2.74/4.17	2.90/4.50	3.13/5.01	3.52/5.93	4.38/8.18
20	1.84/2.42	1.85/2.44	1.87/2.47	1.90/2.53	1.92/2.56	1.96/2.63	1.99/2.69	2.04/2.77	2.08/2.86	2.12/2.94	2.18/3.05	2.23/3.13	2.28/3.23	2.31/3.30	2.35/3.37	2.40/3.46	2.45/3.56	2.52/3.71	2.60/3.87	2.71/4.10	2.87/4.43	3.10/4.94	3.49/5.85	4.35/8.10
21	1.81/2.36	1.82/2.38	1.84/2.42	1.87/2.47	1.89/2.51	1.93/2.58	1.96/2.63	2.00/2.72	2.05/2.80	2.09/2.88	2.15/2.99	2.20/3.07	2.25/3.17	2.28/3.24	2.32/3.31	2.37/3.40	2.42/3.51	2.49/3.65	2.57/3.81	2.68/4.04	2.84/4.37	3.07/4.87	3.47/5.78	4.32/8.02
22	1.78/2.31	1.80/2.33	1.81/2.37	1.84/2.42	1.87/2.46	1.91/2.53	1.93/2.58	1.98/2.67	2.03/2.75	2.07/2.83	2.13/2.94	2.18/3.02	2.23/3.12	2.26/3.18	2.30/3.26	2.35/3.35	2.40/3.45	2.47/3.59	2.55/3.76	2.66/3.99	2.82/4.31	3.05/4.82	3.44/5.72	4.30/7.94
23	1.76/2.26	1.77/2.28	1.79/2.32	1.82/2.37	1.84/2.41	1.88/2.48	1.91/2.53	1.96/2.62	2.00/2.70	2.04/2.78	2.10/2.89	2.14/2.97	2.20/3.07	2.24/3.14	2.28/3.21	2.32/3.30	2.38/3.41	2.45/3.54	2.53/3.71	2.64/3.94	2.80/4.26	3.03/4.76	3.42/5.66	4.28/7.88
24	1.73/2.21	1.74/2.23	1.76/2.27	1.80/2.33	1.82/2.36	1.86/2.44	1.89/2.49	1.92/2.58	1.96/2.66	2.02/2.74	2.09/2.85	2.13/2.93	2.16/3.03	2.22/3.09	2.26/3.17	2.30/3.25	2.36/3.36	2.43/3.50	2.51/3.67	2.62/3.90	2.78/4.22	3.01/4.72	3.40/5.61	4.26/7.82
25	1.71/2.17	1.72/2.19	1.74/2.23	1.77/2.29	1.80/2.32	1.84/2.40	1.87/2.45	1.90/2.54	1.95/2.62	1.99/2.70	2.06/2.81	2.11/2.89	2.15/2.99	2.18/3.02	2.24/3.13	2.28/3.21	2.34/3.32	2.41/3.46	2.49/3.63	2.60/3.86	2.76/4.18	2.99/4.68	3.38/5.57	4.24/7.77
26	1.69/2.13	1.70/2.15	1.72/2.19	1.76/2.25	1.78/2.28	1.82/2.36	1.85/2.41	1.90/2.50	1.95/2.58	1.99/2.66	2.05/2.77	2.10/2.86	2.15/2.96	2.18/3.02	2.22/3.09	2.27/3.17	2.32/3.29	2.39/3.42	2.47/3.59	2.59/3.82	2.74/4.14	2.89/4.64	3.37/5.53	4.22/7.72

556

TABLE V. F Distribution (Continued)

5% (Roman Type) and 1% (Bold-Face Type) Points for the Distribution of F

Degrees of freedom for numerator (v_1)

Each cell lists the 5% point (Roman) / 1% point (Bold-Face).

Degrees of freedom for denominator (v_2)	1	2	3	4	5	6	7	8	9	10	11	12	14	16	20	24	30	40	50	75	100	200	500	∞
27	4.21 / 7.68	3.35 / 5.49	2.96 / 4.60	2.73 / 4.11	2.57 / 3.79	2.46 / 3.56	2.37 / 3.39	2.30 / 3.26	2.25 / 3.14	2.20 / 3.06	2.16 / 2.98	2.13 / 2.93	2.08 / 2.83	2.03 / 2.74	1.97 / 2.63	1.93 / 2.55	1.88 / 2.47	1.84 / 2.38	1.80 / 2.33	1.76 / 2.25	1.74 / 2.21	1.71 / 2.16	1.68 / 2.12	1.67 / 2.10
28	4.20 / 7.64	3.34 / 5.45	2.95 / 4.57	2.71 / 4.07	2.56 / 3.76	2.44 / 3.53	2.36 / 3.36	2.29 / 3.23	2.24 / 3.11	2.19 / 3.03	2.15 / 2.95	2.12 / 2.90	2.06 / 2.80	2.02 / 2.71	1.96 / 2.60	1.91 / 2.52	1.87 / 2.44	1.81 / 2.35	1.78 / 2.30	1.75 / 2.22	1.72 / 2.18	1.69 / 2.13	1.67 / 2.09	1.65 / 2.06
29	4.18 / 7.60	3.33 / 5.42	2.93 / 4.54	2.70 / 4.04	2.54 / 3.73	2.43 / 3.50	2.35 / 3.33	2.28 / 3.20	2.22 / 3.08	2.18 / 3.00	2.14 / 2.92	2.10 / 2.87	2.05 / 2.77	2.00 / 2.68	1.94 / 2.57	1.90 / 2.49	1.85 / 2.41	1.80 / 2.32	1.77 / 2.27	1.73 / 2.19	1.71 / 2.15	1.68 / 2.10	1.65 / 2.06	1.64 / 2.03
30	4.17 / 7.56	3.32 / 5.39	2.92 / 4.51	2.69 / 4.02	2.53 / 3.70	2.42 / 3.47	2.34 / 3.30	2.27 / 3.17	2.21 / 3.06	2.16 / 2.98	2.12 / 2.90	2.09 / 2.84	2.04 / 2.74	1.99 / 2.66	1.93 / 2.55	1.89 / 2.47	1.84 / 2.38	1.79 / 2.29	1.76 / 2.24	1.72 / 2.16	1.69 / 2.13	1.66 / 2.07	1.64 / 2.03	1.62 / 2.01
32	4.15 / 7.50	3.30 / 5.34	2.90 / 4.46	2.67 / 3.97	2.51 / 3.66	2.40 / 3.42	2.32 / 3.25	2.25 / 3.12	2.19 / 3.01	2.14 / 2.94	2.10 / 2.86	2.07 / 2.80	2.02 / 2.70	1.97 / 2.62	1.91 / 2.51	1.86 / 2.42	1.82 / 2.34	1.76 / 2.25	1.74 / 2.20	1.69 / 2.12	1.67 / 2.08	1.64 / 2.02	1.61 / 1.98	1.59 / 1.96
34	4.13 / 7.44	3.28 / 5.29	2.88 / 4.42	2.65 / 3.93	2.49 / 3.61	2.38 / 3.38	2.30 / 3.21	2.23 / 3.08	2.17 / 2.97	2.12 / 2.89	2.08 / 2.82	2.05 / 2.76	2.00 / 2.66	1.95 / 2.58	1.89 / 2.47	1.84 / 2.38	1.80 / 2.30	1.74 / 2.21	1.71 / 2.15	1.67 / 2.08	1.64 / 2.04	1.61 / 1.98	1.59 / 1.94	1.57 / 1.91
36	4.11 / 7.39	3.26 / 5.25	2.86 / 4.38	2.63 / 3.89	2.48 / 3.58	2.36 / 3.35	2.28 / 3.18	2.21 / 3.04	2.15 / 2.94	2.10 / 2.86	2.06 / 2.78	2.03 / 2.72	1.98 / 2.62	1.93 / 2.54	1.87 / 2.43	1.82 / 2.35	1.78 / 2.26	1.72 / 2.17	1.69 / 2.12	1.65 / 2.04	1.62 / 2.00	1.59 / 1.94	1.56 / 1.90	1.55 / 1.87
38	4.10 / 7.35	3.25 / 5.21	2.85 / 4.34	2.62 / 3.86	2.46 / 3.54	2.35 / 3.32	2.26 / 3.15	2.19 / 3.02	2.14 / 2.91	2.09 / 2.82	2.05 / 2.75	2.02 / 2.69	1.96 / 2.59	1.92 / 2.51	1.85 / 2.40	1.80 / 2.32	1.76 / 2.22	1.71 / 2.14	1.67 / 2.08	1.63 / 2.00	1.60 / 1.97	1.57 / 1.90	1.54 / 1.86	1.53 / 1.84
40	4.08 / 7.31	3.23 / 5.18	2.84 / 4.31	2.61 / 3.83	2.45 / 3.51	2.34 / 3.29	2.25 / 3.12	2.18 / 2.99	2.12 / 2.88	2.07 / 2.80	2.04 / 2.73	2.00 / 2.66	1.95 / 2.56	1.90 / 2.49	1.84 / 2.37	1.79 / 2.29	1.74 / 2.20	1.69 / 2.11	1.66 / 2.05	1.61 / 1.97	1.59 / 1.94	1.55 / 1.88	1.53 / 1.84	1.51 / 1.81
42	4.07 / 7.27	3.22 / 5.15	2.83 / 4.29	2.59 / 3.80	2.44 / 3.49	2.32 / 3.26	2.24 / 3.10	2.17 / 2.96	2.11 / 2.86	2.06 / 2.77	2.02 / 2.70	1.99 / 2.64	1.94 / 2.54	1.89 / 2.46	1.82 / 2.35	1.78 / 2.26	1.73 / 2.17	1.68 / 2.08	1.64 / 2.02	1.60 / 1.94	1.57 / 1.91	1.54 / 1.85	1.51 / 1.80	1.49 / 1.78
44	4.06 / 7.24	3.21 / 5.12	2.82 / 4.26	2.58 / 3.78	2.43 / 3.46	2.31 / 3.24	2.23 / 3.07	2.16 / 2.94	2.10 / 2.84	2.05 / 2.75	2.01 / 2.68	1.98 / 2.62	1.92 / 2.52	1.88 / 2.44	1.81 / 2.32	1.76 / 2.24	1.72 / 2.15	1.66 / 2.06	1.63 / 2.00	1.58 / 1.92	1.56 / 1.88	1.52 / 1.82	1.50 / 1.78	1.48 / 1.75
46	4.05 / 7.21	3.20 / 5.10	2.81 / 4.24	2.57 / 3.76	2.42 / 3.44	2.30 / 3.22	2.22 / 3.05	2.14 / 2.92	2.09 / 2.82	2.04 / 2.73	2.00 / 2.66	1.97 / 2.60	1.91 / 2.50	1.87 / 2.42	1.80 / 2.30	1.75 / 2.22	1.71 / 2.13	1.65 / 2.04	1.62 / 1.98	1.57 / 1.90	1.54 / 1.86	1.51 / 1.80	1.48 / 1.76	1.46 / 1.72
48	4.04 / 7.19	3.19 / 5.08	2.80 / 4.22	2.56 / 3.74	2.41 / 3.42	2.30 / 3.20	2.21 / 3.04	2.14 / 2.90	2.08 / 2.80	2.03 / 2.71	1.99 / 2.64	1.96 / 2.58	1.90 / 2.48	1.86 / 2.40	1.79 / 2.28	1.74 / 2.20	1.70 / 2.11	1.64 / 2.02	1.61 / 1.96	1.56 / 1.88	1.53 / 1.84	1.50 / 1.78	1.47 / 1.73	1.45 / 1.70

Table 6 Random Numbers

10 09 73 25 33	76 52 01 35 86	34 67 35 48 76	80 95 90 91 17	39 29 27 49 45
37 54 20 48 05	64 89 47 42 96	24 80 52 40 37	20 63 61 04 02	00 82 29 16 65
08 42 26 89 53	19 64 50 93 03	23 20 90 25 60	15 95 33 47 64	35 08 03 36 06
99 01 90 25 29	09 37 67 07 15	38 31 13 11 65	88 67 67 43 97	04 43 62 76 59
12 80 79 99 70	80 15 73 61 47	64 03 23 66 53	98 95 11 68 77	12 17 17 68 33
66 06 57 47 17	34 07 27 68 50	36 69 73 61 70	65 81 33 98 85	11 19 92 91 70
31 06 01 08 05	45 57 18 24 06	35 30 34 26 14	86 79 90 74 39	23 40 30 97 32
85 26 97 76 02	02 05 16 56 92	68 66 57 48 18	73 05 38 52 47	18 62 38 85 79
63 57 33 21 35	05 32 54 70 48	90 55 35 75 48	28 46 82 87 09	83 49 12 56 24
73 79 64 57 53	03 52 96 47 78	35 80 83 42 82	60 93 52 03 44	35 27 38 84 35
98 52 01 77 67	14 90 56 86 07	22 10 94 05 58	60 97 09 34 33	50 50 07 39 98
11 80 50 54 31	39 80 82 77 32	50 72 56 82 48	29 40 52 42 01	52 77 56 78 51
83 45 29 96 34	06 28 89 80 83	13 74 67 00 78	18 47 54 06 10	68 71 17 78 17
88 68 54 02 00	86 50 75 84 01	36 76 66 79 51	90 36 47 64 93	29 60 91 10 62
99 59 46 73 48	87 51 76 49 69	91 82 60 89 28	93 78 56 13 68	23 47 83 41 13
65 48 11 76 74	17 46 85 09 50	58 04 77 69 74	73 03 95 71 86	40 21 81 65 44
80 12 43 56 35	17 72 70 80 15	45 31 82 23 74	21 11 57 82 53	14 38 55 37 63
74 35 09 98 17	77 40 27 72 14	43 23 60 02 10	45 52 16 42 37	96 28 60 26 55
69 91 62 68 03	66 25 22 91 48	36 93 68 72 03	76 62 11 39 90	94 40 05 64 18
09 89 32 05 05	14 22 56 85 14	46 42 75 67 88	96 29 77 88 22	54 38 21 45 98
91 49 91 45 23	68 47 92 76 86	46 16 28 35 54	94 75 08 99 23	37 08 92 00 48
80 33 69 45 98	26 94 03 68 58	70 29 73 41 35	53 14 03 33 40	42 05 08 23 41
44 10 48 19 49	85 15 74 79 54	32 97 92 65 75	57 60 04 08 81	22 22 20 64 13
12 55 07 37 42	11 10 00 20 40	12 86 07 46 97	96 64 48 94 39	28 70 72 58 15
63 60 64 93 29	16 50 53 44 84	40 21 95 25 63	43 65 17 70 82	07 20 73 17 90

61 19 69 04 46	26 45 74 77 74	51 92 43 37 29	65 39 45 95 93	42 58 26 05 27
15 47 44 52 66	95 27 07 99 53	59 36 78 38 48	82 39 61 01 18	33 21 15 94 66
94 55 72 85 73	67 89 75 43 87	54 62 24 44 31	91 19 04 25 92	92 92 74 59 73
42 48 11 62 13	97 34 40 87 21	16 86 84 87 67	03 07 11 20 59	25 70 14 66 70
23 52 37 83 17	73 20 88 98 37	68 93 59 14 16	26 25 22 96 63	05 52 28 25 62
04 49 35 24 94	75 24 63 38 24	45 86 25 10 25	61 96 27 93 35	65 33 71 24 72
00 54 99 76 54	64 05 18 81 59	96 11 96 38 96	54 69 28 23 91	23 28 72 95 29
35 96 31 53 07	26 89 80 93 54	33 35 13 54 62	77 97 45 00 24	90 10 33 93 33
59 80 80 83 91	45 42 72 68 42	83 60 94 97 00	13 02 12 48 92	78 56 52 01 06
46 05 88 52 36	01 39 69 22 86	77 28 14 40 77	93 91 08 36 47	70 61 74 29 41
32 17 90 05 97	87 37 92 52 41	05 56 70 70 07	86 74 31 71 57	85 39 41 18 38
69 23 46 14 06	20 11 74 52 04	15 95 66 00 00	18 74 39 24 23	97 11 89 63 38
19 56 54 14 30	01 75 87 53 79	40 41 92 15 85	66 67 43 68 06	84 96 28 52 07
45 15 51 49 38	19 47 60 72 46	43 66 79 45 43	59 04 79 00 33	20 82 66 95 41
94 86 43 19 94	36 16 81 08 51	34 88 88 15 53	01 54 03 54 56	05 01 45 11 76
98 08 62 48 26	45 24 02 84 04	44 99 90 88 96	39 09 47 34 07	35 44 13 18 80
33 18 51 62 32	41 94 15 09 49	89 43 54 85 81	88 69 54 19 94	37 54 87 30 43
80 95 10 04 06	96 38 27 07 74	20 15 12 33 87	25 01 62 52 98	94 62 46 11 71
79 75 24 91 40	71 96 12 82 96	69 86 10 25 91	74 85 22 05 39	00 38 75 95 79
18 63 33 25 37	98 14 50 65 71	31 01 02 46 74	05 45 56 14 27	77 93 89 19 36
74 02 94 39 02	77 55 73 22 70	97 79 01 71 19	52 52 75 80 21	80 81 45 17 48
54 17 84 56 11	80 99 33 71 43	05 33 51 29 69	56 12 71 92 55	36 04 09 03 24
11 66 44 98 83	52 07 98 48 27	59 38 17 15 39	09 97 33 34 40	88 46 12 33 56
48 32 47 79 28	31 24 96 47 10	02 29 53 68 70	32 30 75 75 46	15 02 00 99 94
69 07 49 41 38	87 63 79 19 76	35 58 40 44 01	10 51 82 16 15	01 84 87 69 38

Reproduced by permission from The RAND Corporation, "A Million Random Digits," Free Press, Glencoe, Ill., 1955.

Index

WITHDRAWN

3 6289 00273247 4

WITHDRAWN

DATE DUE

DEMCO 38-297